MEDICAL ASTROLOGY

Published by
Blue Turtle Publishing

Also by Blue Turtle Publishing:

SOUL RECOVERY AND EXTRACTION, by Ai Gvhdi Waya/Eileen Nauman, $9.95, 85 pages, paper.

Utilizing her Eastern Cherokee background, Eileen shares a powerful healing technique that was taught to her eight years ago. Soul Recovery and Extraction (SR/E) is about regaining control of your life by retrieving the "lost" pieces of your soul. The loss can occur when pieces of your soul are trapped, stolen by another person (family dysfunction, divorce, etc.), or split off because of a traumatic experience (accident, birth of a child, job loss, etc.). Co-dependence, obesity, and feeling lost or empty are among the fifteen warning signs of soul loss detailed in the book. Extraction, used individually or in conjunction with Soul Recovery, promotes healing by removing blocks from your physical body and/or from the surrounding aura.

COLORED STONES AND THEIR HEALING, by Eileen Nauman and Ruth Gent, $4.95, 28 pages, paper.

Utilizing her Eastern Cherokee background and training, Eileen and her mother, Ruth Gent, have written a handy guide to not only crystals, but 39 colored stones, both precious and semi-precious. Each stone is discussed in relation to the type of health problems it will help, the spiritual use of the stone, a meditation that can be used with it, and a symbol that helps a person tune into the energy of a specific stone.

Arranged in alphabetical order, the book explains how to clean a stone, how to program it and the categories for which a stone may be used, i.e., a money stone, a guard-dog stone, a psychic stone, etc.

MEDICAL ASTROLOGY

by Eileen Nauman
Adjunct Professor

Acknowledgments

A book of this length and depth is never done by one person. Dr. Davidson's works, Mary Vorhezek's work and Robert Jansky's pioneering in the field of medical astrology have all contributed to my understanding of this immense topic. I thank them for their invaluable assistance, knowledge and help in leading the way.

Dedication

To my mother, Ruth Gent-Cramer, who was responsible for my early introduction and training in the nutritional field — without her, this book would never have come into being.

To Karen David, my dearest friend, who is a metaphysical consultant, numerologist, spiritualist medium, psychologist, and shamanic facilitator, for her continued encouragement and support.

To my husband David, who patiently and with understanding supported the thousands of hours it took to compile this monumental project.

To the "Wolf Pack," who made the third, enlarged edition possible — for generously giving of their time to type up the three chapters: Ardella Hecht, astrologer and shamanic facilitator; Marlene Johnson, astrologer and psychic; and Bonnie Birnam, astrologer. Thank you. Your generosity of spirit will be rewarded tenfold.

Copyright © 1982 by Eileen Nauman
Printed in the United States of America
First Printing, July 1982 (5,000 copies)
Second Printing, December 1983 (5,000 copies)

Published by Blue Turtle Publishing
P. O. Box 2513, Cottonwood, AZ 86326
Copyright © 1993 by Eileen Nauman
ISBN 0-9634662-4
Revised Edition, April 1993 (2,000 copies)

ISBN 0-9634662-4-0
Third Revision, May 1996

In the hospitals of Leningrad, Russia, the MST software is being utilized by physicians to help in patient diagnosis—especially in the areas of undiagnosible or hard-to-diagnose patients. My hope is that someday U.S. physicians might be so open minded as to utilize the software, for indeed, it does save the patient much discomfort, pain, as well as quickens the diagnostic process through invaluable information about where to test the body, utilizing medical astrology.

To make way for the chapters on Homeopathy, Bach Flower Remedies and Medical Transits, I have taken out the chapter on herbs and cell salts. I know of no medicine, other than Homeopathy, that can CURE, and this was the reason for placing this chapter into my book. There are small changes throughout the book from the Appendix information to new listings in the Glossary and additions to the Index. It is my hope that this updating of information will continue to help people who use this book around the world.

At one astrological conference a woman came up to me and grabbed my arm. "Your book saved my life," she said with fervor. Since this book has been in print, I have had more than fifty people tell me in person or write to me those same words. I can think of no finer accolade or accomplishment a book can make than this wonderful statement. I hope you enjoy the new Homeopathic and Bach Flower Remedies chapters, as well as astrological information that I have researched in relation to this curative system of medicine. Perhaps it, too, will save lives.

I would like to thank the following women who made this third edition a reality: Ardella Hecht, Marlene Johnson and Bonnie Birnam. Without their enthusiasm, constant help, typing and input, this work would not be available.

Eileen Nauman
Author
April, 1993
Cottonwood, Arizona

Foreword

AN ALTERNATIVE HEALING TECHNIQUE

Eight years ago, I began an interior journey into another form of healing that I'd like to lightly touch upon here, within the purview of the medical astrology book. As an astrologer, I'm always open to new techniques in healing, usually alternative types, such as polarity therapy, acupuncture, homeopathy, laying on of hands, gem therapy or others. Little did I know that I'd be embarking upon an adventure of a lifetime eight years ago.

I have written a book entitled *SOUL RECOVERY AND EXTRACTION*, which will be found in the front of this book. Since I have Eastern Cherokee blood in me (a drop from my great-great grandmother on my father's side of the family), I chose to use my Native American name, Ai Gvhdi Waya.

As a lay homeopath for the last twenty-three years, I noticed that in about 1/3 of my cases, they never got cured. In Homeopathy, cure is the bottom line. I wrestled with WHY on this for many, many years, until I began to undergo a personal, inner transformation, which culminated with becoming a shamanic facilitator.

I was taught by my inner spirit teachers a shamanic technique for healing that finally answered my question as to why 1/3 of the people I worked with homeopathically, could never achieve cure.

Briefly, I want to say that what I was taught falls under the heading of shamanism. I believe this "ability" or skill was genetically in place via not only my Eastern Cherokee gene, but via my Irish genes. I've discovered that certain genetic background imbues people with this gift. It's my understanding that shamanism is practiced all over the world by different cultures and has many varied offshoots. Shamanism, for me, is the ability to achieve an altered state with the beat of a drum (no drugs involved), and visually see into the other dimensions. There are certainly many more definitions of shamanism, but I want to be clear what it is for me.

With this ability, I'm able to retrieve lost or split off pieces of a person's soul and bring them back to them. This ability took five years in the making to learn. Everyone loses parts or pieces or energy of themselves due to trauma—be it mental, physical, emotional or spiritual. We also give away pieces of ourselves to others—particularly family members.

In a small percentage of cases, pieces of ourselves are deliberately and knowingly taken from us, and this falls under the realm of sorcery.

When I began recovering "pieces" for a client, which usually took a nine-month to a year long process (I journeyed in my altered state for them once every three months because I found it took that long to re-integrate the soul pieces). After that, I would then take their homeopathic case, and I could achieve cure for that person. Another interesting phenomena ocurred during the integration process for my client: when s/he integrated pieces back, fifty-percent of the time their illness went away or became markedly better.

This makes sense to me now because if parts of ourselves, or energy, are gone, we aren't whole. And if all of us isn't there to receive whatever form of healing we choose, be it allopathic or alternative, it won't create cure, only partial healing, or the symptoms of the disease will come back over time. However, once Soul Recovery is done for the person, and the homeopathic case is taken, cure is very possible. I might add that regardless of what kind of healing therapy a person chooses and believes will get them well, it will work much better after Soul Recovery.

The other portion of shamanism that was taught to me is what I call "extraction." The easiest way to try and explain it, is to say that it closely parallels what the Philippine healers perform. All the healing takes place in the person's aura. Because of my Native American background, I don't use surgical tools, per se, but items such as a feather, crystal, my hands or whatever is appropriate for that person.

When Soul Recovery and Extraction (I refer to it as SR/E) is performed on a person, the illness can no longer remain the same, and the person does get better on all levels of themselves.

The best thing I was taught was that I could perform SR/E long distances—that is to say, I didn't have to see my client in person or bodily. I could go anywhere in the universe in my altered state, visit a client half-way around the world, and perform SR/E for them. That saves a person a lot of air fare, to say the least! So, over the years, I've seen fewer than 5% of my clients in person, but have communicated with them via phone, letter and fax.

After being given this particular tool for healing, I set about choosing some very wonderful people who came from the heart, to teach them SR/E. Happily, my brother, Gary Gent, who is 3 years younger than me, and from the same genetic pool bloodline, also has developed this same ability—so there are now two of us in the family who perform SR/E.

I'd like to put down the names and addresses of my associates whom I've trained over the years to perform SR/E. They are professionals at this, and if you're interested in this healing technique, we have some simple guidelines for you to follow.

I. If you want SR/E done, you must first purchase the book, Soul Recovery and Extraction from Blue Turtle Publishing. The address is in the front of the book. Why? Because we believe a person should be fully informed on the healing technique they have chosen to utilize to heal themselves. The book is basic, informative, straight-forward and should answer 95% of any questions you might have regarding this technique. If you have questions that remain unanswered, write them down and your next order of business is to select a shamanic facilitator.

II. You should choose a facilitator (all trained by me) that resonates with you. Healing happens when you have TRUST and CONFIDENCE in your healer. Actually, all healing comes from YOU, and the healer is only a physical reflection of that tool you've chosen to get well by! That aside, I normally suggest men go to men, and women go to women. This isn't a prejudicial comment at all, but rather, honors each gender for their particular uniqueness. Women know women much better than they know a male, and vice-versa. However, if you want the opposite gender, this doesn't pose a problem. Pick a name that resonates positively with you and mail off your letter to them. Be sure you tell them you've already read Soul Recovery and Extraction. Here are my associates names:

1. **Roni Lee Bell,** PO Box 23283, Santa Fe, NM 87052, is a metaphysician who has always been close to the heartbeat of Mother Earth. Performing medicine wheel ceremonies, a personal pipe carrier, she also utilizes SR/E among her healing talents on behalf of others.

2. **Mary Buckner,** PO Box 670, Kingston, OK 73439. She is a registered nurse for over thirty years, is a professional astrologer and has performed SR/E for her worldwide cliental.

3. **Karen J. David,** PO Box 39216, Cleveland, OH 44139, is a metaphysician, world lecturer and professional numerologist. She is close to getting her degree in Psychology. Also trained as a spiritualist medium, Karen's wide reaching abilities

to continue to help people around the world, and include SR/E.

4. **Gary Gent,** PO Box 2575, Winston, OR 97496, is the brother of Ai Gvhdi Waya, comes by his Native American blood honestly, and lives in close touch with Mother Earth. He utilizes SR/E for his worldwide cliental, and gives workshops on the topic.

5. **Ardella Hecht,** PO Box 31263, Phoenix, AZ 85046-1263, is a licensed massage therapist who has added SR/E to her broad metaphysical base. She is a lay homeopath for thirteen years, a Bach Flower remedy specialist and gives workshops on all the above topics.

6. **Eileen Lunderman,** PATHWAYS, PO Box 501, Mission, South Dakota 57555, is a Lakota shamanness who lives on the Rosebud (Sioux) Reservation. Highly spiritual, "Tunney," as she likes to be called, walks the Red Road in service of others and practices SR/E for her worldwide cliental.

7. **Glen Malec,** PO Box 186, Wildwood, NJ 08260, is a professional astrologer and does a great deal of teaching and speaking on a broad base of metaphysical topics. He walks the Red Road and utilizes SR/E for those who come to him. Glen has an avid interest in UFO's and aliens.

8. **Coletta Swalley,** PATHWAYS, PO Box 501, MIssion, South Dakota, 57555, is a Lakota shamanness who lives near Tunney on the Rosebud (Sioux) Reservation. Coletta works from her large, generous heart to help her people and those who come to her for SR/E healings.

III. Once the shamanic facilitator has contacted you, usually by phone (be sure and put your phone number in your letter to them!), then s/he can answer your questions about SR/E. If you're comfortable with your facilitator, a date will then be set and agreed upon by both of you, and an SR/E journey will be taken in your behalf. However, if you are uncomfortable with your facilitator, choose another one!

Many times, only soul retrieval will be done on the first journey, and extraction may occur at a later date. This varies from client to client, and there is no set way to go about it. A facilitator cannot perform SR/E for you unless s/he gets permission from their chief guide (or yours) to do so. They won't know if they have permission until they go into the shamanic state. If we aren't given permission, we don't perform SR/E. Why? Because it's karma that you have chosen to work through without outside help. Our facilitators honor this directive and will NEVER perform SR/E on anyone without direct permission of their chief guide.

Also, our facilitators will never perform SR/E

for someone unless they are aware of it. We follow the same procedure by getting that individual (via yourself) to read the book first. Then, they can make an informed decision.

Shamanic facilitators also work with the dead who have crossed over, the dying, and those who are in comas, in mental wards or incapacitated in any number of ways. When we're contacted to help these individuals, we can undertake a journey in their behalf, and must receive permission from either our own chief guide or their guide, before SR/E is potentially performed. We work with babies, who can't read books, either, but we journey to find out if SR/E can be performed on them, too, by the same above method.

To perform SR/E on someone against their will (or their guide's will) is to practice sorcery—and we will not do that. We work for only the highest good for each individual, and will only undertake a case when we're invited to do it—and after the client has taken the responsibility to read the book and fully educated themselves about our technique and we've gotten permission from our chief guide to do it.

For half my life, I've been looking for a technique that would truly heal a person. I've found that SR/E combined with homeopathic treatment afterward (along with diet considerations, and other common sensed changes) gives me what I've been looking for. SR/E and homeopathy aren't the "end-all" for everyone. We've found that if a person pooh-pooh's SR/E, and for that fact, homeopathy, that it won't work on them! This is as it should be and honors each individual's unique make-up. Your reality and what you believe will heal you, will heal you. If you don't believe crystals can heal, then they won't. However, if you believe aspirin can stop your headache, it will. I've seen just as many headaches cured with crystals!

A true healer honors her/his client's reality. We tend to draw people to us who believe that SR/E along with homeopathic after-treatment, will help them the most. And, it does.

I believe that the next healing frontier is going to be the map of the mind, and shamanic facilitating certainly falls into this category. It is a right-brained healing technique.

I write for the *SEDONA JOURNAL OF EMERGENCE!* on a monthly basis under my Ai Gvhdi Waya name, on shamanism, death and dying, metaphysics, Native American topics and homeopathy. If you'd like copies of these articles or receive a subscription to this magazine, write to: PO Box 1526, Sedona, AZ 86336, or call (602) 282-6523.

Introduction

Medical astrology is a science that demands a union of knowledge of both astrology and medicine. Ideally, it takes years of acquiring astrological expertise and then becoming totally familiar with physiology and anatomy to qualify as a medical astrologer who with the cooperation of a physician can accurately diagnose diseases and advise clients on the best procedures for regaining health.

But in varying degrees the tools of medical astrology are available to all people interested in the science, even those with only fundamental knowledge of astrology and/or medicine. After four years of looking for the best system with which to look at a natal chart and discern a practical approach to finding potential medical problems, I discovered the Med-Scan method, a plan that every layperson, student or professional astrologer can use.

The Med-Scan technique is basically simple. In involves using astrology to determine any individual's potential weak spots. In other words, by examining the planetary combinations and placements in a natal or progressed chart, a medical astrologer can ascertain likely psychological or physical weaknesses that may be causing disease. The medical astrologer then can advise the client on the appropriate tests necessary to verify the astrological speculations. After a physician's tests have confirmed the diagnosis, together the medical astrologer and doctor can outline the best diet and program of nutritional supplements for the individual to regain good health.

Since medical astrology is in its infancy, no medical astrologer can work alone, and nothing can be assumed without verification from a physician. A medical astrologer cannot simply throw out suggestions without having them confirmed by a doctor. It is very necessary, therefore, for the medical astrologer to develop a close, working relationship with the physician in charge of the case.

Although in my years of experience I have worked with any and all doctors willing to use astrology, I have found that usually the most sympathetic to medical astrology are homeopathic physicians and those who adhere to holistic health programs aimed at responding to each individual's different needs. My approach in this book and in practice is also definitely homeopathic rather than the allopathic philosophy that most U.S. doctors espouse.

The word *homeopathy* comes from two Greek words meaning "similar affections." Homeopaths believe that "like cures like." As a result they provide remedies that, when given to a healthy person, would create the same symptoms that the sick person has. In essence, it is a concept of "fighting fire with fire" or fighting the disease with its own aggressive characteristics. In the end the ailment has *not* been covered up, as is the case with allopathic medicine.

Allopathic philosophy embraces the notion that the use of drugs to produce effects different from those of the disease will work. Thus allopathic doctors (and most American doctors are trained in allopathy) rely on high dosages of drugs to treat a person. Although this technique may be successful to a point, with the damage incurred along the way by the chemicals given, the body is pressured to fight the adverse effects of the drugs. Furthermore, in allopathic medicine too frequently the root cause of a disease is not sought out, but instead measures are taken simply to provide a drug to give instant relief from the *symptoms* of a disease.

Homeopathic physicians, on the other hand, always seek out the root cause of an illness, and for the most part they use only *natural* remedies to treat it, administering the smallest dosage necessary to effect a cure. Homeopathic remedies stimulate the body's own defenses to throw out the offending ailment, creating no harmful side effects. No warnings or cautions are required on homeopathic remedies. In fact, sometimes a cure can be effected simply by a change in diet: homeopathic doctors recognize that poor diets are the root causes of many diseases.

Any road to health that uses natural remedies, though, will take a long time, especially in chronic illness. Therefore, *patience* is a key word in medical astrology. The medical astrologer must cultivate this quality and instill it in his clients. Most of us are brainwashed into believing that medicine can give instant 30-minute cures to our discomfort or that there is a drug for every conditon. But there really are no miracle cures. Homeopathic treatment requires discipline and patience. Clients must be made to understand that they will have to maintain a program for at least three months and perhaps as long as a year before they will see signs of recovering health.

Patience is especially necessary since medical astrologers usually don't get the easy cases; instead, we get the dying or misdiagnosed—two of the hardest types to deal with. Furthermore, most of the time the client doesn't have just one ailment but other overlapping complications. In the beginning there may only be one, but if the diet is not corrected or other holistic alternatives applied, health begins to fail like toppling dominoes—first one ailment and then another and another contribute to the initial illness.

Since so often medical astrologers are consulted as a kind of last resort, our work can be very frustrating; but for the very same reason it can be most rewarding when a diagnosis proves correct and a suggested regime for recovery brings results. And from seven years of using the Med-Scan method I can say unequivocally that it *does* work. The only time it fails in the diagnostic way is when there is not enough recorded data in the field to make an accurate judgment. In other words, medical astrology has not yet caught up with the more established branches of astrological study. It is my hope that this book, the product of years of experience, will fill in some of the gaps in our knowledge, advancing medical astrology from myth into theory, eventually to become a fact.

The book is divided into two parts—an astrological guide and a medical reference section. Part One explains what is known about medical astrology—the health conditions usually associated with the various planets and their aspects, the houses, signs and astrological crosses. The most innovative and comprehensive chapter in Part One is that on the midpoint structures: the information in this chapter has not been idly lifted from some other sources; instead, the source statements have been checked against case histories and either elaborated upon or changed according to the different facts presented in my experience. This chapter is followed by one on the Med-Scan technique itself, outlining the steps to follow in astrological diagnosis as well as describing some of the tests and diets helpful in diagnosis and remedy.

Part One then concludes with a chapter on case histories, which prove out the old adage that "truth is stranger than fiction." All are actual cases, elucidating the Med-Scan technique in action. Each contains a section entitled "What Astrology Missed" to show that we cannot always be 100 per cent correct in diagnosis.

Part Two was written to save the reader a lot of time and effort in consulting five or six different references to find answers about nutrition. A year of research alone was spent on the section on vitamins and minerals, and I believe these two chapters are the most detailed and complete description of the sources, history, characteristics and properties of the vitamins and minerals yet available. Chapters on herbs and cell salts are also included. Part Two then ends with a special chapter on the endocrine system. Study and experience have convinced me that the glands are often the root cause of poor health. I believe the glands should be checked out *first* because the hormones keep the bodily metabolisms in order, and without proper hormonal release the body needs a basic tuneup to keep the engine running smoothly.

Although a bibliography is supplied at the end of the book, I want to mention a few books that are indispensable to the neophyte medical astrologer: *Taber's Cyclopedic Medical Dictionary*, edited by Clayton L. Thomas; *Materia Medica with Repertory* by Dr. William Boericke; *Dr. Schuessler's Biochemistry* by Dr. J.B. Chapman, and *Eating Naturally Around the Zodiac: Diet and Quadruplicity* by Rebecca Manring (RKM Publishing).

Part One
MEDICAL ASTROLOGY

CHAPTER ONE
The Planets, Uranian Planets, Fixed Stars and Health

THE PLANETS

In medical astrology the planets indicate the functions or malfunctions of specific organs or systems in the body, depending on what sign the planet is posited in at birth. For instance, Mars always implies a potential area of acute inflammation, a flaring up of a specific condition. If Mars is in Gemini, there could be an acute ailment involving any of the Gemini-ruled areas such as the tubes of the body. Which tube is affected would have to be discerned by careful analysis of the entire chart and the person's past and present medical data: if a woman has experienced uterine complaints, there could be an infection involving one of the Fallopian tubes; or if the person has a past history of lung trouble, there could a flare-up of bronchial irritation or pleurisy. The planets, then, indicate how a specific organ or function of the body will be affected.

The Sun

Vitamins: A and D.

Minerals: Iodine and Magnesium.

No number of words can express the Sun's importance to everyday bodily functioning. The Sun should never be overlooked in a natal chart because of its vital importance and energy to a person's entire well-being. All inherent vitality, energy or prana flows through the Sun. The sign it is found in will tell us how the energies are being dispensed within the given lifetime.

Metaphysically, the Sun is our Heart Chakra through which all emotions flow. As Dr. William Davidson has said, it is "the fire of life," ruling the etheric body, a very fine, weblike filament that encases the physical body—the container for the energy that flows into the physical body and keeps it functioning steadily on a daily basis.

This presence of an etheric body is why X-rays, radium or electrical burns do so much damage to the physical body. If the etheric is burned by the invisible, high-frequency rays, the container surrounding the physical shell develops a hole and a leak appears. Taking vitamins, minerals, cell salts, herbs or other internal or external aids can sometimes help this condition. Davidson implies that goose grease applied externally will help to seal the etheric so that the vitality of the Sun's energy is not allowed to dissipate. Sunshine as well as vitamin A, is also healthy in moderation.

There may also be a leak in the etheric web when a person contracts an ailment, although this is not always the case. A medical astrologer who can see auras will notice that the organ or part of the body that is diseased, disabled or not functioning up to par will be pulling in the aura in that area of the egg shell oval surrounding the body. This phenomenon results from more energy being diverted from other areas and pumped into the hole to sustain its minimal functioning. A diseased organ will also appear yellowish-green to the person who can look through the physical shell. But medical astrologers, unless clairvoyant, should stick to the indications of the chart and lab tests to get their answers.

On the physical plane the Sun is the center of life—the life-giver to our physical bodies. Its zodiacal sign in Leo, which medically rules the heart. If the heart is sluggish or impaired, the entire body suffers.

We might think of the Sun as an engine. A faulty diet may cause the engine to falter or sputter. And without a good engine the energy provided by Mars becomes wasted. On the other hand, if we have regular tune-ups by watching our diets and getting physical checkups, we can stay in top running form.

To have a strong, pulsing life force—the heart—we need sufficient vitamin A. If a person is not getting enough of this important vitamin, there will be a short somewhere in the circuitry, and he or she will possibly develop a heart ailment (even though most heart problems are Fixed Cross in origin). Insufficient vitamin A can cause a variety of heart ailments, such as angina pectoris, arteriosclerosis, atherosclerosis, myocardial infarction and congestive heart failure.

The Sun also rules magnesium, found in abundance in most green plants. The Sun, chlorophyl and magnesium have a direct chemical relationship: without the Sun, no chlorophyl and no magnesium. And magnesium is found in such quantity within the body that we cannot live long without it. With insufficient magnesium a long list of ailments can manifest: in fact, with too little magnesium death is inevitable.

The Moon

Vitamins: Riboflavin (vitamin B-2).

Minerals: Potassium.

Whereas the Sun, by sign and aspect, shows the

constitutional quality of the body, the Moon tells the conditions of health. Because of this sensitivity, the Moon is a good indicator of when to undergo operation or not. For example, a person should probably not have surgery on a void of course Moon day. Void of course days usually mean that the surgery won't be done correctly, further complications will be found or a second operation will become necessary. I once had a client who, against my advice, underwent a nose operation on a void of course day, and she had to return two more times. For her fourth operation she came back to me and asked for a good date.

The sign position of the transiting Moon may also indicate favorable or unfavorable times for operations. In general, the transiting Moon should be in a fixed sign (Taurus, Leo, Scorpio, Aquarius). The transiting Moon in fixed signs helps insure that the operation will go as planned and helps keep the hands of the surgeon steady, with no extra complications. Possibly the worst time for surgery is when the Moon is in a mutable sign (Virgo, Gemini, Pisces, Saggitarius). Those are times of too much flexibility: who wants to go in for a gallbladder operation and then have the surgeon decide to also remove the appendix?

A person should probably also not have an operation on that part of the body ruled by the sign in which the Moon is transiting. In other words, for a gallbladder operation (ruled by Capricorn), an individual should not undergo surgery as the Moon transits through Capricorn. A gallbladder operation should also probably not be performed when the Moon transits Cancer, Capricorn's polarity: I usually avoid the opposite sign when possible because there is a definite reflex action involved.

The amount of fluids within the body will also determine the best periods for surgery. In general, the Moon is responsible for the fluid tides in our bodies (the levels of serum, water, blood, etc). Just as the tides of the ocean draw in and out from shore, the body fluids do about the same thing within our physical shells. When the Moon phases, these levels tend to drop or rise. At new Moon time, our fluids are at their lowest points, and there is a resultant weight loss. Thus, the best time for an operation is five days before or after the new Moon, when there is least chance of swelling, bruising or bleeding. In contrast, one should never undergo surgery five days before or after a full Moon, when the body fluids are at their highest and can cause excessive swelling, hemorrhaging or seepage from wounds.

Since the Moon regulates the bodily fluids, its transiting position may also determine whether or not there is a need for riboflavin. For instance, the fluid in the skull is at its highest at full Moon, exer-

ting pressure on the brain and potentially making a person in need of riboflavin more irritable, more easily upset or more sensitive. So, if a person is suffering from a deficiency of riboflavin symptoms may be more severe about five days before the full Moon, and the deficiency may lessen toward the new Moon.

In addition, the amount of potassium a person needs may be determined by the bodily tides. The fluids surrounding the cells as well as our weight losses or gains of water are dependent upon potassium. A woman who has planets in Cancer or a strongly accented Moon in her natal chart can especially incur weight gains and losses of five pounds a month dependent solely upon the fluid distribution in her body. If the fluid is retained and not sloughed off through its various eliminative channels, a weight gain is noticed about five days before the full Moon each month. Toward the new Moon the weight gain will lessen and the body will be at low tide. Much of this problem can be controlled by proper amounts of potassium being available in the body to keep the fluids in balance.

A prominent Moon in the natal chart also generally indicates a drug-sensitive individual. In particular, if the Moon is the singleton of a chart or if it is conjunct the First or Tenth House cusp within eight degrees, the patient should receive a lower dosage of any medication (about ½ the usual dose).

Finally, the position of the Moon in a natal chart will help establish a person's emotional needs. Good health is not just a matter of eating the correct foods; it is a interweaving of diet, emotions and mental attitudes. If emotions are misdirected, suppressed or repressed, they can build up and fester in the subconscious mind. Such festering is the equivalent to a viral microbe entering the body and hibernating until the time that it erupts into an ailment. If emotions such as guilt, anger and jealousy are not properly dealt with, they too can cause illnesses.

Mercury

Vitamins: Thiamine (vitamin B-1).

Since Mercury rules the nervous system, its placement in a natal chart can indicate mental attitudes, and inflexible attitudes can stress the body. Although mental exhaustion is not normally manifested with an afflicted Mercury, the nervous system may take a severe buffeting, perhaps resulting in nervousness, tension and the inability to relax. Such people need to control their worrying, allowing themselves to worry only when they haven't done everything within their powers to change the outcome. The proper attitudes are important for wellbeing, and if we mishandle our emotions we can become sick.

We might also view the planet Mercury as a kind of traffic director influencing various movements within our bodies. The messenger of the gods, it is also the messenger of the nervous system, relaying split second commands throughout the body. Furthermore, in ruling Gemini, Mercury has dominion over all the tubing in the body, the channels through which blood, hormones, enzymes and oxygen move. Finally, Mercury may partially rule the hormones dispensed by the glands in the body: hormones are themselves messengers sent out to gather certain cells together to initiate enzymic functions in the body so that the metabolism can continue on a stable course.

Mercury rules Virgo as well. Thus the planet is involved with the splitting up action and the pancreatic breakdown of sugar into glucose—a process that may be affected when there is insufficient thiamine because of a faulty diet or a predisposition toward too many processed foods. A thiamine deficiency also lowers the amount of hydrochloric acid (HCl) in the stomach; in turn, the food is only semidigested so that when the bile is poured into the duodenum (the first 11 inches of the small intestine) it cannot properly break down the fats. This malfunction causes further problems, such as colitis, diverticulosis, flatulence, heartburn and diarrhea—many of which come under Virgo's rulership.

Mercury is also closely associated with the thyroid, and it seems to have significance in thyroid problems with or without the influence of Taurus, coruler of the thyroid. However, in thiamine-related deficiencies, the thyroid usually presents a second or third symptom and is not a chronic indicator of a thiamine deficiency.

When transiting Mercury is retrograde, it is probably a poor time to schedule an operation. Signals can get crossed: a woman might go in for a simple appendectomy and come out without a uterus! During Mercury retrograde the wrong drugs might be given or the dosage may be wrong for the individual. Misunderstandings may occur between doctors, doctor and nurses, nurses and patient or doctor and patient. Such a transit might even mean a second operation will be necessary.

Venus

Vitamins: Niacin (vitamin B-3) and E.
Minerals: Copper.

Too many students of medical astrology tend to overlook "sweet, l'il ol' Venus" because it has a reputation of being harmless, a "soft" planet, incapable of any foul play. But Venus can be interfered with to such an extent that what it does rule becomes diseased and ailing. Ruling over Taurus and Libra, Venus helps regulate the throat, thyroid and kidneys. The planet also has dominion over half the circulatory system — the venous supply. And it is concerned with skin texture, its beauty and flawless character.

Venus can play a part in diseases of the blood. It rules the venous circulatory system—an intricate series of minute venules of blood vessels that start out as being barely visible and then branch out. The veins differ from the arteries in that they are larger, there are more of them, and they have thinner walls, with valves to prevent the backward wash of blood circulation. Veins, along with the kidneys (Libra) and the heart (Leo), are especially important to blood pressure in general, partially regulated by niacin. Weak artery or vein walls as well as aneurysms under proper configurations, are also Venus phenomena. And in some instances Venus seems to have a secondary effect on red blood cells, partially formed by copper. Venus-ruled vitamin E is also valuable in circulatory ailments, such as phlebitis, embolisms, thrombosis and dilation of the vessels of the arterial and venous systems: it keeps the body supplied with a pure source of oxygen that in sufficient amounts gives the outer body a Venusian radiance or attractiveness and health.

Venus also governs slack muscle tone in the body. Although Mars rules the muscles, Venus has an integral relationship with its sibling planet: Mars represents tight, healthy muscles, whereas Venus, its opposite, indicates a potential lack of tone or tightness, soft or weakened muscles; without sufficient niacin, there can be muscle cramping.

Finally, Venus as well as Jupiter controls what one likes in terms of food—the texture, taste and quality. Since wrong foods can damage a person just as fast in bodily terms as wrong emotions can, Venus must be carefully looked at in the natal chart. For example, its placement may indicate a person with a "sweet tooth" or one who tends towards obesity. An individual with a prominent Venus may go on binges—gorging on sweets and gaining weight. Since Venus also deals with the need for love, a person with a poorly aspected Venus may also eat an inordinate amount of sweets to achieve a sense of affection he or she feels is not supplied by others. Venus dictates how we feel about ourselves. If we like ourselves, we'll probably have a good diet; if we dislike ourselves, we tend to abuse our bodies with less than nutritious foods.

Mars

Vitamins: B-12, folic acid and fatty acids (vitamin F).
Minerals: Chlorine, cobalt, iron, molybdenum, phosphorus, selenium and sodium.

Ruling over the muscles and the adrenal glands, Mars is the energizer and stimulator of all aspects of our bodies. Whereas the Sun is our basic engine, Mars is the gas that fuels it. It is the key planet associated with our physical get up and go, our energy levels.

Depending on its placement in a natal chart, Mars can indicate how active each of us is. For instance, in a fire sign Mars may produce extraordinary athletes or aggressive people who must temper their workaholic tendencies with rest in between their furious spurts of activity. Mars in an air sign can mean great mental energies: these individuals may be cerebral, seeming to grasp scientific theories or equations with ease, but they must be on guard against mental exhaustion and nerve-related breakdowns. Mars in an earth sign often produces people who prefer the sport of sitting in overstuffed arm chairs. And Mars seems least happy in a water sign: energy tends to be in short supply with these people, and they need to monitor just how much they can do without being exhausted. Since everyone needs exercise, Mars will help the medical astrologer evaluate how much and what kind each person needs.

This planet is also very important in indicating how quickly individuals can bounce back from sickness. It seems to work best in the fire or air signs. In earth or water signs it usually indicates slow recuperation.

In terms of health problems an activated Mars can mean inflammation, rapid temperature increase and acute onset of ailments. Depending on which sign it's located in, Mars can also indicate what *may* be hyperfunctioning—in other words, that part of the body, whether it is tissue, bone or organ, that is operating fast and possibly overworking itself so that it will wear out more quickly than other parts.

Mars has dominion over blood: it can be involved in various blood disorders, such as anemia. Thus it is a natural ruler for vitamin B-12, folic acid, cobalt, copper and iron, all of which are essential in the production of red blood cells. Particularly if Mars makes a negative aspect to either Jupiter or Saturn, there may be poor absorption of vitamin B-12, which is closely linked with cobalt, copper and iron—minerals necessary for healthy red blood cells. Folic acid is also essential for red blood cell production and the proper utilization of energy for the body's management: it's a vitamin that seems to stimulate everything around it, including better liver production, hydrochloric acid secretions in the stomach, cell multiplication and healthy flora in the intestinal tract.

Mars rules acids in general. It is an active planet, symbolizing energy, and fatty acids play a direct part in making sure that the body has the necessary get up and go when we ask for it: in many intances blood fat levels are connected with incidences of diabetes or hypoglycemia, or imbalances of insulin and, consequently, energy.

Since chlorine is involved with maintaining the acid-alkaline balance within the body, it is natural that Mars have domain over that mineral. Furthermore, chlorine usually compounds with potassium, ruled by the Moon, or with sodium, another Mars-ruled mineral that supports many bodily functions. Because chlorine is such an active element (a Marslike function in itself), it is responsible for muscle, tendon and ligament health—other Mars-ruled domains. Chlorine is a highly active mineral, befitting Mars' energy and constant movement: it makes sure that the osmotic pressure in and out of the cells is just right all the time. But too much chlorine (or too much sodium) reflects a typical negative Mars trait, unrestrained aggressiveness: too much of a good thing can destroy.

In addition, Mars rules molybdenum, iron, phosphorus and selenium. It governs phosphorus because of that mineral's engagement in so many bodily activites: the brain will not function at peak performance nor will nerve transmissions occur unless this mineral exerts its influence. Furthermore, the confidence usually attributed to Mars is lessened if there is a deficiency of this mineral—a person may cower in his or her home, afraid to move from the premises, a very unMartian reaction. Selenium's active involvement within the body also links it to Mars. And the colors produced by selenium in industry are all Martian—red, orange and yellow.

The worst indication for any type of surgery is probably when Mars is retrograde. Mars retrograde may mean heavy loss of blood, unexpected hemorrhaging or a mistake on the part of the surgeon. Since Mars is the ruler of surgeons, when this planet goes retrograde, surgeons are often not their steadiest or most reliable. There will be interference and misdirected attention. It does not mark a good time for concentration, especially when microsurgery is to be performed.

Jupiter

Vitamins: B-6, biotin, cholin, inositol and pangamic acid (vitamin B-15).

Minerals: Chromium, manganese and zinc.

The word *expansion* is usually applied to Jupiter. In medical terms Jupiterian expansion means overeating and lack of control. Whereas Venus rules our taste buds and how we react to certain foods, Jupiter tends to make for gluttons. Jupiter-ruled people may overeat rich foods that are usually high in acid:

sooner or later uric acid gathers in the body and gout is the result. Jupiter can also indicate swelling, abnormal expansion or too much of something.

Along with Virgo, which governs the splitting up actions within the organ, Jupiter has subdominion over the liver. When liver damage is apparent, a lack of cholin and/or inositol could be indicated since these two vitamins combine to make lecithin, which in turn breaks down the fats and dispenses with them so that they don't clog up the liver. Insufficient amounts of either cholin or inositol can cause cirrhosis of the liver. Pangamic acid may help in the alleviation of certain liver ailments, such as cirrhosis or hepatitis.

Jupiter also rules the fats of the body, their process of breaking down through enzyme reaction and their proper utilization. Cholin is integrally linked with the proper use and assimilation of fats in the body. Inositol, too, is essential for proper metabolization or fats. Another vitamin instrumental in breaking down fats for utilization within the body is B-6. And if Jupiter is found in Gemini, one must suspect a potential problem in the arterial duct work, since Gemini rules the tubing of the body: that placement of Jupiter, linked with a deficiency of vitamin B-6, could initiate atherosclerosis (fats or cholesterol clogging the arteries of the body and impairing circulation). The "new" vitamin—pangamic acid—also has much to do with prevention and treatment of atherosclerosis. Cholesterol levels, another Jupiter phenomenon, are somewhat controlled by the amount of pangamic acid in the tissue; furthermore, pangamic acid helps regulate the fat and carbohydrate metabolism. Manganese is also essential in determining how much cholesterol inhabits the body at any given time. This mineral is an essential regulator of fatty acids, cholesterol and glucose metabolisms—all Jupiter-related functions.

Jupiter is tied into the carbohydrate processes in general. Astrological-medical research indicates that people who have sugar-related problems usually exhibit a hard-aspected Jupiter, which can indicate a possible deficiency of chromium, a mineral also concerned with synthesis of fatty acids and cholesterol as well as helping to prevent arteries from hardening. Zinc, found in insulin, is also vital to proper carbohydrate metabolism, as is the vitamin biotin.

Zinc has traditionally been considered to be ruled by Uranus, but according to the functions of zinc and the characteristics of Uranus, the two don't belong together. Along with Mercury, Uranus rules the central nervous system. It can be involved medically with spasm, cramping, acute jerking or convulsive movements. Even a severe deficiency of zinc does not manifest such symptoms.

Jupiter is a more likely planet for zinc's rulership, especially since zinc plays such an important part in the carbohydrate system. Zinc is also involved with fertility, which, although a Moon-phenomenon, is still an effort of expansion on a physical basis, and expansion is Jupiter's forte. Not enough zinc can also stunt one's bone growth. Whereas dwarfism is a Saturnian affliction, Jupiter encourages growth and extension of the human frame. For now, Jupiter seems the logical choice to rule zinc, until we know more about zinc and its functions within the body; then the controversy surrounding the rulership of this mineral may be cleared up.

Saturn

Vitamins: C, K, PABA and bioflavonoids (vitamin P).

Minerals: Calcium, fluorine, sulfur and vanadium.

Saturn should be scrutinized closely in any natal chart. Most ailments that manifest are usually associated with this planet. For example, whatever sign Saturn is found in at birth might determine what organ, tissue or area of the body is potentially hypofunctioning—that is, sluggish and not working up to normal expectation. If Saturn is found retrograde, the chances of that part of the body malfunctioning are increased.

The transits of Saturn can also indicate medical problems. The planet takes 28 years to make one complete orbit about the Sun. We "feel" its presence about every seven years, when Saturn's main job seems to be to crystallize any problems or insights, particularly at the ages of 7, 14, 21, 28, 42 and 49. Medical problems, diseases and ailments of chronic duration, which are long in building and manifesting themselves and then require a long healing or convalescent period, also tend to crop up during these critical years of the Saturn cycle.

One of the events partially attributable to the transits of Saturn is the midlife crisis, usually happening between the 42nd and 49th years. During this time, at about 45, the aging process, another Saturn-ruled phenomenon, takes place: specifically, the breakdown and eventual destruction of collagen occurs. If medical ailments show up at about the same time, a person can undergo a period of great trial: the mental attitudes may be so poor that the ability to get well is impaired, and the disease may linger chronically.

Proper maintenance with vitamin C can help turn the tide of this crisis. Vitamin C does not guarantee a sickness-free life, but medical research has shown that this vitamin is as necessary as life itself. In particular, vitamin C helps form collagen to keep the cells of proper size and shape so that they may go about their business of maintaining bodily health. Thus with proper amounts of vitamin C careful diets and nonabuse of our bodies Saturn rewards us with long and healthy lives.

Since Saturn is the ruler of vitamin C, it also has an effect on the body's amount of bioflavonoids, whose main function is to aid vitamin C in its work of keeping the collagen healthy and the capillaries elastic and permeable. It is also my belief that vitamin K works in a synergistic relationship with vitamin C. Saturn retards or inhibits, and, like its ruling planet, vitamin K acts as a coagulant, triggering the intricate process of forming a protein web with which to catch the fleeing red blood corpuscles from an open wound or an internal one: the vitamin retards the escaping flow that, if allowed to continue, would eventually cause death. And it's interesting to note that lack of vitamin C can also cause hemorrhaging because the collagen is broken down so that the cells cannot keep their shapes.

Saturn is synonomous with the frame of anything. It is involved with barriers, banks, enclosures, binds, bonds, gels or adhesives. In medical terms it rules the skin and bones that serve as our frames, the bones that hold the muscles in place and the skin that acts as walls or containers.

Because Saturn has dominion over the bone structures of our bodies, including teeth and ears, it rules the minerals calcium, fluorine and sulfur. As is well known, the bones and teeth need adequate amounts of calcium to keep our frames strong enough to carry us around. Proper amounts of fluorine are also necessary to combat tooth decay and bone damage: Saturn's ability to guard, inhibit and block out is a positive attribute in maintaining enough protective fluorine. And sulfur's influence over the skeleton, the skin, bones and cartilage of the body in general is substantial. Furthermore, lack of sulfur may create arthritis, another Saturn-ruled phenomenon, or it may damage the hair and fingernails, also under Saturn's sway. Finally, sulfur plays a part in the protein processes of the body, and proteins are under Saturn's domain as well.

The position of natal, progressed or transiting Saturn also has an effect on the quality of one's skin. Just as Saturn acts as a barrier, the skin, if properly healthy, serves as a barrier against the ultraviolet rays of the Sun, allowing us to tan instead of burning severely. If Saturn is well-aspected, particularly by Venus, which rules vitamin E and is concerned with the youthful beauty and elasticity of the skin, ample amounts of PABA should be available in the body. But when Saturn is negatively aspected, there can be a PABA depletion that allows the skin tissue to become vulnerable to the Sun's rays, and changes in pigmentation and other skin-related ailments begin to surface. Moreover, without enough PABA the skin dries up, becomes scaly, itchy, ulcerous and infected.

Uranus

Although the nervous system is Mercury-guided, the actual impulses that leap from one nerve synapse to another are ruled by Uranus. People with strong Uranuses tend to buckle under stress or to react to it more strongly than other people. Thus they may be in continual states of nervousness, unable to relax. Such stress can cause the Uranian portion of our bodies to disentegrate. These people need to learn to unwind through exercise, meditation or some other form of biofeedback: the quieting of the mind will quiet the screaming nerves.

Depending on what sign it occupies in the natal chart, Uranus may point to possible spasm conditions within the body. In other words, the tissue or part of the body that the sign rules may undergo spasm. If Uranus is retrograde, it's even more possible that at some point in the person's life he or she can expect to have a sudden hypo- or hypercondition. This type of ailment is usually brought on by an emotional, physical or mental shock or other unexpected circumstance such as surgery or accident. Early detection of the possibility of the condition, testing, physical checkup and correction can do much to alleviate the spasm. Since Uranus indicates quick culmination and release of any situation, it offers the person hope of complete and swift recovery.

Neptune

Vitamins: Panthothenic acid and laetrile (vitamin B-17).

Neptune is an important planet to consider in a medical evaluation of the natal chart. The planet has a propensity to be everywhere yet nowhere: now you see it; now you don't. It is diffused, translucent and difficult to pin down or pinpoint. For these reasons it is important to see if the planet is centrally figured in the aspects of a natal chart. If it is, there may be initial misdiagnosis of the medical problem, misinformation about the diagnosis, masked symptoms not pointing directly to the root problem or misread lab or test results. A prominent Neptune may also indicate a potentially drug-sensitive individual, one who should be given a lower than average dosage of any medication.

Whereas Mars implies strength, virility, tone and energy, Neptune signifies the opposite. An undefined sense of tiredness or lethargy may be Neptune-based in many cases. In addition, Neptune can mean weakness and atony (flabby muscle tone). There is a chance of general weakness or laziness in the organ, tissue or part of the body ruled by the sign Neptune is found in. That part may be sluggish to a degree because it cannot withstand physical, emotional or mental strain as much as the rest of the body. It needs to be pampered and fed nutritionally to perform up to its expected normal functions.

The planet also rules the lymphatic system, the pineal gland, the thymus gland and the spleen. And it is involved with infections and poisons in the body. Whereas stings and bites fall under Pluto's influence, any mysterious, inexplicable, confusing element that is toxic is in Neptune's domain.

Thus it is fitting that Neptune should rule the all-pervasive pantothenic acid. This vitamin has been found to mitigate the side effects and toxicity of several antibiotics of the streptomyces variety, which fall under Neptune's dominion. Moreover, this vitamin feeds the adrenal glands and keeps us going: without it our adrenals lag, and we experience a Neptunian phase of exhaustion—not actually sickness but not a feeling of being well. Neptune's secretive personality, its propensity to be everywhere at once, adds significance to its rulership of pantothenic acid: it is sometimes difficult to identify the lack of pantothenic acid as the root cause of certain symptoms.

Neptune is also an especially appropriate choice to rule the controversial vitamin laetrile because of the enigmatic nature of the substance. Neptune is hazy, hidden, unsure, diffusing, bewildering, camouflaging, charlatanic, concealing and secretive, and all of these adjectives apply to laetrile: for the past 15 years it has been smuggled, hidden and sneaked across the Mexican-American border for use by Americans with cancer. And since Neptune is its ruler, it will probably still be years before we have a clear picture of the properties of laetrile.

Another reason that Neptune is the logical choice for ruling laetrile is that laetrile operates on cancer like one poison killing another. But because cancer is the scare of the 20th century, I want to emphasize that my ideas on laetrile and cancer are strictly conjecture, and there is not yet adequate data to back up the theories as solid proof. A checkup with a doctor on a yearly basis is always wise, and anyone who suspects cancer or comes from a family with a history of cancer should visit a doctor regularly, regardless of any other precautions. Despite all of the controversy about how cancer occurs several things have been proven: (1) cancer cells, either through enzyme-producing problems or genetic factors, multiply wildly and without restraint; (2) cancer cells need less oxygen to survive; (3)the enzyme rhodanese is usually absent in people who have cancer. Laetrile contains cyanide. When it is injected into a cancerous body, there is no rhodanese to detoxify the cyanide.

Most cancer cells secrete a substance called glycoidase, and this substance triggers amygdalin, which releases the cyanide at the site of the cancer, causing the cancer cells to die. In simple terms, then, one poison kills another. It is a process of fighting fire with fire—a particularly Neptunian kind of treatment.

I do not mean to imply from this discussion, though, that a poorly aspected Neptune is responsible for cancer. It is my contention that there will never be one specific planet nor sign that will be responsible for it. I believe cancer is a basic genetic and/or metabolic disorder. The planet Pluto rules transforming diseases of the body. And in some ways cancer is like that powerful planet: like Pluto, it will transform a person completely, even from life to death; like Pluto, it alters the cell structures slowly yet irrevocably, until there are alien cells that cannot be destroyed by the body's normal defense mechanisms. But to say Pluto is the only cause is false, and such similarities in no way suggest that anyone who has an ill-aspected Pluto is going to contract cancer. Nor can we say that Neptune *causes* cancer. For that matter to say that any paticular configuration is the root of cancer is a gross misrepresentation of the disease. Cancer is caused by *different* dysfunctions of the body, that is, some part of the body being fragile and breaking down under a lacklusterdiet. Since cancer will attack *any* part of the body it can't possibly be caused by *one* aspect, sign or planet.

Instead, our diets are probably at fault. Cancer had no mass incidence throughout history—except for of late. Our diets have deteriorated so much during the last 100 years that our bodies' metabolisms have become fragile and unstable. When the enzymes, hormones and other substances so necessary to keep our blood healthy and in turn our bodies alive and well become ultrasensitive, then diet changes for the worse will affect the body more quickly. The human body is on the endangered species list as long as we continue our habits of eating unnutritious foods such as nitrite-laden canned foods, dyed meat products, unhealthy white sugar and too much salt—just to name a very few.

Those persons with cancer may compound the dangers of junk food diets with hereditary weaknesses in vitamin or mineral deficiencies. Cell alterations of the calibre of cancer may come about because a family's hereditary history shows a weakness in one area—a lack of vitamin C, for instance—carried on from mother to child: the child may eventually exhibit allergy symptoms because the body has a higher than normal requirement for vitamin C to stop the symptoms. With such a combination of poor eating habits and hereditary weaknesses it is no wonder that our bodies are literally disintegrating on us. We call it cancer.

But our bodies probably will not deteriorate if they get nutritionally balanced diets. Then they will remain healthy and no misshapen cells can appear. To erradicate the disease we must upgrade our diets in general to whole foods. The clinics that deal with laetrile also use wholesome diets in the treatment. They use other vitamins and minerals as well as wholesome foods to help the body rebound to health.

Cancer is one disease showing the medical establishment that drugs don't work. No man-made drugs will ever be able to fight cancer effectively. They may mask or kill the disease, but in killing it they are doing great damage to other fragile parts of our anatomies: we trade one killer for another, dying either of cancer or from the side effects of the drugs, radiation or X-rays—not a very pleasant choice. Yet a lowly vitamin with a jaded history is showing evidence of helping certain kinds of cancer—a vast step forward for people who espouse that sound nutrition, not drugs, is the key to health.

Pluto

Vitamins: Orotic acid (vitamin B-13).

Pluto rules life and death. It reflects a transformation of cells—a continual proliferation and regeneration or the complete halt of all activity, thus inducing death.

On a positive level Pluto helps insure vital and basic changes in metabolism and genetics as well as continued, unbroken chemical processes that eventually transmute and make us functioning and healthy human bodies.

In negative terms Pluto can result in a lack of communication at the very basic levels of many diverse metabolic, enzymic and genetic functions. Hence diseases of a deteriorative nature that we could interpret as complete transformations of our bodies could occur. That is, depending upon the aspects between Pluto and other planets, we could go from strong to weak, from healthy bodies to deformed bodies, from coordination to a lack of coordination, from healthy red blood cells to abnormal-sized red blood cells or from normal white blood cell count to abnormal white blood cell count under Pluto's influence.

The planet is also concerned with the most minute, subatomic particles and how they fit into the schematic of our bodily functions. It affects the molecules, their relationships to a larger molecular structure, their eventual catalytic change into carbohydrates, lipids, proteins or nucleic acids and their eventual formation into more complex chains that all are related to our most basic bodily functions.

Pluto also rules enzyme production as well as the size and shape of red and white blood cells, the bases of our health concerns: a sick cell spells trouble in a big way sooner or later, usually later.

Pluto's most important function, though, is rulership of the endocrine system. Without the glands functioning well with one another the rest of the body is going to feel out of sorts. A strongly aspected Pluto or one near the Ascendant or Midheaven can indicate potential endocrine-related ailments. We then need to look for which gland is malfunctioning. For example, if Pluto is found in Aries, the pineal gland may be affected; in Taurus, the thyroid; in Cancer, the posterior pituitary gland; in Virgo, the pancreas and/or spleen; in Scorpio, the testes or ovaries; in Capricorn, the anterior pituitary gland and in Pisces, the lymph gland system.

Finally, Pluto rules the subconscious depths of our minds. If we persist in keeping a lot of negative emotional reactions hidden in our subconscious minds, sooner or later they will fester and alter our physical health in much the same way an afflicted Moon will.

THE URANIAN PLANETS

I use the Uranian planets in natal or progressed work only on the 90-degree dial, a device used by Uranian astrologers and cosmobiologists to discern hard aspects such as the semi-square (45 degrees), the square (90 degrees) and the opposition (180 degrees). My experience does not include analyzing the transiting Uranian planets or looking at the signs they occupy in natal charts, although research should be conducted in this field. But evaluated on the 90-degree dial, which shows both hard aspects and midpoint configurations, the Uranian planets have the same kind of significance as the known planets, giving the medical astrologer extra information for defining past, present or future health problems.

The three most important Uranian planets for medical analysis are Hades, Admetos and Apollon. Zeus and Vulcanus also have some medical significance. The others—Cupido, Poseidon and Kronos—have minimal effect on a person's health. Chapter Four, on midpoint structures, elaborates the medical attributes of each of the Uranian planets.

Cupido

Cupido is the first of the eight Uranian planets discovered by Alfred Witte of Germany. This planet rules the family, marriage, divorce and childbirth as well as creative, cultural and artistic pursuits. To the medical astrologer Cupido is of use in determining the birth of a child or illness within the immediate family: whenever Cupido is threatened in a person's chart, it is not that individual who may get sick but, instead, a member of his or her family.

By examining the placement of Cupido, the medical astrologer can sometimes help avert a crisis. Upon finding Cupido "under fire" by a planet such as Saturn or Hades, a medical astrologer might question the person about whether or not there is a member currently ailing within the family unit. If the individual says yes and identifies a close family member, the picture in the chart may be a forewarning that the ailing family member might experience a further health setback, and forewarned is forearmed. The astrologer should undertake the progressions of the sick member's chart to confirm this conjecture. Then a physician should take proper medical action to try either to modify or ward off the coming crisis.

On the other hand, if the answer is no, an investigation should be launched into the charts of close family members to see which one may fall ill. All that is normally done to determine the potential illness of a member is to use the 90-degree dial and progress the planets via solar arc. A progressed medical planet conjuncting a natal planet will normally point to the target. As to the question of whether or not the illness will strike a man or woman, Saturn and Kronos might indicate a man and the Moon or Venus, a woman.

Hades

Hades is the planet of sorrow, widows, orphans and grief in general. It rules disintegration, waste, bacteria, depletion, erosion, regression, withering, shriveling and decay. Above all others Hades is one planet that should be treated with all the seriousness the medical astrologer can muster. More than any other planet it hints at the threat of a worsening of a condition or death: through disintegration comes a leveling or breaking down, which left unchecked may mean death. In medical diagnosis I've never seen a time yet that Hades could be totally circumvented. That is, the person will more than likely take ill. By forewarning the person and getting him or her to a doctor for tests, we can modify the projected illness but never totally halt it.

To put it into slang, Hades is literally like "opening up a can of worms." When progressed Hades conjuncts another planet, it is as if the lid of some problem or illness is ripped off and comes into the glaring light of discovery. In death Hades, like Saturn and Pluto, will frequently be activated in midpoint structures over and over again.

Hades is somewhat like Saturn in that it implies long-term ailments, those that take a long time in building and changing and an equally long period to

cure or control. But I consider Hades' threat of devastation more serious than Saturn's. Saturn inflicts damage, but Hades seems to leave little for anyone to work with once it has wreaked its own brand of havoc. It produces vast and long-range effects on the illness it brings forth.

In passing and in fairness to this planet, Hades does have a positive side. A strong Hades may be found in the charts of many medical people—doctors in particular, as well as psychologists and therapists. Hades implies the analyzing process that is necessary to these professions: it is involved with pieces, puzzles, the breaking down of parts. A doctor can see broken bones and mutilated muscles yet have the ability to put them all back together like so many pieces in a puzzle. I would readily trust a doctor with a strong Hades to ferret out and find the root of a problem, whereas a doctor without a strong Hades might grope around a long time trying to discover the root cause.

Zeus

Somewhat like a higher octave of Mars, Zeus seems to be involved in a number of various medical conditions, among them, the procreative urge and conception. Zeus represents leadership, the start of something—the beginning of a seed mating with the ovum to create a child or the beginning of an ailment.

In another way Zeus is almost always prominent in the charts of people who either get burned in fires or wounded by firearms; it may also be implicated in operations. From five years of observation, I have found that Zeus is not so much involved *within* the ailment as being the *cause* of it. For instance, burns may result from steam partially brought on by the influence of Zeus; explosions, fires or wounds may result from gun shots, also influenced by Zeus.

Kronos

If there is such a thing as a higher octave to Saturn, it is Kronos. In mythology Kronos was the father of the gods—the oldest, wisest and most powerful. And a well-placed Kronos in a chart usually gives a generous helping of wisdom to the lucky individual.

Kronos also represents mastery, management, rulership, teaching and positions of authority. In mundane astrology a well-placed Kronos is often in the charts of heads of states, presidents and princes. It can very often indicate a brush with the government (including the IRS), justice officials, the law and bureaucracy in general. It can also mean a lawsuit or questioning by someone in high authority.

The negative manifestion of Kronos is that it can involve a lot of ridiculous red tape or paper work typical of our governmental bureaucracy. Kronos may also bestow a person with a smug image: he or she may be an elitist, who believes to be above the law.

At this point of research Kronos has very little to do with health conditions. Instead, with the best placement it can indicate a good doctor and can thus help insure the best medical treatment. A medical astrologer may want to examine the surgeon's chart for a strong and well-aspected Kronos to determine his or her mastery of the craft. When surgery is to be performed, if progressed Kronos is conjunct another planet, it will very often indicate that the individual will get through the operation because of the steady hands of the physician. Thus it is a good indicator of recovery because of a surgeon's skill.

Apollon

Apollo was the Greek god who rode his chariot through the skies daily to give earth sunlight. He was the golden, fair-haired boy of Zeus, a devotee of the arts and sciences. The Uranian planet Apollon rules science, commerce and industry in general.

Perhaps the most important aspect of this planet is that it usually means two or more of something. Its glyph is a combination of the symbols of Gemini and Jupiter. Thus there is a large amount of knowledge contained in this planet. A person with a strongly placed Apollon will manifest at least two distinct fields of knowledge. Moreover, surprises always seem to come in twos with this planet—either a multitude of trouble or a double dose of good news, depending upon which planets it aspects in the natal chart.

In addition, Apollon has distinct dominion over astrology. When looking for good astrology students, I invariably check out where Apollon is placed, and it's almost always prominent in the chart. It stands for a cosmopolitan knowledge of the world in general—knowledge harnessed with the practical tools of application.

Apollon also represents thinking on a grand scale. If a person with a great deal of Leo thinks big, one with a well-placed Apollon thinks even bigger—sometimes too grandly. One of Apollon's flaws is that an individual under its influence may not pay enough attention to immediate details. Such a person probably has no business working in a career that requires minute attention to details: he or she will probably hate such a job.

In medical terms Apollon always means complications. I very freqently find an active progressed Apollon in the chart of a patient who has already been diagnosed but is getting sicker. The planet often means misdiagnosis or secondary complications.

Admetos

The symbol for Admetos is the glyph for Taurus plus the cross of matter: both Taurus and Admetos suggest earth. Admetos's nature is that of a seed that is planted and watered until it bursts forth into the light of day.

In medical terms the influence of Admetos is too often like that of a seed that sows illness. A badly placed Admetos may be like a seed growing underground until bodily conditions are right for a disease to manifest itself. For example, Admetos is a frequent influence in unwanted pregnancies: a woman may become pregnant, not to discover the fact until two or three months later. In fact, there seems to be a strong connection between this planet and mothers in general: when a family member falls ill, Admetos is frequently an excellent indicator that it will be the mother.

Other medical conditions influenced by Admetos are suffocation, choking, traction (in a cast or bed), conditions simmering beneath the surface that may or may not be known to the person, suspension (in an unconscious state or coma) and many phobias.

A positive medical expression of Admetos, though not a frequent manifestation, is a person's ability to pull back from the depths to ward off or fight off a disease. A strongly placed Admetos in a chart may give an individual the fortitude and discipline needed to overcome some serious debility. A person under Admetos's influence is usually a very good fighter.

Vulcanus

Its name and symbol give a fairly good idea of this planet's innate expression. Vulcanus is like a volcano. It is a planet of great energy. In medical terms it usually represents an addition to an already existing problem or illness: Vulcanus usually makes the ailment worse or more obvious. If there is a festering condition, Vulcanus is the energy that will make it surface.

Vulcanus is also like a chameleon in that it tends to take on the personality of the planet or planets it aspects. For instance, Vulcanus conjunct Neptune would mean more of Neptune's tendencies and expressions; Vulcanus conjunct Mars would indicate more Marslike functions, etc.

On the positive side, if Vulcanus is well-placed in a chart, it may indicate a person who has a tremendous reserve of energy and strength, one who will fight back against illness. Excellent recuperative powers are associated with this planet.

Poseidon

In many ways this planet has little to do with medical astrology. Poseidon has more to do with spiritualization and mental activities than any physical problems. I've encountered it very seldom in health axis problems. But, still, Poseidon may have some influence on illness.

To me Poseidon is the higher octave of Neptune, but without most of the negative traits of Neptune. More than aything else a well-placed Poseidon seems like "guardian angel." It may provide spiritual protection during a time of surgery or perhaps a hope that health can be maintained or an illness overcome with the proper attitude.

At its worst, I suppose, it can point to the possibility of a person having to fill out a lot of governmental and hospital forms—a very minor consideration to a medical astrologer in the overall analysis of a person's health. I also believe it may be somewhat active in the charts of people with mental illnesses, although this conjecture needs to be borne out in research.

TRANSPLUTO

Charles Emerson, a prominent medical and Uranian astrologer, brought Transpluto to national attention several years ago. It was felt by many to be the planet beyond Pluto, hence the name. Other astrologers have redubbed it Bacchus and even assigned it rulership of the sign Taurus.

According to Emerson, Transpluto is a planet of uprooting trauma: anything that Transpluto touches is further changed and transformed. It is a kind of higher octave of Pluto. Emerson believes it influences the psyhological ramifications of birth.

Michael Munkasey, another highly respected astrologer, reports that Transpluto is associated with hypoglycemia. I've checked out the transits of Transpluto in several charts and have found that Munkasey is 100 per cent accurate.

From personal experience, using this planet only in progressions and with solar arc, I've sometimes seen it quite active in relation to medical ailments; at other times, when I felt it should have been active, there was no indication of its power. I don't have an explanation for such on-again, off-again manifestation. My only observation is that when it is active in a 90-degree wheel via progression, it is *very* active—literally a pulverizer or equalizer in any situation.

Indeed, I believe this planet is a formidable enemy to health conditions; however, its influence may be more on the psychological level than the physical. I have noted that mental breakdowns tend to occur when Transpluto is badly placed. It could be

that this planet's vibrations are so high that most of us can't respond to them as yet or that when we do respond it is on a mental plane. At any rate, Transpluto should be thoroughly studied and researched by medical astrologers.

THE FIXED STARS

Thousands of years ago astrologers placed great stock by the constellations and certain stars within them, so-called "fixed" stars (which are not truly fixed). Because medical astrology is in its infancy, there is very little adequate information on these stars and their effects in natal charts. To date the only scientific study has been conducted by Reinhold Ebertin, of Germany, in a small book called *Fixed Stars and their Interpretation* — an excellent study guide and jumping off point for investigating fixed stars in terms of medical astrology. Since so much research needs to be done on these stars in relation to illness, it is my hope that by making notes on the pertinent stars, medical astrologers will begin to determine their actions and influences.

A fixed star in and of itself is not a primary indicator of health conditions; the entire chart must lean in a certain direction for the fixed star to exert any influence. For example, when a natal Saturn has three or four hard aspects to it as well as a conjunction with a fixed star then the medical astrologer has reason to suspect that the star may influence a health situation at some point in the person's life.

In addition, a fixed star must be conjunct a planet or angle to influence the individual. It should ideally be exactly conjunct the position, although a 30-minute conjunction will probably also cause the star to influence the individual. Because of the distance between the earth and the stars, the fixed star should also be in exact orb to activate potential ailments: the tighter the orb, the more influence it will have. The declination of a fixed star does not affect its influence, no matter how close or how far from the ecliptic it may range.

Since an exact conjunction or opposition is usually necessary to activate a star's influence, a fixed-star sitting in an empty house without a conjunction can be ignored except when the fixed star is in the Sixth or Twelfth Houses and is triggered by transits or progressions. Then the star should be noted and the progressed chart examined to see if midpoint structures, conjunctions, etc., are taking place at the same time that there are indications of poor health. If there are, then the fixed star is probably tied into the vibration. Eclipses may also affect a fixed star's power in a chart. And fixed stars on the Midheaven or Ascendant should be carefully noted, since they seem to exert a fairly consistent influence. Finally, a fixed star conjunct any "malefic" planets, such as natal Mars, Saturn, Uranus or Neptune, should be especially noted.

It seems that some fixed stars have characteristics of certain planets, and these stars tend to be the most dangerous in terms of bodily impairment. For instance, a star that has the traits of Venus might influence blood disorders in general, including blood poisoning. A star with the qualities of Mars might bring on hasty or impulsive actions, accidents injuries that may or may not involve operations and animal bites. A star that is like Saturn might induce chronic, long-termed illnesses or weakening or wasting away kinds of disease. A Uranian kind or star might help bring about accidents caused by haste, operations and mental problems. And a star with the features of Neptune might influence the bites of insects that cause severe allergic reactions, drug habits or proclivities for the overuse of drugs and poisons in the body.

Based upon Ebertin's observations, the following stars seem to have direct tie-ins with medical problems. (All positions are as of 1950.)

Deneb Kaitos (1 Aries 51)
This star has Saturnian characteristics. It may bring on bodily and mental inhibition.

El-Scheratain (3 Taurus 17)
This star has the traits of Saturn and Mars. It may cause impulsiveness that results in injury.

El-Nath (6 Taurus 59)
This star has characteristics of Mars and Saturn. It may bring on severe injury at some time in the life of the individual, particularly falls.

Menkar (13 Taurus 38)
This star has Saturnian qualities. Throat or larynx problems are possible if it is conjunct malefic planets.

Zanrak (22 Taurus 50)
This star is also Saturnian. It may bring about chronic illnesses or possible suicidal tendencies.

Algol (25 Taurus 28)
This is a double star: one star is said to have Saturnian characteristics; the other has a Mars/Uranus/Pluto personality. Probably most deadly of all the fixed stars, Algol may exert a tragic influence that could affect individuals. It may bring on chronic illnesses, dental problems or arthritis.

Alcyone (26 Taurus 19)

Alcyone is part of the star cluster known as the Pleiades. It has Moon/Mars characteristics. It may help cause eyesight ailments, including blindness or poor vision in general.

Praesepe (6 Leo 34)
This star has the qualities of Moon/Mars/Neptune. Sitting extremely close to the North and South Aselli, Praesepe is believed to bestow poor eyesight, especially weak eyesight at an early age.

North Aselli (6 Leo 50)
This star has Sun/Mars characteristics.

South Aselli (8 Leo 01)
South Aselli also has Sun/Mars characterstics. Both these stars are linked with poor eyesight. South Aselli may also produce rashness or impulsiveness that can cause injury.

Kochab (12 Leo 24)
This star has the traits of Mars/Saturn. A person under its influence may be extremely tense or nervous, suffering mental anguish.

Alphard (26 Leo 36)
This star is like Saturn/Venus/Neptune. Alphard may cause an individual to be extremely sensitive to any sort of drug or drug habit. It may also influence the outcome of bites by animals or insects, blood poisoning, possible poisoning from toxins and poor eating habits.

Alioth (8 Virgo 09)
Alioth has the traits of Mars. It may cause problems during delivery as well as birth complications.

Zosma (10 Virgo 35)
With the characteristics of Venus/Saturn, Zosma may cause buildup in the body, resulting in disease. It also seems to influence melancholia.

Denebola (20 Virgo 57)
This star has Uranian characteristics. Mental gyrations may occur if Denebola is conjunct Mercury or Uranus in the natal chart.

Algorab (13 Libra 12)
With the traits of Mars and Saturn, Algorab may cause various illnesses, ranging from mental to organic and chronic problems.

The Southern Scales (14 Scorpio 23)
This double star is like Mars and Saturn. If conjunct a malefic planet, it may present health problems.

Unuk (21 Scorpio 23)

This is a Mars/Saturn star. It may induce chronic illnesses, which may not be diagnosed for a long time if the star is conjunct natal Neptune. It also appears to rule operations.

Antares (9 Sagittarius 04)

With the characteristics of Mars/Mercury/Jupiter, Antares may influence various health problems, including eye troubles. It may induce impulsiveness that could account for bodily injury.

Ras Alhague (21 Sagittarius 42)

This star has the traits of Venus/Saturn/Neptune. It may produce toxic conditions that affect the body. It might also affect the results of animal and insect bites and other infectious states.

Fomalhaut (3 Pisces 09)

With the characteristics of Mercury/Venus/Neptune, this star may help bring on problems with drugs, including addiction.

THE PLANETS AND OPERATIONS

The positions of the planets and luminaries often determine the best and worst times for a person to undergo surgery. Following are guidelines for planning operations astrologically:

1. Try to plan an operation five days before or after the new Moon. At this time, fluids are at their lowest ebb; consequently, there is less chance of swelling.

2. Avoid operations five days before or after a full Moon. At this time bodily fluids are at their highest and can cause excessive swelling, hemorrhaging or seepage from wounds.

3. A day in which the Moon is void of course is a bad one for surgery. On such a day there is a good possibility that the operation won't be performed correctly, that complications will arise or that a second operation will become necessary.

4. Avoid an operation on that part of the body ruled by the sign in which the Moon or the Sun is transiting. (See Chapter Two for a discussion of the signs and parts of the body they rule.)

5. Avoid surgery when the Moon is in a mutable sign—Virgo, Gemini, Pisces or Saggitarius.

6. Try to plan an operation when the transiting Moon is in a fixed sign—Taurus, Leo, Scorpio or Aquarius. With such a placement the operation should go as planned, the surgeon's hands should be steady, and no further complications should arise.

7. Avoid surgery when the transiting Moon is combust or within 17 degrees of the natal Sun, Moon or Mars.

8. Avoid surgery when the transiting Moon is square, opposite or inconjunct the natal or transiting Sun, Mars, Saturn, Neptune, Uranus or Pluto. Mars in a tension aspect with the transiting Moon can mean excessive bleeding or inflammation after surgery. Saturn can mean chronic or very serious complications.

9. Try to plan an operation when the transiting Moon is sextile or trine to natal, progressed or transiting Venus, Mars or Jupiter. Such an aspect will help the surgery go smoothly. The transiting Moon sextile or trine Mars will also help insure that the surgeon will have a quick, clean cutting hand and will know what he or she is doing.

10. Avoid surgery when Mercury or Mars is retrograde. Mercury retrograde can mean misunderstandings, mistakes and confusion. Sine Mars is the planet of surgeons, when it goes retrograde surgeons tend not to be at their steadiest or most reliable: they may not be able to concentrate well. Furthermore, Mars retrograde can mean heavy loss of blood.

CHAPTER TWO
The Signs, Crosses, Houses and Diagnosis

THE SIGNS

The signs help pinpoint what part of the body is potentially suspect of dysfunctioning. Of course, not all signs with planets within them will represent malfunction. In medical astrology the most important planets are the outer ones—Saturn, Uranus, Neptune and Pluto. Mars also needs to be carefully examined. Although the Sun, Moon, Mercury, Venus and Jupiter should never be disregarded, a higher percentage of medical ailments stem from the action of the five other planets when they are in hard aspect, particularly if there are two or more inconjuncts to a specific planet.

ARIES

Bones: Cranium and face.
Muscles: The frontales, occipitals, attolens, deprimens, articularum, zygomaticus, temporalis and buccinator.
Arteries: The temporal and internal carotids.
Veins: The cephalic veins.
Cell Salt: Kali phosphoricum.

Aries rules the head in general, specifically the motor centers of the brain and the circulation of the blood through the skull region. The action of Aries is said to show epilepsy and sleeping sickness (encephalitis) that may infect the brain through virus. Aries is also involved with inflammation of the brain that may cause delirium, frenzy, vertigo, dizziness, sharp pains in the head along the course of a nerve and congestion. Those people with planets in Aries may suffer from frequent headaches caused by clogged or sluggish kidneys (Libra) that have a reflex action to the head, digestive disturbances (Cancer), resulting in headaches and sluggish gallbladders (Capricorn)—other Cardinal Cross diseases. And various skin eruptions affecting the head or face as well as baldness plague some Aries people.

Other diseases influenced by Aries are various forms of toxemia. By a reflex action to the kidneys toxemia may induce skin ailments, usually caused by poor diet. Uremic toxemia is also a possibility in pregnant women. A more subtle and insidious form of toxemia can also invade the blood and cause havoc in many ways.

Sun in Aries

This placement might result in an unusual amount of blood congestion, causing headaches, brain fevers, cerebral meningitis, sunstrokes or heatstrokes (apoplexy) or the inability to express oneself properly through speech patterns or loss of verbal comprehension (aphasia). There is also the possibility of an imbalance of the sodium-potassium exchange, with too much sodium causing weight gain and edema. There is a further probability of acidosis because Aries people tend to eat a lot of meat, high in acid. Thus the acid-alklaine exchange may be out of balance, especially if Libra is involved. Acidosis can also bring on tension and headaches.

Moon in Aries

The Moon in Aries can mean weak sight and eye strain since Cancer, ruled by the Moon, governs the sac containing the eyeballs. Migraine headaches are also possible because of emotional strain and tension. And there can be insomnia from a lack of potassium (Moon) in the body.

Mercury in Aries

Headaches caused by nervous tension or strain may result from this configuration. Brain disorders are also possible because of a lack of proper nerve synapse release: muscle coordination problems or speech/thinking impediments could occur as a result. In addition, neuralgia or shooting pains in the head may come about because of the nerves. And there is the potential for Bell's palsy, wherein nerves are inflamed and paralysis sets in, as well as spells of vertigo or delirium.

Venus in Aries

Venus in Aries may affect mucus congestion in the head and nasal passages. There can also be eczema of the head and face as well as gastric headache from overeating carbohydrates or other rich foods.

Mars in Aries

This placement may produce violent pains in the head, rupture of the blood vessels in the brain, stroke, extreme restlessness, blows, cuts and wounds or surgery to the head and face, cerebral congestion and a tendency toward headaches.

Jupiter in Aries

Excess blood in the head, causing stress on vessels, may result from Jupiter in Aries. The placement also presents the potential for aneurysms if the veins and/or arteries do not remain flexible and elastic.

Saturn in Aries

With this placement constriction or lack of blood to the head may cause strokes or mucous buildup in the ears, resulting in earaches and deafness. Saturn in Aries can also signify apathy, listlessness or dullness because of a lack of blood supply to the brain.

Uranus in Aries

Uranus in Aries may indicate sharp, shooting pains in the head, sudden headaches, pain in the eyes or spastic constrictions of the blood vessels of the eyes. By reflex action to Libra spasms of the kidneys might result in cyclical albuminuria.

Neptune in Aries

This placement may mean weakened adrenal gland function, mucous buildup in the head area in general, causing mental fatigue, allergies involving the sinus cavities and weakened kidney function by reflex action to Libra. The blood vessels in the brain may be weak and unable to take high blood pressure; thus a stroke may result.

Pluto in Aries

Since Aries rules the general site of the head, where the pituitary gland is located, and since Aries is ruled by Mars, which in turn rules the adrenal glands, there can be a possible malfunction of the pituitary hormones that directly affects the adrenal secretions. Depending on Pluto's aspects to other planets, the adrenal glands may be sluggish, hypo- or hyperactive. Aneurysms in the head area are also a possibility.

TAURUS

Bones: Cervical vertebrae.

Muscles: Sternohyoid, mastoid, trapezius, sternomastoids, esophagus, stylopharingaeus, splenius and complexus, longus, scalenus, biventres cervicis and spinales cervicis.

Arteries: External carotids and basilar artery.

Veins: Occipitals, jugulars and veins of the thyroid gland.

Cell Salt: Natrum sulphuricum.

Taurus rules the adenoids, tonsils and larynx; its main function, however, is corulership with Mercury of the thyroid gland. This gland frequently malfunctions because of severe emotional stress, a lack of sufficient iodine in the diet or a diet that is lacking in fiber and roughage. Very often, by reflex action to Taurus's opposite sign, Scorpio, the thyroid may go hyper- or hypoactive because of colon toxemia.

Some symptoms of a hyperthyroid condition are tenseness, inability to relax, shaking, heart palpitations, weight decrease, heat intolerance, excessive sweating and increased bowel activity. Unfortunately, few people are aware that their thyroids are hyperactive and blame their nervous conditions on themselves or something within their immediate environment. The mental anguish a hyperthroid can cause is great. Some people feel as if they are tiptoeing on the boundaries of insanity. Getting a T-3, T-4, T-7 blood test to check out the thyroid is easy, quick and worth a person's mental and physical well-being.

Hypothyroid symptoms are obesity, dry skin, lackluster and brittle hair, low blood pressure, slow pulse, sluggishness of all functions and depressed muscular activity. People with hypothyroids feel mentally dull and listless, quickly forgetting what they just said and displaying poor memories in general. These people are sensitive to cold draughts and continually overdress to keep warm. Constipation also tends to be a problem. The congenital form of hypothyroidism is called cretinism. In Canada all babies are given mandatory blood tests to make sure they don't have the disease.

Sun in Taurus

This placement may produce sore throats, nasal mucus, polyps in the throat region or on the vocal cords and diptheria.

Moon in Taurus

The Moon in Taurus can mean sore throats as well as swelling in the throat or ulcers. A person with this configuration in a natal chart is also likely to overeat because of emotional unhappiness.

Mercury in Taurus

Hoarseness from nervousness or talking at length, croup, difficulty in swallowing at times, choking on objects and laryngitis are all potential ailments with Mercury in Taurus.

Venus in Taurus

This configuration can indicate swelling in the neck, mumps, thrush or fungus infection of the mouth or throat and abscesses in the pharynx region.

Mars in Taurus

Mars in Taurus may create a hyperthyroid condition, laryngitis, enlarged tonsils, tonsillitis, polyps in the throat area, adenoid problems and inflammation of the nasal passages.

Jupiter in Taurus

Enlarged adenoids or tonsils, dry coughing spells, sore throats and an enlarged thyroid are possibilities with this placement. People with Jupiter in Taurus also tend to overeat and desire too many rich foods that put on weight.

Saturn in Taurus

This placement may cause phlegm in the throat, a dry cough, loss of voice, choking, suffocation and hypofuncton of the thyroid gland.

Uranus in Taurus

Spasm in the thyroid gland, causing it to go from normal to either hyper- or hypoactive, may result from Uranus in Taurus. Stress, especially any sudden or unexpected shock to the system, may cause the thyroid to malfunction. Colon stasis can also contribute to the problem. This placement may produce a sudden loss of voice or hoarseness attributable to nervousness. And there is the potential danger of choking or gagging on objects.

Neptune in Taurus

The thyroid may malfunction with this placement, especially during stress. There may be lethargy or loss of memory with a hypothyroid and nervousness and heart pounding with a hyperthyroid. By reflex action to Scorpio, Neptune in Taurus can also mean weak or slowed peristalsis of the large intestine. The result can be toxemia, and as the poisons filter back into the bloodstream, symptoms such as headaches and skin rashes may appear. If the toxemia persists, the entire cardiovascular system may be affected. Glaucoma and/or cataracts may also result if the person has a family history of such ailments.

Pluto in Taurus

With Pluto in Taurus there is the possiblity of thyroid complications of a severe and chronic nature as well as polyps, tumors or growths on the vocal cords, thyroid or within the neck region.

GEMINI

Bones: Clavicle, scapula, humerus, radius, ulna, carpal and metacarpal bones and upper ribs.
Muscles: Deltoid, biceps, supinator radii, subclavians, triceps, serratus anticus minor, pectoralis and palmaris.
Arteries: Subclavians, brachial, right and left bronchials, intercostals, radials and ulnars.
Veins: Pulmonary, basilic, subclavians, azygos, vein of the thymus and mediastinum.
Cell Salt: Kali muriaticum.
Gemini rules the hands, arms, shoulders (with

the exception of the sternum and breastbone, ruled by Cancer) and central nervous system in general. But it has the much more subtle and important job of governing the tubes of the body—not the arteries or the veins but the eustachian tubes of the ears, the fallopian tubes connected with the uterus, the bronchial tubes of the lungs, the trachea, the ureter tubes from the kidneys to the bladder and the urethra from the bladder to its outside opening.

The lungs also fall under Gemini's domain. Whereas Sagittarius represents exhaled breath, Gemini represents inhaled breath. This oxygenation that reaches the blood is of utmost concern: without proper amounts of oxygen, a person will feel mentally dull and tired.

Sun in Gemini

The Sun in Gemini may produce bronchitis, nervous disorders, pleurisy, hyperventilation, shallow breathing that should be deepened to get proper amounts of oxygen into the bloodstream and injuries to the arms and fingers.

Moon in Gemini

Female complaints involving the fallopian tubes, the erratic flow of the menstrual blood that can be corrected with kali muriaticum, edema of the lungs, pneumonia and varicose aneurysms are all potential ailments with this placement.

Mercury in Gemini

This configuration can mean pains in the arms, lungs and hands of a nerve-related origin as well as bronchitis, intercostal pain, asthma and pleurisy.

Venus in Gemini

With Venus in Gemini whitlow or inflammation and suppuration from the fingers as well as papilloma or tumors of the skin or mucous membrane of the hands and arms are possibilities.

Mars in Gemini

This placement can indicate disorders of the nervous system, cuts, fractures and wounds of the arms, hands and collar bone, bronchial congestion, acute pneumonia and acute pains in the lungs or extremities.

Jupiter in Gemini

Blood and lung disorders, hemorrhaging in the lungs, pleurisy and arterial ailments may result from Jupiter in Gemini.

Saturn in Gemini

This configuration may produce a myriad of

ailments: constriction of some tube in the body; partial blockage of a small opening by either a stone or other sedimentary waste that has not been washed out of the body; rheumatism or arthritis of the arms, hands or shoulders; dislocation of the arm or shoulder; chronic bronchitis, pneumonia or emphysema; tuberculosis; lung congestion, fibrosis of the lungs or tumors in the lungs; and nervous trembling from a lack of calcium and manganese to feed the nervous system.

Uranus in Gemini

Uranus in Gemini can signify the spasmodic constriction of one of the tubes of the body: in a woman, it may be the fallopian tubes that constrict, resulting in tubal pregnancies. Cramps or spasms in the hands and arms are also possible, as are spasms in the ureters or urethra, spasms that can cause renal retention or recurrent bladder infections.

Neptune in Gemini

Weakness of one or more tubes in the body is possible with this placement. There may also be poor oxygen capacity in the lungs: deep breathing and physical exercise will expand and strengthen the lungs. In addition, there is the potential for chest colds and continued bouts with pneumonia in childhood, lung sensitivity to pollution and lung ailments, such as emphysema, caused by smoking.

Pluto in Gemini

With Pluto in Gemini the tubes of the body may experience blockage because of tumors or cysts in them. There may also be fallopian tube blockage preventing pregnancy. Chronic lung, arm or hand ailments are other possibilities.

CANCER

Bones: Sternum, ensiform cartilage and part of the ribs.
Muscles: Diaphragm and intercostals.
Arteries: Axillary, diaphragmatic, posterior mediastines and esophagian.
Veins: Diaphragmatic, gastric, gastroepiploic and mammary.
Cell Salt: Calcarea fluorica.

Cancer rules a wide and varied array of functions. It has domain over coverings such as the brain, lung and heart membranes, sinus cavities, eyeballs, bone marrow, the cheeks of the face and the glycogen storage within the liver. Anemia, as brought about by the marrow of the bones, also comes under Cancer's dominion. And during pregnancy the womb comes under its rulership because the womb "contains" the fetus; when not in use, the womb reverts to the domain of Scorpio. In addition, Cancer rules the posterior pituitary gland where many hormonal functions take place, as well as the breasts, sternum and chest.

Cancer's primary rulership, however, is of the stomach and the digestive processes that take place within the organ. The action of Cancer is said to involve digestive ailments, gastric mucus, dipsomania and craving for alcoholic beverages. Such malfunctioning can be triggered, in part, by improper storage and release of glycogen via the liver. Furthermore, lack of one of the many gastric juices, such as the intrinsic factor, which aids vitamin B-12 and iron to be assimilated into the body, or hydrochloric acid, needed to break down meat to get valuable proteins, will cause vitamin and mineral deficiencies.

The peristaltic action of the stomach is ruled by Cancer (whereas the antiperistaltic action falls under the dominion of Capricorn and Saturn). Without good, thorough peristalsis the food is not broken down properly before entering the duodenum and intestinal tract where nutrition is absorbed and used by the body.

Sun in Cancer

This placement may cause dyspepsia (imperfect digestion in the stomach) breast disorders and edema caused by the hypofunctioning of the pituitary gland or lack of sufficient potassium (Moon) to regulate the balance with sodium in the body.

Moon in Cancer

With the Moon in Cancer there may be general problems with overweight. A person may put on weight because of emotional stress, or there may be tendencies towards edema. Furthermore, there can be an imbalance in the sodium-potassium exchange or a weak kidney that does not empty out waste properly. A person may be prone to sickness of an acute nature. And the tympanic or ear drum covering may cause partial loss of hearing.

Mercury in Cancer

Indigestion, gas or cramping of the stomach brought on by emotional duress as well as bloating of the stomach or distension caused by gas related to nervous disorders are potential symptoms of this configuration.

Venus in Cancer

Venus in Cancer can indicate nausea and vomiting, cysts on the breasts, swelling of the breasts five days before the menstrual cycle and a potential deficiency of vitamin B-6.

Mars in Cancer

This placement may produce ulcers in the stomach or a sensitive or touchy stomach. Moreover, the walls of the stomach may be irritable or prone to inflammation from spicy foods, or there may be vomiting from emotional stress.

Jupiter in Cancer

Jupiter in Cancer may result in edema, digestive disorders from overeating, stretching of the stomach and hiatus hernia. A person with this placement should eat small, frequent meals rather than three large ones a day.

Saturn in Cancer

With this configuration there may be loss of appetite from emotional strain as well as low hydrochloric acid levels in the stomach, producing poor digestive processes. The gastric secretions in the stomach may be below normal standards, and if they are, there can be gastric complaints, bloating, croup in babies, poor digestion of food and, therefore, an inability of nutrients to get back into the body. Saturn in Cancer can also produce anemia brought on because the intrinsic factor is hypofunctioning. Vitamin B-12 and iron may be poorly assimilated into the body. And there may be tumors or cysts in the breast region.

Uranus in Cancer

Spasms in the stomach, stomach cramps brought on by emotional duress, spasmodic release of gastric juices depending on emotional stress, poor digestion and a "nervous" or "hourglass" stomach are all potential symptoms of Uranus in Cancer.

Neptune in Cancer

This placement can mean weak peristalsis of the stomach during the digestion phase and diluted gastric juices when liquids are drunk with meals, thus interfering with digestion. In addition, there may be a weakened ovary condition that creates cysts in the reproductive area as well as a weakened state of any covering rule by Cancer in general.

Pluto in Cancer

A woman who has this placement conjunct the Ascendant may have problems with water-weight gain, commonly known as edema. The root cause may well be the posterior pituitary "going out" after the woman gives birth: the basal metabolism is upset and there is weight gain and the inability to lose weight. The ADH factor could be tested at the discretion of an endocrine specialist, since it has control over how much or how little water is released from the body through the kidneys. A secondary possibility is the TSH factor that affects the thyroid: TSH may not be released properly and a hypothyroid condition may be responsible for the weight gain.

LEO

Bones: Dorsal vertebrae.
Muscles: Longissimus and latissimus dorsi, transversalis, diaphragm and the heart muscles.
Arteries: Aorta, anterior and posterior coronary.
Veins: Vena cava and coronaries.
Cell Salt: Magnesia phosphorica.

Leo rules just one organ, but it is the most important one—the heart. Nearly all forms of heart ailments fall under this sign's domain. Leo may also be responsible at times for back ailments of many varieties, in a kind of reflex action with Aquarius, its opposite sign: although Aquarius rules the spinal cord, Leo rules the vertebrae that protect the spinal cord's vulnerability.

Sun in Leo

The Sun in Leo may mean heart and back problems as well as fever of an acute origin.

Moon in Leo

Fainting, convulsions and heart problems, especially enlarged heart conditions, may result from this configuration.

Mercury in Leo

With this placement there may be convulsions, fainting, pains in the back, palpitations of the heart that may be thyroid-connected and pain in and around the heart.

Venus in Leo

Venus in Leo can result in diseases of the bone marrow and the vertebrae as well as aortic diseases.

Mars in Leo

Heart attacks, palpitations (perhaps brought on by a thyroid problem), aneurysms resulting from severe physical stress, hypertrophy, dilatatio cordis, angina, pericarditis, endocarditis, sunstroke, muscular rheumatism in the back and scarlet and rheumatic fever are all possibilities with this configuration.

Jupiter in Leo

Jupiter in Leo can indicate feverish complaints, strokes, cholesterol-related degeneration of the heart or aortic arteries, palpitations and a larger than normal heart.

Saturn in Leo

With this placement there is the potential for hardening of the arteries; constriction of the arteries or veins leading to the heart; atrophy of the heart; weak, muscular action of the heart; locomotor ataxia from lack of enough calcium, magnesium or potassium; heart "skipping"; a smaller than normal heart; and a malformed spine.

Uranus in Leo

Uranus in Leo may produce arrhythmia of the heart, spasmodic palpitations (potentially a thyroid problem) and sudden attacks of angina pectoris.

Neptune in Leo

Neptune in Leo can mean a weak heart, low blood pressure from sluggish activity of the heart and a weak back and commensurate problems: light to moderate exercise will strengthen both the heart action and flabby back muscles.

Pluto in Leo

Sudden heart attacks of a chronic nature, heart transplants because of a severe injury to that muscle and back problems of a chronic and long-lasting nature are all possible ailments caused by Pluto in Leo.

VIRGO

Bones: None
Muscles: Obliquus, transversalis of abdomen and rectus pyramidalis.
Arteries: Gastric, superior and inferior mesenteries.
Veins: Portal, hepatics, umbilical and intestinal.
Cell Salt: Kali sulphuricum.

Virgo's main job is to breakdown, analyze and organize. These functions are especially evident in the pancreas, which Virgo rules. This gland is concerned with the proper release of pancreatic juices that will digest all kinds of food. The internal secretion from the pancreas also includes the hormones insulin and glycogen, both of which play a vital role in the carbohydrate metabolism. Without Virgo's proper breaking down and utilization of these two products people can become prone to diabetes or hypoglycemia, both sugar-related diseases.

Thought by many sources to be ruled by the Sun, the spleen also falls under Virgo's domain. Besides producing many types of blood cells, the spleen splits up the prana on an etheric level. Without proper trafficking of the vitality globules the body would degenerate. Both Virgo and Neptune are concerned with this important function.

Integrally involved with absorption, Virgo also rules the intestinal tract. The duodenum is of primary concern: it is here that food receives the proper amount of bile from the gallbladder and juices from the pancreas. Only the food is chemically broken down and distributed through the body, good health can be maintained. Assimilation of all nutrients as they pass through the intestines is also under Virgo's dictate. Without proper absorption a person will become nutrition-poor and deficiencies are sure to develop.

In addition, Virgo has co-rulership of the liver along with the planet Jupiter and the sign Cancer: whereas Cancer rules the outer covering of the organ and Jupiter rules the organ in general, Virgo is concerned with the inner workings of enzyme production. Furthermore, it is involved with the storage of glycogen in the liver.

Since Virgo is the polar opposite of Pisces, people who have planets in Virgo are usually sensitive to drugs. They generally require only a minimal dosage of any medication for best results.

Sun in Virgo

This placement may produce diabetic or hypoglycemic complaints as well as colitis and diarrhea. There is the possibility of poor assimilation of food, requiring a strict, healthful diet with fiber.

Moon in Virgo

The Moon in Virgo may bring on looseness of the bowels and abdominal swellings and tumors. Moreover, there is the possibility that women who take birth control pills will have sugar problems caused by endocrine malfunction. Hypoglycemia is another potential illness.

Mercury in Virgo

With this placement diverticulosis or colitis from nervousness may occur. These people are prone to worry, creating nervous tension. Other possible ailments are colic, insomnia and flatulence of the abdomen caused by poor digestion.

Venus in Virgo

This configuration may result in sugar problems and irregular bowel action.

Mars in Virgo

Pancreatitis, inflammation of the spleen or liver, dysentery, worms and bowel inflammation in general, gastroenteritis, peritonitis, cholera, ventral hernia, typhoid and hyperinsulinism are all potential illnesses with Mars in Virgo.

Jupiter in Virgo

Jupiter in Virgo may create liver problems related to enzyme functions, an enlarged liver, abscess of the liver, jaundice, fatty degeneration of the liver and cholesterol deposits.

Saturn in Virgo

This placement may bring about the beginning or last stages of diabetes, hypoinsulinism, intestinal blockage or constriction, poor peristaltic motion creating bouts with diarrhea and constipation, colitis, sclerosis of the liver and poor enzyme action within the liver.

Uranus in Virgo

The sudden onset of diabetes or hypoglycemia caused by severe emotional stress may result from Uranus in Virgo. Spasms and cramping may also occur in the intestinal tract. Furthermore, there may be intermittent sugar problems resulting from an individual's living through a traumatic shock. Other potential ailments are the twisting and telescoping of the bowels and a type of diabetes caused by the malfunctioning of the posterior pituitary hormonal release mechanism.

Neptune in Virgo

Neptune in Virgo may produce prolapsed intestines and weak intestinal peristalsis; consequently, food stays longer in the tract, causing toxins to be reabsorbed through the walls and poisoning the individual. Diabetes or misdiagnosed hypoglycemia may also occur: the person may be placed under psychiatric care or put in a mental ward when the root of the problem is actually organic and not mental. Toxemia is another potential disease.

Pluto in Virgo

With this placement disorders of the pancreas may be suspect. As a result there may be chronic sugar problems, such as hypoglycemia and diabetes: both can be easily checked with a five-hour glucose tolerance test. Anyone having a family history of sugar disorders is especially susceptible to such diseases and should undergo the test. In addition, Pluto in Virgo can mean enlargement of the spleen or splenic problems involving white blood cells. A person with this placement may have to undergo removal of the spleen or may suffer regrowth of the spleen after surgery. He or she may also have chronic problems involving the intestines, such as colitis and diverticulosis.

LIBRA

Bones: Lumbar vertebrae.

Muscles: Quadratus lumborum and sacrolumbars.

Arteries: Suprarenal, renal and lumbar.

Veins: Renal and lumbar.

Cell Salt: Natrum phosphoricum.

Since Libra rules the kidneys, it's an important sign to consider in medical astrology. The elimination of poisonous waste material is essential to life. Without the kidney's filtering capacity to clean blood during a 24-hour period we would be dead in a relatively short time.

Because of the kinds of food we consume today, the miles of tubules within each kidney can potentially become blocked with debris such as cholesterol, calcium or other waste. Debris that should have been plucked out of the bloodstream and filtered down through the ureters to the bladder to be emptied out of the body may swing back into the circulation. A gradual poisoning then occurs.

The symptoms of partially blocked kidneys are numerous. Although there may not be inflammation or nephritis, there can be lower back pain or a minor aching sensation in the region of one or both kidneys. Other potential problems include edema, weight gain and the inability to loose it, mild to severe headaches, adrenal gland stress and skin rashes ranging from dryness to dermatitis and eczema.

Blood disorders varying from simple anemias to a pseudoleukemia and high white blood cell counts can also be caused by a malfunctioning kidney. Such ailments are usually blamed on the spleen: sometimes, when a doctor cannot find the reason a person has a dangerously high white blood cell count, he or she will remove the spleen in an effort to halt the formation of the cells. Actually, though, the reason the body manufactures many more white blood cells is to fight the infection that is flowing through the body in the form of toxemia. Manufacturing white blood cells is the body's main way of combating something that the body automatically realizes could kill it. At the same time the person may experience soreness of the lymph glands, swelling or even lumps that are often mistaken for cancerous tumors. Other symptoms, such as continual colds, sniffles and stuffy sinus conditions, can be signs of toxicity as well.

Libra also rules the basal metabolism, specifically the acid-alkaline metabolism. A person who is a heavy meat eater may get acidosis: meat is very high in acidic properties that build up in a person's system. When the body is unable to supply enough alkalinity, the result is nervousness without reason, insomnia or unrestful sleep, tenseness and the inability to relax, headaches and heartburn.

Finally, if Libra is found on the Ascendant or

Midheaven, a glandular malfunction may be suspected.

Sun in Libra

This configuration may create various diseases of the kidney, such as nephritis or Bright's disease, as well as skin ailments or diseases that are kidney-related by renal retention.

Moon in Libra

The Moon in Libra may cause edema of the hands and feet or an inability to lose weight because of a weakened or clogged kidney.

Mercury in Libra

With this placement there is the potential for kidney tubule obstructions, pain of a nerve-related origin within the kidneys and nephritic colic.

Venus in Libra

Kidney disorders in general, high color to the urine and uremia are all possible with this configuration.

Mars in Libra

Mars in Libra can indicate kidney inflammation of a nephritic variety or a sudden flare-up or inflammation to the kidneys from a physical injury.

Jupiter in Libra

This placement can mean changes in the blood circulation because of the fluctuation of kidney regulation or cholesterol deposits in the kidney tubules. Sugar-related problems, such as the consumption of too many sweets, can also occur.

Saturn in Libra

The various ailments that may result from Saturn in Libra are thickening of the tubule walls of the kidneys, poor filtering conditions to remove urea from the blood, renal or urine retention, kidney blockage by gravel or stones of a calcium nature, suppression of urine, blood ailments caused by unfiltered toxic waste and sluggish or hypofunctioning kidneys.

Uranus in Libra

With Uranus in Libra the kidneys may work intermittently or spastically, causing a problem like cyclical albuminuria, wherein urine is not completely filtered out of the blood.

Neptune in Libra

This configuration may indicate weak or sluggish kidney function: the kidneys may be weakened because of illness or heredity. There may also be poor filtering of urine from the blood, causing anemia and potential problems with the spleen.

Pluto in Libra

Pluto in Libra may result in tumors in the kidneys, toxemia caused by poor kidney function and kidney diseases that are chronic or terminal. Pluto in Libra conjunct the Ascendant, if in hard aspect, always hints at some sort of glandular disorder. There can also be an imbalance of the acid-alkaline metabolism.

SCORPIO

Bones: Tuberosity of ischium, brim of pelvis and symphysis pubis.

Muscles: Cremasters, sphincter, levatores, penis, clitoris and sphincter of bladder.

Arteries: Internal iliac.

Veins: Spermatic, mesenteric, colic and hemorrhoidal.

Cell Salt: Calcarea sulphurica.

Ruling over the prostate gland and the reproductive system, Scorpio's main function is governing the colon. A well-functioning colon is essential to good health. Since diets high in natural roughage and fiber have decreased during the twentieth century, fecal matter cakes the walls of our intestines. As much as five to thirty pounds of old fecal matter can be expelled during enemas or high colonics; this matter may have remained caked on the walls for upwards of five to fifteen years. It's logical to assume that the poisons contained in the feces will be reabsorbed through the walls and placed back into the bloodstream to reinfect the person. Furthermore, a toxemia may occur that can harm the organs, tissue and bones over a period of years as well as influence the quality of the blood, upset the metabolism and be responsible for placing a strain upon the heart as it labors to circulate the tainted blood.

There is an old adage among medical astrologers: Scorpio implicates diseases of the back and heart (Leo), thyroid (Taurus) and eyes (Aquarius)—the other signs in the Fixed Cross. The upshot is that cataracts or glaucoma, back ailments or heart conditions may actually be caused by a malfunctioning colon.

Sun in Scorpio

This placement can indicate constipation, hemorrhoids, diseases of the reproductive system or prostate gland and bladder infections.

Moon in Scorpio

The Moon in Scorpio can mean genitourinary

complaints, cystitis, reproductive problems in women and hernial aneurysms.

Mercury in Scorpio

With this configuration there is the possibility of pains and disorders of the generative organs, the ureters, urethra, fallopian tubes or testicles. There may also be menstrual hemorrhaging and pain or spasms in the bladder.

Venus in Scorpio

Venereal diseases, weakness of the bladder, womb disorders and problems connected with the vaginal passage or ovaries may occur with Venus in Scorpio.

Mars in Scorpio

This placement may result in urinary disorders, cystitis, inguinal and scrotal hernia, hemorrhoids, venereal ulcers—particularly in the throat region—and pains in the bladder. Moreover, there may be problems with menstrual flow, ovaries, vaginitis, hypertrophy of the prostate gland and inflammation of the prostate.

Jupiter in Scorpio

Jupiter in Scorpio may produce vaginitis, piles, urinary and seminal complaints, edema, tumors in the bladder or uterus and abcesses of the urethra.

Saturn in Scorpio

With Saturn in Scorpio there may be a variety of illnesses: colon stasis; poor peristalsis resulting in constipation; caking of fecal matter on the walls of the large intestine; toxemia, potentially affecting the thyroid, heart, throat and back; stones in the bladder; suppression of urine; small or undeveloped ovaries or testicles; problems in the birthing process; and a small womb or tipped uterus.

Uranus in Scorpio

Uranus in Scorpio may cause spasm of the colon, especially when there is emotional stress or the sudden onset of tension, creating constipation and then diarrhea. In addition, this placement may cause the thyroid to spasm, especially under stressful conditions. There may also be palpitations of the heart, pressure on the vertebrae of the back and back ailments. ailments.

Neptune in Scorpio

With this configuration there is the potential for a weakened colon or poor or sluggish peristalsis: the walls may become caked with fecal matter, resulting in a toxic condition in the body. Furthermore, there

can be a hypothyroid condition, weakened heart action, a high white blood cell count, anemia, weak female organs and poor or low sperm count.

Pluto in Scorpio

Tumors in the colon, chronic ailments of the prostate, reproductive system or colon, a severe heart condition, a weak thyroid or back disorders may all result from Pluto in Scorpio.

SAGITTARIUS

Bones: Ilium, femur, coccygeal and sacral.

Muscles: Iliopsoas, iliacus, pectineus, sartorius, rectus, quadriceps extensor and gluteus muscles forming the buttocks.

Arteries: External iliac, femoral and sacral.

Veins: Vena sacra, iliacs and great saphenous.

Cell salt: Silicea.

Generally known to rule the thigh, Sagittarius also governs the sciatica nerve and the great saphenous vein—both of which may cause ache, cramping or feelings of discomfort radiating from the lumbar region, buttocks, thighs or calves. Sagittarius also rules the expiratory functions of the lungs: fresh oxygen cannot be used effectively if the carbon dioxide is not expelled properly.

Sun in Sagittarius

The Sun in Sagittarius may cause sciatica nerve problems that may involve the body from the lumbar to the calf of the leg. There may also be paralysis from injury to the coccyx, injury to the back because of falls from horses and injury from firearms in general.

Moon in Sagittarius

This placement can indicate gout and nervous disorders.

Mercury in Sagittarius

Pains in the region of the hips and thighs, sciatica, paralysis and nervousness may result from Mercury in Sagittarius.

Venus in Sagittarius

Gout and tumors or skin ailments involving the hips and thighs may occur with this placement.

Mars in Sagittarius

With this configuration sciatica, ulcers of the hips and thighs, injuries to the hips and thighs from riding horses or other violent physical exertions and pelvic operations may take place.

Jupiter in Sagittarius

Jupiter in Sagittarius can indicate pains or swelling in the hip and thigh region, gout and rheumatism. It can also mean large, well-formed and heavy thighs.

Saturn in Sagittarius

Sclerosis or constriction of the sciatica femoral or saphenous may occur with this placement. There may also be chronic sciatica problems, hip-joint disease, dislocation of the pelvis and shallow exhalation of breath, requiring deep-breathing exercises.

Uranus in Sagittarius

Spasms and cramping occurring in the thighs, severe and sporadic problems with the sciatica nerve and hyperventilation from a nervous conditon are possibilities with Uranus in Sagittarius.

Neptune in Sagittarius

This configuration can signify weak thighs. Pains in the back or calves may be misdiagnosed since the root cause may be the sciatica nerve. There is also the potential for poor exhalation and lung capacity.

Pluto in Sagittarius

Chronic problems with the sciatica, tumors or cysts in the hip and thigh area and paralysis from destruction of the coccyx because of a physical injury or heredity are possibilities with Pluto in Sagittarius.

CAPRICORN

Bones: Patella.
Muscles: Patellar ligament and popliteus.
Arteries: The iliac and popliteal (to a partial extent).
Veins: Poplitea and exterior saphenous.
Cell Salt: Calcarea phosphorica.

Closely connected with the digestive system, Capricorn rules the processes of the gallbladder. This organ secretes a dark green liquid called bile into the duodenum. The bile is then spurted into the food, chemically emulsifying the fats and promoting strong peristalsis. Without sufficient bile, fats go undigested, precipitating many serious problems.

Symptoms of a sluggish, partially blocked or stone-ridden gallbladder are a burning sensation in the upper chest, often referred to as heartburn; pain beneath one or both shoulder blades; sharp, cutting pains in the chest cavity, especially around the heart; inability to breathe deeply because of lung-related pain (blamed on pleurisy in the lungs); inability to get breath; and spasmodic pains in the area of the heart, especially from 10 p.m. to midnight (frequently blamed on a heart attack when it is really a gallbladder attack). Other serious complications, such as diverticulitis, diarrhea, constipation, colitis and stomach cramping, can also occur with unwelcomed regularity. Lecithin, one of the ingredients in bile, will help the organ function and also break down the fats that are causing the above problems.

Capricorn also rules the knees. People having their natal Sun in this sign or on the Sixth House cusp will often experience cracking knees upon standing or bending. Moreover, arthritis will sometimes lodge in the knees, causing stiffening of the joints in later years.

Sun in Capricorn

Rheumatism or general aches and pains with age as well as skin disorders may occur with this placement.

Moon in Capricorn

The Moon in Capricorn may cause skin eruptions and problems with the synovial fluids of a joint.

Mercury in Capricorn

This configuration may cause rheumatism, gout, psoriasis caused by nerves and stored up tension or emotion and pruritus (severe itching of skin).

Venus in Capricorn

Potential ailments with Venus in Capricorn are nausea caused by gallbladder disorder, bursitis of the knee, gout in the knees and skin diseases.

Mars in Capricorn

With this placement there may be bruises in and around the knee joints, knee injuries and inflammation of the gallbladder.

Jupiter in Capricorn

Eczema, swollen knees, cholesterol stones or partial blockage in the bile duct or gallbladder are possibilities with Jupiter in Capricorn.

Saturn in Capricorn

This placement can mean a hypofunctioning gallbladder, the release of too little bile, causing digestive problems, and knee problems of an arthritic origin.

Uranus in Capricorn

With Uranus in Capricorn, spasms in the gallbladder may cause what seems to be a heart attack. In addition, there may be poor digestion and bouts with diarrhea and constipation when one is under sudden or severe stress. Laparotomies (exploratory surgery of the abdominal cavity) may be performed because there are sharp, spasmodic pains in the area of the uterus that seem totally divorced from the gallbladder. Gallstones may cause a reflex pain activity in the reproductive area for women. And stones of a calculi or calcium nature may be found in the gallbladder.

Neptune in Capricorn
People with Neptune in Capricorn may have a weak or sluggish gallbladder, with not enough bile secreted during the digestive phase. They may also have weak knees. Drugs used for arthritis, such as cortisone and steroids may interfere with digestion.

Pluto in Capricorn
Pluto in Capricorn may create excess cellular buildup of tissue in and around the knees, chronic arthritic tendencies and tumors or stones in the gallbladder. Since Capricorn rules the anterior pituitary gland, this configuration may indicate a malfunctioning of the gland.

AQUARIUS
Bones: Tibia, fibula and inner and outer ankles.
Muscles: Tibialis anticus, peronaeus tertius, achilles tendon, gastrocnemius and soleus.
Arteries: Tibial.
Veins: Internal saphenous.
Cell Salt: Natrum muriaticum.

Commonly known for ruling the calves and ankles of the legs, Aquarius has several more important functions that are little known. For one, it is concerned with the oxygenation process of the body. Too little oxygen deprives the cells of their ability to work at peak efficiency. And since foods high in starch rob the body of oxygen during the digestive phase, a person with a strong Aquarius in a natal chart should adhere to a low-starch diet and conserve the oxygen for better use. Deep breathing exercises also help to eliminate the carbon dioxide from the body.

In addition, Aquarius influences the blood circulation in general. This sign is involved with blood poisoning that can be traced to toxemia resulting from colon stasis by reflex action to Scorpio.

Furthermore, Aquarius regulates the rods and cones of the eyes. When the colon is sluggish or regulating inconsistently, eye weakness often occurs. In severe cases, glaucoma and cataracts can develop.

Finally, Aquarius has domain over the spinal cord protected by the back vertebrae. Thus nerve-related diseases having to do with the spinal column are under this sign's sway. Ailments having to do with coordination of muscle, nerves and brain, such

as multiple sclerosis, lateral sclerosis and myelitis, are not uncommon.

Sun in Aquarius
The Sun in Aquarius can mean poor circulation, blood disorders connected with the colon, carbon monoxide poisoning, lumbar disorders and lower leg cramping.

Moon in Aquarius
This placement can induce varicose veins of the lower legs, blood poisoning and eye problems, such as cataracts and glaucoma.

Mercury in Aquarius
Muscular dystrophy or any nerve-related ailment having to do with muscle and brain disruption may be caused by Mercury in Aquarius. Muscle cramping, pain in calves or ankles and weak ankles may also occur.

Venus in Aquarius
With this configuration there is the potential for blood disorders, varicose veins and swelling of the ankles.

Mars in Aquarius
Mars in Aquarius can indicate overheated blood, intermittent fevers, blood poisoning of the legs, back problems from heavy physical exercise and erysipelas of the lower legs or back.

Jupiter in Aquarius
Lumbago, blood poisoning, swollen ankles, heart dropsy or edema may result from this placement.

Saturn in Aquarius
There may be various illnesses with Saturn in Aquarius: lack of sufficient oxygen in the body, muscle cramping in the lower legs from lack of calcium, anemia because of a weak colon, sprained ankles, club foot, spinal curvature, caries of the spine, compression or sclerosis of the spinal cord, arterial sclerosis and cataracts.

Uranus in Aquarius
With this placement nerve degeneration related to diseases of the muscles, nerves and spinal column may occur. There may also be spasms in the calves, blurring of vision and strokes.

Neptune in Aquarius
Neptune in Aquarius can mean weak eyesight, with a propensity to cataracts or glaucoma—

formations caused by faulty, nonfibrous diets and heredity. In addition, there can be weak ankles and lower legs. The quality of the blood may be poor, with the individual contracting blood poisoning from lack of oxygen in the blood: such poisoning may give one a poor memory as well as a listlessness and fatigue.

Pluto in Aquarius

Tumors or growths concerned with the eyes and spinal cord as well as degeneration of the spinal cord in relation to nerve tissue destruction may occur with this configuration.

PISCES

Bones: Tarsus, metatarsus and phalanges.
Muscles: Short extensor of toes, short flexor of toes, abductors of great and little toes, short flexor of great toe and accessory flexor toes.
Arteries: Internal and external plantars, tarsal and metatarsal.
Veins: Of the feet.
Cell Salt: Ferrum phosphate.

Pisces is the health poor sign of the zodiac. People with planets in this sign can expect some weakness attributed to it. They must find out that they cannot push themselves: *moderation* in all forms is a good watch word to live by.

Furthermore, the healing process may take longer for Pisces individuals. To develop stronger constitutions, Pisceans should be treated with water. Baths are also an integral part of the recuperation process from mental, physical or emotional problems. Fresh air, walks and sunshine help greatly as well.

Pisces rules the complete lymph gland system, which protects us in a first line of defense against all foreign bacteria and viruses. The lymph uses white blood cells to their fullest extent. When the diet is poor and toxins are reabsorbed into the body, the glands may become tender, sore and swollen as well as even form lumps, which are sometimes mistaken for tumors or cancer. If the toxicity continues to recirculate through the bloodstream and various organs, a high and noticeable white blood count will occur. At times this condition may baffle doctors, and they may even remove the spleen: when they cannot discern why the body is creating an abnormally large white blood cell count, they will remove this organ since it manufactures the majority of these kinds of cells.

Pisces is also directly connected with the amount of mucus in our bodies. Since Americans eat so many mucus-forming foods, there is a danger of overabundance of that substance. Mucous excess or catarrh

can clog up many organs, adversely affecting their respective functions. The result is a general feeling of sluggishness or fatigue.

Sun in Pisces

This placement may cause lymphatic problems, swollen glands, susceptibility to colds, flu, childhood diseases and poor circulation.

Moon in Pisces

Alcoholism is a possibility for people with the Moon in Pisces. Other potential ailments are edema and swelling of the tissue of the body in general, colds, weak lungs inducing pneumonia, poor resistance to viruses, deformed feet or foot problems, poor circulation and a hypofunctioning thymus gland (Neptune).

Mercury in Pisces

Sugar ailments brought about by nervousness and stress in a hostile environment may result from Mercury in Pisces. In addition, there may be pains in the feet and coldness of the extremities. These people tend to worry a good deal and thus bring on a general deterioration of health, mental problems involving unfounded fears and paranoia.

Venus in Pisces

This configuration may bring on gout involving the feet, bunions, tenderness and extreme sensitivity of the feet.

Mars in Pisces

Mars in Pisces may produce hyperinsulism and other sugar ailments. There may also be injury to the feet, broken bones, cuts and sweating feet. Excessive drinking, alcoholism and very weak vitality are also possible. In addition, there may be acute lymphatic conditions and early childhood ailments, including sudden fevers, colds and flu on a continual basis.

Jupiter in Pisces

With Jupiter in Pisces there may be cirrhosis of the liver from excessive drinking as well as sugar problems. Swollen feet or cysts on the feet are also possible. The quality of the blood may become poor because of a malfunctioning liver.

Saturn in Pisces

With this placement the cecum tends to be large and inactive. The liver may be sluggish. Constipation is likely. Lymphatic stasis may incline one toward severe and continued colds and flu. There may also be fallen arches and deformed feet with poor or restricted circulation. Sugar problems are possible, with poor insulin function. Moreover, there may be a low white blood cell count, an inactive spleen, sluggish reproductive cells and a hypofunctioning thymus gland.

Uranus in Pisces

Uranus in Pisces may produce unpredictable sugar problems, such as spasmodic release of insulin from the pancreas because of an emotional state. There may be foot deformity, cramping and spasms of the muscles in the feet as well. Functional diabetes caused by the posterior pituitary gland in relation to the carbohydrate metabolism is another possibility.

Neptune in Pisces

Weak pancreatic action, causing a mild case of either diabetes or hypoglycemia, may occur with this placement. Weak feet, poor arches and poor circulation in the feet are other potential ailments.

Pluto in Pisces

Chronic pancreatic ailments, foot-crippling ailments, tumors, cysts or growths on the feet or in the lymph gland system and chronic diseases involving the lymph system are all possible diseases with this placement.

THE CROSSES

The crosses, or quadruplicities, are very important in medical astrology. By determining which cross or crosses are activated in a natal chart, a medical astrologer may be able to ascertain the root cause of health ailments. Vitamin and mineral deficiencies may also be discerned, as may potential weak points of the body. Thus determining the cross will aid a medical astrologer in outlining the correct dietary considerations and reestablishing health. Certain philosophies of medicine believe that once the root cause of a disease is found, with proper dietary considerations all symptoms will disappear.

When I use the word *cross*, I am not referring to a grand cross or t-square, although such configurations may play a part in the final analysis of a chart. Instead, I mean the cardinal, fixed or mutable configurations. Deciding which cross is most active in a chart and therefore most suspect of initiating disease takes time and patience.

First, a tally should be made of how many planets occupy the cardinal, fixed and mutable signs and houses. The highest tally *usually* indicates the most active cross. To make sure of the right cross, the individual's past medical history should be matched with the various parts of the body, vitamins, minerals, etc., ruled by the cross. When the medical data agrees with the health circumstances of a cross,

that cross is the most activated. If the data does not coincide, the next highest tally should be consulted and cross-referenced with the symptoms of that cross.

In determining the correct cross, a medical astrologer will many times find planets in only three out of the four signs, with the fourth sign empty. About 65 per cent of the time such a cross is completed by the Ascendant or Midheaven. But it may also be the case that the cross has planets and/or the Ascendant or Midheaven in only three "arms." In such circumstances it is very often the empty arm of the cross that is most active—i.e., the individual has the problem most representative of that sign. For example, if a person with a heart-related illness has planets in Scorpio and Aquarius with Taurus on the Ascendant, the ailment is originating from the empty arm of the cross, Leo

There is also the possibility that two arms of the cross will be empty. For instance, a stellium (more than two planets in a sign) may occur with an additional planet in another sign of the cross, such as three planets in Virgo, one in Gemini and no planets in Sagittarius or Pisces. One of these empty signs may be on the Ascendant or Midheaven, and the other empty arm may help explain the ailment the person is manifesting.

About 20 per cent of the time there is a double-cross phenomenon. That is, a person will exhibit ailments indicate of two different crosses. A medical astrologer then must determine which root cause to treat or decide if both should be treated, a difficult assessment to make without years of experience. Although it will be necessary to treat both disorders, it's usually best to take the most active of the two crosses, label it the major cause and treat the corresponding disease first.

Cardinal Cross (Aries, Cancer, Libra and Capricorn)

The root cause of Cardinal Cross illnesses is usually the kidneys, ruled by Libra. An innumerable and surprising number of ailments occur because the kidneys are either plugged up or the tubes constricted so that spasm or renal retention takes place. There are many tests to check the kidney's functioning, and a physician will know best which ones to administer to find out about a potential condition: tests such as the IVP, BUN or creatinine test discussed in Chapter Five can ascertain whether or not urine is being emptied completely into the bladder or if some of it is floating back into the blood circulation.

A secondary root cause may be the gallbladder, ruled by Capricorn. Many heart symptoms, such as pains in the arms or under one or both shoulder blades, heartburn around the heart and shallow breathing, are caused by gallstones or stricture of the bile duct(s). The cholecystography test can determine whether or not the gallbladder contains cholesterol or calculitype stones. The test will also show if the bile duct is partially clogged.

Cardinal Cross people are the delight of the medical world. They are easy to treat since they tend toward ailments that involve organs, and they are rather quick to respond to treatment. They are also willing to cooperate with the doctors and therapists.

Cardinal Cross people can be reasoned with, even though the approach to them may vary depending on which sign is most prominent in their charts: Aries and Capricorn types usually would rather the doctor shoot straight from the hip and give them no-nonsense answers; Cancer and Libra individuals usually need diplomatic and carefully worded descriptions about their ailments. But no matter what their signs once Cardinal Cross people are adjusted to their health predicaments and understand the basis for a medical discussion, they usually can be counted on to stick to the prescribed program. They will normally take the nutrients on a daily basis, adhere to proper diet and generally make life easier on themselves and the attending physician. They tend to be fighters of the first order and do not give up easily, although an encouraging word at the proper time usually will increase their tenacity and efforts.

Since Cardinal Cross people tend to be pioneers and leaders, they are willing to try "new" techniques and medications. As a result, they are more likely to take herbal preparations, homeopathic remedies or cell salt treatments. Cardinal Cross patients can also be expected to respond quite well to normal dosages of medication without ensuing complications.

Fixed Cross (Taurus, Leo, Scorpio and Aquarius)

The root cause of Fixed Cross ailments is the Scorpio-ruled colon. An affected colon can mean poor peristalsis or heavy buildup of fecal matter lining the intestinal walls. In addition, weak or sluggish colon action can be brought on by years of eating the wrong foods or foods not high in fiber and roughage content. The major outcome of a clogged colon is heart attacks: as fecal matter remains on the walls, the toxins contained therein are reabsorbed through the walls and move back into the bloodstream, where they place a heavy strain on the heart, eventually resulting in heart problems.

A secondary root case is the thyroid gland, ruled by Taurus. Toxicity in the colon can trigger the thyroid to go either hyper or hypo and upset the basal metabolism. A hyperthyroid condition will result in extreme nervousness, heart palpitations and tenseness. With a hypothyroid there is extreme fatigue, sluggishness, lethargy and mental dullness. Furthermore, the thyroid is susceptible to emotional upsets that can trigger a hyper- or hyposituation. Drugs, such as the birth control pill, can also alter the thyroid's performance.

Other colon-related ailments via Aquarius are the formation of cataracts and glaucoma. If a person has no personal or familial history of heart trouble, he or she should be checked for eye-related problems. Eye as well as heart and thyroid ailments probably run in the family if this cross is activated. Moreover, with Leo implicated, there may be back trouble.

Fixed Cross ailments are chronic in nature. These people are known as centrapetal: that is, their bodies aggregate or hold in toxins instead of throwing them out. Fixed Cross diseases may take a long time to develop—perhaps 30 years—but when they do, it will also take a long time to erradicate the diseases completely. For these reasons cancer is most commonly linked with this cross: it is a sickness that takes a long time to come on and a long time to cure.

When it comes to helping themselves back to health, Fixed Cross people can be their own worst enemies, and they are usually the most difficult to treat. Known for being stubborn and opinionated, they may resist any change, usually feeling safe and secure in their day-to-day routines. And since being sick is a change in routine, they resist the idea. As a consequence, doctors may experience much difficulty with these individuals. They will rarely listen, and if they do, they may doubt the doctor's innate and trained abilities.

Unlike Cardinal Cross people, Fixed Cross people usually don't want to try anything new or innovative; they would rather stick to what is proven. "If so-and-so took this drug, why can't I?" they may ask. "If Mom did this, why can't I?" And God help the doctor who prescribes a medication that doesn't work the first time! Fixed Cross patients may never go back to the doctor, distrusting his or her ability to prescribe any other medication. In fact, Fixed Cross people are most apt to take matters into their own hands, even at potential risk to their health.

Because Fixed Cross individuals often have trouble in breaking from tradition, it may be difficult to get them to take herbs, homeopathic or cell salt therapy. Therefore, it may be better to give them vitamin and mineral supplements only and to treat them with dietary changes. However, changing their diets can also be a problem. Fixed Cross people usually have eaten the same foods for twenty years and aren't apt to change their eating habits for a doctor, a medical astrologer or themselves. It is often difficult to introduce them to new or more natural foods—much to their own detriment and eroding health. Their years of bad eating habits will very likely catch up with them and give them chronic health problems. But once Fixed Cross individuals make up their minds to get well, they will usually adhere religiously to a holistic health plan—without the periodic encouragement Cardinal Cross people seem to need.

Medicating Fixed Cross individuals can also be frustrating. They seem to need two to three times the normal doses of any medication to affect the ailment that is being treated. Similarly, they may require higher than normal dosages of vitamins and minerals. Any megadose portions should obviously be administered under a doctor's supervision.

Mutable Cross (Gemini, Virgo, Sagittarius and Pisces)

The root cause of the diseases of this flexible quadruplicity is the lymph gland system, ruled by Pisces. Once it becomes clogged with debris many symptoms occur that don't seem directly related to these valuable guardian glands. For instance, many lumps found in and around the neck, under the arms or in the chest or groin region are often caused by lymph congestion. There can also be a high frequency of colds, flu and bronchial and chest problems. In addition, fatigue and mental slowness may be evident without any hint as to what is the cause of the tiredness. But if the lymph glands are cleaned out through diet, these mysterious and seemingly unrelated disturbances usually will disappear.

There is no secondary root cause in the Mutable Cross. Instead, the primary cause of disease is shared with the pancreas, ruled by Virgo and responsible for glucose production. Many hypoglycemics and diabetics fall under this cross. For the most part, sugar problems are easily tested with a five- or six-hour glucose tolerance test.

People with this cross activated in their charts tend to contract anything acute—that is, sudden illnesses that have short incubation times and fast recovery rates. These individuals are susceptible to any disease—especially colds and the flu—that sweeps the country each year. They are said to be centrifugal in that their bodies throw disease and sickness off quickly via colds, sinus infections, fevers or the flu.

Just a little discipline could make Mutable Cross individuals the healthiest in the world, and if they would adhere to prescribed programs, theirs would probably be the easiest cure rate of all. But Mutable Cross people tend to lack determination and tenacity. Unfortunately, they often do not stick to disciplined regimens, and they end up with more aches and pains

or lingering illnesses that other people.

Since Mutable Cross people as a rule will not stay on daily schedules, they are usually the most frustrating to work with. They tend to dive eagerly into any new program, barely listening to the doctor, half-hearing the instructions for taking medication and then rushing home to try on this "new" system. Fortunately, Mutable Cross people will generally try anything once. But they tend to be very sensitive to taste, texture and smell. If the product doesn't taste good, they may never take it again. Or if they do not receive instant reprieve from pain or discomfort, they may call the doctor and demand something different and more speedy. Furthermore, these people normally have many up-and-down days when fighting health problems, and they may either take or not take their medication, entirely depending on their moods.

Mutable Cross people tend to think, "If a little helps me, why not take some more and get better even faster?" Unfortunately, medication doesn't work that way and overdoses occur. On the contrary, underdosing is usually necessary for Mutable Cross individuals. Even normal dosages may trigger adverse reactions in these individuals. Instead, the physician should probably prescribe ½ the normal dose of any medication.

Because this is the most flexible cross, diet is usually the best way to treat these people. They also tend to respond rapidly to homeopathic and cell salt therapies, since their bodies are so finely tuned: in many instances such treatment will have a positive effect within a matter of minutes. On the other hand, getting herbs down Mutable Cross individuals is difficult. Virgo or Pisces individuals, especially, may react adversely to the taste, texture or smell of the herbs. Gemini and Sagittarius individuals generally do not like having to mix and match herbs and then encapsulate them: precapsuled pills are good for such people, but since they hate taking a handful of pills, it might be better to eliminate pills as much as possible. In fact, it may be best to side step herbal application completely with Mutable Cross people, who tend to want quick *relief* that herbs can't supply.

Finally, the doctor should deal diplomatically with Mutable Cross people. He or she must carefully describe whatever disease is involved. Since these individuals tend to dwell on the worst attributes of the ailment, it's best to sugar coat the news rather than to be blunt and candid.

THE HOUSES

Ailments develop for different reasons. Some are caused by societal pressures; others may be triggered by psychological factors. The houses tell the astrologer why various disorders manifest. Positive handling of the energy of afflicted houses will help insure health.

First House

Aggressiveness is usually very pronounced for people with planets in this house. They tend to strive on physical and mental levels to be "first." Such rash use of energy may promise depletion. Since First House individuals usually have difficult times resting, their bodies may break down from the stress of hard, forceful driving without breaks. These people need to learn moderation to insure good health.

First House people also tend to be strong individualists. If these people are not allowed to express themselves without the help of others they may become frustrated. Health may be maintained when pure, individual expression is pursued, either through hobbies or business.

If Neptune is in the First House, especially within eight degrees of the First House cusp, these individuals may be sensitive to drugs. Particularly if Neptune aspects other natal planets, the dosage of any medication should be lower than normal.

Second House

People with planets in the Second House tend to have overwhelming desires to prove their self worth: they may need to establish themselves as reputable to the rest of society by building big houses, getting degrees, establishing businesses, making millions, etc. Such obsessions with "making something" of themselves will, of course, place great strain on their bodies. For example, they may work 16 hours a day to achieve their goals, in the process neglecting to eat or developing poor eating habits.

After they have established their nest eggs, rich eating habits usually get in the way of health maintenance. Gluttony is not uncommon. These people also tend to consume food that is high in sugar and carbohydrates. Second House people need to realize that earthly monuments will not give them happiness: happiness is the one thing that cannot be bought. They must learn that other people like them for who and what they are, not for what they own, how much they are worth or what clothes they wear. When Second House people learn the real nature of happiness, they place their bodies under less stress and get rest and relaxation every once in a while.

Third House

Since they are usually very good at being "Dear Abbeys," people with planets in the Third House often become the centers of attention where they live. And if they are asked too often to help siblings or other people in their homes or on their blocks, their bodies can react adversely to the environmental stress. Such people need some private moments for "downtime" for their bodies.

The disease of "peopling" can lead to a state of great frustration. Indeed, for Third House individuals the nerves are the most likely to suffer because of environmental pressures. They need to learn to say *no* to those who hound them, to make phone conversations short and to keep coffee breaks with neighbors to a minimum. If they control such situations, health may be improved.

Fourth House

Since the Fourth House concerns parents, parental conditioning may play a major part in how people with planets in the Fourth House maintain their health after they leave the security of the home. Parents many times inflict their personality traits upon their children, not realizing that their sons and daughters need to express themselves differently to grow into their own. Neurosis caused by repressed anger may develop and lead to inner struggles that individuals may not be consciously aware of. If these negative emotions are not worked out on a conscious and positive level, health may deteriorate and chronic problems may be established in the middle part of life, from age 42 to 49.

The healthy approach is one of confrontation. These people need to examine themselves in terms of parental conditioning. Psychological counseling is sometimes necessary to dredge up these hurts and talk about them. By getting their feelings into the open, these individuals may be relieved of terrible subconscious burdens, and health may be improved.

Fifth House

The Fifth House is concerned with love. That is, those individuals with planets in this house feel a great need for love. They tend to feel a lack of love and try to get ample love from those around them. The kind of big emotional expenditure caused by such a search may eventually create health problems—ailments that are often long in coming and not obvious at first. The need for love may drive these people into a series of chaotic affairs, leading to fragmented, frustrated lives. Furthermore, Fifth House individuals may experience great loneliness that deprives them of their desires to live.

Fifth House people need to realize that the root of their desires for affection is probably insecurity. They need to cultivate a healthy view of self. They need to learn that they can receive attention best through creative self-expression. These people usually have one major talent and several minor talents and should develop them.

They also must learn to love themselves first and foremost. The old adage that to receive love one must love onself is true. Therapy may help these individuals discover the reasons for their insecurity and help cultivate new attitudes so that they like themselves. Self-acceptance may breed good health and inner contentment so that energies will flow smoothly.

Sixth House

Although the Sixth House is one of the two well-known health houses, people with planets in this house generally have a lack of self-esteem, and they tend to gravitate toward stronger, more confident individuals. In doing so they may succumb to other people's needs, ignoring their own. Therein lie the seeds of destructive ailments.

Sixth House individuals too often are plagued by guilt—one of the most vicious emotions that humans have acquired. Other people—spouses, children, relatives or friends—tend to make such individuals feel guilty because they have not become involved with the desires of others. If they don't help others, Sixth House people believe, others will think less of them. But, of course, the price they pay for the approval of others is often sickness—a hefty payment for ignoring their own needs. If these people continue to bow to the needs of others before their own, nerve-related ailments, sugar problems and intestinal disorders will crop up with frequency.

For good health Sixth House individuals should come to terms with what guilt is, what it does if allowed to continue and how to cope with it. The word *no* is a healthy rejoinder for Sixth House people to use frequently. Learning to work for themselves first and then making the choice to help others second will keep them in good states of health.

Neptune in the Sixth House, especially if in hard aspect to other planets, may indicate allergic reactions to drugs. Such individuals should probably receive half dosages of any medication, at least at first.

Seventh House

People with planets in the Seventh House often feel as though they can never stand on their own two feet to accomplish anything; consequently, they may follow the leads of their partners. Such compromise can become a negative attribute. Although the need to be partners with others is all right in and of itself, bowing to the needs of the spouses or business partners can become very frustrating, perhaps leading to poor health. These Seventh House individuals may give up their self-identification and personal needs to help their "other halves." In time the need to be

themselves will arise and create emotional and mental stress.

Some Seventh House individuals work better in teams and not as individuals: there is nothing wrong with such cooperation. But the reasons for the partnerships should be minutely examined. Seventh House people many times take on partners for reasons of insecurity, lack of confidence in themselves or the fear of living their own lives. None of these are healthy reasons, and a little psychology and honesty may be needed to change the situation.

Eighth House

This particular house tends to place the cruelest test upon the body. Individuals with planets in the Eighth House tend to be psychologically intense and complicated. Those deep, psychological ramifications may deteriorate physical health. With such people emotional scarring tends to be internalized, hidden in the dark vaults of the subconscious. Under such circumstances it takes years for bodies to give out; but when they do, they usually succumb to chronic ailments—a long time developing and a long time healing—around the ages of from 42 to 49 years old.

In addition, Eighth House people often have burning needs to purge themselves of some past emotions or memories and brutally punish their bodies in doing so. They can also be expected to undergo transformations at some points in their lives—the experiencing of pain to move over thresholds or suffering to transcend emotional suppression.

Finally, because of hidden emotional insecurity, these people many times will push the hardest to attain success: they may spend 12 to 16 hours a day toward a business goal. Such psychological problems inevitably take their toll and although these people have the strength of ten to persevere and survive, their bodies may crack.

Psychological counseling, therapy or psychiatry are usually the best means of helping Eighth House individuals to open up their subconscious. There is very little else that can be done for people with planets in this position, since they tend to be highly introverted and inflexible in their beliefs. Perhaps they need to wrestle silently within their own internal structures to work problems out.

Ninth House

Because this house has to do with higher ideals, beliefs and philosophies, people with planets in this house are among the least likely individuals to have health problems. One's faith in God, some supreme force or onself can overcome even the most severe disease upon occasion: faith heals and mends on mental, emotional and physical levels. However, a negative attitude can bring on health ailments sooner or later. We are what we think, and if we think ill we will become ill.

Tenth House

People with planets in the Tenth House are usually very susceptible to societal pressures. These people often aspire to be at the top so that their parents, friends or colleagues will be accepting and proud of them. At the same time parents of Tenth House individuals may cajole their children into believing that the only way to be accepted is to follow the norms established by society.

With such pressures from parents, peer groups and society in general Tenth House individuals may put their bodies under great stress. They may bow to society's demands and work 12 to 16 hours a day to make something of themselves—establishing a home with a spouse and two children or climbing up the corporate ladder. They may not know the meaning of the words *relaxation* and *vacation* and may not give their bodies proper time to regroup for the next push. Some Tenth House people after being laden with 18 years of conditioning at home may work hard for peer recognition, encountering much frustration in their searches for popularity. The worries, internal pressures and incessant drives to work harder may produce chronic ailments that will manifest in the middle years. Only with age, when such people realize that they want to work toward specific goals for themselves and not for parents or society, will health tend to improve.

Neptune within eight degrees of the Tenth House cusp of the natal chart can indicate a drug-sensitive individual.

Eleventh House

Somewhat like the Nine House, this is not a position for health problems. People with planets in the Eleventh House tend to work toward their hopes and wishes, many times through large groups and organizations. In some instances under proper circumstances, friends, acquaintances and clubs may place inordinate demands upon Eleventh House individuals, causing them undue stress.

Twelfth House

Like the Sixth House, the Twelfth House is directly concerned with health matters. Specifically, it is the house of hospitalization. It is also a house that can indicate psychological problems. People with strong Twelfth Houses tend toward introversion, and they hide their feelings in their subconscious minds. And as with the Fourth and Eighth Houses, people with planets in the Twelfth House can build up negative emotions until there is a physical manifestation in illness. Since this is one house position that does not allow emotions to ferment forever, progressed or transiting planets can trigger release of this backlog of repressed or suppressed emotions—perhaps resulting in hospitalization.

But if Twelfth House individuals can remain honest with themselves about their emotions and feelings, they may avoid hospitalization. Therapy is the best bet. Good friends or spouses can also provide sounding boards for unleashing feelings in positive ways. Talking out their feelings is the best remedy for Twelfth House individuals. (They must learn that harboring envy, jealousy, hatred or anger will inevitably result in ailments.) The karmic law that applies in this case is, "What goes around, comes around." Conversely, keeping their thoughts pure and their ethics and morals above question will help insure hospital-free lives.

CHAPTER THREE
The Hard Aspects and Health

The aspects used in determining health matters are the hard aspects: the conjunction, square, inconjunct (or quincunx) and opposition. These are considered "hard" configurations because the energy between the two planets or a planet and a house cusp is blocked. Sickness is simply a mismanagement of energy on either a mental or emotional level.

Two other minor aspects, the semi-square (45 degrees) and the sesquiquadrant (135 degrees), also play a role in the manifestation of disease. These minor aspects can provide a degree of irritation and continual abrasive activity that weakens an organ or metabolic function so that severe illness or breakdown may occuᵣ when a major aspect by progression takes place. But the influence of these minor aspects is slight in that a full-blown condition will not manifest unless there are accompanying major hard aspects present.

Whereas the sign the planet is in will indicate where illnesses occur and the house placement will suggest why ailments may develop, the hard aspects indicate the severity of the diseases that may take place. Hard aspects create stress that eventually may manifest in physical ailments.

Conjunction (0-degree aspect between two planets)

Depending upon which planets are involved, a conjunction generally infers a melding of two energies that work in tandem; thus twice the energy and twice the nutritional needs are created. Any conjunction that involves Pluto should be watched and checked out carefully by the medical astrologer. Neptune conjunctions, especially with the Sun, Moon, Mars or Saturn, can also be indicators of poor health.

Square (90-degree aspect between two planets)

The old adage that a square can be a stumbling block or a building block also applies in medical astrology. A square implies that some stress is being applied. It can also show the loss or overuse of whatever vitamins or minerals are involved. But square aspects can be worked out and used beneficially for good health.

Opposition (180-degree aspect between two planets)

An imbalance is most likely with this aspect. One of the two planets involved is receiving more energy than the other, creating health problems. One of the planets (but not both) will be deficient in some vitamin or mineral; however, when the energies are balanced, there will be no health problems or nutritional deficiencies because an opposition allows us to see clearly what is wrong with our present diets and how to correct the situation so that no deficiencies exist.

Inconjunct (150-degree aspect between two planets)

This is *the* health aspect, the *most* suspect of high and low conditions of the body. It is the most difficult and impregnable of the aspects to deal with. People who have two or more inconjuncts in their charts are prone to diseases at some time in their lives. Moreover, a yod (two planets sextile and inconjunct a third) may implicate illness: you can tell where the ailment is likely to manifest by noting the center, or inconjunct planet.

The inconjunct can be likened to a pressure cooker. The accumulating steam has to go somewhere; it will eventually have to escape. On a psychological level, an inconjunct indicates that a person cannot get in touch with himself or herself very easily. He or she is poor at identifying internal needs or even recognizing the presence of suppressed or repressed emotions. The buildup of such emotional dross has to explode somewhere, and sickness may develop.

On a purely physical level, the inconjunct indicates very poor absorption of nutrients: it can denote an enormous appetite for a vitamin or mineral ruled by the planets involved in the aspect. A careful diet is going to have to be tailor-made by a nutritionally conscious physician, particularly if any of the B complex vitamins are involved.

The inconjunct involves the First and Sixth or Eighth Houses. The Sixth House inconjunct is the easier of the two to deal with. It mainly means paying careful attention to diet to help sidestep possible health situations. The Eighth House inconjunct, on the other hand, involves a Pandora's box of subconscious manifestations that have to be worked out by the individual, often with the help of a therapist.

The best word for people with inconjuncts to remember is *adaptation*. If they can adapt positive attitudes to different circumstances and changing environments, health will probably not be impaired; however, people with two or more inconjncts, especially those with yods, court ill health if their attitudes are inflexible and negative.

Although any inconjunct should be seriously

considered and given more weight than other hard aspects when deciding potential areas of nutritional deficiency, some of the more potent inconjuncts are Sun-Moon, Sun-Saturn, Sun-Neptune, Moon-Pluto, Mars-Saturn, Mars-Pluto, Jupiter-Saturn and Saturn-Neptune.

HARD ASPECTS OF THE SUN

Sun-Moon

A hard aspect between the Sun and the Moon implies poor health and low vitality. When the energy of the Sun is blocked by the Moon, which rules all the bodily fluids, there is the possibility of a very basic flaw in a person. Ill health can be expected at some point if eating habits are poor and emotions negative. At the least such a person will have a weak beginning as an infant, perhaps with stronger health toward middle age. The individual cannot afford junk food diets because his or her body will probably retaliate.

A hard configuration between the Sun and the Moon can indicate a deficiency in vitamin A (Sun). As a result there may be sterility, female complaints and disorders, reproductive infections—such as vaginal yeast infections (Scorpio)—and digestive upsets.

Since the Moon rules Cancer, the "coverings" in the body, such as the pericardium of the heart, the sinuses and the cheeks, may be affected. Since bone marrow also falls under Cancer's domain, a lack of vitamin A may cause softening or abnormal lengthening of the long bone in the body.

There may also be problems with pregnancy with a hard aspect between the Sun and the Moon. Especially when a hard aspect to Saturn is present, a lack of iodine (Sun) in the mother and fetus may be indicated if the planets are in the sign Taurus or its opposite polarity, Scorpio, thyroid imbalance may occur during or after pregnancy, affecting the basal metabolism so that the mother is unable to lose weight and return to normal metabolic functions: a thyroid test should be conducted when the patient is found to be pregnant to ascertain whether an iodine supplement of natural origin should be included in her diet. Furthermore, such an aspect can signal a long labor because of insufficient magnesium (Sun), especially if there is also a hard aspect to Saturn. Without enough magnesium the pituitary gland may be unable to stimulate the release of uterine hormones to insure healthy contractions: this problem will especially tend to affect women with either the Sun or the Moon in Cancer or Capricorn as well as a hard aspect from Saturn.

In fact, a hard aspect between the Sun and the Moon is very likely to produce a deficiency of magnesium, especially if the person is a heavy milk

and dairy product user—a good possibility since the sign Cancer is involved. Insufficient magnesium in turn can lead to a lack of potassium (Moon). If there is not enough potassium in the cells, edemalike situations can occur. If one planet is in Cancer and the other in Libra, there may be a possible fluid imbalance from lack of potassium. And if Leo or Aquarius is involved, potential heart palpitations and racing may be caused from a lack of potassium.

On the other hand, if Pluto is trine the Sun, there may be too much magnesium in the body. This abundance of magnesium can interfere with the potassium exchange in nerve-related activity, causing impaired muscular and respiratory functions.

The transiting Moon in hard aspect to the Sun may also affect conditions for surgical operations. Operations should not normally be scheduled when the transiting Moon is within 17 degrees of the natal Sun. Nor should an operation be contemplated when the transiting Moon is in close square, opposition or inconjunct to the natal or transiting Sun.

Sun-Mercury

Since Mercury is never more than 28 degrees from the Sun, there are no major aspects possible, except for the conjunction.

Mercury rules Gemini; consequently, with a Sun-Mercury conjunction there can be various disorders related to the Gemini-directed tubes of the body, such as the eustachian tubes of the ears, the bronchial tubes of the lungs, the ureters leading from the kidneys to the bladder, the urethra leading from the bladder to the outer opening, the fallopian tubes carrying eggs from the ovaries to the uterus and the cerebrospinal system. With an accompanying hard aspect from Saturn and one of the planets in Gemini, a deficiency of vitamin A could manifest as bronchial asthma attacks. In addition, ear infections might occur if Saturn is in aspect and one of the planets is in Aries. Bladder infection (cystitis) or menstrual problems are possible if Scorpio is involved. And if one of the planets is in Libra, the lower back may be helped with adequate vitamin A.

Since Mercury also rules Virgo, a lack of vitamin A may cause ailments associated with that sign. Virgo guides the splitting-up processes that take place in the intestines, liver and pancreas. A deficiency of vitamin A may create intestinal problems, such as colitis or diverticulosis. The aging process or the slow renewal of RNA through the liver may also be caused by a lack of vitamin A. And with the pancreatic disease diabetes vitamin A cannot be stored properly and must be replenished daily. Rashes, itching, flaking, psoriasis, liver spots, dryness and tightness may also appear, partially caused by the nerves, ruled by Mercury.

Nerve-related problems are another possibility with the Sun in hard aspect with Mercury. If Mercury is in an air sign (Gemini, Libra or Aquarius), the person is apt to be high-strung to begin with. This condition may be aggravated by a deficiency of thiamine (Mercury) so that the person is easily irritable and grouchy. An individual with Mercury in a fire sign (Aries, Leo or Sagittarius) is more apt to have inflammation of the nerve endings, such as neuritis or inflammation of the sciatica. Another disease linked to a deficiency of thiamine is Bell's palsy, more likely to occur if Mercury is in Aries, which rules the face, the motor centers of the brain and the circulation therein. Any such nervous condition may be intensified by an additional hard aspect from Saturn.

A deficiency of thiamine may bring on heart problems as well, since the Sun rules that vital organ. For example, there is the possibility of cardiomegaly or bradycardia. A planet in the sign Leo or an activated Fixed Cross in a natal chart could enhance such a possibility.

Moreover, a lack of thiamine could cause disorders of the spinal cord, coruled by the Sun and Uranus. For instance, the myelin sheaths that cover the cord could become destroyed or partially disintegrated because of insufficient thiamine coupled with pernicious anemia.

Since Mercury co-rules the thyroid with Taurus, thyroid complications are also possible. With a hard aspect from Saturn the thyroid may hypofunction because a lack of vitamin D (Sun) means there is not enough calcium (Saturn) available in the system. Or with a hard aspect from Saturn the thyroid may hypofunction from lack of iodine, particularly if any of these three planets is in Taurus or Scorpio. On the other hand, with a hard aspect to Sun-Mercury from Mars or Uranus the thyroid may hyperfunction.

Finally, a hard aspect between the Sun and Mercury can indicate a deficiency of magnesium and accompanying illnesses. For instance, a lack of magnesium can contribute to Virgo-related diseases, such as diarrhea or pancreatitis. With a hard aspect from Jupiter vitamin B-6 (Jupiter) may not be supplied in adequate quantities because of insufficient magnesium, creating a potential diabetic situation or leading to celiac diseases. And if there is a hard aspect from Jupiter or Saturn and the sign Virgo is involved, there may be liver damage.

Sun-Venus

Because Venus is never farther away than 48 degrees from the Sun it is impossible for the Sun to be in a major hard aspect to Venus, except for a conjunction. Therefore, the semi-square or 45-degree angle should be considered a minor hard aspect and noted in any medical condition.

The main problems involved with an aspect between the Sun and Venus concern a lack of vitamin E (Venus). Although Venus cannot be a direct cause of heart problems because of its close orbit to the Sun, a hard aspect from Saturn could indicate a vitamin E deficiency that could contribute to cardiac malfunctions. Furthermore, since vitamin A and magnesium are both essential for proper use of vitamin E, a negative aspect from Saturn and Uranus could show at least a sporadic deficiency in one of these nutrients—a deficiency that could secondarily aid heart ailments. A hard aspect from Saturn could also indicate a lack of copper (Venus) and/or vitamin C (Saturn), deficiencies that might make the aorta susceptible to aneurysms and create heart problems. In addition, with a hard aspect from Saturn, not enough vitamin E may be available to help absorb the iodine that is ingested. There may also be afflictions of the skin related to a deficiency of vitamin E.

Because Venus rules Libra there may be troubles with the acid-alkaline metabolism when Venus is in aspect with the Sun. Acidosis may become a problem, possibly initiating nephritis. This disorder might evolve into a bone ailment if a hard aspect to Saturn is present.

Thyroid difficulties are other possibilities. Venus rules Taurus, which, along with Mercury, corules the thyroid. Abnormal function of that gland may occur because of insufficient vitamin A. A hard aspect from Saturn would suggest that vitamin E is deficient and cannot absorb the iodine ingested. A hard aspect from Pluto, with the sign Libra involved, may also point to thyroid inefficiency.

With a hard aspect from Saturn, there may be other problems. For example, there may be a magnesium deficiency, which can create calcium deposits in the kidneys. Clots in the veins are also possible with a hard aspect to Saturn.

Finally, there is speculation that the Sun conjunct Venus may cause a person to burn up great amounts of energy, contributing to a deficiency of niacin (Venus).

Sun-Mars

Heart problems are possible with a hard aspect between the Sun and Mars. For example, there may be potential cardiovascular ailments involving high blood pressure. Heart palpitations or irregular beats may be caused by a deficiency of phosphorous (Mars). Anemic conditions may create an enlargement of the heart, placing a strain upon the organ. With a trine from Jupiter there may also be accumulation of fat in the arteries (atherosclerosis) as well as too much intake of chlorine (Mars), resulting in potential heart ailments. And an additional hard aspect from Saturn could indicate cardiac problems because there is too few fatty acids (Mars) to help vitamins A and D to be synthesized.

Insufficient vitamins A and D may create other difficulties. A lack of vitamin A may mean kidney inflammation or nephritis by reflex action of Mars to Libra, which rules the kidneys: additional vitamin A can soothe the inflamed tissue and reduce the swelling. Without enough vitamin D the Mars-ruled minerals sodium and phosphorus may not be properly absorbed. Excessive perspiration as well as heatstroke or sunstroke may occur from loss of sodium. In addition, if either the Sun or Mars is in Libra, high acidity may develop from too little sodium. With the Sun trine either Jupiter or Pluto in hard aspect with Mars phsophorus may be washed out of the system, leaving too much magnesium instead.

In fact, a magnesium imbalance is strongly indicated with a hard aspect between the Sun and Mars. Too little magnesium can cause problems with the adrenal glands. If the sign Libra is involved, the adrenal glands probably won't secrete enough aldosterone to help regulate the rate of magnesium excretion via the kidneys and urine. Too little magnesium could cause the adrenals to be hyperactive, especially with a trine to Mars from Jupiter or Pluto. If the Sun or Mars is in Aries or Cancer, with a hard aspect from Pluto, the adrenal glands could also be hyperfunctioning, whereas the pituitary gland could be hypofunctioning. When the adrenals overproduce hormones and the pituitary gland is sluggish, brittle bones (osteoporosis) may result. With a lack of magnesium in the muscles an alcoholic may suffer from delirium tremens when a hard aspect to Neptune is also present.

A Sun-Mars hard aspect may also cause an imbalance of calcium in the body. For instance, if vitamin D is not being synthesized by enough fatty acids, calcium may not be reaching its destination. An additional hard aspect from Saturn could also indicate either too much or too little calcium. Calcium in the urinary tract could be formed because of an imbalance of phosphorus. Or there could be a deficiency of calcium resulting in poor muscle coordination.

If there is an additional aspect from Mercury, a hyperthyroid condition is also possible with a hard aspect between the Sun and Mars. Since iodine is used at a higher rate when Mars is involved, more natural supplementation of that mineral may be necessary to keep the bodily metabolism normal and the thyroid well-regulated. A hypermetabolic situation is also probable if either the Sun or Mars is in Libra, especially if Pluto is in hard aspect as well.

In addition, a hard configuration between the Sun and Mars may indirectly contribute to a deficiency of PABA (Saturn), a deficiency that could have a direct effect on the efficiency of folic acid (Mars) in the body. And by weak implication vitamin B-12 (Mars) could be affected.

Finally, when the Sun and Mars are conjunct in a natal chart, the person tends to push to the limits of his or her physical endurance. With such a conjunction health impairment often comes from not recognizing that the body needs periods of recuperation.

Sun-Jupiter

Any time Jupiter is conjunct and in tight orb with the Sun (five degrees or less), there may be either too much or too little of the vitamins and minerals ruled by these two planets: the vitamins A and D (Sun) and B-6, biotin, cholin, inositol and pangamic acid (all ruled by Jupiter); and the minerals iodine and magnesium (Sun) and chromium, manganese and zinc (Jupiter). A person with such a configuration in the natal chart should undergo physician's tests to determine if there is a deficiency or overabundance of one or more of these nutrients. And any hard aspect between the Sun and Jupiter could result in too much or too little of these vitamins and minerals.

A deficiency of vitamin A can result in upper respiratory infections, since Saggitarius, ruled by Jupiter, is the opposite polarity of Gemini, which rules the lungs. High cholesterol, always a potential problem when Jupiter is involved, can also be caused by insufficient vitamin A, a vitamin necessary for good heart maintenance as well. And insufficient vitamin A will inhibit the assimilation of zinc, which is needed for clearing up fatty deposits in the arteries. Lack of zinc can also halt conception in women.

With a hard aspect between the Sun and Jupiter there may be a large and disproportionate need for vitamin D, too. Or perhaps there will be too much vitamin D, creating a toxic condition in the body. With too little vitamin D plus an aspect from Saturn, there is a possibility of the loss of calcium (Saturn), since vitamin D plays a major role in distributing that mineral.

A larger dose of magnesium than the average person usually needs is probably also indicated with a Sun-Jupiter hard aspect. Tests should be undertaken to determine whether or not this is the case. Instead, there may be too much magnesium, which could cause a deficiency of cholin, in turn affecting the nerve synapses and inducing loss of muscle control. If, however, there is too little magnesium (a more likely occurrence), clots in the arteries may develop with a hard aspect from Saturn. In addition, with high-protein diets there may be high cholesterol levels, especially if the planets are in Aries, Leo or Scorpio. There may also be hair loss.

A deficiency of magnesium usually goes hand-in-hand with a lack of vitamin B-6, producing the potential for several problems. If not enough magnesium is available and there is a hard aspect to Saturn, there may not be enough vitamin B-6 to control the blood cholesterol levels. If vitamin B-6 and magnesium are needed, there may also be tics and tremors, as well as diabetes. Cramps and menopausal arthritis are also possible. In addition, heart conditions and glaucoma can be set off by lack of vitamin B-6 in the system.

A hard aspect between the Sun and Jupiter may also produce heart conditions. With a hard aspect from Saturn a shortage of pangamic acid could cause hardening of the arteries leading from the heart. The arteries could also harden from the lack of a necessary amount of chromium in the diet. There is additional speculation that some heart ailments develop from a manganese deficiency caused by arrhythmic disturbances, especially if Saturn is in hard aspect and either of the planets is in Leo.

Sun-Saturn

Since Saturn rules the entire skeleton, the bones, the skin and the teeth, a hard aspect between the Sun and Saturn may mean calcification of the organs in general but primarily of the kidneys and the endocrine gland. A hard aspect between the Sun and Saturn is the major culprit in most problems related to deficiencies of vitamin D. For example, psoriasis is possible, as are arthritis, rheumatism, osteomalacia and all other bone conditions discussed under the section on vitamin D in Chapter Seven. The possible presence of such conditions should be confirmed through testing by a physician.

Because vitamin D is necessary to help assimilate calcium (Saturn), insufficient vitamin D will produce a lack of the mineral. If either the Sun or Saturn is in Libra, a lack of calcium resorption within the kidney tubules may cause stones later in life. If either planet, particularly the Sun, is in Cancer or Pisces, there may be puffiness in the body caused by excess salt retention from too little calcium available to wash the salt out. There may also be sunburn or skin problems from insufficient amounts of vitamin A and calcium as well as middle or lower back pains implicated by the Leo-Aquarius polarity.

A calcium imbalance in turn may produce an insufficient amount of magnesium, especially if Libra is involved with a hard aspect from Pluto. And with Saturn trine Pluto a calcium overload and severe

magnesium deficiency may result. Soft enamel forming on the teeth may ensue from such a magnesium deficiency begun in childhood. Insufficient calcium and magnesium could also cause hypoparathyroidism, which can further prevent absorption of magnesium. (A hard aspect between the Sun and Saturn may also result in hyperparathyroidism since the parathyroid is under Saturn's domain.) Without enough calcium and magnesium insomnia may result as well. And magnesium is needed to maintain the normal, regulatory pulse of the heart and prevent coronary thrombosis. If either planet, particularly Saturn, is in the sign Cancer, there may be poor healing of broken bones from a low HCl factor in the stomach plus the need for more vitamin D and magnesium.

A hard aspect between the Sun and Saturn can also indicate insufficient amounts of vitamins A and C (Saturn), especially since vitamin C is necessary to help vitamin A be assimilated and used in the body. If either planet is in Cancer or Capricorn and especially if Saturn is retrograde, there may be gallstone problems that can be partially or complete controlled by adequate amounts of vitamins A and C. Difficulties with bones, teeth, ears and kidney stones can also occur with insufficient amounts of vitamin A. Furthermore, deficiencies of vitamins A and D, both fat-soluble vitamins, may inhibit the production of sulfate and chondroitin, causing malformation of cartilage and stiffening of joints. If either planet is in Leo or Aquarius with a hard aspect from Venus, a need for vitamin C as well as vitamin E (Venus) may be indicated to keep discs between the vertebrae supple and free of lesions. Vitamin C and magnesium are also necessary to prevent kidney stones.

A test should be conducted to find out if there is lack of necesssary iodine in the body. If either the Sun or Saturn is in Taurus or Scorpio or if Mercury is in hard aspect, there is the potential for hypothyroidism. In addition, pink eye is possible when either planet is in Aquarius.

Finally, there is speculation that with an aspect from Jupiter and either the Sun or Saturn in Leo, there may be a deficiency of bioflavonoids (Saturn), causing the arteries surrounding the heart to harden.

Sun-Uranus

Uranus in hard aspect with the Sun always indicates that a spasm condition may be present, with the constriction usually taking place when a person is under stress. At such times, an individual will probably need one of the vitamins or minerals ruled by the Sun.

For example, there may be a sporadic need of

vitamin A because of stressful conditions. At one time, the person may be tested for a deficiency of vitamin A and not have one; six months later, a deficiency may exist. Such a situation can lead to perplexity and frustration. There is also speculation that sudden, unexpected stress can drain the body of vitamin D reserves.

In addition, when the body is placed under sudden, stressful situations, heavy iodine usage may be required. There is conjecture that such lack of iodine may induce polio. Or, if the Sun or Uranus is found in Taurus or Scorpio, a spastic thyroid condtion is possible: the gland may go either hyper or hypo, depending upon the nature of the stress and of the individual.

There may also be sporadic needs for higher dosages of magnesium when one is under sudden, unexpected stress. With a hard aspect from Saturn and insufficient magnesium epilepsy may be suspect. If Jupiter is also implicated, then there could be a probable deficiency of vitamin B-6 (Jupiter) as well.

Finally, since Uranus rules Aquarius a hard aspect with the Sun could indicate glaucoma, cataract problems or retina ailments involving the rods and cones of the eyes. Ingestion of too much preprocessed food and not enough raw fruits and vegetables or fiber can clog up the colon—the root cause of many eye problems.

Sun-Neptune

Anytime these two planets are in hard aspect there may be poor vitality, frail health, bodily weakness and prolonged healing time. Infections, continual colds, flu and swollen lymph glands in the neck, under the arms or near the groin are all probable. Furthermore, earaches involving the eustachian tubes may occur, especially if one of the planets is in Aries or Gemini with a hard aspect from Saturn.

A hard aspect between the Sun and Neptune may result in a malfunctioning thymus, especially during childhood. Although the body may probably never be strong and vital, adequate amounts of vitamin A can insure fewer secondary acute types of illnesses usually present in children.

A configuration between these two planets can also result in poor usage of calcium (Saturn). Without adequate amounts of vitamin D calcium will not be fairly dispensed throughout the body, and a deficiency will develop. The problem may originate in the duodenum, where low blood calcium or lack of calcium assimilation can take place and bring on muscle cramping, lack of muscle tone, an infant's inability to walk until much later, insomnia, inability to sleep soundly, soft bones and teeth, forgetfulness and many other symptoms of a deficiency of calcium. True to Neptune's nature to disguise things, the illness may seem to be a hypoparathyroid condition (tetany) when it is not.

In addition, there can be problems with the assimilation of vitamin D and iodine. For instance, mineral oil (Neptune), if taken in immoderate dosages, may be robbing the body of vitamin D. There is also speculation that iodine poisoning is possible if Saturn is in hard aspect. Or the thyroid may be the root cause of a condition that is seemingly undiagnosable, especially if either the Sun or Neptune is in Taurus or Scorpio, with an attending hard aspect from Pluto.

Whenever Neptune is prominent in a natal chart, especially conjunct the Sun, an individual is likely to be sensitive to drugs and perhaps should receive only ½ the normal dosage of any medication. Moreover, hormones used as drugs, such as thyroxine or thyroid supplements, may upset the magnesium serum levels, causing insomnia and deficiencies of magnesium and pantothenic acid (Neptune). Drugs in general may retard magnesium assimilation.

Finally, with hard aspects from Saturn or Pluto and especially if the sign Taurus or Scorpio is involved, there is the possibility of such problems as cancer of the throat, colon, bladder or prostate gland.

I want to emphasize that any discussion of the probable causes of cancer in this book is strictly speculative, and no one configuration in any way implies that a person will get cancer. Research is sparse on this ailment. If cancer is suspect, a physician should be consulted.

Sun-Pluto

With a hard aspect between the Sun and Pluto, especially with Pluto conjunct the Sun, there may be severe deficiencies of vitamins A and D as well as the minerals iodine and magnesium. A medical astrologer should elicit symptoms or have a client undergo tests to find out which deficiencies exist.

If there is too little vitamin A, there can be sinus or catarrhal conditions or ureter, vaginal or anus infections—all diseases under the domain of Scorpio, ruled by Pluto. Poor intestinal flora, gas, colitis and diverticulosis may also result with too little vitamin A.

If iodine is lacking and either the Sun or Pluto is in Taurus or Scorpio, with a hard aspect from Saturn, a potentially severe hypothyroid condition is possible—perhaps even cretinism. On the other hand, a hard aspect from Mars or Uranus may indicate a severe hyperthyroid if the Sun or Pluto is in Taurus or Scorpio.

A shortage of magnesium can indicate problems

with the prostate gland. And if there is an accompanying hard aspect from Saturn, urinary and/or bladder problems caused by calcium deposits may result.

Finally, a Sun-Pluto conjunction is much like a Sun-Mars conjunction. A person with this configuration in a natal chart tends to push to the limits of the body's endurance. Health impairment comes from not recognizing that the body needs periods of recuperation.

Sun-Ascendant

The most likely hard aspect between the Ascendant and any planet or luminary to cause health problems is a conjunction. Very few medical problems occur when the Sun is conjunct the Ascendant, unless the Sun has three or more hard aspects to it: in that case, the sign the Sun is posited in can indicate where the ailments are likely to be found. Since the Sun represents the body, a conjunction between the Sun and the Ascendant may mean health problems or bodily weakness that will never be normalized. This person must pamper his or her fragile body to keep healthy.

HARD ASPECTS OF THE MOON
Moon-Mercury

With a hard aspect between the Moon and Mercury a person may show a propensity toward any of the diseases caused by a lack of thiamine (Mercury). Since the Moon's sign, Cancer, rules the digestive processes in the stomach, hydrochloric acid, which helps to break down the food components properly, may be missing, particularly if Saturn is in Cancer in negative aspect to Mercury. A deficiency of thiamine, can also cause gastric atony, wherein the stomach muscles become weak and flabby, contributing to poor digestion. And the liver, ruled by one of Mercury's signs, Virgo, can suffer from insufficient thiamine. The liver may not be able to produce the coenzymes necessary in the carbohydrate metabolism, a problem that *might* result in hypoglycemia if Jupiter and/or Saturn is also in the picture.

Since the Moon rules potassium and Virgo guides the small intestine, there is a possibility of tendencies toward constipation because of a lack of the mineral.

Moon-Venus

Digestive disturbances may occur with a hard aspect between the Moon and Venus. With an additional hard aspect from Saturn or with Saturn in Cancer there can be too little hydrochloric acid available to absorb the copper (Venus) in the food. And since Venus rules niacin, there may be digestive

upsets such as diarrhea caused by a lack of that vitamin. Bad breath (halitosis) from poorly digested food is also a possibility.

The sweet tooth inclinations of Venus can cause problems as well. Eating too many sweets can contribute to obesity, causing possible liver damage. Then a deficiency in riboflavin (Moon) could contribute to hypoglycemia. Eating too many white sugar products will also cause the leaching of potassium from the cells, resulting in problems with overweight. If there is an accompanying hard aspect from Mars, too little potassium in turn can result in an imbalance of sodium (Mars): with too little potassium and too much sodium the eliminating function of the kidney will weaken, perhaps causing edema.

There could also be female problems caused by a lack of vitamin E (Venus), especially with a hard aspect from either Saturn or Pluto. Miscarriage, abortion or resorption of the fetus could occur from lack of the vitamin. And if Venus or Saturn is in Cancer or Capricorn, there is the potential for anterior or posterior pituitary malfunction, causing a lack of necessary hormones and further upsetting the delicate female metabolic system.

Finally, any aspect between the transiting or progressed Moon and Venus should be examined when considering an operation. For best results, the transiting Moon should be sextile or trine to natal, progressed or transiting Venus and not afflicted by Mars. A favorable aspect to Venus is very desirable to insure that the operation proceeds smoothly and as anticipated, without complications.

Moon-Mars

It is important to consider the transiting or progressed Moon in relation to Mars when preparing for an operation. Surgery should be avoided when the transiting or progressed Moon applies to Mars in conjunction, square, inconjunct or opposition: Mars in a tension aspect with the transiting Moon may mean excessive bleeding or inflammation of an area of the body during or after surgery. On the other hand, an operation is advised when the transiting Moon is sextile or trine Mars: such an aspect may help insure a quick, clean, concise cutting hand of the surgeon.

Since Mars rules both the red blood cells and iron, the Moon in hard aspect with Mars always hints at the possibility of anemia, especially if a person is not getting enough riboflavin (Moon) as well. An accompanying hard aspect from Saturn will enhance the chances of the ailment. Since the Moon's sign, Cancer, rules the marrow of the bones, pernicious anemia may be implicated. If the Moon is in Cancer, there is the possibility a person will drink too much milk or eat too many dairy products, thereby inducing blood anemia (hypochromic anemia), especially if either Jupiter or Pluto is trine to the Moon, indicating overindulgence or an immoderate diet.

High blood pressure is another blood disorder indicated by a hard aspect between the Moon and Mars. With Mars ruling activity in general and the Moon ruling potassium there is an ideal situation for high blood pressure if a person ingests a great deal of salt, with too little riboflavin to keep the sodium-potassium level stabilized. The potential for this ailment is heightened if either the Moon or Mars is in Libra and/or there is an accompanying hard aspect from Saturn.

With insufficient iron (Mars) and a hard aspect between the Moon and Mars women may suffer menstrual difficulties, especially if Saturn is also in hard aspect to the Moon or Mars. The problems may be compounded by a lack of vitamin B-12 or fatty acids, Mars-ruled vitamins necessary to create a normal menstrual flow.

Pregnancy may also be difficult when the Moon is in hard aspect with Mars, especially if either planet is in Cancer. For example, there is the potential for an anemic state in pregnancy if Saturn is also in hard aspect or if Saturn is in Cancer, indicating potential poor assimilation of cobalt, vitamin B-12 and folic acid (all ruled by Mars) because of minimal amounts of hydrochloric acid being released in the stomach. A deficiency of folic acid, especially, can mean before and after problems related to the birthing process. In addition, there may be difficulties with conception caused by a deficiency of selenium (Mars). There is also speculation that miscarriages may occur if the levels of Mars-ruled sodium are too high.

Furthermore, the adrenal glands (Mars) are apt to malfunction with a hard aspect between the Moon and Mars. Adrenal gland sluggishness of the cortex tissue may make a person susceptible to stress symptoms of irritability, oversensitivity and emotional displays: riboflavin can be used to help correct the situation. The adrenals are also suspect as the root cause of an ailment if a person has edema or overweight from water retention: with a hard aspect from Saturn or Pluto the aldosterone hormonal levels should be tested, since the amount of the hormone produced may be causing a potassium-sodium imbalance.

Other potassium-related disorders are also possible. For instance, there is speculation that the potassium exchange with chlorine may be disrupted, causing a metabolic imbalance in the acid-alkaline levels, especially if the sign Libra is involved or if there is a hard aspect from Pluto: Libra on the Midheaven is particularly suspect of acidosis. The

potassium-sodium relationship may also be at odds, pointing to a metabolic imbalance if Libra is involved with a hard aspect from Saturn or Pluto. Moreover, loss of potassium may cause an imbalance of iron. And a deficiency of potassium as well as phosphorus (Mars) can cause lack of oxygen to the brain, bringing on headaches and mental dullness, especially if either the Moon or Mars is in Aries. Finally, there is speculation that muscular dystrophy may partially result from a lack of potassium.

Some other potential ailments indicated by a hard aspect between the Moon and Mars are states of emotional anxiety from a lack of phosphorus, especially if the signs Cancer, Virgo or Pisces are involved in the configuration; inflammation of the face and eyes, correctable by riboflavin; and too much hydrochloric acid in the stomach, causing digestive upset and potential ulcers.

Moon-Jupiter

Since the sign Cancer, ruled by the Moon, has authority over pregnancy and the birthing process and, along with Scorpio, corules the menstrual cycle, a hard aspect between the Moon and Jupiter may point to problems with female reproduction. Therefore, any pregnant woman with this configuration in her natal or progressed chart should receive enough cholin (Jupiter) or lecithin to insure proper fetal growth: research indicates that insufficient cholin in a pregnant woman can produce a child with a smaller-than-normal thymus gland. Using breast milk to feed the infant helps insure that the thymus gland will function properly in the child. With the Moon in hard aspect to Jupiter, especially if one of the planets is in Cancer, a deficiency of manganese (Jupiter) may cause the "postpartum blues," or dislike of the newborn infant. Furthermore, soreness or tenderness of the breasts before menstrual periods may occur, a symptom relievable with proper amounts of vitamin B-6 (Jupiter).

Liver ailments are other possibilities with the Moon in hard aspect with Jupiter. The liver, coruled by Jupiter and Virgo, can fall prey to inflammation caused by a virus or toxin (yellow jaundice or hepatitis). Lecithin is needed to cure this ailment, but without sufficient vitamin B-6 in the body lecithin cannot be formed: vitamin B-6, then, is a vital vitamin for people with a hard configuration between these two planets. There may also be riboflavin-related liver problems caused by a lack of the coenzyme action in the breaking down of insulin in the bloodstream: the insulin is converted into fat (Jupiter) and hypoglycemia may result. Liver injury from obesity or other causes can also bring on hypoglycemia, a disease that is especially possible if either planet is in Libra, Virgo or Pisces, with an accompanying hard aspect from Saturn to Jupiter: precipitation of the disease could be caused by too little potassium being available to help in the glucose process.

Digestive ailments, too, are likely with the Moon in hard aspect to Jupiter. Without sufficient vitamin B-6 in the liver to hook up cholin and inositol (Jupiter) to form lecithin, there can be many digestive problems. In addition, there may be a deficiency of biotin (Jupiter), since the gastric juices may not be available to unbind the vitamin, especially if the Moon is in Capricorn or if Saturn is in Cancer in negative aspect. If the Moon or Jupiter is in Cancer with a hard aspect from Mars, there could also be digestive problems involving ulcers because of a lack of zinc (Jupiter). And by reflex action to Cancer's opposite sign, Capricorn, there could be difficulties with the gallbladder (Capricorn), especially since lecithin is one of the necessary elements that makes up bile.

With the Moon in hard aspect to Jupiter the pituitary gland (Cancer) may be involved as well. For example, sterility or impotence may occur from a lack of manganese if there is an accompanying hard aspect from Saturn. A supporting hard aspect from Saturn could also mean that not enough vasopressin is released, and diabetes insipidus may result. The loss of great amounts of inositol in the urine would be evident, pointing to a potential case of the disease.[1]

In addition, an imbalance of vitamin B-6 is very likely with a hard aspect between the Moon and Jupiter. With Jupiter involved one must suspect either too much or too little riboflavin; consequently, there can be either too much or too little of vitamin B-6. Either way, other ailments can result. For instance, a deficiency of vitamin B-6 could upset the sodium-potassium metabolism. Too much sodium could produce edema that ebbs and flows with the phases of the Moon.

Finally, for best results the transiting Moon should be sextile or trine to natal, progressed or transiting Jupiter and not afflicted by Mars for undergoing surgery.

Moon-Saturn

Problems with the female reproductive system can be indicated when the Moon is in hard aspect with Saturn. For example, since Cancer rules the pituitary gland and ovaries, there may be menstrual problems, such as cramping and irritability before each period or a scanty or irregular menstrual flow—all caused by a lack of calcium (Saturn). A lack of bioflavonoids (Saturn) may also cause menstrual problems. And if the Moon is in Cancer with a hard aspect from Pluto and insufficient bioflavonoids, a possible abortion could be indicated. Miscarriage and other female complaints may occur from a lack of vitamin K (Saturn) as well. In addition, a possible deficiency of vitamin B-12 could create child-bearing problems that might be alleviated with vitamin C (Saturn).

Skin problems are also possibilities. Since Saturn rules the dryness of things—including people's exoskeletal regions, the skin—and rules the depletion of organic material, insufficient riboflavin may result in skin problems, such as flaking or scaling. Eczema may also come about from a deficiency in potassium.

Furthermore, potential bone ailments are always indicated when Saturn is in hard aspect. For instance, with an accompanying hard aspect from Mars, which rules phosphorus, rickets may occur. And if either the Moon or Saturn is in Cancer or Capricorn, the pituitary gland may be hyperfunctioning, especially with an aspect from Mars or Pluto that could trigger increased resorption of bone tissue back into the bloodstream, with not enough magnesium to halt the process: the end result could be osteoporosis. It may also be that there is not enough hydrochloric acid in the stomach to assimilate the calcium, especially if Saturn is retrograde in Cancer.

The levels of potassium in the body may be off, too, with a hard aspect between the Moon and Saturn. If the potassium-calcium relationship is disturbed, the muscles may not be receiving adequate neuromuscular activity, especially if there is an accompanying hard aspect from Mars to indicate muscle weakness or flabbiness. Saturn in Scorpio can show colon stasis brought about by insufficient potassium. And if either of the planets is in Libra, there may be kidney stones because not enough potassium is available in the body.

Other possible disorders with the Moon in hard aspect to Saturn are ulcers, especially with an additional aspect from Mars in Cancer or Pisces, and hemorrhoids, caused by a lack of bioflavonoids if the Moon is in Scorpio.

Finally, no one should probably undergo an operation when the transiting Moon is applying closely to a square, opposition or inconjunct to natal or transiting Saturn: an inconjunct, especially, is the worst possible aspect for operations. Saturn in adverse aspect with the Moon can mean chronic or very serious complications with any operation.

---

[1] All data on inositol is highly speculative and needs further research: too little is known about the vitamin at this point to make strong prognoses in relation to planetary designations.

Moon-Uranus

A person should avoid surgery when the Moon is in negative aspect to Uranus. And with any hard aspect between these two planets sudden stress, such as that caused by surgery, can create a quick loss of potassium. Watch for a postoperative condition known as hypokalemia, caused by a severe depletion of potassium during the operation. A lack of potassium could also result in swelling of the ankles from edema, since the ankles fall under the domain of Uranus-ruled Aquarius.

In addition, this configuration may help create sporadic needs for riboflavin because of stress factors. Since the rods and cones of the eyes are ruled by Aquarius, eye problems caused by a lack of riboflavin may occur. There is also speculation that irregularities in childbirth can result if the mother's diet is deficient in riboflavin and she is on drug therapy as well during the pregnancy.

Moon-Neptune

With a hard aspect between the Moon and Neptune, especially if the Moon is conjunct Neptune, a person will probably be extremely sensitive to drugs. And if Neptune is in Leo, any drugs being taken, such as diuretics, produce a weakened heart condition. Since drugs are responsible for flushing potassium out of the body, a deficiency of that mineral may occur, putting further strain on the heart.

Other potassium-related problems may come about. If Neptune is in Virgo or Scorpio, the intestinal flora and bacteria may be lacking, consequently lowering the potassium levels. Moreover, there is some speculation that if Mars is in hard aspect, too, a deficiency of potassium may result in leukemia.

Disorders of the female organs, of course, are always suspect when the Moon is in hard aspect. And female problems of an infectious nature— specifically, vaginitis—may occur when the Moon is in hard aspect to Neptune. Especially if either the Moon or Neptune is in Scorpio, there may be itching, inflammation or discharge in the genital area, caused by a deprivation of riboflavin. With a hard aspect from Saturn and/or Pluto there may also be ailments of the breast, stomach, uterus and urinary tract, particularly when either the Moon or Neptune is in Cancer or Scorpio.

Since Neptune rules pantothenic acid, there may be insufficient amounts of that vitamin and resultant diseases. Particularly with an accompanying hard aspect from Saturn allergies may crop up. A deficiency of pantothenic acid can also cause cholesterol to turn into hormones, affecting the pituitary gland.

And with either the Moon or Neptune in Cancer or Pisces there can be extrasensitivity to environmental surroundings: an individual with a hard aspect between the Moon and Neptune may not be able to take stress as well as other people and may be more prone to stress-related problems.

There is also some speculation that a hard aspect between the Moon and Neptune may cause cancer of the lymph glands, since Neptune, along with Pisces, rules this part of the body.

Finally, one should avoid surgery when the Moon is in hard aspect to Neptune.

Moon-Pluto

A severe deficiency of potassium might occur when the Moon is in hard aspect with Pluto. Without sufficient potassium the endocrine glands (Pluto) may be hypofunctioning. To determine the specific gland affected, you will need to look at the signs the planets are in: if they are in Cancer or Capricorn, the pituitary gland may be affected; in Taurus, the thyroid; and in Scorpio, the ovaries and testicles. If the Moon is conjunct Pluto in Scorpio, it's especially possible there will be troubles, including swelling, with the ovaries and testicles. If either planet is in Taurus or Scorpio, there is the additional potential for constipation or other ailments of the colon from lack of potassium. If one of the planets is in Scorpio, there may also be infections of the urethra or bladder, such as the inability to urinate. The tubes of the body (Gemini) may be affected, too, from a deficiency of potassium.

In addition, there may be insufficient amounts of riboflavin or vitamin B-6 (Jupiter) with a hard aspect between the Moon and Pluto. There is speculation of the possibility of tumorous cancers in the body with a deficiency of riboflavin or vitamin B-6, especially with an accompanying aspect Jupiter. Jupiter in the configuration can also point to too much riboflavin and too little vitamin B-6 or vice versa.

People should avoid operations when the transiting Moon is in negative aspect to Pluto; they should wait for harmonious aspects or none at all. I know a woman who went in for two heart surgeries when there was a strong negative aspect between the Moon and Pluto, and she died twice on the table. Fortunately, she survived. But her experience emphasizes the importance of waiting for harmonious aspects for surgery.

Moon-Ascendant

The emotions are quite vulnerable when the Moon is conjunct the Ascendant: anyone can knock such an individual emotionally off-center with little effort. Consequently, health problems involving sudden weight gain and loss are possible. For a woman, especially, this combination may mean an eternal battle with edema or fluid retention, particularly around the time of her period each month: a loss or gain of five pounds is common.

HARD ASPECTS OF MERCURY

Mercury-Venus

Since Mercury and Venus can never be more than 76 degrees apart in orbit, there are no possible negative aspects between the two planets; however, the semi-sextile (30 degrees) and the semi-square (45 degrees) may furnish potential irritation if Venus is likewise afflicted by any of the outer planets—Saturn, Uranus, Neptune or Pluto. There is speculation that a semi-square can bring about an imbalance of niacin and thiamine, ruled by Venus and Mercury respectively—an imbalance that can contribute to ailments such as a malfunctioning thyroid. With Venus ruling both Taurus and Libra the deficiency of thiamine may result from a love of sweets and other carbohydrates.

With a hard aspect between Mercury and Venus and an accompanying hard aspect from Saturn potential problems with the Gemini-ruled tubes of the body may occur. For example, the tubes may become less elastic and flexible, indicating a potential loss of copper (Venus) and vitamin C (Saturn). Or there may be problems with the capillaries.

Because Mercury rules Virgo as well as Gemini, an aspect between Mercury and Venus may produce Virgo-related ailments. Intestinal disorders, such as sprue and celiac diseases, may occur because of insufficient copper. A lack of vitamin E (Venus) can produce pancreatic disturbances: if Mars is also in hard aspect, there may be inflammation of the pancreas; if Saturn is in hard aspect, the gland may be sluggish. And with Jupiter and/or Virgo implicated, there is the possibility of liver disturbances because of a deficiency of vitamin E.

The general health of the nervous system may also be affected, particularly if Mercury is in Aquarius with a hard aspect from Pluto. Such a placement indicates possible degeneration of the myelin sheaths about the nerves. If Saturn is also in hard aspect, multiple sclerosis may develop from lack of copper.

Mercury-Mars

Nervous disorders are definite possibilities with a hard aspect between Mercury and Mars. There may be general inflammation of the nerves. Or since Mars rules Aries, which has domain over the face, there is the potential for Bell's palsy. Nerve transmission may be faulty, too, causing unexplained tenseness because of a deficiency of phosphorus (Mars). And the central nervous system may become impaired, possibly resulting in a shuffling gait, slurred speech patterns and eventual paralysis—all connected with a deficiency of vitamin B-12 (Mars). There is speculation that as well as general nervous tension epilepsy may result from a hard aspect between Mercury and Mars because of an imbalance of sodium (Mars) affecting the central nervous system. And Mars in Virgo in poor aspect with Mercury may incite a case of nerves that will probably be helped by adequate dosages of thiamine (Mercury).

In fact, a deficiency of thiamine is highly likely with a hard aspect between these two planets, especially since Mars regulates how we burn our energy and how we exert ourselves mentally and physically. Mars in a fire or air sign will tend to induce a deficiency of thiamine more readily than if the planet is found in water or earth signs: Mars in Cancer in hard aspect to Mercury may even infer that supplemental thiamine should be avoided because of too much hydrochloric acid in the stomach. Another possibility is that too little thiamine is assimilated from lack of sufficient phosphorus.

Intestinal disturbances may also occur. A hard aspect between Mercury and Mars may mean a deficiency of folic acid (Mars). Without enough of this important vitamin diseases such as diarrhea, diverticulosis or sprue could possibly manifest. Diarrhea could occur from a lack of fats in the digestive process as well. And since Mars rules chlorine, colitis caused by too much intake of chlorinated water and the eventual destruction of flora bacteria in the intestinal tract could also develop.

Other Virgo-related problems possible with a hard aspect between Mercury and Mars are liver dysfunction from a lack of natural chlorine in the body for maintenance of the organ, especially with an additional hard aspect from Jupiter; and pancreatitis or impairment of the pancreatic functions with a hard aspect from Saturn.

An accompanying hard aspect from Saturn can also indicate that the tubes of the body will be blocked: i.e., cholesterol deposits may build up in the bile duct, kidney tubules, etc., if fatty acids (Mars) are missing.

Mercury-Jupiter

A hard aspect between Mercury and Jupiter can point to a moderate deficiency of thiamine. If a hard aspect from Saturn is present as well, this deficiency may be caused from a lack of manganese (Jupiter). A lack of vitamin B-6 (Jupiter) can also prevent thiamine from being assimilated properly, causing symptoms. of a thiamine deficiency. Since Jupiter rules Sagittarius, which holds sway over the thigh and sciatica nerve, there may be inflammation of that area without adequate thiamine.

Lack of vitamin B-6 can cause a variety of ailments. For example, since Mercury rules Virgo, diseases such as diabetes, hypoglycemia or pancreatitis may occur when vitamin B-6 is in short supply over a long period. Vitamin B-6 is also known to keep the central nervous system healthy: lack of the vitamin can induce nervousness, a well-known disorder of Mercury. And it is speculated that with Jupiter in Gemini clogging of the arteries could occur from lack of vitamin B-6, causing atherosclerosis.

Since Gemini rules the lungs as well as the bronchi and bronchial tubes, respiratory ailments, indicating a deficiency of pangamic acid (Jupiter), are possible with a hard aspect between Mercury and Jupiter. Especially if Saturn is in Gemini, bronchial asthma may occur. Emphysema is also possible with Jupiter in Gemini and an accompanying hard aspect from Neptune—a configuration that that indicates a weakening in that area of the body from distension of the sacs with excess air. With a hard aspect from Saturn and a lack of pangamic acid angina can result, showing constriction that could bring on possible suffocation.

There may also be diseases of the pancreas (Virgo). A potential deficiency of zinc (Jupiter), for example, could manifest a diabetic condition. With a hard aspect from Saturn there could be insufficient manganese to control glucose levels. A lack of chromium (Jupiter) could also affect the glucose process. In addition, there is some speculation that insufficient inositol (Jupiter) can contribute to diabetes. And there is the possibility that biotin (Jupiter) is not being unbound for assimilation, thus affecting the splitting-up process of the pancreas as well as the liver and the intestine: the glands located in the pancreas (the isles of Langerhans) are co-ruled by Jupiter, Cancer and Virgo, so that glucose and insulin production may be affected, pointing a potentially higher need of biotin to keep insulin levels normalized in diabetic cases.

Nerve disorders are other possibilities with a hard aspect between Mercury and Jupiter. Some impairment of the central nervous system has been noted with a lack of biotin. And if either planet is in Virgo, with a hard aspect from Uranus, nerve degeneration or "faulty wiring" is indicated—a condition that can be helped with manganese.

Furthermore, the thyroid, coruled by Mercury and Taurus, may be adversely affected when Mercury is in hard aspect with Jupiter. There is speculation that with an accompanying hard aspect from Saturn too little cholin (Jupiter) could halt production of tyrosine so that thyroxine would not be available—a condition that could trigger hypothyroidism. If Jupiter is also sextile or trine Pluto, too much manganese may settle in the thyroid. And with a hard aspect from Neptune estrogen supplements may be responsible for lowering the basal metabolism of the thyroid.

Finally, an additional hard aspect from Saturn, indicating a deficiency of chromium, could point to liver disorders.

Mercury-Saturn

With Mercury ruling Virgo a hard aspect between Mercury and Saturn may cause intestinal disorders. Virgo rules the intestinal tract and everything concerned with it, including the growth of healthy bacterial flora. There is speculation that Mercury in hard aspect to Saturn can indicate a lack of flora, which, in turn, may cause poor synthesis of PABA and vitamin K, both ruled by Saturn. As a result there may be such problems as diarrhea and colitis. Possible intestinal tract malabsorption may also indicate that bioflavonoids (Saturn) are not being utilized properly, creating further complications with the capillaries. Moreover, with an additional aspect from Neptune or with Mars in Cancer, Pisces or Virgo, as well as involved in the configuration, there may be poor assimilation of thiamine, producing duodenal ulcers.

Other ailments may result from a probable lack of thiamine. For example, poor bone growth in infants can be attributed to a deficiency of thiamine. Skin disorders, such as herpes and its various manifestations (simplex, zoster and zoster ophthalmicus), may also occur. The teeth are affected by the amount of thiamine in the body, too, and not enough thiamine can aggravate the pain and discomfort before and after dental surgery. Finally, insufficient thiamine may inhibit the functions of sulfur (Saturn). Especially if the sign Taurus is involved, the thyroid gland may be interfering with the sulfur uptake, since thyroxine is necessary for the mineral to be used successfully. With a deficiency of sulfur the insulin functions of the pancreas may be malfunctioning.

A hard aspect between Mercury and Saturn may also cause a lack of calcium (Saturn). If one of the planets is in Taurus and especially if Saturn is retrograde in Taurus, the thyroid may be hypofunctioning, producing a deficiency of calcium and related arthritic problems. Without enough calcium nerve ailments such as tremors, shaking, insomnia, restlessness, morbid states of mind and depression can occur. With an accompanying hard aspect from *to much or to little?*

the Sun nervousness may indicate too little magnesium (Sun) to work with calcium to stop tremors, restlessness or vague nervousness.

Mercury-Uranus

Since a person with this configuration will be inclined toward great nervousness anyway, care should be taken to make sure the nerves are well supplied with all vitamins and minerals affecting the nervous system, especially thiamine. There will probably be sporadic needs for thiamine because of sudden stress. Although Mercury is said to be a coordinator and cooperator, in negative aspect, especially with Uranus, it can mean incoordination, spasm or twitching—all helped by thiamine. In addition, Uranus rules Aquarius, which governs the spinal cord, and thiamine in short supply can cause potential damage to the spinal cord.

Mercury-Neptune

A deficiency of thiamine is a strong possibility with a hard aspect between Mercury and Neptune, although because of the deceptive nature of Neptune the problem may be misdiagnosed or overlooked. For instance, since Virgo rules much of the pancreatic function, a case of "hidden" diabetes may occur: a five-hour glucose tolerance test will determine if diabetes does indeed exist; instead, the ailment may be a carbohydrate problem that can be straightened out with adequate dosages of thiamine to provide better oxidation in the metabolic process. Moreover, the antivitamin vitamin enzyme thiaminase may be at work destroying thiamine through a diet of raw fish, oysters and mussels. Addiction to alcohol can produce an added need for the vitamin. Without adequate thiamine there may be a general weakness of the thyroid.

With Mercury ruling Virgo there may also be intestinal complaints from a lack of flora, perhaps caused by insufficient pantothenic acid (Neptune).

The possibility of cancer of the lungs, pancreas or liver should not be discounted when Mercury is in hard aspect to elusive Neptune, especially with an additional hard aspect from Saturn or Pluto. The sign Gemini or Virgo must also be implicated.

Mercury-Pluto

First and foremost, a hard aspect between Mercury and Pluto may imply either a lack of or an overabundance of thiamine, situations probably caused by a person's diet. Especially if Mercury is conjunct Pluto, a severe deficiency may occur, with resultant thyroid ailments. Furthermore, since Pluto rules Scorpio, which governs the colon, the root of

Fixed Cross diseases, an imbalance of thiamine could indicate heart problems as discussed under the section about the aspects of the Sun to Mercury. The pancreas could also be involved. And there could be a hormonal imbalance in general.

There is some speculation that a hard aspect between Mercury and Pluto provides a possible link to multiple sclerosis, since Mercury rules the central nervous system. Mercury in Aquarius in hard aspect with Pluto is especially suspect of creating this disease because of a deficiency of orotic acid (Pluto). But since so little valuable information has yet become available on orotic acid, this idea should be treated purely as hypothetical until there is enough data to compare multiple sclerosis with other diseases that seem to be caused by deficiencies of orotic acid.

Mercury-Ascendant

When Mercury is conjunct the Ascendant, a person is apt to run on nervous energy, producing frayed nerves. He or she needs to learn to relax and turn off the mind and its careening mental faculties. Since such an individual will probably never sit still, he or she should use a rocking chair to be able to sit in one place and yet be in motion. Worry is a great deteriorator of health with a conjunction between Mercury and the Ascendant, and only attitudinal change can assuage this tendency. A person with this configuration in a natal chart must be encouraged to use his or her native acumen—without worry.

HARD ASPECT OF VENUS

Venus-Mars

There is the potential for a lack of vitamin E (Venus) when Venus is in hard aspect with Mars. The deficiency may be aggravated by the ingestion of too much chlorinated water, since Mars rules chlorine and overdoses of that mineral can destroy vitamin E in the body. Vitamin E also needs fatty acids (Mars) for assimilation, and there may be a lack of these fatty acids, especially if there is a hard aspect from Saturn as well; thus the normal functions of the glands, particularly the thyroid and the adrenals, could be interrupted, and the kidney (Venus) could malfunction. With Mars governing the adrenal glands, insufficient vitamin E and fatty acids could cause low secretion of hormones, affecting the sexual drive.

Of course, with insufficient vitamin E a person can suffer skin ailments, especially since there may also be a deficiency of folic acid and/or selenium, both ruled by Mars. With an attending hard aspect from Saturn, wrinkling may occur, and insufficient selenium may precipitate the aging process. In addition, scars from burns (always a possibility when

Mars is in aspect) may need applications of vitamin E to heal properly. And if Uranus is also in aspect, scars from surgery or accidents may require applications of vitamin E.

With an accompanying hard aspect from Saturn there could also be poor absorption of iron (Mars) because of insufficient vitamin E, necessary to assimilate natural iron. A hard aspect from Neptune could create a potential negative chemical reaction between vitamin E and iron, too, if the iron is from an inorganic source.

When Mars is in hard aspect, blood disorders are always possible. There is speculation that with a hard aspect between Venus and Mars menstrual irregularities, such as decrease or cessation, may be linked to a dual need of vitamins E and B-12 (Mars), especially if a hard aspect from Saturn is present. With Saturn involved there may also be problems with the veins, such as high blood pressure, possible hemorrhaging or stroke. High blood pressure is especially probable, since the kidneys help control the blood pressure. Hardening of the arteries is another possibility, which may be avoided through the use of less sodium and more vitamins E and C (Saturn). An accompanying hard aspect from Saturn can also indicate that the cobalt-copper (Mars-Venus) relationship is out of balance, inducing anemia that an iron supplement alone will not cure. An imbalance of copper can result in other problems. A deficiency in copper may create poor iron absorption. High concentrations of copper might induce a deficiency of molybdenum (Mars), especially with an accompanying hard aspect from Saturn; on the other hand, a hard aspect from Pluto could hint at an excess of molybdenum, creating a deficiency of copper.

With a hard aspect between Venus and Mars there may also be insufficient niacin (Venus). Too little niacin in the body may be caused from lack of phosphorus (Mars) to help niacin become assimilated. Especially with a hard aspect from Saturn or Pluto the calcium-phosphorus metabolism may be out of balance. The tendency to eat too many sweets or white sugar products will also generally interfere with phosphorus assimilation. At any rate, a deficiency of phosphorus can deplete the niacin, causing such problems as swollen lips, sore tongue, canker sores, trench mouth or migraine headaches—all Mars-related problems.

Other disorders indicated by a hard aspect between Venus and Mars are an acid-alkaline imbalance, especially with a hard aspect from Pluto; dropsy, correctable in part with dosages of vitamin B-12 and folic acid; reproductive problems caused by a deficiency of selenium, if a hard aspect to the Moon

and/or Saturn is also present; muscle damage that may be chronic, debilitating or transforming in nature, occurring because of a lack of vitamin E, if Saturn and Pluto are also implicated.

Venus-Jupiter

A person with Venus in hard aspect with Jupiter in a natal chart might require larger-than-average quantities of vitamin E. With a deficiency of vitamin E and an accompanying hard aspect from Saturn, there may be arterial damage. With Saturn involved there may also be the possibility of certain types of muscular dystrophy, which seems to respond to a joint application of vitamin E and inositol (Jupiter). With insufficient pangamic acid (Jupiter) as well, heart ailments are other possibilities. A lack of cholin (Jupiter), in addition to a deficiency of vitamin E, may also cause problems with the kidneys. And a lack of vitamins PABA, E and B-6 (Jupiter) can result in cholesterol problems.

Furthermore, there is always the potential for sugar-related ailments when Venus is in hard aspect with Jupiter. Both Venus and Jupiter can indicate overindulgence, especially of sweets. With an accompanying hard aspect from Saturn there can be diabetic tendencies caused by a deficiency of manganese (Jupiter).

If either Venus or Jupiter is in Virgo or its opposite sign, Pisces, liver problems may also be indicated. With a trine from Pluto to Jupiter and the sign Virgo involved hepatolenticular disease could occur, signalling an above-average need for copper.

A deficiency in copper can create other disorders. For instance, if the copper-zinc (Venus-Jupiter) balance is disturbed, there may also be an imbalance of iron (Mars). And insufficient zinc (Jupiter) can result in skin problems. In addition, there may be a metabolic block in the copper enzyme factor synthesis from a missing cofactor, vitamin B-6, if a hard aspect from Saturn is present. If either Venus or Jupiter is in Leo with an aspect from Saturn, there can be possible rupture of the aorta or arteries, caused by inelasticity of the artery walls from a loss of copper and vitamin C (Saturn).

A person with a hard aspect between Venus and Jupiter in a natal chart may have an above-average need for niacin, too. And a deficiency of niacin can reduce the availability of vitamin B-6.

Finally, with a hard aspect between Venus and Jupiter and an additional hard aspect from Saturn it's possible that whatever sign Jupiter is in could pinpoint the site of an aneurysm, caused by a deficiency of copper: if Jupiter is in Leo, it could be an aneurysm of the aorta; in Virgo, the abdominal arteries; and in Aries, the head.

Venus-Saturn

Lack of vitamin E is a major possibility when Venus is in hard aspect with Saturn, and a lack of the vitamin can cause a variety of skin disorders. For example, skin may bruise easily. Or the aging process of wrinkles and sagging skin may hasten, especially since a hard aspect between Venus and Saturn also indicates a deficiency of the antiaging nutrient PABA (Saturn). Skin problems such as eczema, dermatitis, lupus, vitiligo, wrinkles, dry skin and dark spots may also occur, requiring the external application of PABA cream.

Vitamin E is also concerned with the blood and clotting process, particularly in the veins, ruled by Venus. An inability to assimilate vitamin E can result in loss of venous elasticity. Moreover, clotting or thrombosis formation can occur from a lack of vitamins C (Saturn) and E in combination: if either planet is in Aquarius, the clotting will probably take place in the legs if in Gemini, the lungs.

Other potential deficiencies can also cause problems with the veins. For instance, the veins may become fragile from lack of sufficient bioflavonoids (Saturn) to keep them elastic and permeable: skin bruising easily could indicate a need for more bioflavonoids as well as vitamins E and C to keep the blood and veins healthy in general and to discourage clotting (phlebitis) from occurring. Copper is also necessary to keep veins elastic, and with a hard aspect from Mars or Pluto there can be possible aneurysms from insufficient copper, especially if Jupiter is also involved.

Kidney ailments are possible with a hard aspect between Venus and Saturn, too, since Venus rules Libra, the regulator of the kidneys. There is some speculation that kidney damage can be inflicted by too much fluorine (Saturn), which causes blockage of the tubules. With an aspect from Mars or Pluto there may be kidney stones. If the Sun is involved, there could be kidney calcification because vitamin D (Sun) is not present in sufficient quantities to distribute the calcium properly. And if Venus or Saturn is in Libra with an additional aspect from Mars, there may be inflammation of the kidneys from lack of vitamin E.

Other potential ailments with this configuration are an acid-alkaline imbalance in the body from insufficient calcium (Saturn) with a hard aspect from Pluto; skin lesions over the body, dermatitis from pellagra, ulcerations, pustules or any tumors of the outer skin from a lack of niacin; possible copper poisoning and resulting destruction of vitamin C with an aspect from Pluto or Neptune; problems in protein metabolism without sufficient copper; and possible osteoporosis of the bones.

Venus-Uranus

With a hard aspect between Venus and Uranus there may be sporadic needs of niacin when sudden stressful situations occur, especially if a person is on a high starch-carbohydrate diet. Uranus rules Aquarius, which governs the oxygenation process of the body. If too many starch products are eaten, a great amount of oxygen is stolen from the bloodstream to digest the starch. Oxygen loss accompanying a deficiency of niacin will bring on dementia, confusion, disorientation, mental imbalance and depression. Furthermore, cramping in the region of the calves is a possibility, since Aquarius rules over the calves and ankles.

A hard aspect between Venus and Uranus may also bring on sporadic needs for higher quantities of copper when a person is under severe and sudden stress. With an aspect from Mercury to Uranus there may be degeneration of the myelin sheaths from lack of copper, especially if a hard aspect from Saturn or Pluto is also present. In addition, sensitivity to radiation can disturb the copper reserves in the body, causing a loss of the mineral.

Finally, there may be sporadic needs for larger-than-normal dosages of vitamin E with a hard aspect between Venus and Uranus, paticularly when a person is under stress, creating the potential for heart ailments.

Venus-Neptune

Since Venus rules Libra, the metabolism in general may be upset or out of balance with a hard aspect between Venus and Neptune, especially with aspects from other planets. More specifically, with poor aspects from Jupiter and/or Saturn there is the potential for blood sugar problems, such as hypoglycemia, caused by a deficiency of pantothenic acid (Neptune).

A hard aspect between Venus and Neptune can also indicate disorders of the skin. There is the potential for loss of vitamin E because of consumption of rancid oil, mineral oil or cod liver oil—all ruled by Neptune. Moreover, there is the possibility of pigmentation changes, especially in pregnant women, caused by deficiencies of niacin and pantothenic acid. And there is some speculation that a hard aspect between Venus and Neptune can mean lack of adequate laetrile (Neptune), perhaps causing skin cancers with a hard aspect from Saturn or Pluto.

A hard aspect between Venus and Neptune may signify possible poisoning from inorganic copper sources, too, especially if there is a hard aspect from Saturn. Since Neptune rules liquids, they would be highly likely as the poisoning agent, but any copper source should be suspect until proper lab testing can prove otherwise.

Venus-Pluto

Venus in hard aspect with Pluto can indicate an abnormal need for vitamin E to keep the endocrine system healthy, especially the pituitary glands: if Venus is in Cancer, the posterior pituitary may be affected; if in Capricorn, the anterior pituitary. On the other hand, Venus in Aries can implicate the adrenal glands, and Venus in Taurus shows potential thyroid problems. With an accompanying aspect from Saturn female problems related to a deficiency of vitamin E may manifest, if Venus is in Scorpio.

There is also some speculation of an abnormal requirement of niacin in the daily diet with a hard aspect between Venus and Pluto. Since Pluto rules Scorpio, which governs the colon, a lack of the vitamin B complex in the intestines can mean that the amino acid tryptophane cannot convert to niacin, triggering a severe deficiency of that vitamin.

In addition, there is the potential for abnormal needs of copper in the daily diet with a hard aspect between Venus and Pluto, a probability that should be confirmed through testing by a physician. With a hard aspect from Saturn such a possible copper shortage could affect the RNA genetic coding. With Aquarius involved a hard aspect from Saturn could also point to disintegration of the myelin sheaths surrounding the nerves because of insufficient copper.

Finally, a hard aspect between Venus and Pluto, especially a conjunction, may mean potential sugar problems if the sign Virgo is involved—perhaps pancreatic disruption occurring because vitamin E is lacking.

Venus-Ascendant

A person who has Venus conjunct the Ascendant in a chart will probably love sweets, perhaps turning to them when in need of affection. As a result an insecure individual may put on weight. In addition, the pancreas may suffer from the unnecessary amounts of sugar and carbohydrates consumed.

HARD ASPECTS OF MARS

Mars-Jupiter

Any time blood disorders manifest, Mars is implicated. With a hard aspect between Mars and Jupiter there can be possible overproduction of red blood cells, a problem that may be caused by a loss of zinc (Jupiter). If either planet is in Gemini, there may be difficulties with circulation of the arteries, particularly arteriosclerosis, caused by an imbalance of sodium (Mars). Megaloblastic anemia is another possibility. Furthermore, high blood pressure may occur because of insufficient cholin (Jupiter). And with a hard aspect from Saturn there may not be enough vitamin B-6 (Jupiter) to help iron (Mars) become assimilated; thus an anemic state may exist.

With Jupiter ruling vitamin B-6 there is always the possibility of a deficiency of that vitamin if Mars is in hard aspect. When vitamin B-6 is not present in sufficient quantity to break down iron for assimilation and use, hypochromic anemia is a possibility. In addition, since Mars rules Aries, which governs the region of the head, ear inflammations, such as labyrinthitis or Meniere's syndrome, may occur from a deficiency of vitamin B-6. Vitamin B-12 (Mars) also cannot be assimilated at all unless vitamin B-6 is available. And without enough vitamin B-6 to create lecithin and without enough vitamin B-12 to promote a fast breakdown of lecithin, high cholesterol levels can result. Since vitamin B-6 is also essential for the assimilation of fatty acids (Mars), hypoglycemia may manifest with an aspect from Saturn, especially if Mars or Jupiter is in Libra.

Hair loss is another possibility with a hard aspect between Mars and Jupiter: Mars in Aries or Leo tends to precipitate the problem, especially if there is an affliction from Saturn. Such hair loss may be induced by a deficiency of biotin (Jupiter). Insufficient folic acid (Mars), along with a lack of vitamin B-6, may also bring on baldness. And there is speculation that an imbalance of inositol (Jupiter) can contribute to the problem.

Whenever Jupiter is in hard aspect in a natal chart, a person may have either too much or too little of whatever vitamins or minerals are involved. With a hard aspect between Mars and Jupiter there is the potential need for larger-than-normal amounts of folic acid and vitamin B-12 to keep the body healthy. A greater dosage of fatty acids may also be needed for daily bodily maintenance: there is the possibility of cholesterol or fat plugging the arteries if inadequate amounts of fatty acids are not ingested or enough lecithin is not produced by the body.

The minerals, too, may be out of balance in the body with a hard aspect between Mars and Jupiter. For example, if there is any liver dysfunction, tests should be conducted to determine if there is a larger-than-normal need of natural chlorine (Mars); on the other hand, arterial clogging may result from too much chlorine, especially if there is a sextile or trine aspect from either Mars or Jupiter to Pluto. There is also speculation that a hard aspect between Mars and Jupiter may bring about greater needs for cobalt and selenium, both ruled by Mars. There may also be too much or too little sodium in the body: a person with a hard aspect between Mars and Jupiter in a chart tends to overuse salt on food. In addition, a high intake of chromium (Jupiter) may be necessary to keep carbohydrates functioning properly because of a voracious high-energy metabolism. And a trine to Jupiter from Pluto can indicate that iron is not getting properly absorbed because of a high amount of manganese (Jupiter) in the body.

An imbalance between phosphorus (Mars) and zinc is also possible with a hard aspect between Mars and Jupiter, especially if the sign Libra is involved or either planet is on the Ascendant. Prostate enlargement may occur if zinc is not sufficiently supplied, particularly if there is a hard aspect from Pluto or the sign Scorpio is involved. Mars trine Pluto could point to an overabundance of phosphorus, thereby creating a shortage of manganese. In contrast, low phosphorus levels could interfere with the production of lecithin.

Finally, since Mars rules the muscles, a person with a Mars-Jupiter hard aspect in a chart might be prone to muscle injuries that could be alleviated with dosages of pangamic acid (Jupiter).

Mars-Saturn

Ailments involving the blood are possible with a hard aspect between Mars and Saturn. For example, clotting or thickening may take place from lack of sulfur to create heparin, the natural blood thinner. Blood clot problems may also be caused by insufficient bioflavonoids (Saturn), if there is an accompanying hard aspect from Venus, ruling vitamin E. Moreover, since Mars rules Aries, which governs the head region, there may be problems with the teeth and gums, such as bleeding or excess hemorrhaging, from a lack of calcium (Saturn). There may also be nose bleeds and bleeding in the muscles from a lack of vitamin K (Saturn).

But the most probable blood disorder with a hard aspect between Mars and Saturn is anemia. Insufficient amounts of vitamin C (Saturn) may result in poor assimilation of iron, thereby inducing anemia. Deficiencies of folic acid and vitamin B-12 can also cause anemia, which can be related to premature aging or death of red blood cells. In fact, folic acid and vitamin B-12 are helpmates, and deficiencies in both may trigger pernicious anemia.

The reasons for the anemia may be confusing if Neptune is also in hard aspect. For instance, if Neptune is involved, anemia may be created by an overdose of vitamin K, but Neptune's influence may make a person unable to figure out exactly what is causing the disease. Anemia may also be initiated by insufficient cobalt, but with Neptune in the configuration the illness may be masked by a higher-than-normal intake of folic acid without a comparable amount of cobalt and vitamin B-12 to avoid an anemic condition.

Since Saturn rules bone structure, bone-related problems are very probable when Saturn is in hard aspect with Mars. If the Sun is also in hard aspect, thus triggering a lack of vitamin D (Sun) to help assimilate calcium and phosphorus, ailments such as arthritis, rickets or osteoporosis may occur. If either Mars or Saturn is in Libra, there may be some forms of inflammatory arthritis because of insufficient vitamin C. Furthermore, a person may have trouble wearing dentures if the sign Cancer is involved. And there is some speculation (and I emphasize that this is pure speculation) of the possibility of brittle bones caused by an excess of molybdenum (Mars) if Pluto is trine Mars.

If Saturn is in the sign Cancer in hard aspect with Mars, there may be troubles with the stomach, the pituitary glands or the gallbladder. Especially if Saturn is retrograde in Cancer, there may not be enough chlorine to stimulate sufficient quantities of hydrochloric acid for proper digestion of foods. Low HCl content in the stomach can negate phosphorus absorption as well as hinder the absorption of iron. An affected pituitary gland may cause the loss of sodium. And if Saturn is in either Cancer or Capricorn, a lack of fatty acids may bring on cholesterol deposits, indicating gallbladder blockage of bile duct or cholesterol stones within the organ: if too little bile is released, it cannot break down fat molecules for use.

If, instead, either Saturn or Mars is in Libra in hard aspect with each other, there may be a metabolic imbalance of selenium-sulfur and/or calcium-phosphorus, particularly if Pluto is also involved or if either Saturn or Mars is on the Ascendant. Insufficient selenium may result in muscle flabbiness and atrophy. A calcium-phosphorus imbalance usually indicates acidosis. A possible overabundance of phosphorus could result in poor absorption of iron, also indicating a need for more vitamin C. There may not be sufficient calcium available either.

As I've already indicated, there is also the strong possibility of a lack of folic acid with a hard aspect between Mars and Saturn. The deficiency may result from the inability of PABA (Saturn) to grow in the intestinal tract. But, whatever the reason, insufficient folic acid can result in poor assimilation of iron. Without enough folic acid vitamin B-12 may also be ineffective in some enzymatic or metabolic function. Furthermore, a want of folic acid can mean loss of hair or premature graying. At any rate, a person with a hard aspect between Mars and Saturn in a natal chart will probably have a greater need for folic acid when under sudden or severe stress.

A hard aspect between Mars and Saturn can also signify decreased levels of sodium in the body. With a hard aspect from Pluto the adrenal glands may be suspect as the root cause of such a deficiency. There also may not be enough calcium to support the sodium in its functions.

Other disorders potentially resulting from a Mars-Saturn hard aspect are vitamin C-related ailments involving the muscles, tendons and cartilage of the body; hair problems, underweight or lack of growth caused by a lack of fatty acids; and adrenal exhaustion, if there is an aspect from Neptune, indicating insufficient pantothenic acid.

Mars-Uranus

With a hard aspect between Mars and Uranus there is the possibility of sudden accidents, surgery or the onset of stress, requiring supplements of vitamins and minerals. For example, burn-related accidents may occur, necessitating a sudden supply of sodium. And when a person is under shock or sudden, unexpected stress, the adrenals may become exhausted, eventually upsetting the sodium balance. When there is the sudden onset of stress from surgery, there can be a greater need for phosphorus. With a hard aspect from the Moon, emotional stress of sudden origin may also necessitate extra supplementation of phosphorus. And there is some speculation that cobalt as well as vitamin B-12 may be required in higher amounts when a person is under sudden and severe stress for long periods of time. Stomach secretions may not be normal because of stress. With little of the intrinsic factor vitamin B-12 may not be assimilated, and anemia may develop.

Since Uranus rules Aquarius, disorders related to that sign may be caused with a hard aspect between Mars and Uranus. For instance, Aquarius governs the spinal cord, where most of the body's chlorine is stored; therefore, a person may have a sporadic need of natural chlorine when under sudden stress. With Aquarius also ruling the calves an accompanying hard aspect from Saturn may result in varicose veins, caused by insufficient fatty acids, which can also be destroyed by X-rays. And there is some speculation that when either Mars or Uranus is in Aquarius with an accompanying hard aspect from Saturn, muscular dystrophy can occur: selenium may aid in erradicating the disease.

On the other hand, if Mars or Uranus is in Libra, there may be a metabolic imbalance of phosphorus occurring when a person is under sudden or extreme emotional duress as well as on a diet heavy in phosphorus. With an overabundance of phosphorus iron will not be readily absorbed.

Finally, there is some speculation that poisoning may take place with a hard aspect between Mars and Uranus because of excessive intake of supplemental molybdenum, especially if Saturn is also in hard aspect.

Mars-Neptune

With a hard aspect between Mars and Neptune, especially a conjunction, there may be poor vitality and lack of energy in general. A person with such a configuration in a chart may also be prone to stress-related ailments. And he or she may be especially sensitive to drugs, usually requiring only ½ the regular dosage of any medication.

Because of this drug-sensitivity, a person with Mars in hard aspect with Neptune in a chart may be highly susceptible to poisoning. Iron poisoning may occur, especially with an accompanying hard aspect from Saturn. There is also the potential for poisoning through overconsumption of selenium-bearing herbs. Furthermore, a hard aspect between Mars and Neptune points toward possible chlorine poisoning when a hard aspect from Saturn is involved: chlorine levels in the body should be tested by a physician, because the mineral may be the root cause of an allergic reaction.

Mars in hard aspect with Neptune also can indicate the potential for weak adrenal glands and the poor production of hormones therein. The adrenal glands may be susceptible to drug poisoning. Or there may be a deficiency of pantothenic acid (Neptune), needed to support the adrenals so that aldosterone can keep sodium in balance.

Since Mars is involved, there may be blood problems as well, especially is either or both planets is in Pisces and/or Virgo, indicating lymph-related ailments that could result in high white blood cell count. With an accompanying hard aspect from Saturn or Pluto leukemia may occur. Low blood pressure is another possibility with Jupiter or Saturn also in hard aspect. In addition, there can be seemingly blood conditions that are not diagnosable. For instance, especially with a hard aspect from Saturn, an individual may experience fatigue for no discernible reason: the condition may be caused by an imbalance of folic acid, vitamin B-12 or cobalt, creating borderline anemic conditions that persist for long periods. And with an aspect from Saturn fatty acids may not break down properly within the body, leaving undigested fat to combine with iron and calcium (Saturn) to form an insoluble soap, bringing on anemia or fragile bone conditions (and constipation if Mars or Neptune is in Scorpio).

A Mars-Neptune hard aspect may also induce deficiencies of phosphorus or folic acid. The ingestion of the poisonous metal aluminum (Neptune) may halt phosphorus absorption. A hard aspect from Saturn can indicate a loss of phosphorus, too. As a result the parathyroid gland may function poorly. And insufficient folic acid may result from drug therapy.

On the other hand, there may be too much sodium in the body. The sodium may be retained because of drug therapy, such as cortisone injections. If Neptune is in Libra, weakened kidneys, renal insufficiency or acidosis may develop, causing sodium retention and edema. Too much sodium may result in gout if there is also a hard aspect from Saturn: without sufficient pantothenic acid sodium settles with uric acid needles into the soft tissue surrounding the joints, causing inflammation because of insufficient vitamin C (Saturn) to stop the process.

There is also some speculation that a hard aspect between Mars and Neptune may cause a lack of laetrile, resulting in cancer of the mouth or tongue or muscle deterioration in some part of the body—with a hard aspect from Saturn or Pluto.

Finally, it should always be remembered that Neptune is very deceptive, and misdiagnosis may occur when that planet is in hard aspect with Mars. For example, a shortage of iron, vitamin B-12 or pantothenic acid may be the root cause of a seemingly undiagnosable condition or of a disease whose symptoms seem unrelated to such shortages.

Mars-Pluto

Whenever Pluto is in hard aspect, there is the potential for glandular malfunction. Mars in hard aspect with Pluto indicates possible problems with the adrenal glands: especially if Pluto is in Aries, the adrenals may be hyperactive. With an accompanying hard aspect from Saturn the adrenals may atrophy, resulting in Addison's disease. Severe stress on the adrenal glands may create sugar problems, such as hypoglycemia. Disorders of the endocrine glands may also occur because of an overabundance of sodium caused by exhausted adrenal glands. If Pluto is in Cancer, the posterior pituitary gland may be hyperfunctioning. And if Mars is conjunct Pluto in a man's chart, prostate problems may take place in later life.

In addition, since Pluto rules transformations within the body, blood-related and cellular problems are possible with Mars in hard aspect with Pluto. Septic inflammation of the blood, blood poisoning and macrocytic anemias, wherein red blood cells are abnormally large, may occur, indicating a severe deficiency in cobalt and/or vitamin B-12. There is also some speculation that abnormal red blood cell production may cause megaloblastic anemia from insufficient orotic acid (Pluto). And with Pluto involved a severe depletion of vitamin B-12 might evidence itself, creating pernicious anemia.

As well as a possible abnormal need for vitamin B-12, a hard aspect between Mars and Pluto can signify greater-than-average needs for folic acid and

selenium to keep the body healthy. There is some conjecture that a deficiency of folic acid could cause red blood cell transformation, resulting in a specific type of anemia. Certainly, adequate amounts of folic acid are necessary to maintain the DNA structure. There is also some speculation that an accompanying hard aspect from Saturn can produce immature white blood cell (leucocyte) production that may be arrested by selenium. Doctor's tests should be initiated to determine if above-normal quotas of selenium are really necessary.

Since Pluto is known for its gluttonous characteristics, a hard aspect with Mars can indicate abnormal needs for several other vitamins and minerals. There may be a severe vitamin B-12 deficiency, resulting in allergies such as asthma, hives or eczema. Moreover, tests should be conducted to find out if there is a greater-than-average need of iron. An abnormal requirement for fatty acids may also be necessary for daily bodily maintenance: a deficiency in fatty acids may cause possible constipation if an aspect from Saturn is present and the sign Scorpio is involved. Finally, there is some conjecture that a hard aspect between Mars and Pluto may result in greater-than-average needs for natural chlorine and molybdenum; however, physician's tests must first confirm the requirements for these minerals because too much of them can be deadly.

On the other hand, a Mars-Pluto hard aspect can indicate an overabundance of certain minerals. A trine from either planet to Jupiter can especially mean gross indulgence in a potentially poisonous product. For instance, if Pluto is trine Mars, there may be too much iron in the body: if Jupiter is also in hard aspect, hemosiderosis of the liver may occur; a Saturn involvement may indicate a lack of vitamin B-6 (Jupiter) to help distribute the increased iron properly throughout the body. Such an overabundance of iron may interfere with absorption of phosphorus, particularly if a hard aspect from Saturn is involved. Sodium may also be high; consequently, water weight problems will ensue. In addition, a person with Mars in hard aspect with Pluto in a natal chart may consume excessive amounts of table salt, causing chlorine poisoning: there is some speculation that with an accompanying hard aspect from Saturn too much chlorine ingestion can cause DNA damage, thereby affecting the offspring of the individual.

Mars-Ascendant

A person with Mars conjunct the Ascendant in a natal chart probably loves speed of any kind. Such haste adds up to accidents. The physical drive may outweigh the condition of the body, which is normally quite athletic, and the individual may become exhausted or develop anemia. The adrenal glands may also be overstressed, and adrenal exhaustion may occur cyclically.

HARD ASPECTS OF JUPITER

Jupiter-Saturn

Not everyone can take synthetic nutrients and improve in health. The relationship between Jupiter and Saturn in a natal chart helps determine an individual's ability both to assimilate and absorb vitamins or minerals once they are ingested. Since Jupiter stands for expansion, enfoldment or envelopment of something and Saturn stands for walls, blockage, stoppage or sluggishness, if the two planets have a friendly relationship via a sextile or trine, then the proper assimilation will probably be achieved within the body. Synthetic nutrients can be taken without any problems.

On the other hand, Jupiter in adverse aspect to Saturn can indicate halted growth, stagnation, inhibited activity or death—and poor absorption of nutrients. If a person has Jupiter square or inconjunct Saturn, that individual should avoid taking synthetic supplements or should take as few as possible. Instead, 100 per cent natural supplements as well as a diet rich in those nutrients should be considered.

A person who has Jupiter either conjunct or in opposition to Saturn has to decide if there is a nutritional deficiency that involves one of the planets. If there is, the deficiency may be mild and easily corrected by diet alone: supplements may not even be needed.

Jupiter in hard aspect with Saturn may also indicate a diabetic-hypoglycemic combination, particularly if the planets are square or inconjunct. If the sign Libra is involved, the carbohydrate metabolism may be interfered with, possibly from a deficiency of chromium (Jupiter). And if one of the planets is in Libra, there is the potential for a lack of manganese (Jupiter) that may upset the glucose metabolism.

A deficiency of vitamin B-6 (Jupiter) is another possibility when Jupiter is in hard aspect with Saturn. Since Saturn is concerned with the skin and bones of the body, insufficient vitamin B-6 can induce seborrhea, acne or dermatitis. If the Sun is also in hard aspect, the lack of vitamin B-6 may be accompanied by an undersupply of magnesium (Sun), precipitating a loss of calcium (Saturn). With Jupiter or Saturn in Libra and a trine aspect from Mars to Jupiter, there may be high intake of phosphorus (Mars) and not enough calcium to balance the phosphorus out, thus creating kidney calcification.

On the other hand, a Jupiter-Saturn hard aspect can signify an overabundance of calcium, especially if Saturn is also trine Pluto. Too much calcium can result in deficiencies of manganese and zinc, both ruled by Jupiter. An inhibited intake of zinc can result in stunted bone growth or possibly dwarfism. With a hard aspect from Mars there is the further possibility of underdevelopment of the male genitalia as well as weakened sexual interest.

Whenever Jupiter is involved, diseases of the liver may also be suspect. With a hard aspect to Saturn and a deficiency of vitamin K (Saturn), there may be jaundice problems. Glycogen conversion may also be inhibited. Furthermore, biotin (Jupiter) may be lacking so that sulfur (Saturn) is not assimilated or utilized properly: without ample sulfur the ability of the liver to make bile for secretion into the duodenum may be impaired. There may also be a lack of lecithin in the bile to break down the fats, indicating a vitamin B-6 deficiency as a root cause. And there is conjecture that a potential lack of inositol (Jupiter) could affect the liver.

Depending on what signs the planets are posited in, a hard aspect between Jupiter and Saturn can hint at various other disorders. If either planet is in Capricorn or Cancer, absorption of fat (the lipids) may be hindered; or this position could signify a lack of gastric enzymes in the stomach for the unbinding of biotin, since Cancer rules the stomach; or the configuration could mean formation of gallstones because of Saturn's calcification aspect and because Capricorn, ruled by Saturn, governs the gallbladder. But if either planet is in Libra, kidney stones are possibilities, or the kidneys could be affected by a deficiency of inositol. Either planet in Taurus might result in dysfunctioning thyroid. With either planet in Gemini there may be cyanosis. Either planet in Leo or its opposite polarity, Aquarius, could indicate lack of oxygen, causing heart angina. And Saturn in Aquarius could mean too little oxygen is available, necessitating deep breathing exercises.

Other potential problems with a hard aspect between Jupiter and Saturn are the buildup of cholesterol deposits from insufficient vitamin C (Saturn) and manganese, especially if one of the planets is in Taurus or Leo; atherosclerosis induced by lack of vitamin C and in turn causing loss of arterial strength and allowing plaque to accumulate; fragile arteries or arteries that lose their elasticity (atherosclerosis) because of insufficient bioflavonoids (Saturn); skin problems, such as eczema, dermatitis and seborrhea, resulting from a lack of biotin; tooth enamel or bone problems from too much fluorine (Saturn), if an aspect from Pluto is present; lack of absorption of PABA (Saturn) or a larger need of PABA; and insufficient cholin (Jupiter).

Jupiter-Uranus

Because Uranus rules all spasm conditions of the body, tics, tremors, twitches and some types of noncalcium-related cramping may occur when Jupiter is in hard aspect with Uranus and an individual is under stress. As a result there may be sporadic needs for vitamin B-6 and pangamic acid, both ruled by Jupiter, to relieve such symptoms. There is also speculation about greater needs of biotin and inositol when there is sudden stress.

With Uranus ruling part of the nervous system as well, a Jupiter-Uranus hard aspect may indicate sporadic needs for zinc, manganese and cholin when there is stress. Zinc has been found very necessary for the continued health of the nerves. In addition, there is conjecture that epilepsy can be linked to a lack of zinc. And the nerve-related disease myasthenis gravis may be linked to deficiencies of manganese or cholin, especially if there is an accompanying hard aspect from Saturn and either Jupiter or Uranus is in Aquarius.

Finally, with Jupiter in hard aspect to Uranus and an additional hard aspect from Mars, there is the potential for sugar problems brought on by sudden, unexpected emotional stress: the involvement of Mars implicates the adrenal glands. Therefore, there may be sporadic needs for extra chromium to keep up health.

Jupiter-Neptune

If Jupiter is in hard aspect with Neptune, acompanied by a hard aspect from Saturn, the body is prone to infection in general, and there may be serious ailments. For example, there may be problems with the white blood cells, such as anemia, leukemia or leukopenia, or problems with the red blood cells in the form of polycythemia—all disorders related to an imbalance of zinc or manganese. There is also the potential for zinc or manganese poisoning.

Cancer is another possibility with Jupiter in hard aspect to Neptune. Tumors may develop. And cancer of the liver is conceivable if either planet is in Virgo with an accompanying hard aspect from either Saturn or Pluto. There is some speculation that an individual with a Jupiter-Neptune hard aspect in a natal chart may have a greater-than-normal need for nitriloside foods in the diet to stay free of cancer.

Since Neptune rules drugs in general, alcoholism, related to a deficiency of pangamic acid, may be a problem with a hard aspect between Jupiter and Neptune, especially if the sign Pisces is involved. The administration of drugs may result in other problems. For instance, oral antibiotics may destroy the biotin production in the intestinal tract. And the intake of other drugs may destroy inositol, thereby creating hair loss, high blood cholesterol or possibly diabetes: the lack of inositol may be undiagnosed as the root cause of the disease.

With Neptune's deceptive nature, a chromium deficiency may also be masked when there is a hard aspect with Jupiter. Blood sugar levels should be checked to determine if hyper- or hypoglycemia is a problem caused by insufficient chromium, especially if Saturn is in hard aspect.

Furthermore, especially with Saturn in hard aspect, the thymus gland may be weakened from a deficiency of cholin. If, instead, Mars is in hard aspect, adrenal exhaustion may result because of the loss of vitamin B-6 and pantothenic acid (Neptune). Or, with either Jupiter or Neptune in Pisces, painful, itching feet may occur, indicating higher amounts of pantothenic acid needed for daily maintenance of bodily functions.

Finally, Jupiter in favorable aspect to Neptune (conjunction, sextile or trine) implies very good absorption of synthetic or natural nutrients, regardless of whether or not Saturn is in hard aspect.

Jupiter-Pluto

Jupiter in hard aspect with Pluto in a natal chart may lead to a severe and continued vitamin or mineral deficiency all of a person's life. Since both Pluto and Jupiter represent voracious appetites, more can possibly go wrong with a hard aspect between these planets, especially a conjunction, than with any other combination of planets. The gluttony signified by these planets will probably go unchecked unless Saturn is strongly and well-aspected. The only position where some of these gluttonous tendencies may be decreased is in the Twelfth House, where some of the innate needs of Jupiter and Pluto are tamed down.

For instance, with a hard aspect between Jupiter and Pluto there may be a severe deficiency of vitamin B-6, chromium, cholin and pangamic acid as well as inositol, biotin, sulfur and manganese. Insufficient chromium or vitamin B-6 may result in sugar ailments. With Pluto involved, allergies may also occur from a lack of vitamin B-6. And a severe deficiency of vitamin B-6 may cause depletion of other vitamins in the vitamin B complex. Moreover, if Jupiter or Pluto is in Libra, there may be an imbalance in the metabolic rate, with a chromium deficiency affecting the carbohydrate functions. A lack of cholin may halt the enzymatic action of the liver. And there is speculation that the endocrine system, ruled by Pluto, may be adversely affected by insufficient pangamic acid.

Zinc may also be deficient, possibly causing a variety of disorders. If the sign Scorpio is involved in a man's chart, there is the potential for sexual dysfunction. There may also be loss of fertility with a hard aspect from Saturn. Prostate problems with a hard aspect from Mars and one of the planets in Scorpio is another possibility. In addition, there can be enzyme malfunctions. And there may be blood problems of a chronic nature with a hard aspect from Saturn.

Finally, orotic acid (Pluto) may be needed in larger-than-normal dosages for health maintenance. A lack of the vitamin may be the root cause of liver dysfunction. And with a hard aspect from Saturn and either Jupiter or Pluto in Aquarius there is the potential for multiple sclerosis, possibly caused by a deficiency of orotic acid or manganese.

Jupiter-Ascendant

Somewhat like Venus, Jupiter conjunct the Ascendant makes for gluttony, but the cravings won't be limited to sweets. A person with this configuration in a natal chart probably will have a rich palate and adore excellent food prepared with the finest of ingredients. Such preferences would be all right except that the individual will tend to overindulge in these morsels, causing obesity. He or she must acquire control and discipline or else there may be weight problems sooner or later.

HARD ASPECTS OF SATURN

Saturn-Uranus

With a hard aspect between Saturn and Uranus there may be sporadic needs for the vitamins and minerals ruled by Saturn—vitamin C, bioflavonoids, vitamin K, PABA, calcium fluorine and sulfur. The high requirements for the nutrients will usually be brought on by sudden stress situations, such as surgery or emotional duress.

Furthermore, since Uranus rules Aquarius, there may be problems with the legs with a hard aspect between Saturn and Uranus. For example, varicose veins may occur, perhaps aided by dosages of bioflavonoids. Or there may be spasms in the legs related to a deficiency of calcium.

With Uranus involved spasms are always suspect. In the case of a hard aspect with Saturn the spasms may be caused by insufficient calcium. If Uranus is in Scorpio, especially retrograde, there may be spasms of the colon, inducing constipation, particularly with an accompanying hard aspect from the Sun or the Moon, ruling magnesium and potassium respectively.

Saturn-Neptune

A hard aspect between Saturn and Neptune represents a major disease configuration, implying chronic, long-term ailments or a genetic or hereditary weakness. For instance, there may be a hereditary shortage of pantothenic acid (Neptune), causing several problems. With an accompanying hard aspect from Mars there may be low blood pressure. With either Saturn or Neptune in Capricorn arthritis is a possibility. A hard aspect from Jupiter can mean that the liver is manufacturing insufficient antihistamines, thus precipitating allergies, particularly if any of the planets is in Pisces. Finally, an aspect from Mercury, which rules the nervous system, in addition to a deficiency of pantothenic acid, may result in bruxism.

With Neptune involved the individual may also have troubles with drugs. A Saturn-Neptune hard aspect may imply that drugs will alter the absorption of calcium. Or vitamin K may be destroyed by antibiotics, especially if Pisces or Virgo is involved, since Virgo rules the intestines. There is also speculation that bioflavonoids are lost through administration of antibioitics or drugs. Moreover, cortisone injections may potentially block chondroitin sulfates from being assimilated. There may be potential drug damage to the intestinal flora so that PABA is not synthesized, in turn meaning that no pantothenic acid is created. And a deficiency of vitamin C can occur because of the administration of drugs and/or antibiotics or the consumption of alcohol.

When Neptune is in hard aspect, poisoning is always suspect as well. With a hard aspect to Saturn there may be high amounts of lead, cadmium and mercury, beryllium all poisonous metals ruled by Saturn, with not enough vitamin C available to wash the pollutants out of the body. With a hard aspect from Pluto fluorine poisoning may indicate that calcification is taking place. And people working in chemical companies may be susceptible to chemical poisoning — especially sulfur poisoning.

A hard aspect between Saturn and Neptune may also represent insufficient amounts of calcium in the body. As a result, if either planet is in Pisces and there is an additional aspect from Uranus, cramping may occur in the feet. With an aspect from Pluto tetany (hypocalcemia) may result. With aspects from Mars or Pluto there may be a high release of parathyroid hormone (PTH), causing osteoporosis, which will take calcium from the bones to elevate blood calcium levels. With an aspect from Mercury as well as a deficiency of pantothenic acid bruxism may occur. And if either planet is in Pisces or Virgo, there may be heightened sensitivity to pain from a lack of calcium and pantothenic acid.

Other potential ailments with a hard aspect between Saturn and Neptune are general weakening of the veins with a hard aspect from Venus or, with a hard aspect from Jupiter, general weakening of the arteries, causing hardening or fragility through inadequate supplies of vitamin C or bioflavonoids.

Finally, there is some speculation that Saturn in hard aspect with Neptune may indicate a laetrile (Neptune) deficiency, causing bone cancer or bone deterioration—if there is also a hard aspect from Pluto. There may be a need of more nitrilosides in the diet to prevent such cancer.

Saturn-Pluto

Saturn in hard aspect with Pluto must be examined closely by the medical astrologer. Pluto and Saturn are like big brothers fighting for supremacy over one another: Pluto represents power; Saturn, tenacity and perseverance. When the two planets are in hard aspect, especially when they conjunct each other, a potential ailment is almost always implied.

A hard aspect between Saturn and Pluto can indicate possible chronic, long-term, degenerative diseases. For example, low white blood cell count (leukopenia) can occur. There also may be lack of growth from a deficiency of orotic acid (Pluto) as well as inherited orotic acid disorders. Since Saturn corules Aquarius with Uranus and Aquarius is thought to be the progenitor of multiple sclerosis, that degenerative disease may result from insufficient orotic acid if Mercury is also in hard aspect.

The glands may also be strongly affected. There may be sluggish endocrine glands in general as well as malfunctioning adrenals, thymus, pancreas, pituitary or parathyroid. Which gland is faulty will depend on the position of Pluto in a chart. If Pluto is in Cancer, the posterior pituitary gland may be hypoactive; if in Aries, the adrenal glands may be hypofunctioning. Whatever Pluto's position, the parathyroid is suspect of malfunctioning, but especially if Pluto is in Capricorn: a diseased parathyroid gland may be the root cause of a deficiency of calcium.

In addition, a severe deficiency of vitamin C, bioflavonoids or vitamin K may exist. A person with Saturn in hard aspect with Pluto in a natal chart may need large doses of vitamin C to maintain health, and insufficient amounts of the vitamin may make the individual highly susceptible to various bites and stings, especially if there is an accompanying deficiency of calcium. If either Pluto or Saturn is in Scorpio and Venus or the Moon is aspected, abortion or menstrual problems may result from lack of bioflavonoids. And poisons may destroy vitamin K.

Although it is doubtful that deficiencies will be found in PABA, fluorine, sulfur or vanadium when Saturn is in hard aspect with Pluto, tests should be conducted to determine if these substances are indeed lacking. There is some conjecture that with a Saturn-Pluto hard aspect an abnormal amount of PABA may be needed for the body to function properly. A high requirement of fluorine for daily health maintenance is also possible in children: an adverse aspect between the two planets might indicate dental decay. (On the other hand, a trine aspect between Saturn and Pluto could mean too much fluorine, resulting in uncontrolled bone growth.) And the healing processes may be slowed from lack of sulfur. Insufficient sulfur can also cause amino acid interference, upsetting the protein metabolism. The synthesis of collagen may be partially inhibited, too. Moreover, with a hard aspect from Venus the skin may show effects of a deficiency of sulfur, as may the hair and fingernails.

An added hard aspect from Neptune hints that lead, cadmium, mercury or aluminum poisoning may occur—particularly to an infant with a hard aspect between Saturn and Pluto in a natal chart. Lead should be suspected first among the poisonous metals.

Finally, this configuration can indicate poor cell division caused by a deficiency of calcium.

Saturn-Ascendant

With a hard aspect between Saturn and the Ascendant, especially a conjunction, bone, teeth and ear problems may manifest. There may also be a calcium deficiency that may be attributed to a sluggish parathyroid gland. And there is the potential for chronic diseases that take a long time to manifest, usually occurring between the ages of 28 and 30 or 42 and 45.

HARD ASPECTS OF URANUS
Uranus-Neptune

Since Uranus rules Aquarius, there may be spinal deterioration or weakness with a hard aspect from Saturn. There is also some speculation that to combat cancer of the spine there may be sporadic, abnormal needs of laetrile (Neptune) added to the diet during sudden, stressful periods in the life.

In addition, there may be sporadic needs for pantothenic acid (Neptune) because of sudden stress.

Uranus-Pluto

A hard aspect between Uranus and Pluto, especially a conjunction, may subject organs or bodily functions to great stress. As a result stress-related ailments may crop up if a person does not take proper precautions, exercising moderation in all areas of life. For example, spasms, tremors and nerve-related problems may manifest: Uranus's sign, Aquarius, is implicated in multiple sclerosis. To combat such ailments there may be sporadic needs for orotic acid (Pluto) when stressful situations arise.

Other disorders that are possible with a hard aspect between Uranus and Pluto are brittleness, such as brittle diabetes, and deterioration of the spinal cord and the myelin sheaths, ruled by Aquarius.

Uranus-Ascendant

A person with Uranus in hard aspect to the Ascendant in a natal chart, especially a conjunction, may be prone to tension-related ailments and must learn to relax. He or she may be vulnerable to stress-related diseases, such as high blood pressure or ulcers. Nervous complaints, cramps, spasms or tics may also evolve.

HARD ASPECTS OF NEPTUNE

A well-aspected Neptune usually means protection. A harmonious Neptune acts like the guardian angel of a natal chart, indicating that spiritual benefactors are at work and that no matter how poor the health is there will be a time when the person will get better. Neptune sitting well-aspected in the Sixth or Twelfth House is in an especially excellent position for conquering health problems.

The aspects of Neptune in a natal chart may also indicate an individual's ability to assimilate and absorb nutrients. Neptune represents gossamer, gaseous liquids, able to permeate anything. Thus a well-aspected Neptune signifies the ability of nutrients to pass through the walls of the intestines, be picked up by the bloodstream and distributed to where the vitamins and minerals are needed. But a poorly aspected Neptune or one in hard aspect with Saturn signifies the incapacity of the intestinal tract to absorb nutrients properly. A heavily aspected Neptune will imply an individual who may be sensitive to drugs of any kind, thereby requiring only ½ of the usual dosage of a medication.

Neptune-Pluto

Glandular malfunctions are possible with a hard aspect between Neptune and Pluto. A deficiency of pantothenic acid may produce infections of the thymus or spleen, causing those glands to function poorly. And if Pluto is in Aries, the adrenal glands may be sluggish; if in Cancer, the posterior pituitary gland may be atonic, causing a multitude of ailments elsewhere in the body.

Since Pluto rules Scorpio, which governs the colon, intestinal disorders may occur with a hard aspect between Neptune and Pluto. Especially if Neptune or Pluto is in Scorpio or if Saturn in Scorpio is also in hard aspect, there may be chronic constipation caused by a deficiency of pantothenic acid (Neptune) and an abnormal quantity of that vitamin may be needed on a daily basis for bodily maintenance. Moreover, with an aspect from an inner planet in Scorpio and with Saturn involved there is the possibility of cancer of the colon, rectum, prostate or urinary area: there may be an abnormal need for laetrile (Neptune) in the diet for an individual to remain free of cancer.

A severe deficiency of orotic acid (Pluto) is another possibility when Neptune is in hard aspect with Pluto. With an accompanying hard aspect from Saturn such a deficiency could indicate an abnormal white blood cell count, since Neptune rules white blood cell production. There is also the potential for poisoning with this configuration and a lack of orotic acid. For example, with Saturn in hard aspect there could be ammonia in the red blood cells, causing orotic aciduria. And since Neptune rules Pisces and Pisces' opposite sign is Virgo, there is some speculation that there could be liver-enzyme problems caused by a lack of orotic acid but misdiagnosed because of Neptune's deceptive nature.

Finally, a hard aspect between Neptune and Pluto with an attending hard aspect from Saturn could indicate poor health or prolonged recovery from illness.

Neptune-Ascendant

A person with Neptune conjunct the Ascendant in a natal chart may be susceptible to many infectious or viral complaints, easily catching colds and the flu and having a hard time throwing the diseases off. Allergies may also occur because not enough pantothenic acid is supplied to the adrenal glands to make sufficient antihistamines.

Misdiagnosis of problems is possible with a hard aspect between Neptune and the Ascendant. A second opinion on any serious ailment may be necessary at times, since too many mistakes are made when Neptune is involved.

Furthermore, minimal drug dosage should be considered with a hard aspect between Neptune and the Ascendant, since the individual's body will probably be so finely calibrated to everything, including food, that he or she will have an allergic reaction to normal dosages of medication.

HARD ASPECTS OF PLUTO

Pluto represents immoderation in all matters. When it is heavily aspected in a natal chart, that person tends to be an intense workaholic or athlete who stresses the body to the limits of physical exertion. In addition, when Pluto is in hard aspect, especially in conjunction, there appears to be voracious long-term needs for specific vitamins or minerals.

Conversely, a hard aspect of Pluto can imply that the person is getting *too much* of some vitamin or mineral. For instance, Mars conjunct Pluto may mean the person is getting too much iron, causing poisoning. Proper tests should be conducted to determine if there is a deficiency or an overload of a nutrient: the tests, of course, should be monitored by a doctor to make sure no overdose of any supplement occurs.

Any hard aspect to Pluto from another planet can also suggest potential degeneration of some basic cycle within the body, eventually bringing on chronic, slow changes. If severe enough, the transformation can induce death.

Another consideration with Pluto in hard aspect is potential endocrine problems.

Pluto-Ascendant

Inherent genetic disorders may occur with a conjunction between Pluto and the Ascendant, or a person may tend to inherit the health problems of his or her mother, father or grandparents. For instance, if there is a strong family history of cancer, the individual should get checkups and maintain a careful, well-balanced diet to prevent this potential disease. Cellular disturbance, disintegration, tumors, cysts, fibrous tissue or any other kind of replicative activity may manifest.

Endocrine disorders may also occur if Pluto is conjunct the Ascendant, especially if Pluto is in the First House.

Pluto conjunct the Ascendant in the Twelfth House, however, is more medically threatening. This position may pose several problems. For example, if by solar arc progression Pluto comes into the First House, it may mean a chronic ailment coming to light or the beginning of treatment for an ailment that has simmered beneath the surface for many years. Pluto in the Twelfth House also may mean potential hidden endocrine problems. That is, the doctor has probably overlooked the glands as the potential reason for a certain ailment.

HARD ASPECTS OF THE ASCENDANT

The First House cusp is an important health consideration in a natal or progressed chart. The Ascendant is medically the most sensitive angle in a chart, with the Midheaven as a close second. (A planet within 10 degrees of either side of the Midheaven is, in essence, shining down upon the individual; and if that planet has three or more hard aspects to it, it may be strongly involved in an individual's health.)

The conjunction is the most significant hard aspect in terms of the Ascendant. Any planet found within 10 degrees of either side of the Ascendant may have a serious effect on the health of an individual. The outer planets particularly indicate health hazards when they are conjunct the Ascendant. Other hard aspects to the Ascendant appear to have much less medical power, although research needs to be conducted in this area, particularly with the minor hard aspects. But if enough hard aspects hit the Ascendant, there may be a potential health problem involving that sign, regardless if a planet is conjunct this angle or not.

CHAPTER FOUR
Midpoint Structures and Medical Diagnosis

A midpoint can be either an occupied or an unoccupied space between two other planets; it is the exact number of degrees between the bordering, or bracketing, planets. In Uranian astrology as well as in cosmobiology a midpoint structure within a very small orb—usually no more than two degrees if the Sun or Moon is involved and one to one and a half degrees for any other planet—is an astrological phenomenon that can affect a person psychologically and/or physically. The middle point between the bracketing natal planets sets up a harmony or vibration; and when a natal planet, progression or transit "hits" that midpoint, the chord is struck and the vibration energizes into a physical, mental or emotional manifestation.

A yod, consisting of two planets sextile and inconjunct a third planet, is simply a midpoint structure, with the inconjunct planet sitting in the middle of the other sextile planets. For years astrologers have known that planets progressing or transiting that inconjunct planet or in opposition to it can cause many medical problems. A midpoint, too, is most activated by a conjunction or opposition.

To find a midpoint, using the chart below, add the longitude of the two bracketing planets and divide by two, thereby arriving at the middistance between them.

Aries 0-30°	Libra 180-210°
Taurus 30-60°	Scorpio 210-240°
Gemini 60-90°	Sagittarius 240-270°
Cancer 90-120°	Capricorn 270-300°
Leo 120-150°	Aquarius 300-330°
Virgo 150-180°	Pisces 330-360°

EXAMPLE

Sun 2 Gemini 58 = 62 degrees 58 minutes Moon 10 Pisces 41 = 340 degrees 41 minutes 62.58 + 340.41 = 402.99 402.99 divided by 2 = 201.49.
Since the Moon is more than 180 degrees, or beyond Libra, we must add another step, subtracting 180 degrees from the above computation:

201.49 - 180.00 = 21.49

The midpoint between the Sun and the Moon in this example, then, is 21 Aries 49.

EXAMPLE

Uranus 16 Gemini 41 = 76 degrees 41 minutes Saturn 21 Cancer 33 = 111 degrees 33 minutes 76.41 + 111.33 = 187.74 187.74 divided by 2 = 94.07

In this case the 74 minutes must be subtracted from 60 minutes, with one degree added to the degree column, making the figure 94 instead of 93. The left over minutes are 14, which must be divided by 2, giving us 7 minutes as the final answer. Thus the midpoint between Uranus and Saturn is 4 Cancer 07.

EXAMPLE

Moon 10 Pisces 41 = 340 degrees 41 minutes Jupiter 18 Libra 07 = 198 degrees 07 minutes 340.41 + 198.07 = 538.48; 538.48 divided by 2 = 269.24.

The midpoint between the Moon and Jupiter is 29 Sagittarius 24.

If there is no natal planet at the midpoint, then a transit may activate it; a transit in opposition to the midpoint may also trigger a medical complication. When any of the outer planets transits a midpoint, medical ailments are especially probable, providing that the bracketing planets are also medical indicators. The active orb on transits varies with each individual, but I normally begin to look for symptoms when the transiting planet is within five degrees of a natal midpoint planet in the 360-degree work chart. (In the 90-degree chart I do not use transits—only progressions.)

A transiting planet that retrogrades over a midpoint can indicate several possible medical occurrences. As the planet passes over the midpoint the first time, a person may experience the onset of an illness—often acute in nature. (Chronic ailments usually do not manifest from a transit only; there must be a progression as well as a transit that activates the midpoint.) As the planet retrogrades back over the midpoint, the ailment will normally come to light enough so that a person is aware of it. If the planet moves forward and crosses the midpoint for a third time, there can be a worsening of the ailment, the condition may stabilize, or there may be a cure for the disease. In some rare instances the ailment may not even manifest until the third contact with the planet. To be able to gauge when the illness will occur, a medical astrologer must go over the person's astrological and medical history, checking out the results of other retrogrades, when they took place and what ailments surfaced.

Progressions conjunct or in opposition to a midpoint may also indicate serious medical complications, especially if there is a natal planet at the midpoint. In the 360-degree dial if that midpoint planet is being conjuncted by another progressed planet, the possibility of illness occurring is increased. If concurrent transits are also in hard aspect to any of the planets involved, the chances of serious ailments occurring are further enhanced.

The only kind of progressions I recommend for medical work is mean solar arc. (I know of other astrologers who get better results with the true solar arc; so a medical astrologer should try both ways to ascertain which works best.) Through experimentation I have also found that I get better results with the mean motion of the Sun, averaged out at 59 minutes per year. Using solar arc and the 90-degree dial, I allow only ½ degree or 30 minutes of orb to apply a progressed planet to a natal midpoint structure, with the 30 minutes standing for six months. That is, when medical planets are involved, we can see a disease beginning to build to a crisis six months before the date of the conjunction. A progressed planet to an unoccupied midpoint is usually far weaker in its ramifications, with the period of vulnerability lasting only one month—two weeks applying and two weeks separating.

In addition, eclipses can activate midpoints, perhaps causing health problems. Although there has been little research conducted on how much an eclipse conjunct or opposite a midpoint affects health, it is my opinion that when an eclipse occurs in a midpoint without a natal planet present there will be little manifestation of disease—except if the eclipse takes place in the Sixth or Twelfth Houses. If the eclipse does conjunct or oppose a natal midpoint planet, the medical astrologer must decide upon the importance of the planet. For instance, if Saturn or any of the other outer planets is involved, there is ample reason to take the eclipse into medical consideration, especially if the midpoint planet resides natally in either the Sixth or Twelfth Houses.

Although an eclipse may involve medical planets, the ailment may not erupt at the time of the eclipse. The influence of an eclipse lasts approximately six months. Almost 90 per cent of the time, when the eclipsed luminary squares its own position exactly three months later, there is normally a physical manifestation of the illness—not before this date and not after. This "fallout" date should be checked with progressions and other transits. If there is to be little activity via progressions or transits at the fallout date, not too much importance should be placed on the eclipse midpoint—unless it is one of the health axes discussed below. If, on the other hand, other progressions or transits conjunct or opposite a midpoint are occurring at the same time, the eclipse should be given full consideration and importance in any medical diagnosis.

Following are midpoint structures normally thought of as the most important in terms of health. The midpoint planet may either be natal or progressed, or another progressed planet may activate the configuration. A note of caution: one picture does not an ailment make. Midpoints, whether they are in a natal chart or on a 90-degree dial, are only part of the overall view. The presence of one medically suspect midpoint structure does not necessarily mean a person will contract a sickness. It takes further correlation in the chart to diagnose an illness accurately.

THE SUN AS MIDPOINT BETWEEN BRACKETING PLANETS

Su-Mo/Me

This configuration may bring on female complaints. There may also be a thyroid imbalance causing fluid retention. For example, the thyroid may malfunction because of a woman's nervousness if either the Moon or Mercury is in Taurus. A transit or progression of outer planets, including Saturn, to the midpoint might manifest a ailment.

Su-Mo/Sa

Depression is possible with this midpoint structure.

Su-Mo/Ur

Nervousness is possible with this configuration.

Su-Mo/Ne

A person with this midpoint structure in a natal or progressed chart may be sensitive to drugs, requiring a less-than-normal dosage of any medication. There may also be weakness in the female organs.

Su-Mo/Pl

The endocrine glands may be affected with this configuration. The pituitary gland may malfunction, or there may be problems involving fluid retention if the sign Cancer is involved.

Su-Mo/Cu

This configuration could indicate a woman with many children or one desiring a family.

Su-Mo/Ha

With this midpoint structure there may be ailments involving the uterus of the female, long-term problems with the menstrual cycle or a possible hysterectomy later in life.

Su-Me/Sa

Mental retardation is possible with this midpoint structure. A person may have slower comprehension than normal.

Su-Me/Ne

With this configuration a person may be ultrasensitive to surroundings, especially hospitals. Every effort should be made to keep such an individual away from ailing people, since he or she will pick up on the pain, suffering and negativity involved. Such a person should recuperate at home if possible. He or she may have hypochondriacal tendencies.

Su-Me/Pl

With this midpoint structure nerve-related ailments may occur, mostly from overtaxing the brain, thereby inducing nervous strain.

Su-Me/Ha

Chronic nerve-related ailments and a faulty nervous system are possibilities with this midpoint structure.

Su-Ve/Ma

This configuration could indicate conception or birth if progressed Uranus, Zeus or Cupido is also conjunct the midpoint.

Su-Ve/Sa

Infertility or lower fertility in a woman or man is possible with this combination. There could also be a low sexual appetite.

Su-Ve/Ur

If progressed Cupido is on the midpoint, birth is possible; if progressed Zeus, conception may occur.

Su-Ve/Cu

There could be a birth to a woman or to someone in her family if progressed Zeus is on the midpoint.

Su-Ve/Ze

This midpoint structure could signify procreative ability. If progressed Cupido is conjunct the midpoint, there may be conception or birth.

Su-Ma/Ju

This midpoint structure could indicate birth, especially if progressed Cupido, Zeus or Uranus is present at the midpont.

Su-Ma/Sa

With this configuration there may be poor health, indicating susceptibility to chronic conditions requiring long recuperative healing. Since health may be fragile, the body may not be able to take much physical, emotional or mental abuse before it breaks down. Progressed Admetos in the picture could mean that the ailment has either just begun or that it will become physically active; progressed Hades could indicate a severe worsening of the condition; progressed Uranus might indicate surgery to save one's life; pro-

gressed Apollon may indicate complication with the illness.

Su-Ma/Ur

This combination hints at the possibility of injury to self from foolhardy or impetuous activities. Surgery, birth or accident are also possible. If progressed Zeus is conjunct the midpoint, injury from firearms or fires is possible. Progressed Saturn in the picture could indicate potential surgery.

Su-Ma/Ne

This midpoint structure can indicate lowered vitality. A person may be prone to infections of a viral or bacterial strain as well as liable to have adverse reactions to drugs, experience an overdose of drugs or contract allergies from drugs. Ilnesses may be continually misdiagnosed. The thymus gland should be checked: it may be hypofunctioning, causing lowered resistance to infections, especially in newborn infants and young children. An individual with this configuration in a chart may have acute fevers and is likely to catch any ''bug,'' such as the flu, that is around. He or she may be especially susceptible to illness in winter and spring. A warm, dry climate is probably best for good health. Progressed Saturn in the picture may indicate poisoning from a metal source as well as fatigue and malaise; progressed Pluto may indicate blood disorders, such as anemia; progressed Admetos conjunct the midpoint could show the seed of a chronic disorder coming to light or just beginning; progressed Hades could indicate a severe worsening of a condition and perhaps crisis.

Su-Ma/Pl

A person with this configuration in a chart may be prone to injury of a violent nature: progressed Uranus could indicate electrical shock; progressed Zeus, injury through firearms or fire.

Su-Ma/Cu

Conception or birth is possible with progressed Zeus present at the midpoint.

Su-Ma/Ha

This midpoint structure can indicate injury through an attack. Chronic illness is also possible if progressed Saturn is involved.

Su-Ma/Ze

There may be conception or birth if progressed Venus is involved. Progressed Uranus may indicate injury through burns or firearms.

Su-Ma/Ad

This configuration implies a hidden condition that comes to light when progressed Saturn is also involved.

Su-Ju/Ur

Birth is possible with progressed Venus involved; there may be conception with progressed Zeus at the midpoint.

Su-Ju/Cu

If progressed Venus is involved, there may be conception or birth.

Su-Ju/Ze

Birth or conception is possible if progressed Venus or Cupido is at the midpoint.

Su-Sa/Ur

This configuration can mean nervous exhaustion from overwork. A person with this midpoint structure in a natal or progressed chart probably needs to learn when to quit working and relax. The involvement of progressed Mars could indicate a sudden operation or the manifestation of a chronic ailment.

Su-Sa/Ne

A person with this combination in a chart may be prone to bodily weakness, poor health and long-term viral or bacterial infections. He or she may find it hard to throw off colds, flu or other common conditions. Such an individual may also be extremely sensitive to drugs, perhaps susceptible to overdoses or adverse effects from them: less-than-normal dosages of medication usually are required.

Su-Sa/Pl

Endocrine-related ailments are possible. There may be a chronic ailment of a particular gland, perhaps the parathyroid gland. Tetany is also possible. And growth may be retarded from poorly functioning glands. The involvement of progressed Mars might indicate the manifestation of an acute of a condition; progressed Admetos could indicate either the beginning or the physical manifestation of illness; progressed Hades may indicate a severe health crisis.

Su-Sa/Ha

This configuration hints at slow degeneration of the body, especially if progressed Neptune is conjunct the midpoint.

Su-Sa/Ze

With progressed Mars on the midpoint there may be injury through burns or firearms.

Su-Sa/Ad

This midpoint structure could mean a chronic ailment with a long-term recuperation period. Progressed Pluto at the midpoint could indicate the beginning of an ailment or the physical manifestation of the ailment.

Su-Ur/Ne

An individual with this midpoint structure in a chart may be sensitive to anesthetics, suffering adverse side effects from them and general weakness of nerves. With such a person's inability to stand great emotional strain, the body may break down. If progressed Mars is involved, there may be paralysis through sudden injury; if progressed Saturn, the condition may be brought to the awareness of the person; if progressed Hades, the condition may worsen and build to a crisis.

Su-Ur/Pl

A person with this configuration in a chart may suffer from nervousness, tenseness and an inability to relax. Progressed Mars may indicate a sudden operation to save the life; progressed Saturn may indicate that health is deteriorating to a crisis point; progressed Hades may indicate sudden worsening of illness.

Su-Ur/Cu

This configuration may mark the date of conception or birth if progressed Venus, Mars or Zeus is at the midpoint.

Su-Ur/Ha

Injury from unusual or unique circumstances may occur, especially if progressed Mars or Zeus is at the midpoint.

Su-Ur/Vu

With this midpoint structure there is the danger of injury through explosions, such as dynamite or nuclear blast, especially if progressed Mars is at the midpoint.

Su-Ne/Pl

There is the possibility of alcoholic problems from disorder of the pancreas and faulty insulin secretions with this midpoint structure. There may be weakness of the endocrine glands in general, such as atonic or sluggish activity. Progressed Saturn or Hades involved may bring out symptoms of a disease that may not be identified for a long time. Misdiagnosis is possible.

Su-Ne/Ha

A person with this configuration in a chart may be prone to infections of a bacterial or viral strain. Progressed Saturn involved might indicate the beginning of a chronic condition—a long-term, debilitating disease.

Su-Pl/Cu

This midpoint structure can indicate the death of a family member or chronic illness of a close relative when progressed Saturn or Hades is on the midpoint.

Su-Pl/Ha

A chronic disease, a long-term condition, is possible, especially if progressed Saturn is conjunct the midpoint. Severe endocrine disorders are also likely.

Su-Pl-Ad

This configuration can mean that a hidden glandular condition will manifest with progressed Saturn at the midpoint—a glandular disorder that may change one's personality from a Jekyll to a Hyde.

Su-Cu/Ha

Death or severe illness in the immediate family is possible with this midpoint structure: if progressed Saturn is involved, a male member of the family might be affected; if progressed Moon, a female member.

Su-Cu/Ze

This midpoint structure might mark conception or birth with progressed Venus or Mars at the midpoint.

Su-Ha/Ze

This configuration can indicate a poor conception rate or infertility. Progressed Cupido at the midpoint in the chart of a woman could indicate complications with childbirth.

Su-Ha/Ap

General complications are possible with this configuration, especially if progressed Saturn or Admetos is at the midpoint.

Su-Ha/Ad

A person with this midpoint structure in a chart may suffer from depression. Progressed Saturn involved could indicate the beginning or the manifestation of a possible chronic illness.

THE MOON AS MIDPOINT BETWEEN BRACKETING PLANETS

Mo-Su/Ve

This configuration can indicate conception with progressed Zeus at the midpoint.

Mo-Su/Sa

A woman with this midpoint structure in her chart may suffer from depression or emotional fluctuation.

Mo-Su/Ne

Problems involving the female reproductive organs are possible with this configuration. A person may also suffer general weakness or an atonic condition that would benefit from exercise.

Mo-Su/Pl

The occurrence of this midpoint structure might bring on an endocrine imbalance, especially if the sign Libra is involved. Progressed Saturn at the midpoint could indicate a change in glandular activity that should be monitored.

Mo-Su/Ha

Chronic female problems are possible with this combination, even if progressed Saturn is at the midpoint.

Mo-Su/Ze

This configuration may help in the procreation of children. A woman with it in her chart may have the desire to be a mother. Progressed Venus, Mars or Cupido at the midpoint could indicate conception or birth.

Mo-Me/Ne

A person with this midpoint structure in a chart may tend to worsen an actual, existing ailment because of unfounded fears. Doctors should be diplomatic with such an individual: placebos may work well in getting him or her on the road to recovery. Since hospitals negatively influence such a person, recuperation at home is advised when possible.

Mo-Me/Pl

Glandular problems, especially affecting women, are possible. The thyroid may be hypofunctioning, inducing edema and weight gain.

Mo-Ve/Ma

Conception or birth is possible if progressed Cupido or Zeus is at the midpoint.

Mo-Ve/Ju

Birth is possible if progressed Mars or Cupido is at the midpoint. Progressed Zeus at the midpoint may indicate conception.

Mo-Ve/Sa

An individual with this midpoint structure in a chart may experience depression from lack of love or affection. He or she may need to feel wanted or important.

Mo-Ve/Ur

This configuration can signify birth if progressed Mars, Cupido or Zeus is at the midpoint.

Mo-Ve/Cu

The birth of a child within the immediate family may take place if progressed Mars or Zeus is at the midpoint.

Mo-Ve/Ze

The occurrence of this midpoint structure may mark a date of conception.

Mo-Ma/Ju

Birth is possible with the occurrence of this midpoint structure, especially if progresed Venus, Cupido or Zeus is involved.

Mo-Ma/Sa

Female complaints, such as scanty menstruation, cramping and miscarriage, are possible with this configuration. If a woman is pregnant and progressed Admetos is at the midpoint, there is the possibility that the baby will be strangled by the umbilical cord before being born. The involvement of progressed Zeus or Hades can indicate birthing complications: such a woman should probably not have a child at home but should be under the care of a doctor throughout the delivery. Progressed Cupido could indicate the death or illness of a family member.

Mo-Ma/Ur

A woman with this midpoint structure in a chart may have a Caesarean section, surgery in the area of the womb or a hysterectomy, especially if progressed Saturn is at the midpoint. Progressed Venus, Cupido or Zeus involved may indicate birth, with a quick delivery possible.

Mo-Ma/Ne

Infections of an acute nature may occur in reproductive organs with this combination. A person may be sensitive to drugs and anesthetics in general, needing less-than-normal doses. There may be adverse side effects from drugs that upset the bodily functions, inducing edema. The sodium-potassium (Mars-Moon) metabolism may also be out of balance.

Mo-Ma/Pl

Possibilities with this configuration are endocrine disorders, a sodium imbalance causing water retention and adrenal exhaustion from intense emotions.

Mo-Ma/Ha

Complications with birth are possible if progressed Saturn is at the midpoint. For example, there may be a stillborn child, severe hemorrhaging at childbirth or miscarriage.

Mo-Ma/Cu

This midpoint structure can indicate conception or birth if progressed Venus or Zeus is at the midpoint.

Mo-Ju/Ze

Procreation is likely with this combination, especially if progressed Venus, Mars or Cupido is at the midpoint.

Mo-Sa/Ur

Mood swings, melancholia, nervousness and tension may all be indicated with this midpoint structure: the parathyroid should be checked for a possible calcium (Saturn) deficiency that could be responsible for these symptoms. Progressed Admetos may bring on a manic depressive state; Hades may encourage suicidal tendencies.

Mo-Sa/Ne

This configuration might bring on female illness involving the reproductive system. For instance, there may be the inability to conceive a baby, the possibility of a hysterectomy or misdiagnosis of female complaints. In addition, a woman may be susceptible to infections of long duration, with the emotions chiefly responsible for any ailments that are contracted: a better self-image is probably necessary to improve health. As a patient, such a woman may not fight to get better but, instead, may maintain the attitude of a loser. Recuperation at home, if possible, and an interest in hobbies are advised to take her mind off her condition: she will need a sunny room and confident people about her. Progressed Hades involved may indicate severe problems with the uterus.

Mo-Sa/Pl

Endocrine disorders involving the parathyroid gland are possible with this midpoint structure. There may also be the inability to conceive children.

Mo-Sa/Cu

The death of a woman in the immediate family may be indicated with the occurrence of this midpoint structure, especially if progressed Saturn or Hades is involved.

Mo-Sa/Ha

A woman with this midpoint structure in her chart may suffer chronic problems in her reproductive organs. She may be sterile, she may be unable to carry a baby, or she may experience miscarriage or abortion.

Mo-Sa/Ad

Depression is a possibility with this configuration.

Mo-Ur/Ne

General weakness of female organs may be indicated with this combination. Emotional tension may create problems during the menstrual cycle. Nervousness or emotional tension may be the root cause of female complaints.

Mo-Ur/Pl

With this midpoint structure endocrine problems may be directly precipitated by some sort of emotional shock, such as an accident or the death of someone close, or by a prolonged period of stress without a chance for a person to recuperate from the emotional state.

Mo-Ur/Cu

With the involvement of progressed Mars, Venus or Zeus in this midpoint structure there may be either conception or birth. Progressed Saturn at the midpoint may indicate the sudden illness of a woman in the family; progressed Hades may indicate the death of a woman in the family.

Mo-Ur/Ze

Birth is possible if progressed Venus or Cupido is at the midpoint.

Mo-Ur/Ad

If progressed Venus, Zeus or especially Cupido is at the midpoint, there may be complications at the time of birth, such as choking or suffocation of the infant, perhaps because the umbilical cord wrapped around the baby as it was being born; or there may be

an unexpected situation arising during the delivery.

Mo-Ne/Ha

In a woman's chart this configuration can mean water retention or edema: the thyroid and the sodium-potassium metabolism should be tested as potential causes.

Mo-Ne/Ad

A hidden, weakened condition in women, perhaps in the reproductive organs, might occur with this midpoint structure.

Mo-Pl/Cu

Progressed Venus, Mars or Zeus at the midpoint could indicate birth to an individual or to someone within his or her family. Progressed Saturn or Hades at the midpoint may indicate the sudden illness of a woman in the family; progressed Hades may indicate the death of a woman in the family.

Mo-Ur/Ze

Birth is possible if progressed Venus or Cupido is at the midpoint.

Mo-Ur/Ad

If progressed Venus, Zeus or especially Cupido is at the midpoint, there may be complications at the time of birth, such as choking or suffocation of the infant, perhaps because the umbilical cord wrapped around the baby as it was being born; or there may be an unexpected situation arising during the delivery.

Mo-Ne/Ha

In a woman's chart this configuration can mean water retention or edema: the thyroid and the sodium-potassium metabolism should be tested as potential causes.

Mo-Ne/Ad

A hidden, weakened condition in women, perhaps in the reproductive organs, might occur with this midpoint structure.

Mo-Pl/Cu

Progressed Venus, Mars or Zeus at the midpoint could indicate birth to an individual or to someone within his or her family. Progressed Saturn or Hades at the midpoint could indicate an illness or death in the family.

Mo-Pl/Ha

This midpoint structure may bring on endocrine problems that could show up as bizarre or abnormal emotional behavior. There may also be trouble conceiving children.

Mo-Pl/Ad

A hidden endocrine disorder responsible for a woman's emotional problems is possible with this combination.

Mo-Cu/Ha

Progressed Venus, Mars or Zeus at the midpoint may indicate problems during delivery. Progressed Saturn at the midpoint may indicate an even more difficult delivery, perhaps resulting in a stillborn baby.

Mo-Cu/Ze

The involvement of progressed Venus or Mars may hint at conception.

Mo-Cu/Ad

This midpoint structure usually means problems in a marriage, especially hidden problems that come to light. Progressed Venus or Mars involved could also indicate complications during delivery: for example, an infant may be too large to pass through the birth canal, forcing a Caesarean section or resulting in suffocation of the unborn child.

Mo-Ha/Ad

This configuration may bring about female reproductive ailments that are long-term—such as sterility, blockage in the Fallopian tubes or a malformed or atrophied ovary.

Mo-Ha/Vu

A woman with this midpoint structure in her chart may have acute ailments involving the reproductive organs. If progressed Mars or Uranus is at the midpoint, an existing condition may flare up.

Mo-Ze/Ad

There may be problems with conception, perhaps caused by a blockage in the Fallopian tubes with this combination. A woman may also become pregnant without intending to do so if progressed Venus or Mars is at the midpoint.

MERCURY AS MIDPOINT BETWEEN BRACKETING PLANETS

Me-Su/Sa

This configuration indicates an individual who has a pessimistic or depressed outlook on life. As a patient, he or she should be placed in a sunny room with confident nurses and/or doctors as part of the staff for best recovery.

Me-Su/Ne

Misdiagnosis is possible with this configuration: the possible root problem may be a nervous disorder or a hypofunctioning thyroid gland. A person with this midpoint structure in a chart will probably be easily influenced, with a tendency to empathize with other sick individuals. So, for best recuperation, he or she should be placed with confident patients. Under the proper circumstances, such a person can probably be encouraged into getting well. Placebos may also work well.

Me-Su/Pl

This midpoint structure may bring on endocrine problems that seem symptomatic of a nervous disorder: the thyroid should be tested. Progressed Saturn or Hades at the midpoint may indicate the beginning of a chronic, nerve-related ailment.

Me-Su/Ha

The mental outlook of a person with this midpoint structure in a chart may produce ailments: adjustment of attitudes, therapy or psychological counseling could help the individual get well. Since hospitals are usually extremely depressing to such a person, every effort should be made for outpatient or home recovery for best results. The individual may also harbor hidden fears about sickness or operations in general, sometimes thinking he or she will get cancer or some other wasting disease: such a mind needs to be turned toward positive and productive activities.

Me-Su/Ad

This configuration may indicate a hidden disorder of the nerves that will come to light with a progression of Saturn or Hades to the midpoint.

Me-Mo/Sa

A woman with this configuration in her chart may be inclined to morose or depressive states as menstrual periods approach: the thyroid gland should be tested as a root cause of these manifestations.

Me-Mo/Ur

A person with this midpoint structure in a chart may be nervous because of continual, intense, emotional states. If the individual is under emotional stress for a continued period, the thyroid gland may begin to malfunction and should be tested as the root cause of the nervous condition.

Me-Mo/Ne

As a patient in a hospital, a person with such a

configuration in a chart may be easily influenced by the surroundings. Care must be taken to provide a sunny, cheerful environment for best recovery. The doctor should choose words carefully so that the patient does not overreact. Verbal encouragement usually works well. The patient should not be allowed to rely too much on a member of the hospital staff but must be taught to be a self-healer.

Me-Mo/Pl

This midpoint structure can indicate disorders of the endocrine glands, which should be tested first before any diagnosis is made. The thyroid or the pituitary gland may be suspect. In a woman the reproductive organs should be checked.

Me-Mo/Ha

In a woman's chart this configuration suggests morbid or depressive states of anxiety: the thyroid gland should be tested as a possible root cause of the behavior.

Me-Mo/Ad

A person with this midpoint structure in a chart may harbor a negative or pessimistic outlook on life in general. He or she may be a poor patient, not fighting to get well. Such an individual will probably need a sunny room and positive staff members around for best results.

Me-Ma/Sa

Chronic nerve-related problems are possible with this configuration. The thyroid may be malfunctioning, causing states of depression or melancholia. A person may be a manic depressive because of an endocrine disorder. Nervous exhaustion may be caused by a malfunctioning adrenal gland.

Me-Ma/Ur

A person with this midpoint structure in a chart may be high-strung or continually nervous: the root cause may be a hyperthyroid. Progressed Saturn or Hades at the midpoint may indicate chronic nerve degeneration; progressed Admetos at the midpoint could trigger a nerve ailment that might remain hidden for years, with few symptoms that a doctor could diagnose.

Me-Ma/Ne

Nerve-related ailments are possible if an individual with this configuration in a chart does not protect himself or herself from various influences. The nervous condition may be misdiagnosed, with the thyroid or adrenal glands as the root cause. Such a person may use alcohol or drugs to reduce sensitivity to the world.

Me-Ma/Pl

Major endocrine disorders involving the thyroid or adrenal glands are possible: malfunction may begin when progressed Saturn or Hades is at the midpoint. There may also be chronic nerve disorders brought on by excessive work or stress.

Me-Ma/Ha

This configuration in a chart can bring on depression because of a thyroid condition. Suicidal tendencies can occur if the depression continues. Speech impediments are also possible.

Me-Ju/Ne

A person with this combination in a chart will probably be easily influenced in a hospital environment. Care must be taken not to arouse his or her powers of imagination.

Me-Sa/Ur

Chronic nerve disorders or the onset of nerve-related strain without warning are possible. In addition, there may be a spastic thyroid condition: that is, the thyroid may go out under stress and after the stress has gone gradually go back to normal functioning.

Me-Sa/Ne

This midpoint structure can indicate a chronic, nerve-related ailment whose symptoms the doctor is unable to diagnose properly: the parathyroid may be causing problems in the levels of calcium (Saturn) in the body, bringing on nervous ailments; a weak thyroid may also be the cause. The mental outlook of such a patient is usually poor because he or she is overwhelmed in a hospital by the suffering and dying. A private room, sunshine and a quietly confident staff are probably needed. Recuperation at home, if possible, is best.

Me-Sa/Pl

An individual with this configuration in a chart may have a chronic nerve condition: endocrine functions should be checked first, particularly the thyroid and the parathyroid glands.

Me-Sa/Ha

A person with this midpoint structure in a chart may suffer depression and may even be suicidal if the progressed Moon is at the midpoint: endocrine disorders of the thyroid or parathyroid should be tested.

Me-Ur/Pl

With this configuration an endocrine gland may

suddenly begin to malfunction because of unexpected stress: the thyroid should be tested.

Me-Ne/Pl

With progressed Saturn at the midpoint a person with this configuration in a chart may develop a nervous ailment of long duration, perhaps caused by a weakly functioning thyroid gland.

Me-Ne/Ha

A person with this midpoint structure in a chart may be susceptible to morbid thoughts. His or her mind may be delicately balanced and easily influenced by surroundings. There may also be hypochondria and the fear of death. Furthermore, there is the possibility of water retention in a woman, caused by a hypothyroid.

Me-Ne/Ad

The slow decay or degeneration of nerves is possible with this combination: a hidden thyroid condition may be the root cause of the problem with the nerves. Since drugs may drastically alter such an individual's state of mind, they must be carefully administered: drug overdose and adverse reactions to drugs are possible.

Me-Pl/Ha

A person with this midpoint structure in a chart may suffer from melancholia and depression and have a poor outlook toward recovery. A chronic endocrine ailment, especially a thyroid condition, is also possible.

Me-Pl/Ad

Progressed Saturn to this midpoint may trigger a long-term, hidden endocrine problem.

Me-Ha/Ad

An individual with this configuration in a chart may experience chronic depression, melancholia or pessimism: the thyroid should be tested.

VENUS AS MIDPOINT BETWEEN BRACKETING PLANETS

Ve-Su/Ma

Progressed Zeus at the midpoint could indicate conception of a child; progressed Cupido, birth.

Ve-Su/Cu

This midpoint structure may mark the birth of a child if progressed Mars is involved or conception if progressed Zeus is at the midpoint.

Ve-Su/Ha

This configuration may bring on skin ailments, such as eczema or dermatitis, possibly caused by a deficiency of vitamin E (Venus) or vitamins A and D (Sun).

Ve-Su/Ze

Conception is possible with progressed Mars at the midpoint or birth with progressed Cupido at the midpoint.

Ve-Ma/Ju

Birth may occur (usually of a girl) with progressed Zeus or Cupido at the midpoint; the progressed Sun at the midpoint can mean conception.

Ve-Ma/Ur

With the occurrence of this midpoint structure a birth is possible, although it may be accompanied by complications, such as the necessity for a Caesarean section. Progressed Admetos, Saturn or Hades at the midpoint especially indicates complications with delivery. Progressed Zeus or Cupido at the midpoint can mean birth to a woman or to someone else in the family.

Ve-Ma/Ne

Infections involving women's reproductive systems are possible with this configuration.

Ve-Ma/Cu

Progressed Zeus at the midpoint could indicate the birth of a child within the family.

Ve-Ma/Ha

Abortion is possible if progressed Saturn or Admetos is at the midpoint.

Ve-Ma/Ze

There may be conception of a child with the progressed Sun or Cupido at the midpoint.

Ve-Ju/Ze

If progressed Cupido is at the midpoint, birth may take place with no complications.

Ve-Sa/Ne

Ailments involving the reproductive organs, infections, weakness or poor fertility are all possible with this midpoint structure.

Ve-Sa/Pl

Chronic ailments involving the reproductive region are possible with this combination. Vitamin E may be useful in alleviating some of the symptoms.

Ve-Sa/Ha

The occurrence of this midpoint structure may bring on miscarriage or premature birth.

Ve-Ur/Cu

With this midpoint structure there may be unexpected birth and labor may be particularly short, coming sooner than expected by the mother or the doctor.

Ve-Ur/Ze

Conception is possible with this configuration. (Some sources believe the child will be female.)

Ve-Ne/Ad

Possible ailments with this midpoint structure are problems with the female reproductive organs or a condition that goes undetected for a long time. Decay or atrophy of the Fallopian tubes or the ovaries may also occur.

Ve-Pl/Cu

Birth is possible with progressed Mars or Zeus at the midpoint.

Ve-Pl/Ha

There may be complications during delivery with progressed Zeus or Cupido at the midpoint.

Ve-Cu/Ze

Birth may occur with progressed Mars at the midpoint.

Ve-Ha/Ad

With this configuration the female reproductive organs may be shrunken or atrophied. There may be the inability to produce children or sterility.

Ve-Ze/Ad

If progressed Mars is at the midpoint, a child may be conceived without the knowledge of the man or woman involved.

MARS AS MIDPOINT BETWEEN BRACKETING PLANETS

Ma-Su/Mo

Conception is possible if progressed Venus, Zeus or Cupido is at the midpoint.

Ma-Su/Ve

There may be conception with progressed Zeus or Cupido at the midpoint.

Ma-Su/Ur

Accidents arising from impulsive acts or sudden, unexpected surgery may happen with the occurrence of this midpoint structure.

Ma-Su/Ne

With this configuration general health may be weak, there may not be much "get-up-and-go," vitality may be poor and recuperation slow. There may also be weak adrenal gland function. Moreover, a person may be susceptible to infection, drug overdose or side effects from drugs. Sexual impotence or lack of a strong sex drive are other possibilities.

Ma-Su/Cu

The occurrence of this midpoint strucutre may mean a marriage, although, on some occasions, with progressed Zeus involved, it can indicate conception.

Ma-Su/Ha

Deformity, chronic, long-term ailments that may involve physical therapy, muscle impairment caused by disintegration of tissue and blood problems involving the red corpuscles are all potential ailments with this configuration.

Ma-Su/Ze

Conception or birth is possible with progressed Venus or Cupido at the midpoint.

Ma-Mo/Ve

Birth may occur if the progressed Sun, Zeus or Cupido is at the midpoint.

Ma-Mo/Ju

Birth is possible with progressed Venus, Zeus or Cupido at the midpoint.

Ma-Mo/Sa

A person with this midpoint structure in a chart may suffer from ailments involving the reproductive system. There is also the potential for edema, resulting from adrenal gland malfunction and an unbalanced sodium-potassium (Mars-Moon) metabolism. Progressed Zeus or Cupido at the midpoint may indicate problems with delivery.

Ma-Mo/Ur

With this configuration explosive emotions may get out of hand, causing injury to a person.

Ma-Mo/Ne

A woman with this midpoint structure in her chart may be susceptible to general weakness of the reproductive system, such as infections and acute disturbances. Weight control problems caused by a sodium-potassium imbalance are also possible: the adrenals should be tested.

Ma-Mo/Pl

Injuries caused by intense emotional reactions are possible with this configuration.

Ma-Mo/Ha

This midpoint structure can indicate ailments involving the reproductive organs. A hysterectomy is possible with progressed Uranus at the midpoint. Tubal pregnancy is another possibility.

Ma-Me/Ur

A person with this midpoint structure in a chart may experience nervous ailments, with tremendous stress being placed upon the adrenal glands. There is the potential for adrenal exhaustion with progressed Saturn at the midpoint.

Ma-Me/Ne

An individual with this configuration in a chart may suffer from frayed nerves because he or she works too hard and does not take time off to relax.

Ma-Ve/Ju

Birth is possible with the progressed Sun, Zeus or Cupido at the midpoint.

Ma-Ve/Sa

This configuraton can mean a low level of fertility, with either a man or woman having problems conceiving.

Ma-Ve/Ur

Birth is possible with the occurrence of this midpoint structure.

Ma-Ve/Ne

Infections involving the female reproductive system, particularly the vaginal area, may occur with this midpoint structure.

Ma-Ve/Pl

Conception is possible with progressed Zeus at the midpoint.

Ma-Ve/Ze

There may be conception with the progressed Sun, Jupiter or Cupido at the midpoint.

Ma-Ju/Ze

Conception is possible with the occurrence of this configuration.

Ma-Sa/Ur

This is one of the most active midpoint structures, indicative of major accidents. It can also imply sudden injury or operation with progressions of the Sun, Zeus or Hades to the midpoint.

Ma-Sa/Ne

This is a major health axis. Bodily resistance to disease may be very low, with the thymus gland responsible. The adrenal glands may also be weak, causing adrenal exhaustion. A person may be sensitive to normal doses of drugs, requiring only half the usual amounts. Other possibilities are allergies to drugs and allergies in general, caused by malfunctioning adrenal glands. Muscles may also be flabby or weakened, and bones may be soft or deformed from a lack of sufficient calcium (Saturn): the parathyroid glands should be tested.

Ma-Sa/Pl

This midpoint structure can indicate an ailment involving total transformation of the bone, cell or blood structure—a transformation that may manifest when a progressed planet hits the midpoint. Progressed Admetos to the midpoint may suggest the start of an undetected disease that may take several years to become apparent. Progressed Hades on the midpoint may indicate a health crisis and a possible worsening of a health condition. Endocrine problems involving the adrenal or parathyroid glands are also possible.

Ma-Sa/Ha

A long-term illness may occur, perhaps involving hypofunctioning of the adrenal glands.

Ma-Sa/Ze

This configuration may help bring on injury through the use of firearms or through fires: progressed Uranus at the midpoint could especially suggest unexpected injury from such conditions.

Ma-Sa/Ad

A blockage or obstruction may occur in some part of the body with this midpoint structure. Progressed Pluto at the midpoint hints at an aneurysm.

Ma-Ur/Ne

The occurrence of this midpoint structure can mean a coma lasting for an indeterminate amount of time. Loss of vitality or endurance is also possible.

Ma-Ur/Pl

With progressed Saturn at the midpoint there may be a sudden, unexpected and debilitating accident, perhaps resulting in complete or partial paralysis.

Ma-Ur/Ha

This configuration can mean sudden injury or accident with progressed Saturn at the midpoint. Progressed Zeus at the midpoint may imply accidents from firearms or burns incurred in a fire.

Ma-Ur/Ze

This configuration may mark the date of the conception of a child, usually a boy. Injury from explosions or electrical equipment is also possible.

Ma-Ur/Ad

A sudden rupturing of a hidden condition, such as a stroke or aneurysm, may take place with the occurrence of this midpoint structure. Another potential problem is sudden blockage in the arteries, vessels, intestines or tubes of the body: as a result, the appendix may burst or peritonitis may develop, especially if progressed Saturn, Zeus or Hades is at the midpoint.

Ma-Ur/Vu

This midpoint structure may represent the possibility of severe injury through explosion, electrocution or burns suffered from electricity: progressed Zeus at the midpoint could indicate burns; progressed Saturn, explosions. If progressed Saturn is involved, there may be a sudden, unexpected operation.

Ma-Ne/Pl

A person with this configuration in a chart may experience weakness of the adrenal glands, causing general symptoms of fatigue and apathy. The thymus gland may be weak, lowering resistance to infection.

Ma-Ne/Ha

Edema and problems with water retention caused by the adrenal glands and affecting the sodium-potassium balance are possible with this combination. There may also be water-related injuries, especially if progressed Zeus is at the midpoint, indicating injury from steam or boiling water.

Ma-Ne/Ze

This midpoint structure can indicate low fertility and poor ability to conceive.

Ma-Ne/Ad

With this midpoint structure poisoning through narcotics or other chemicals is possible, especially if progressed Saturn is at the midpoint. A doctor may misdiagnose a condition that is caused by poisoning.

Ma-Pl/Ad

The adrenal glands may atrophy with this midpoint structure. There may be adrenal-related ailments in general.

Ma-Pl/Ad

This configuration may indicate tumors or growths that remain undetected for many years or something hidden or suppressed in general. There is also the possibility of the improper functioning of the adrenal glands.

Ma-Ha/Ze

Injuries involving burns or firearms are possible with this midpoint structure. Electrical injuries may occur if progressed Uranus is also at the midpoint.

Ma-Ze/Ad

Conception may occur without a woman's knowledge with this combination.

Ma-Ad/Ze

This midpoint structure may bring on sudden blockage or stoppage in the tubes of the body, including the arteries or veins.

JUPITER AS MIDPOINT BETWEEN BRACKETING PLANETS

Ju-Su/Mo

Birth may occur with progressed Zeus or Cupido at the midpoint.

Ju-Su/Ur

An operation undertaken at the time of this configuration should be successful.

Ju-Su/Ne

A person with this midpoint structure in a chart probably will have a weak body and will be inclined toward corpulence from lack of exercise and the consumption of rich foods without proper exercise to burn off the carbohydrates.

Ju-Su/Pl

A person with this midpoint structure in a chart probably will be a glutton, prone to excess in everything. He or she may be fat.

Ju-Su/Ha

Problems with blood from a malfunctioning liver are possible with this combination.

Ju-Mo/Ur

Delivery without complications may occur when progressed Zeus or Cupido is at the midpoint.

Ju-Mo/Ha

This midpoint structure may indicate conditions involving fluid retention in the body: the potassium-sodium balance should be tested.

Ju-Mo/Ze

Conception is possible when progressed Venus or Cupido is at the midpoint.

Ju-Ve/Ur

Birth may occur with progressed Mars, Zeus or Cupido at the midpoint.

Ju-Ma/Sa

The occurrence of this configuration may bring on improvement in an illness or a quick, peaceful death.

Ju-Ma/Ur

A successful operation is indicated with the occurrence of this midpoint structure.

Ju-Ma/Ne

Blood poisoning or poor quality of blood is possible with this configuration. The liver may also be weak and susceptible to infections, such as hepatitis.

Ju-Sa/Ne

This configuration can indicate a chronic condition involving the liver or infections of the liver.

Ju-Sa/Pl

A chronic condition that will take more time than expected to heal is possible with this combination.

Ju-Sa/Ha

This midpoint structure can indicate chronic ailments involving the liver or calcification of the liver.

Ju-Ne/Ha

Edema, water retention, liver infection and a general wasting away are all possibilities with this midpoint structure.

Ju-Pl/Ha

The occurrence of this midpoint structure can mean the worsening of an illness.

SATURN AS MIDPOINT BETWEEN BRACKETING PLANETS

Sa-Su/Mo

Illness in infancy and early childhood is possible with this midpoint structure: health probably will improve with age. There is also the possibility of chronic illness around the ages of 30 or 42 to 45. And there may be a shortage of calcium (Saturn) or an imbalance of potassium (Moon).

Sa-Su/Me

This configuration can indicate mental slowness and a conservative or pessimistic outlook on life that is inhibitive to health. Sunshine, activities and a confident staff are best for a person to regain health.

Sa-Su/Ve

With this midpoint structure female complaints may occur, such as atrophy to some parts of the reproductive system.

Sa-Su/Ma

The occurrence of this midpoint structure may dampen a person's natural vitality, or it may indicate the start of an illness. Fatigue may occur from the hypofunctioning of the adrenal glands.

Sa-Su/Ju

Long recuperation may be required for a person with this configuration in a chart to get back to a state of health.

Sa-Su/Ur

This midpoint structure may indicate a sudden, unexpected obstruction or blockage in some part of the body. Surgery may occur, especially if progressed Mars is at the midpoint. Progressed Cupido at the midpoint may indicate the birth of a child—but with great difficulty.

Sa-Su/Ne

This midpoint structure can indicate a lowered state of resistance to infections: the thymus may be sluggish. An individual may be prone to misdiagnosis or side effects from drugs. Since the body is probably delicate and fragile to begin with, care must be exercised for a person to stay in good health.

Sa-Su/Pl

With this configuration bodily changes that tend to be irreversible may take place, such as changes in the blood or bones or hardening in organs, arteries or veins. A health crisis may occur.

Sa-Su/Ha

This configuration can mean an illness that lingers, slow recuperation and health that deteriorates after the age of 30. With the progressed Moon at the midpoint abortion is possible.

Sa-Su/Ze

Progressed Cupido at the midpoint may indicate a difficult delivery.

Sa-Su/Vu

One's innate physical strength is limited with this midpoint structure. Endurance may be shortened.

Sa-Mo/Me

The mental outlook of a person with this configuration in a chart may be negative or pessimistic. His or her moods may be easily influenced by surroundings: all efforts should be made to keep the environment bright and cheerful during convalescence.

Sa-Mo/Ve

This midpoint structure can indicate sterility or the inability to conceive a child without difficulty. The involvement of Cupido suggests birth but with complications or long labor. In addition, there may be ailments of the reproductive organs, such as atrophy of the ovaries.

Sa-Mo/Ma

With this configuration a person's emotions, such as suppressed anger or anxiety, may trigger ailments. A woman with this midpoint structure in her chart may have reproductive complaints in general.

Sa-Mo/Ur

Supressed emotional reactions may suddenly manifest in the form of an accident or injury with this midpoint structure, particularly if progressed Mars is at the midpoint.

Sa-Mo/Ne

A woman with this midpoint structure in her chart may have a weak reproductive system. Furthermore, she may become sick because she has a low threshold for anxiety, worry or environmental pressures: she probably cannot take a great deal of stress or her body will succumb to poor health. This configuration also hints at depression, insomnia and pessimism. A person will probably be ultrasensitive to surroundings and should be in a positive environment for best results.

Sa-Mo/Pl

Endocrine problems involving the pituitary or parathyroid glands may occur with this configuration. There may also be chronic problems or tumors in the reproductive organs. A person with this midpoint structure in a chart may tend to be gloomy and depressed, experiencing intense moods, such as melancholia or manic-depressive states.

Sa-Mo/Cu

The occurrence of this midpoint structure can indicate the death of a woman or a member of the family, especially if progressed Hades is at the midpoint.

Sa-Mo/Ze

This configuration suggests an inability to conceive.

Sa-Ma/Ad

There may be an undetected blockage or stoppage in the body with this midpoint structure. An individual may harbor secret fears.

Sa-Me/Ur

Chronic nerve-related ailments are possible with this midpoint structure. A person may be inwardly tense without manifesting the condition outwardly.

Sa-Me/Ne

A person with this configuration in a chart may have a negative outlook that hinders the healing process: he or she may not have the ability to fight back against disease.

Sa-Me/Pl

An individual with this midpoint structure in a chart may suffer from mental strain from overwork. He or she needs to learn to balance work and play more evenly.

Sa-Me/Ha

This configuration can indicate an obsession with death or dying or a fear of death. On the positive side, an individual with this midpoint structure in a chart may have the ability to be a therapist or psychologist.

Sa-Ve/Ma

Sexual inhibitions are possible with this midpoint structure. There may also be low fertility or the inability to conceive.

Sa-Ve/Ur

This midpoint structure can mean long labor or

problems during delivery, particularly if progressed Cupido is at the midpoint.

Sa-Ve/Ne

Reproductive infections are possible with this combination.

Sa-Ve/Ze

A person with this midpoint structure in a chart may be sterile or unable to conceive.

Sa-Ma/Ju

Progressed Cupido or Venus at the midpoint could indicate childbirth—but with long labor. Progressed Apollon at the midpoint may indicate complicatons during delivery.

Sa-Ma/Ur

Sudden, unexpected accident or injury requiring an operation may happen with the occurrence of this midpoint structure. There is the possibility of the loss of an arm or a leg. Progressed Cupido at the midpoint may indicate a Ceasarian section.

Sa-Ma/Ne

This is a major health axis. The body will probably be prone to infections, overdoses or side effects of drugs and slow recovery time. Chronic illness from toxic conditions in the body may result. Misdiagnosis is very possible.

Sa-Ma/Pl

Chronic illness that may become irreversible is possible with this midpoint structure. For instance, the blood, bones or muscles may waste away for a long time.

Sa-Ma/Ha

A person with this configuration in a chart may contemplate suicide when progressed Mercury is at the midpoint.

Sa-Ma/Ze

In a man's chart this combination can mean sterility or lowered fertility.

Sa-Ma/Ad

This midpoint structure can indicate a hidden condition that will manifest after a long time.

Sa-Ma/Vu

A tremendous blockage or stoppage may occur in the body with this combination.

Sa-Ju/Ze

There is the possibility of miscarriage with this midpoint structure, especially with progressed Mars or Hades at the midpoint.

Sa-Ur/Pl

Sudden loss or injury may take place with this configuration, especially if progressed Mars is at the midpoint.

Sa-Ur/Ze

This configuration can indicate accidents involving firearms or fires. Progressed Mars at the midpoint can mean burns, wounds or electrical injury.

Sa-Ur/Ad

A partial blockage may unexpectedly block completely with the occurrence of this midpoint structure: progressed Mars on the midpoint could trigger a stoppage or rupture.

Sa-Ne/Ha

Long-term illness and misdiagnosis are possible with this configuration. Poison could be the root cause of the confusing array of symptoms.

Sa-Ne/Ze

A person with this midpoint structure in a chart may be in danger of being poisoned by gases from exploding containers or from a chemical factory.

Sa-Ne/Ad

The occurrence of this midpoint structure may bring on the beginning of a chronic ailment that may take years to manifest physically.

Sa-Pl/Ha

A chronic health ailment that will eventually surface over a long period of time may be the result of this configuration.

Sa-Pl/Ad

This midpoint structure can indicate a possible tumor or cyst condition that will remain undetected for many years before it is discovered.

Sa-Cu/Ha

Death in the family is possible with the occurrence of this combination.

Sa-Ha/Ap

Health complications in general may occur with this midpoint structure. With progressed Neptune at the midpoint diagnosis may be faulty: a doctor may find only one cause of an illness when there are really two causes; further testing may be necessary to discover the additional cause.

Sa-Ha/Ad

The worsening of an already chronic illness or a health crisis is possible with the occurrence of this midpoint structure.

URANUS AS MIDPOINT BETWEEN BRACKETING PLANETS

Ur-Su/Mo

There is the potential for injury or an unexpected accident with progressed Mars at the midpoint.

Ur-Su/Ma

A person with this midpoint structure in a chart may be accident-prone because of impulsive, impetuous actions. Progressed Zeus at the midpoint could indicate wounds from firearms or burns.

Ur-Su/Ju

The occurrence of this configuration could mark an excellent time for a successful operation with quick recuperation.

Ur-Su/Sa

Nerve-related ailments are possible with this combination.

Ur-Su/Ne

Misdiagnosed cases involving nerve ailments, convulsions or fits may occur with this midpoint structure. There may be weak nerves in general. A person may be unable to withstand strain or stress for a long period of time.

Ur-Su/Cu

A marriage or birth may take place with the occurrence of this midpoint structure, particularly if progressed Venus, Zeus or Mars is at the midpoint.

Ur-Su/Ha

Nerve disintegration or nervous disability is possible with this configuration.

Ur-Su/Ze

This midpoint structure can indicate injuries from explosions, firearms or electricity if progressed Mars is at the midpoint.

Ur-Mo/Ve

Birth may occur with this combination, especial-

ly if progressed Mars, Zeus or Cupido is at the midpoint.

Ur-Mo/Ju

A woman with this configuration in her chart may expect easy labor and delivery. Delivery may be sooner than expected with progressed Mars at the midpoint.

Ur-Mo/Sa

A woman with this midpoint structure in her chart may experience a great deal of nervousness, perhaps from a lack of calcium (Saturn). Progressed Cupido at the midpoint could indicate complications during delivery.

Ur-Mo/Pl

This configuration can indicate a sudden change in glandular functions, particularly of the pituitary gland. Tests should be conducted to determine the cause of extreme nervousness.

Ur-Mo/Ha

Complications with delivery may result if progressed Saturn or Admetos is at the midpoint.

Ur-Mo/Ad

A person with this midpoint structure in a chart may experience a hidden nervous condition, inner tension or the inability to relax.

Ur-Me/Ha

The occurrence of this midpoint structure may make a person highly excitable, a state that may cause accident or injury. Progressed Saturn at the midpoint may trigger a chronic nerve ailment.

Ur-Me/Sa

An individual with this configuration in a chart may suffer from chronic nervous debility or a gradual destruction of nerve sheath fiber: the condition may worsen if progressed Hades is at the midpoint. This configuration can also indicate a health crisis.

Ur-Me/Ne

A person with this midpoint structure in a chart may have a weak nervous system. He or she should avoid high-stress jobs or environments that will contribute to deterioration of the nerves. In addition, an individual may experience convulsions that come from an undetermined origin: a doctor may have problems in diagnosing the cause of the convulsions.

Ur-Me/Pl

This midpoint structure can indicate severe nerve stress that may cause eventual malfunction if an individual does not rest occasionally. A mental breakdown is possible, especially with progressed Saturn or Hades at the midpoint.

Ur-Ve/Cu

Conception is possible when progressed Zeus or Mars is at the midpoint.

Ur-Ve/Ze

Unexpected pregnancy may occur with this midpoint structure.

Ur-Ma/Ju

Miscarriage or abortion can take place if progressed Hades is at the midpoint.

Ur-Ma/Sa

This configuration may bring on sudden, violent accidents that can cause death. A person may also suffer from a chronic nerve ailment or sustain a severe injury.

Ur-Ma/Ne

This configuration can indicate conditions that may paralyze a person or a weak nerve response. There may also be sudden weakness or debility. Acute infection or high fever of an unknown origin are other possibilities. Toxic conditions in the body may suddenly become acute, and poisoning may also occur.

Ur-Ma/Pl

There may be severe physical, mental or emotional stress with this midpoint structure. With progressed Saturn or Hades involved a person's life may hang in the balance, and there may be a health crisis.

Ur-Ma/Ha

The occurrence of this midpoint structure can mean sudden violence and bodily harm: there may be especially severe injury if progressed Mars is at the midpoint. An operation that does not go as planned because of mistakes that may occur: progressed Apollon at the midpoint may mean unexpected complications during surgery.

Ur-Ma/Ze

Injury from fires, firearms or explosions might occur with this configuration: the injury may be especially severe if progressed Saturn is at the midpoint.

Ur-Sa/Ne

This configuration may bring on stress, causing poor health. A person may be unable to take continued stress for a long time.

Ur-Sa/Pl

This midpoint structure can indicate a long-term ailment that will suddenly appear without warning.

Ur-Sa/Ha

The onset of a health crisis, with a condition worsening unexpectedly, may happen with the occurrence of this configuration.

Ur-Sa/Ze

Injury from fire, lightning or electrical damage may result with progressed Mars at the midpoint.

Ur-Sa/Ad

With the occurrence of this midpoint structure a chronic, hidden condition may come to light without warning.

Ur-Pl/Ha

A person's health may deteriorate rapidly, with ensuing crisis, when this configuration comes about.

Ur-Pl/Ad

A long-term, deep-seated ailment remaining undetected until its sudden appearance is possible with this midpoint structure.

Ur-Pl/Vu

This midpoint structure can mean a sudden, transforming change in health.

Ur-Ha/Ad

Suffocation or the inability to breathe properly may occur with this combination.

Ur-Ha/Vu

There may be unexpected worsening of a health condition with the occurrence of this configuration.

Ur-Ad/Vu

This midpoint structure can indicate a turn for the worse in a health crisis. Furthermore, unknown factors regarding an illness may suddenly come to light.

NEPTUNE AS MIDPOINT BETWEEN BRACKETING PLANETS

Ne-Su/Mo

A person with this configuration in a chart may

have fragile health. He or she must take good care of bodily health, since there is a propensity to illness from stress.

Ne-Su/Me

An individual with this midpoint structure in a chart may be easily influenced by the environment and may lose perspective about his or her illness. A doctor should be tactful but not vague, since vagueness will probably only increase the patient's unfounded fears.

Ne-Su/Ma

This is one of the major health axes. A person may have poor vitality and little endurance, be prone to infections, be susceptible to drug overdose and the side effects of drugs and require a long period of recuperation. There may also be a tendency for illnesses to be misdiagnosed.

Ne-Su/Ju

An individual with this configuration in a chart may be prone to drug overdose and sensitive to the side effects of drugs. Health will probably be fragile, and the person may lose perspective about illness, thus increasing health risks.

Ne-Su/Sa

This midpoint structure may indicate a tendency toward a long, chronic illness, with a long recuperation period needed to regain health.

Ne-Su/Ur

A person with this combination in a chart may suffer from a weakened nervous system. He or she may be unable to stand stress for long periods.

Ne-Su/Pl

With this configuration a person's health may erode gradually over a long period of time.

Ne-Su/Ha

An individual with this midpoint structure in a chart may be suicidal. In addition, he or she may have problems taking drugs or have bad experiences with them, such as allergic reactions. Progressed Saturn at the midpoint could indicate the beginning of a disease or a worsening of a condition, producing a crisis.

Ne-Su/Ze

This midpoint structure can indicate an inability to conceive children or a low fertility rate.

Ne-Su/Kr

A person with this configuration in a chart may end up consulting an incompetent doctor or a quack. He or she should seek a second opinion before undergoing an operation.

Ne-Su/Ad

Erosion to the body or a long, wearing illness may occur with this midpoint structure. A person may be neglectful of health, bringing on a crisis.

Ne-Su/Vu

With this configuration reserves of strength may be sapped away. This midpoint structure can also mean the worsening of a disease.

Ne-Mo/Me

A person with this configuration in a chart may be easily persuaded, a factor that can work positively or negatively in case of hospitalization. Efforts should be made to provide such an individual with a sunny room and a quietly confident doctor and staff for moral support. A doctor should use tact but not vagueness. Such a person may easily succumb to groundless fears.

Ne-Mo/Ma

This midpoint structure can indicate acute infections in a woman. Her emotional reactions may also impair reproductive functions, perhaps causing premenstrual problems. A diet of natural foods will help keep reproductive organs clear of infection and other ailments.

Ne-Mo/Sa

A person with this combination in a chart may have a tendency toward long-term depression: the levels of calcium (Saturn) should be checked. There may also be chronic reproductive ailments. Efforts should be made to keep such an individual in a positive, confident atmosphere for best health.

Ne-Mo/Ur

This configuration can mean a weakened nervous system or nerves highly influenced by stress or intense emotional reactions.

Ne-Mo/Pl

A person with this midpoint structure in a chart may be overly sensitive so that he or she will exaggerate an illness, interfering with the recovery process. Such an individual may not tolerate vagueness from a doctor.

Ne-Mo/Ha

Long-term, reproductive ailments involving infections or decay are possible with this midpoint structure.

Ne-Mo/Ad

This configuration may produce self-deception about health conditions so that an individual is persuaded that he or she is well when actually there is sickness.

Ne-Me/Ma

A person with this midpoint structure in a chart may have the ability to blow things out of proportion, thereby influencing health conditions. A doctor should use factual forthrightness, leaving no vague fears for a patient to suffer.

Ne-Me/Sa

This configuration can indicate morbid states of mind, depression or melancholia: calcium levels as well as the thyroid should be checked. Such an individual may display a pessimistic attitude about getting well. He or she may need a sunny room and a confident doctor and staff for best results.

Ne-Me/Ur

Because of overstress of the mental faculties, a person with this configuration in a chart may have frayed or weakened nerves.

Ne-Me/Ad

An individual with this midpoint structure in a chart may submit to hidden, unspoken fears.

Ne-Ve/Ma

This midpoint structure may indicate an inability to conceive or a low fertility rate. There may also be infections of the reproductive organs.

Ne-Ve/Ze

The inability to conceive, sterility or weakened procreative powers are possible with this combination.

Ne-Ma/Ju

This configuration can indicate complications with delivery, such as long labor and weak contractions.

Ne-Ma/Sa

This is a major health axis. Vitality and endurance may be limited. Moreover, stress may cause illness if care is not taken. A person with this configuration in a chart will probably be susceptible to poisons, such as lead, chemicals or gas. A misdiagnosed, chronic ailment may occur. In addition, such an individual may have allergic reactions to individual drugs and be prone to parasites and infections in general.

Ne-Ma/Ur

A person with this midpoint structure in a chart may be prone to sudden infections, especially after an operation. He or she may be unable to stand too much stress. Since vitality may be limited, actions should be moderate and not impulsive.

Ne-Ma/Pl

This midpoint structure can indicate an endocrine disorder that goes undetected or is misdiagnosed. If pushed too hard too fast, a person with this configuration in a chart may suffer rapidly dropping energy levels. Such an individual probably cannot sustain an effort and needs to learn his or her limitations for best health.

Ne-Ma/Ha

This configuration can indicate diseases caused by poisons, such as heavy metals, gas or other caustic agents. Allergic reactions or injurious side effects from drugs may also occur.

Ne-Ma/Ze

Weak procreative powers are possible with this configuration. In the chart of a pregnant woman this midpoint structure could signal miscarriage with progressed Saturn or Hades at the midpoint.

Ne-Ma/Ad

This midpoint structure could mean a hidden ailment that may fester below the surface for a long time. A physical examination once a year is the best way of detecting the start of this kind of health problem.

Ne-Ma/Vu

A person with this configuration in a chart will probably be unable to gather energy or endurance to withstand a severe illness or operation.

Ne-Sa/Ur

An individual with this combination in a chart may recall strange or unusual sensations during an operation. There may also be problems with anesthetics.

Ne-Sa/Pl

A chronic, long-term illness and poor recuperation powers are indicated with this midpoint structure.

Ne-Sa/Ha

Slow decay of some bodily function or an insidious ailment is possible with this midpoint structure.

Ne-Sa/Kr

This configuration can mean that a person may consult a professional in medicine who is incompetent or who is a fraud, unable to help in the particular situation.

Ne-Sa/Ad

This midpoint structure may bring on an illness that festers undetected; once the disease manifests, there may be an extended recuperation period. Progressed Mars at the midpoint may bring the illness to light.

Ne-Sa/Vu

A person with this midpoint structure in a chart will probably be susceptible to a drug habit, perhaps relying on drugs for a long time, thus jeopardizing health.

Ne-Ur/Ha

This configuration can indicate unexpected events during an operation.

Ne-Ur/Vu

Loss of motor activity, inhibited nerve activity and weak nerves are possibilities with this midpoint structure.

Ne-Pl/Ha

Slow deterioration within the body, undetected and perhaps misdiagnosed, may occur with this configuration.

Ne-Pl/Ad

This midpoint structure can indicate an undetected ailment, with very few symptoms in evidence until it has finally manifested. Progressed Mars or Saturn at the midpoint may bring the disease to light.

Ne-Ha/Ap

Excessive water retention and edema are possible with this midpoint structure. The adrenal glands should be tested to check the hormonal secretion of sodium (Mars).

Ne-Ha/Ad

This configuration can indicate a chronic, hidden illness that may manifest itself when progressed Mars or Saturn is at the midpoint.

Ne-Ap/Ad

A person with this midpoint structure in a chart may suffer from a hidden health condition, or a second condition may come to light when there was thought to be only one. The midpoint structure suggests complications in general.

Ne-Ad/Vu

Worsening of health, crisis and general weakening may be indicated with this midpoint structure.

PLUTO AS MIDPOINT BETWEEN BRACKETING PLANETS

Pl-Su/Mo

Endocrine disorders are possible with progressed Saturn at the midpoint.

Pl-Su/Me

Nervous ailments that could be attributed to a problem with the thyroid may occur with this midpoint structure.

Pl-Su/Ma

A person with this configuration in a chart may have great recuperative powers, strength and abundant vitality. Such an individual should not overwork but use this energy in a constructive manner. Progressed Saturn at the midpoint can indicate possible adrenal exhaustion if a person has pushed too hard for a period of time.

Pl-Su/Ju

This configuration indicates robust health. If an individual with the midpoint structure in a chart does get sick, he or she probably will make a swift, uneventful recovery.

Pl-Su/Sa

Chronic health problems are possible with this midpoint structure. The parathyroid should be tested for secretions of calcium (Saturn). There may also be deformity of the bones.

Pl-Su/Ur

A person with this midpoint structure in a chart may suffer from extreme nervousness or be under continued stress for long periods of time.

Pl-Su/Ne

Progressed Saturn to the midpoint may indicate the beginning of a chronic condition that will go undetected for a time.

Pl-Su/Ha

This midpoint structure can indicate a chronic illness or malfunction of an endocrine gland.

Pl-Su/Vu

A person with this midpoint structure in a chart may have tremendous physical strength and good recuperative powers.

Pl-Mo/Me

There may be problems with the thyroid caused by emotional shock with this configuration. As a result there may be a nervous condition or fluid changes in the body, such as edema.

Pl-Mo/Ma

This configuration may affect the female reproductive system, perhaps causing hemorrhaging during the menstrual cycle. Endocrine malfunction and estrogen imbalance in a woman are other possibilities.

Pl-Mo/Sa

This midpoint structure may cause depression in a woman from an endocrine-related origin: the thyroid should be tested. A woman may also have problems conceiving.

Pl-Mo/Ur

A person with this combination in a chart may suffer from unrelieved tension usually brought about by an emotional state: the thyroid should be tested.

Pl-Mo/Ne

If found in a woman's chart, this configuration can mean a possible endocrine disorder that goes undetected. There may also be edema or water-weight problems.

Pl-Mo/Ha

This midpoint structure can indicate sterility or great difficulties during delivery.

Pl-Me/Ur

Strain on the nervous system from mental stress is possible with this combination.

Pl-Ve/Ze

Birth and extreme fertility are possibilities with this midpoint structure. An individual may realize that he or she wants many children.

Pl-Ma/Ju

A person with this midpoint structure in a chart should enjoy robust health and have a great reserve of strength or endurance.

Pl-Ma/Sa

This is a major health axis. Health may hang in a precarious balance. Chronic disease may manifest with the progressed Sun or Hades at the midpoint. The endocrine system, particularly the adrenals or parathyroid, may be the root cause of disease.

Pl-Ma/Ur

A sudden, unexpected operation to save one's life may take place with the occurrence of this midpoint structure.

Pl-Ma/Ne

This configuration may indicate weakened vitality, perhaps caused by adrenal exhaustion. There is the chance of major infections and lowered immunity: the thymus should be tested.

Pl-Ma/Ha

Sickness brought on by overwork or unhealthy working conditions may result with this midpoint structure. The adrenal glands may be impaired.

Pl-Ma/Ad

With this midpoint structure in a chart a person's health may dwindle, causing loss of strength or energy.

Pl-Ma/Vu

An individual with this combination in a chart may have great energy and quick recuperative powers. He or she will probably exert effort to become well.

Pl-Ju/Ur

This configuration can indicate a life-saving operation or the sudden onset of a chronic ailment.

Pl-Sa/Ne

With this midpoint structure there is the possibility that a health condition neither gets better nor worse. A chronic ailment is also possible.

Pl-Sa/Ha

This configuration can indicate illness that will cause bodily decay or deterioration.

Pl-Sa/Ad

A hidden, chronic illness that lingers without a patient's or doctor's awareness may occur with this midpoint structure.

Pl-Ur/Ad

A hidden condition may suddenly come to light

with the occurrence of this configuration. Exploratory surgery is possible with progressed Mars at the midpoint.

Pl-Ne/Ha

This midpoint structure can indicate the decay or deterioration of the body. There may also be misdiagnosed or not diagnosable conditions that ravage the body. And a person may have adverse reactions to drugs or allergies.

Pl-Ne/Ad

A person with this combination in a chart may be sensitive to drugs, suffering side effects. A slow accumulation of chemicals within the body may cause damage.

Pl-Cu/Ha

This configuration can indicate a death in a family: progressed Saturn at the midpoint can mean a man; the progressed Moon, a woman.

Pl-Cu/Ze

Birth may take place with the occurrence of this midpoint structure.

Pl-Cu/Ad

There may be sickness within a family with this midpoint structure, but it may not be common knowledge. Progressed Mars or Saturn at the midpoint may bring it to everyone's attention.

Pl-Ha/Ad

This midpoint structure can mean chronic endocrine problems. The onset of a chronic ailment is also possible with progressed Saturn at the midpoint.

Pl-Ha/Vu

A health crisis is indicated with this midpoint structure. The condition may worsen.

CUPIDO AS MIDPOINT BETWEEN BRACKETING PLANETS

Cu-Su/Ve

Birth is possible with the occurrence of this configuration.

Cu-Su/Sa

Sickness in a family is possible with this midpoint structure: the illness may not be too serious unless progressed Hades is at the midpoint. The sickness probably will happen to immediate family members, such as children, wife or husband.

Cu-Su/Ha

A serious illness to an immediate family member may result from the occurrence of this configuration.

Cu-Mo/Ha

This midpoint structure can indicate an illness to a woman in a family.

Cu-Ve/Ma

When this midpoint structure occurs, birth is possible, with easy labor and delivery. Progressed Saturn, Hades or Admetos at the midpoint warns of prolonged labor or complications during delivery.

Cu-Ma/Sa

The occurrence of this configuration can mean death to a family member or the manifestation of a chronic illness. Progressed Hades at the midpoint may indicate the worsening of a condition.

Cu-Ma/Ur

This midpoint structure can indicate an unexpected birth in a family, or a child may be born early or late.

Cu-Ma/Ha

Death of a family member through violent means, such as an accident, is possible with this midpoint structure. Progressed Saturn at the midpoint could indicate illness or harm to a male member of the family.

Cu-Sa/Ur

An accident may happen to a family member with the occurrence of this midpoint structure, especially if progressed Mars or Zeus is at the midpoint.

Cu-Sa/Ne

This configuration can mean illness of a chronic nature to a family member. He or she may be a drug addict or have to undergo drug rehabilitation.

Cu-Sa/Pl

The occurrence of this midpoint structure can indicate the death of a family member who has been terminally ill for a long time: progressed Hades at the midpoint could indicate illness or harm to a male member of the family.

Cu-Sa/Ur

An accident may happen to a family member with the occurrence of this midpoint structure, especially if progressed Mars or Zeus is at the midpoint.

Cu-Sa/Ne

This configuration can mean illness of a chronic nature to a family member. He or she may be a drug addict or have to undergo drug rehabilitation.

Cu-Sa/Pl

The occurrence of this midpoint structure can indicate the death of a family member who has been terminally ill for a long time: progressed Hades at the midpoint could indicate death; progressed Uranus, the sudden loss of a male family member.

Cu-Sa/Ha

This configuration can indicate that a family member has a hereditary disease that may either manifest itself or worsen.

Cu-Ur/Pl

Sudden developments within a family are possible with this combination: if progressed Mars is involved, there may be an accident or birth: if Saturn, sudden illness or death.

Cu-Ur/Ha

There may be an unexpected accident to a family member with the occurrence of this midpoint structure. An operation or death is possible with progressed Mars or Saturn at the midpoint.

Cu-Ur/Ze

Conception or the beginning of pregnancy may occur with this midpoint structure.

Cu-Pl/Ha

This midpoint structure can indicate death in a family with progressed Saturn at the midpoint.

Cu-Pl/Ze

Birth may take place with the occurrence of this midpoint structure.

Cu-Ha/Ad

This configuration can mean the death of a family member, especially with progressed Saturn or Pluto at the midpoint.

Cu-Ha/Vu

Violent injury to a family member is possible with this configuration, especially with progressed Mars, Uranus, Saturn or Pluto at the midpoint.

Cu-Ap/Ad

There may be complications during delivery, such as choking or suffocation of the undelivered baby, with the occurrence of this midpoint structure.

HADES AS MIDPOINT BETWEEN BRACKETING PLANETS

Ha-Su/Mo

With this midpoint structure a deep-seated illness involving the total body or the survival of a person may manifest: the involvement of progressed Neptune may weaken the foundations of health.

Ha-Su/Ma

Serious accidents may result with progressed Uranus at the midpoint.

Ha-Su/Sa

This configuration can indicate the worsening of an illness or a health crisis. Progressed Pluto at the midpoint may indicate death.

Ha-Su/Ne

Ailments involving water retention of the body, such as edema, are possible with this midpoint structure. A person may also be susceptible to infections or any viral strain, drug overdose, side effects from drugs, drug-related allergies, weakening of the body or sapping of strength. If a person is suceptible to infections, the thymus gland should be treated.

Ha-Su/Pl

This midpoint structure can mean growth-related problems. Enzyme deficiencies may cause poor assimilation of food and loss of viral nutrients.

Ha-Su/Ze

Miscarriage or problems in conception are possible with this midpoint structure. There may be a stillborn child.

Ha-Su/Ad

This configuration can indicate the ability to exhaust oneself to the detriment of health.

Ha-Su/Vu

This midpoint structure can mean lack of physical strength or endurance. Injury that may cause disfigurement is also possible.

Ha-Asc/Cu

Death of a distant relative or the news of his or her chronic illness may result from the occurrence of this midpoint structure.

Ha-Mo/Me

A person with this configuration in a chart may suffer from depression, morbidity or pessimism.

Ha-Mo/Ve

This combination can indicate female complaints. A woman's reproductive system may be faulty, causing miscarriage or a necessary abortion.

Ha-Mo/Sa

Chronic female ailments are possible with this midpoint structure. There may also be the death of a woman. Progressed Cupido at the midpoint may also indicate the death of the mother in a family or the death of another woman.

Ha-Mo/Ne

With the occurrence of this midpoint structure there may be vague or misdiagnosed complaints by a woman. An individual with this combination in a chart may be emotionally sensitive and unable to withstand severe stress.

Ha-Mo/Pl

This configuration can mean chronic endocrine problems, especially in a woman.

Ha-Mo/Cu

Illness to a woman within the family is possible with this midpoint structure.

Ha-Mo/Ad

A hidden, chronic ailment involving the reproductive organs may come to light with the occurrence of this midpoint structure. The death of the mother in a family or the death of another woman is possible with progressed Saturn at the midpoint.

Ha-Me/Ur

Nerve-related deterioration may occur with this configuration.

Ha-Me/Ne

This midpoint structure can indicate decay of nerves, although the condition may not be readily discernible or may be misdiagnosed. A person with this combination in a chart may be easily and morbidly influenced by surroundings.

Ha-Me/Pl

There may be extensive damage to the nerves with the occurrence of this configuration: the thyroid may be malfunctioning.

Ha-Ve/Ze

A person with this configuration in a chart may have problems in conceiving or may be unhappy in conceiving.

Ha-Ma/Ju

Problems during pregnancy, such as miscarriage or complications with delivery, may occur with this midpoint structure. With progressed Uranus at the midpoint there is the possibility of a Caesarean section.

Ha-Ma/Sa

This configuration can indicate severe illness, which in some cases may result in death. Progressed Uranus at the midpoint could indicate severe injury or death from an accident.

Ha-Ma/Ur

Severe injury because of an unexpected accident, complications during surgery and the poor outcome of an operation are all possible with this midpoint structure.

Ha-Ma/Ne

Death or near death from infections, poisons, drug overdoses or side effects from drugs may occur with this midpoint structure. In addition, there may be weak adrenal or thymus glands.

Ha-Ma/Pl

This configuration can indicate major illness with chronic implications. Death is possible with progressed Saturn at the midpoint.

Ha-Ma/Ze

A woman with this midpoint structure in her chart may suffer miscarriage or abortion. She may also be unable to procreate under some circumstances.

Ha-Sa/Ur

An accident that results in severe injury is possible when this midpoint structure takes place.

Ha-Sa/Ne

Wasting diseases of the body are possible with this midpoint structure. A person may have poor immunity against viral and bacterial illnesses. The thymus should be tested.

Ha-Sa/Pl

This configuration may mean chronic ailments, bone deformity, parathyroid problems or possibly even death.

Ha-Sa/Cu

News of an illness or death in the family, probably of a man, may result from this midpoint structure.

Ha-Sa/Ad

A disease that incubates a long time in the body before manifesting or a chronic ailment may occur with this midpoint structure.

Ha-Ur/Ne

This midpoint structure can indicate a state of unconsciousness, a coma or death occurring while a person is in a coma.

Ha-Ur/Pl

There may be a sudden manifestation of an illness with the occurrence of this configuration. Chronic blood diseases are also possible. With progressed Mars at the midpoint complications during surgery may mean death on the operating table.

Ha-Ur/Ad

With this configuration unsuspected, unexpected illnesses may come to light.

Ha-Ur/Vu

Complications with surgery may occur with progressed Mars at the midpoint. Severe hemorrhaging is also possible with this midpoint structure.

Ha-Ne/Pl

This midpoint structure can indicate a viral disease that is insidious and lingering in nature.

Ha-Ne/Ad

A person with this combination in a chart may suffer from the side effects of drugs building up in the body, reactions to drugs or allergies.

Ha-Pl/Cu

With progressed Saturn involved a death in the family, probably of a man, is possible.

Ha-Pl/Ad

This configuration can indicate the continued deterioration of health or a health crisis.

Ha-Cu/Ap

Death or illness of two members of a family is possible with the occurrence of this midpoint structure.

Ha-Ap/Ad

Complications to an already existing illness may result with the occurrence of this midpoint structure.

ZEUS AS MIDPOINT BETWEEN BRACKETING PLANETS

Ze-Su/Mo

With progressed Venus or Mars at the midpoint conception is possible.

Ze-Su/Ju

This midpoint structure can indicate a person's ability to have many children. Such an individual may be very fertile. With a progressed planet such as Venus, Mars, Uranus or Cupido at the midpoint conception may occur.

Ze-Su/Ur

This configuration in a chart can indicate a highly excitable person, someone who is explosive and temperamental. Blood pressure may rise because of the individual's personality.

Ze-Su/Ne

This midpoint structure may result in the passing on of weak, hereditary traits that may mean sick children.

Ze-Su/Cu

A person with this combination in a chart may be very fertile, with the ability to have many children.

Ze-Su/Ha

An individual with this midpoint structure in a chart may experience high fevers and acute conditions as a child. Progressed Mars or Uranus at the midpoint may indicate injuries from firearms or fires.

Ze-Su/Vu

A person with this configuration in a chart may have tremendous energy and strength to live or fight back against illness.

Ze-Mo/Ve

The birth of a child is possible with the occurrence of this midpoint structure.

Ze-Mo/Ma

This midpoint structure can indicate birth or the ability to have many chidren.

Ze-Mo/Ju

Conception and easy delivery are possibilities with this configuration.

Ze-Mo/Cu

Pregnancy may result from the occurrence of this midpoint structure.

Ze-Me/Ur

With progressed Mars at the midpoint there is the possibility of injury or accident from fires or guns.

Ze-Ve/Ma

Conception may take place with the occurrence of this midpoint structure. With progressed Cupido at the midpoint birth is possible.

Ze-Ve/Ur

This configuration can indicate impulsive, unexpected conception.

Ze-Ve/Ne

A person with this midpoint structure in a chart may be infertile, with a tendency to hemorrhage easily.

Ze-Ve/Pl

This is an excellent combination to indicate easy labor and delivery.

Ze-Ve/Ad

Unsuspected conception or pregnancy may occur with this configuration.

Ze-Ve/Ha

A person with this midpoint structure in a chart may be unable to conceive children because of a disease of the reproductive system.

Ze-Ma/Sa

An individual with this configuration in a chart may be childless. Severe injury may occur from guns or fires. Progressed Uranus at the midpoint may indicate electrical burns; progressed Hades, death or severe injury through fire or firearms.

Ze-Ma/Ur

Injury through electricity, explosions, auto engines or guns may occur with this midpoint structure.

Ze-Ma/Ne

A person with this combination in a chart may suffer from inherited deficiencies, such as blood ailments. Injury through gas, chemical explosions or leakage is also possible.

Ze-Ma/Cu

Birth may result from the occurrence of this midpoint structure.

Ze-Ma/Ha

A person with this combination in a chart may

be unable to conceive children. Progressed Saturn at the midpoint may indicate severe injury from auto accidents, guns or fires.

Ze-Ju/Cu

An individual with this configuration in a chart may be very fertile, with an ability to have many children.

Ze-Ju/Ha

A man with this midpoint structure in his chart may be unable to father children.

Ze-Sa/Ur

With progressed Mars at the midpoint an operation in which some part of the body is removed (such as a gallbladder or appendix) is possible.

Ze-Sa/Ne

This midpoint structure can indicate hereditary deficiencies that are passed on to children.

Ze-Sa/Ha

Inherited ailments are possible with this configuration.

Ze-Ur/Ne

Progressed Mars or Saturn at the midpoint could indicate injury or possible death from an auto accident or gas or chemical explosion.

Ze-Ur/Pl

Progressed Mars at the midpoint could indicate a sudden and severe accident caused by an engine, auto, fire or explosion.

Ze-Ur/Vu

A person with this midpoint structure in a chart probably will have a vast reservoir of energy. He or she may be a fighter, especially if ill, with good recuperative powers. Progressed Mars at the midpoint may indicate injury through an explosion, fire or auto accident.

Ze-Ne/Ha

Injury from steam is possible with progressed Mars at the midpoint.

Ze-Ne/Ad

A person with this midpoint structure in a chart may manifest the will and desire to survive. When gravely ill, he or she will probably have the ability to get better through sheer will or at least will try to get better.

Ze-Pl/Cu

Birth is possible with the occurrence of this midpoint structure.

Ze-Pl/Ha

A person with this configuration in a chart may lack the energy to fight illness.

Ze-Pl/Vu

An individual with this combination in a chart probably has the ability to fight back and overcome disease through sheer will.

Ze-Cu/Ha

A person with this midpoint structure in a chart may have children who are sickly, weak or ailing or may have to take care of sick family members.

Ze-Cu/Ad

There is the potential for conception remaining unknown to a woman with the occurrence of this midpoint structure.

KRONOS AS MIDPOINT BETWEEN BRACKETING PLANETS

Kr-Su/Ma

The occurrence of this midpoint structure marks an excellent time for surgery: the best surgeon will probably be available.

Kr-Su/Ju

The presence of this configuration indicates a person's ability to choose the best surgeon or doctor for an ailment.

Kr-Su/Ha

The occurrence of this midpoint structure means that it is not a good time for an operation: the doctor may be incompetent or fraudulent, charging more money than is due for his or her services.

Kr-Me/Ad

This configuration in a chart is a sign of a good surgeon, who is able to concentrate totally on his or her job and may have innovative techniques.

Kr-Ma/Ju

This is one of the best configurations for a surgeon to have in a chart. The surgeon will probably be both thorough and quick, highly competent and extremely fortunate, even under the most demanding conditions.

Kr-Ma/Sa

Progressed Cupido at the midpoint can indicate death of the father or another male in a family.

Kr-Ma/Ur

This configuration is normally found in the charts of doctors who are best at performing surgery.

Kr-Ma/Ha

This is not usually a good combination for a surgeon, who may lose more patients than he or she saves.

Kr-Ma/Ze

This configuration indicates a masterful surgeon, who is extremely competent and enjoys his or her role.

Kr-Ma/Po

This midpoint structure in a chart may indicate a highly moralistic or ethical medical person.

Kr-Ju/Ur

The occurrence of this configuration usually marks an excellent time to schedule surgery.

Kr-Sa/Ur

A surgeon with this midpoint structure in a chart may lose a patient on the operating table.

Kr-Sa/Pl

The occurrence of this configuration can mark the loss of a patient on the operating table.

Kr-Sa/Ad

This midpoint structure can mean a malpractice suit for a doctor, with the outcome not in the doctor's favor.

Kr-Ur/Ze

This configuration in a chart can signify an innovative doctor or surgeon with new techniques—perhaps a specialist.

Kr-Ne/Ha

The occurrence of this midpoint structure may indicate a poor time for a surgeon to operate. There may be danger of infection, side effects from drugs or mistakes by the surgeon.

Kr-Pl/Ha

This configuration in a chart can mean an incompetent doctor or surgeon. With the occurrence of this midpoint structure operations should probably not be risked. In addition, there may be a malpractice suit against a doctor.

Kr-Ha/Ze

When this midpoint structure occurs, it is usually not a good time to go to a hospital. There may be mismanagement and incompetence that a patient could pay for in terms of health.

Kr-Ha/Ad

This configuration can indicate negligence on the part of a doctor, members of the staff or lab personnel.

Kr-Ze/Ap

This midpoint structure in a chart can mean an outstanding doctor, who has the grasp of his or her trade or science, perhaps an excellent surgeon.

APOLLON AS MIDPOINT BETWEEN BRACKETING PLANETS

Ap-Su/Ha

The occurrence of this configuration can indicate an epidemic. A person may catch a viral infection that many others have contracted. There may be complications with progressed Saturn at the midpoint. This combination in a chart can also signify a doctor or one who deals with mass epidemics.

Ap-Su/Vu

A person with this midpoint structure in a chart may possess great energy and endurance, with the ability to bounce back quickly after sickness.

Ap-Me/Ne

An individual with this combination in a chart may be highly strung, with sensitive nerves.

Ap-Me/Kr

This configuration can indicate a doctor who is highly regarded in his or her own profession, an innovator.

Ap-Ma/Ju

A person with this midpoint structure in a chart may be extremely fertile, with an ability to have many children.

Ap-Ma/Sa

This midpoint structure can indicate a chronic condition that may manifest a secondary ailment.

Ap-Ma/Ne

An individual with this configuration in a chart may be susceptible to many infections, sensitive to drugs and allergic to many items.

Ap-Sa/Ur

This configuration may bring on complications during surgery.

Ap-Sa/Ne

When this midpoint structure appears, a hospital may not be as clean as expected, with infections around scientific or medical premises. There may also be an infectious epidemic. A person may be allergic and sensitive to drugs.

Ap-Sa/Ha

Complications or new developments during a chronic or terminal illness may occur with this midpoint structure.

Ap-Ne/Ha

Injury resulting from chemicals or gases is possible with this configuration. In addition, poisoning to water that could affect many people might occur.

Ap-Pl/Ha

This configuration can indicate a transformative illness in the body that multiplies rapidly and threatens health.

Ap-Pl/Vu

This midpoint structure is a primary indication of an illness. The occurrence of the configuration may mark the beginning of a sickness that may develop complications later.

Ap-Ad/Vu

The occurrence of this combination can mean the worsening of a condition. Complications may suddenly set it.

ADMETOS AS MIDPOINT BETWEEN BRACKETING PLANETS

Ad-Su/Mo

Admetos progressed to the midpoint may indicate a person who is bedridden or who has to remain motionless, perhaps in traction. Progressed Saturn or Hades to the midpoint may indicate the beginning of a chronic ailment.

Ad-Su/Ma

The occurrence of this configuration can indicate an illness that is at a standstill. Enforced rest may be necessary for recuperation.

Ad-Su/Sa

A person with this midpoint structure in a chart

may be handicapped in some way. There may also be slow bone formation.

Ad-Su/Ur

The occurrence of this midpoint structure can mean the sudden halt of some bodily function, such as the heart. There may be an aneurysm or stroke. An injury that may put a person in bed for recuperation is also possible.

Ad-Su/Ne

An individual with this midpoint structure in a chart may have a sluggish body or poor or hindered circulation, such as phlebitis. Viral conditions may incubate in a person. Or there may be inhibiting viruses or bacteria that go undetected. An individual may be a carrier of a viral disease.

Ad-Su/Pl

This configuration can indicate abnormal weight gain from a malfunctioning endocrine gland.

Ad-Su/Ha

Problems from poor nutrition or assimilation are possible with this midpoint structure. The occurrence of the configuration can also mean the beginning of a chronic condition, especially with progressed Saturn at the midpoint. Growth may be hindered in some way, either through lack of sufficient food or improper absorption.

Ad-Su/Vu

A person with this configuration in a chart may be unable to sustain energy or endurance for long periods.

Ad-Mo/Me

An individual with this midpoint structure in a chart may be a depressive brooder, prone to morbidity.

Ad-Mo/Ve

Progressed Mars or Cupido at the midpoint can indicate problems with pregnancy or complications during delivery.

Ad-Mo/Sa

This midpoint structure in the chart of a woman can indicate a hidden ailment of the reproductive system. A person may also be sterile.

Ad-Mo/Pl

Endocrine disorder, such as sluggish or inhibited secretions of a gland, may affect a woman with this configuration in her chart. Weight gain from water retention is also possible.

Ad-Mo/Ha

A chronic condition affecting the reproductive system is possible with this midpoint structure. There may also be hidden deterioration or disease within the womb: a Pap smear should be taken every six months.

Ad-Mo/Ze

A person with this combination in a chart may have problems conceiving and may have low fertility.

Ad-Me/Ma

An individual with this configuration in a chart may suffer from inhibited speech, the inability to express himself or herself quickly or efficiently or speech impediments.

Ad-Me/Sa

This midpoint structure may cause inhibited endocrine function: the thyroid or parathyroid may be considered in the low to normal range but still not functioning properly.

Ad-Me/Ur

Sudden, unexpected bouts of severe depression may occur with this midpoint structure.

Ad-Me/Ne

Since a person with this configuration in a chart is likely to be easily persuaded, therapy will probably work well in the healing process.

Ad-Me/Ha

An individual with this combination in a chart may have a pessimistic and limited outlook. He or she may even be suicidal, especially with the progressed Moon or Saturn at the midpoint.

Ad-Me/Ma

This midpoint structure can indicate a suppressed sexual function. If the configuration occurs in the chart of a man, there may be low fertility. The adrenal glands should be tested.

Ad-Ve/Ze

A person with this midpoint structure in a chart may have limited procreative abilities and lowered fertility.

Ad-Ma/Ju

With this midpoint structure problems during pregnancy, such as a miscarriage, complications during delivery or a premature baby, may occur.

Ad-Ma/Sa

This configuration can indicate a chronic condition that remains hidden for a time or a long-term disease. Suppression of the adrenal or parathyroid glands is also possible.

Ad-Ma/Ur

The occurrence of this midpoint structure may bring on injury that may halt the breathing processes, choking, a stroke or an aneurysm.

Ad-Ma/Ne

A person with this combination in a chart may be susceptible to many types of infections, perhaps from suppressed thymus functions. Allergies from a malfunction of the adrenal glands are also possible. Furthermore, an individual may be a carrier for disease or virus that can infect others. He or she may be allergic to drugs or become poisoned in some unexpected way.

Ad-Ma/Pl

With the occurrence of this midpoint structure a severe ailment may come to light, perhaps involving the suppression of the adrenal glands. This configuration can also indicate diseases that deal in duplication of cells and take a long time to be detected. With progressed Saturn at the midpoint such a condition may mainfest itself.

Ad-Ma/Ha

This configuration can indicate chronic ailments involving the endocrine glands, particularly the adrenals. There may be the manifestation of severe illness with progressed Saturn at the midpoint. Poor circulation is another possibility.

Ad-Ma/Ze

Difficult birth or prolonged labor may resul from the occurrence of this midpoint structure. Hid den problems during the birth of a child may also occur.

Ad-Ma/Vu

A person with this midpoint structure in a chart may experience loss of strength, depletion of energy reserves or worsening of a condition.

Ad-Sa/Ur

With the presence of this midpoint structure injury may occur from unforeseen or hidden circumstances. There may also be a sudden blockage somewhere within the body.

Ad-Sa/Ne

This is a major health axis. It implies a long, deteriorating condition that goes undetected for some time: progressed Mars or Hades at the midpoint may bring the condition to light. A person with this configuration in a chart probably will be susceptible to allergies and infections.

Ad-Sa/Pl

This is one of the major health axes. It can indicate a slow, proliferating or multiplying disease. It may also indicate endocrine disorder, possibly with the parathyroid. Progressed Mars or Hades at the midpoint may bring the disease to light. Bone diseases or bone growth suppression may also occur.

Ad-Sa/Ha

This configuration can indicate chronic, long-term diseases. If progressed Admetos is at the midpoint, there may be the triggering of a condition or an indication of continued deterioration of health; possible complications may also come to light at that time.

Ad-Sa/Ze

Sterility or the inability to conceive children is possible with this configuration.

Ad-Ur/Pl

The occurrence of this midpoint structure can mean the sudden beginning of an ailment. Unexpected rest may be demanded of an individual.

Ad-Ur/Ze

With this midpoint structure a hidden condition may result in abortion or sudden loss of a child during pregnancy.

Ad-Ur/Vu

The occurrence of this configuration can indicate sudden blockage or suppression somewhere within the body, possibly a stroke or aneurysm or a burst appendix.

Ad-Ne/Pl

With this midpoint structure a hidden or undetected condition may cause a lingering or proliferating condition. A weakened endocrine function is also possible.

Ad-Ne/Ha

A person with this midpoint structure in a chart may experience water retention problems: the condition may be misdiagnosed. A chronic disease that goes undetected may also occur. Infections may be deadly to such an individual. He or she may have unusual allergies.

Ad-Pl/Ha

This midpoint structure can indicate an illness of long duration that remains undetected for years. There may also be endocrine problems. Proliferation of a multiplying disease within the body is another possibility. The basic cell structure formation may be changed as well.

Ad-Pl/Vu

A tremendous blockage or suppression may threaten life with the presence of this midpoint structure: a stroke, angina or trouble with the gallbladder is possible under the right circumstances.

Ad-Cu/Ze

Delivery may be difficult and long with unexpected complications if progressed Mars or Uranus is at the midpoint.

VULCANUS AS MIDPOINT BETWEEN BRACKETING PLANETS

Vu-Su/Mo

A person with this midpoint structure in a chart probably will have tremendous reserves of energy or strength. To avoid overdoing things, such an individual should be moderate in all activities.

Vu-Sa/Ma

A person with this configuration in a chart will probably have great strength and endurance as well as quick recuperative powers after an operation or illness.

Vu-Su/Ur

An individual with this combination in a chart may be a workaholic, overworking and stressing the nerves. If not moderate, such a person may contract ailments induced by stress, such as high blood pressure.

Vu-Su/Ne

The occurrence of this configuration can indicate a terrific weakening of the body: if a person is ill, the condition may worsen. An individual with this combination in a chart may be susceptible to a broad range of viral or bacterial infections and allergies. He or she may have an adverse reaction to drugs.

Vu-Su/Pl

A person with this midpoint structure in a chart will probably have a strong and durable body and be able to throw off most nagging illnesses without problem. He or she will probably enjoy great

recuperative powers. But with such an individual's tendency to overdo activities, injury is possible.

Vu-Su/Ha

This midpoint structure can indicate bodily injury that may destroy tissue or bone, especially with progressed Uranus at the midpoint. There may be extensive damage to the body from injury.

Vu-Mo/Ma

A person with this combination in a chart may come under great emotional stress. He or she may tend toward overemotional actions or reactions that could result in injury.

Vu-Mo/Sa

This configuration can indicate inhibited reproductive functions or problems with the menstrual cycle.

Vu-Mo/Ur

Birth is possible with progressed Venus or Cupido at the midpoint.

Vu-Mo/Ad

During pregnancy there is the chance of miscarriage when this midpoint structure is in a woman's chart.

Vu-Me/Sa

Stuttering or the inability to express oneself as one would wish may result from this midpoint structure.

Vu-Me/Ur

This configuration could indicate irritation of the nerves or an overload on the mental circuits from concentration or intensity. A person with this midpoint structure in a chart will probably need to relax or learn moderate habits to take stress off the nerves.

Vu-Ve/Ze

Conception may take place with the occurrence of this midpoint structure.

Vu-Ma/Ju

An individual with this configuration in a chart will probably be robust; however, injury or illness may occur from lack of moderation.

Vu-Ma/Sa

If a person is ill when this midpoint structure occurs, a chronic condition may become worse, indicating an hour of crisis.

Vu-Ma/Ur

A person with this configuration in a chart may be involved in a tremendous explosion or some other sort of unexpected accident, undergo sudden extensive or complicated surgery or spend long hours in surgery.

Vu-Ma/Ne

An individual with this combination in a chart may be sensitive to allergies or drugs and their side effects. With lowered immunity such a person may catch any type of infection: the thymus should be checked. Anemia or blood-related problems are also possible.

Vu-Ma/Pl

An individual with this midpoint structure in a chart may display tremendous strength and energy as well as a will to live and battle against any odds.

Vu-Ma/Ze

Injury through firearms, explosions or fires may happen when this midpoint structure occurs.

Vu-Ma/Ad

A blockage or suppression in the body that could affect the life of a person may take place with the occurrence of this configuration.

Vu-Ju/Ur

The occurrence of this midpoint structure usually marks a good time for surgery, with an excellent outcome.

Vu-Sa/Ur

A person with this midpoint structure in a chart may have to remain hospitalized because of injuries sustained.

Vu-Sa/Ne

This configuration can indicate the worsening of a disease or a condition. A person with the midpoint structure in a chart may be prone to infection that may be uncontrollable or halted by drugs. Poisoning is another possibility.

Vu-Sa/Pl

It is usually not a good time for surgery with progressed Uranus at the midpoint: there may be loss of life.

Vu-Sa/Ha

This configuration can indicate the worsening of a condition.

Vu-Sa/Ad

The occurrence of this midpoint structure may bring on enforced hospitalization for a long time.

Vu-Ur/Ha

When this configuration occurs, it is usually not a good time for surgery: complications or unexpected changes may take place.

Vu-Ur/Ze

Injury through firearms, explosions, electricity or fire is possible with progressed Mars at the midpoint.

Vu-Ur/Ad

Unexpected blockage or stoppage may take place somewhere in the body with the occurrence of this midpoint structure. In addition, there may be danger to a life through suffocation or choking.

Vu-Ne/Pl

The occurrence of this midpoint structure can indicate the crisis of an illness or a festering condition that manifests itself.

Vu-Pl/Ha

Disintegration of the body from a chronic illness is possible with the occurrence of this midpoint structure: the disease may become worse instead of better.

Vu-Pl/Ad

The occurrence of this configuration can indicate hidden and transforming conditions that may come to light, especially with progressed Saturn or Neptune at the midpoint.

Vu-Cu/Ad

Prolonged labor with tremendous effort exerted to birth the baby may result from the occurrence of this midpoint structure, especially with Venus at the midpoint.

POSEIDON AS MIDPOINT BETWEEN BRACKETING PLANETS

Po-Ve/Ne

A person with this midpoint structure in a chart may be highly susceptible to radiation and its subsequent damage. In addition, an individual may be sensitive to his or her environment: if he or she is ill, efforts should be made to keep the atmosphere quiet and sunny for best recuperation.

Po-Ma/Sa

Mental illness may occur with this midpoint

structure. The mind may wander from stark reality to more fanciful creations.

Po-Ma/Ur

The occurrence of this midpoint structure usually marks a good time for surgery, especially with progressed Mars at the midpoint.

Po-Ma/Ne

This configuration can mean sickness of the mind and possible insanity if other conditions exist.

Po-Sa/Ur

This midpoint structure can indicate mental indecision and confusion.

Po-Sa/Ne

The mind of a person with this midpoint structure in a chart may be in disorder, with flights of fantasy and possible mental illness.

Recommended reading: *The Uranian Planets* by Sylvia Sherman.

CHAPTER FIVE
The Med-Scan Technique

Every body has its own particular weak spots that tend to dysfunction under mental, physical or emotional stress or through poor diet. The Med-Scan technique helps determine potential weaknesses within a body. It relies on medical astrology to find out what diseases a person may be susceptible to or what vitamin or mineral deficiencies might occur. That is not to say that because specific configurations appear in a natal or progressed chart a person will have a certain disease or nutritional deficiency. The Med-Scan technique simply provides *clues*.

In medical astrology nothing is assumed: all findings are cross-checked with the present symptoms and past medical history of the patient and then proven through tests or physical examinations conducted by a physician. A medical astrologer examines a natal chart to locate potential vitamin and mineral deficiencies and likely weak areas of the body, comparing the astrological findings with the person's medical history. In addition to looking at the sign and house placements of the planets and the hard aspects, a medical astrologer determines which cross is activated. He or she also looks closely at critical degrees in the natal chart, evaluates a progressed chart for the client and looks at transits and eclipses. From all this information a medical astrologer can then suggest the best nutritional supplements, diet and therapy for the patient—after the astrological conclusions have been verified by a physician.

THE MEDICAL QUESTIONNAIRE

For the Med-Scan technique to be successful a medical astrologer must first find out all he or she can about a client's present symptoms, medical history and eating, drinking and smoking habits as well as determine what drugs and/or nutritional supplements the person is taking. One of the best methods for gathering this information is a systematic questionnaire. Figure 1 reproduces an abbreviated form of a questionnaire I use with my clients. In addition, I am providing an explanation for each of the questions to show how the questionnaire can help in ascertaining the root problems of a person's health.

1. Childhood Diseases?

Clients often have severe childhood diseases, such as polio or rheumatic fever, that can have medical ramifications in later years. Rheumatic fever, for example, a disease that manifests through a strain known as A beta hemolytic streptococci (Neptune), a bacteria that causes high fever and aching in the joints, can cause minimal to major damage to the heart and/or kidneys many years afterward. The fact that a client may or may not still have a heart murmur because of the rheumatic fever can be another factor in an analysis. Therefore, information about childhood diseases is very important in the final diagnosis of a client's chart.

2. Allergies?

It is important to know about a person's allergies for several reasons. For one, the adrenal glands may not be triggering enough antihistamines to combat the pollen, pollution or whatever is causing the allergy. An astrologer should also be aware if a person is allergic to such substances as brewer's yeast, whole grains or other natural products that are normally suggested in a diet to get a person well: if allergies exist, of course, these products must be eliminated from the diet. Furthermore, any allergic symptoms to certain types of drugs should be noted and compared with drugs that are being taken. In rare instances a drug may contain an ingredient that a person is having a mild allergic reaction to, and the doctor must be so informed.

Allergies usually mean that a person needs dosages of pantothenic acid (Neptune) and vitamin C (Saturn), since both are antihistaminic in action: the chart should be examined to see if there are two or more hard aspects to Neptune or Saturn. If there are, then proper dosages of these vitamins should be considered to alleviate the allergic condition.

3. Do you smoke?

If a client answers *yes* to this question, a medical astrologer should examine the natal chart to help determine why the person smokes. People usually smoke for two reasons—habit and/or nervousness. Nerves are ruled by Mercury and Uranus respectively. A habit, on the other hand, indicates the influence of a fixed sign and/or a strongly placed Saturn. In fact, Saturn may be said to rule smoking: many doctors feel that the most important vitamin for smokers to take, in megavitamin doses, is vitamin C, because smokers lose up to 30 per cent more vitamin C from their bodies than nonsmokers. But since smoking is considered a pleasurable habit, Venus may also be somewhat of an influence.

Smoking is obviously not good for the human body. One cigarette can paralyze the hairlike processes projecting from the cells that line the nose and lungs (cilia). This hairlike motion propels mucus, pus and dust particles as well as bacterial and viral material, out of sensitive passages and breathing areas, washing them from the body so they cannot produce harm or begin infection.

Smoking also influences the constriction of the blood vessels, cheating the body of its needed circula-

Date:_____ Medical Scan for _____

Time: _____ Vocation _____

Address _____

_____

Telephone ( ) _____

1. Childhood diseases? ☐ YES ☐ NO

_____

_____

2. Allergies? ☐ YES ☐ NO

(a) at what age?_____

(b) on medication presently? _____

3. Do you smoke? ☐ YES ☐ NO

(a) how many packs?_____

4. Do you drink? ☐ YES ☐ NO

(a) what? _____

(b) how often or much? _____

(c) why? _____

5. How much milk do you drink? _____

_____

6. Do you take a bath or shower? (circle one)

7. Are you a Meat Fruit Vegetable eater? (circle one)

8. Do you eat sweets and sugar products? ☐ YES ☐ NO

(a) how much? _____

(b) specify foods: _____

_____

(c) frequency: _____

9. What drug medication are you on presently? Specify what, how much and frequency of dose for symptom: _____

_____

_____

10. What drug medications do you take that are over-the-counter (aspirin, sleeping pills, digestive aids, cold formulas, etc.)? _____

_____

(a) how often do you take them? _____

(b) any noticeable side effects from taking them? _____

what? _____

_____

_____

Figure 1
MEDICAL QUESTIONNAIRE

11. Are you presently taking natural vitamin supplements? (If so, specify what, strength in mg.'s or I.U.'s and how often taken.)

Vitamin   Frequency

_____   _____

_____   _____

_____   _____

_____   _____

_____   _____

12. Any side effects or benefits from #11?

_____

_____

_____

_____

13. How long have you been taking vitamins?

_____

14. Have you ever had any operations?

When   Part of Body   Outcome

_____   _____   _____

_____   _____   _____

_____   _____   _____

_____   _____   _____

15. Have you ever had or do you have presently any of the following ailments (if 'yes' explain further on a separate piece of paper:

heart problems _____   digestive disturbances _____

sugar problems _____   endocrine problems (specify gland)_____

constipation_____   high blood pressure _____

blood problems _____   kidney ailments _____

headaches_____   urinary disorders _____

   (a) frequency _____   diarrhea _____

menstrual problems _____   nervous disorders _____

   (a) describe _____   dizziness _____

_____   chief complaints

pregnancy _____   (comment on separate piece of paper)

   (a) when_____

tion, especially to the extremities. In addition, intermittent claudication (a deficiency of blood supply to the peripheral blood vessels in the feet, ruled by Pisces) is aggravated by smoking. This disorder can range from an aggravating pain when a person walks to a sharp pain like a muscle cramp in one or both legs—in the foot, calf or even the thigh.

Moreover, a medium to heavy smoking habit is now known to cause increased acidity in the bone tissue. And bone minerals, mostly calcium (Saturn) and phosphorus (Mars), are known to be more soluble in acid solutions. The bone minerals are dissolved and absorbed into the bloodstream at an accelerated rate, inducing osteoporosis, wherein the bones (Saturn) become porous and fragile and can eventually crack or shatter with the slightest bump or fall. There may also be a loss of vitamin D (Sun) and calcium with smoking: the high calcium content in the blood (hypercalcemia) may increase the loss of calcium from the bone structures.

Another relatively rare and often misdiagnosed health problem that can be brought on by smoking is tobacco blindness (tobacco amblyopia). Smoking can cause partial or complete loss of visual acuity, loss of color perception and even blindness. According to the *Canadian Medical Association Journal* (28 February 1970), the disease can result from large amounts of cyanide in tobacco. The poison causes degeneration of myelin, the lipoprotein that sheathes the nerves. The optic nerve is the first to disintegrate when there is too much cyanide in the body. Vitamin B-12 (Mars) combats the problem as well as helping to stop the smoking habit.

Both arteriosclerosis and atherosclerosis, the thickening and hardening of the walls of the arteries, can also be induced by smoking. Arteriosclerosis is characterized by the gradual buildup of calcium deposits in the artery walls, restricting the flow of blood to other parts of the body: this is a Saturn-ruled affliction, since calcium is under that planet's sway. Atherosclerosis is a buildup of cholesterol or fatty deposits in the artery walls that clog the tubing involved: this disease is ruled by Jupiter, which has domain over fat.

In addition, cigarette smoking is linked to strokes (cerebrovascular accidents, or CVA), which occur when the blood supply in a part of the brain is cut off for a time, and the cells die from lack of oxygen. Strokes can be caused by atherosclerosis, clotting or hemorrhaging.

Indigestion (dyspepsia) can also be caused by smoking before or during a meal and swallowing too much air with the meal. This problem can lead to heartburn, flatulence, swelling of the abdomen and uneasiness in the stomach.

Another disease associated with smoking is emphysema, which occurs when the air sacs in the lungs become thin and stretched and lose their elasticity. With emphysema used air sits in the lungs, making a person unable to utilize the fresh, incoming air. Smoking irritates the already-laboring lungs and causes further shortness of breath as well as coughing.

The elevation of blood pressure (hypertension) is also aggravated by smoking. Symptoms range from headaches, nervousness, insomnia and edema to shortness of breath. Athough an abnormal amount of bodily sodium (Mars), which causes retention of fluids, is the main reason for hypertension, smoking abets the situation.

4. Do you drink? What? How often or much? Why?

This question pertains to any liquid, from water to alcoholic beverages. What we put into our systems our kidneys must eventually deal with. Too little water prevents the kidneys from dispensing toxic waste material that has accumulated. Hence, many people who drink perhaps only one glass of water a day at the most end up with an inflammation of the bladder (cystitis) that may have secondary complications affecting the kidneys, prostate gland or urethra. Thus the medical astrologer should ascertain how much water a person drinks per day.

The astrologer also needs to find out what kind of water an individual drinks—i.e., faucet water, distilled water or spring water. Faucet water in most places in the United States is polluted with chemicals. This is one reason processed sodas and powdered drink mixes are so popular: they disguise the horrible taste and smell of local, city water. Distilled water is certainly better than faucet water; however, because all the minerals have been washed out of it, if a person drinks it for a prolonged time he or she should take a mineral supplement. Bottled, fresh spring water still has the minerals intact and is even better to use than distilled water.

Americans often substitute caffeine drinks, such as coffee, black tea and sweetened, carbonated sodas, for water. All of these substances are nutritionally poor and may produce health repercussions if drunk in excess; therefore, a medical astrologer needs to pay careful attention to a person's habits with such drinks.

For instance, coffee can cause the loss of 35 to 40 essential nutrients required for health by washing them out of the urine. Furthermore, it stimulates the respiratory process and kidneys, excites the brain functions and raises blood pressure. Although it makes a person feel less fatigued for a while, in excess it causes nervousness, irritates the lining of the stomach and heart and creates problems with the arteries. Coffee may also force the loss of inositol and biotin (both ruled by Jupiter), prevent iron (Mars) from being used properly and cause many other vitamins to be pumped through the body before they can be absorbed.

Coffee acts as a stress to the body, causing a prompt rise in blood fats and cholesterol. In one study involving 2,000 men over a seven-year period, individuals who developed coronary problems drank five cups or more of coffee daily. Caffeine is also known to make the liver torporific or sluggish, affecting that organ's ability to manufacture glycogen, filter out and destroy bacteria in the bloodstream and perform several other equally important functions.

Black tea normally purchased in stores is high in caffeine, too. In addition, it contains tannic acid. Thus tea has little nutritional value other than supplying flouride (Mars). It can especially have a harmful effect on the mucous membranes of the mouth and the gastrointestinal system. And, like coffee and cocoa, tea is alkaline in reaction. Its residue, combined with uric acid and other colloids, is manufactured into crystal urates, which can become deposited in the body, causing rheumatism, arthritis and kidney stones. Herbal teas are highly recommended, instead, because of their high nutritional value. (See Chapter Nine.)

There is also little nutritional value in sweetened, carbonated drinks. All such drinks contain either orthophosphoric or citric acid that eats away the enamel protection on teeth. Furthermore, there is a large dose of caffeine in such drinks to overstimulate the metabolism and wash out needed nutrients from the body. And, most importantly, carbonated drinks are potentially dangerous to anyone with sugar-related problems—that is, to almost all Americans. A 16-ounce bottle of soda pop contains *six teaspoons of white sugar*! And we wonder why American children are so overweight, sluggish and unhealthy and why hypoglycemia and diabetes are so rampant among Americans.

Finally, a medical astrologer should find out the kinds and amounts of alcoholic beverages a person drinks. Some alcoholic beverages are mildly helpful to the body. Wine made from natural grape sugar (fructose) is fine when taken in moderation, i.e., one glassful a day. Beer contains some protein. But pure alcoholic spirits do nothing positive; instead, they disrupt the body in many ways. Once the alcohol hits the stomach, it acts, first, upon the central nervous system, changing the mental functions and destroying brain cells. Then the liver works to neutralize the alcohol by breaking down its composition. Heavy

drinking may trigger scarring of the liver (cirrhosis), pancreatic and gastrointestinal reactions as well as mental and emotional problems. Alcohol can also force the loss of great amounts of magnesium (Sun) from the body, causing jitters, nervousness and tension.

Knowing the amount of alcohol a person drinks will clue a medical astrologer in on how hard the liver is working to keep up with the intake: a supplement of B vitamins can be suggested to help support the liver if a client insists on maintaining his or her drinking habits. Knowing the amount consumed can also indicate whether or not a client has emotional problems. But a note or warning: a person does not have to drink a quart or two of a beverage a day to be an alcoholic; alcoholism is a disease and a blood disorder, and a medical astrologer must sometimes look for other signs to diagnose alcoholism—such as the presence of planets in Virgo, ruling the pancreas, or its opposite sign, Pisces. Many other factors must be present before one can diagnose alcoholism. In many instances the consumption of much alcohol is really triggered by hypoglycemia or prediabetic tendencies.

5. How much milk do you drink?

There is much confusion about the role of milk in today's diet. At one time milk was very good taken in moderation. Moreover, lactose, a natural sugar that is beneficial to us, appears only in milk: it helps maintain a healthy bacterial balance in the body and assists in the assimilation of calcium, phosphorus and magnesium.

But nowadays the milk we buy is hardly fit for human consumption. It is peppered with toxic chemicals, such as DDT, pesticides and other herbicides found on the grass that the cows consume. It also contains excessive antibiotics, notably penicillin and Aureomycin, used to prevent mastitis in the udder: a heavy milk drinker can literally build up a reaction to pencillin. Furthermore, pasteurization of the milk destroys the nutritional value: boiling the liquid kills both the harmful and beneficial bacteria as well as changes the chemical structure of the protein, making the milk nearly indigestible.

Too much milk also creates too much mucus. And too much mucus can block the necessary assimilation of vital minerals, vitamins and nutrients in the body. It can also cause constipation and interfere with oxygen exchange.

Mucus buildup adversely affects the digestive process, too. A diet of highly processed foods and proteins creates the secretion of strong digestive juices. As a result, the stomach cells that create mucus to protect the lining go into double-time production to protect the gastrointestinal tract. The mucus then interacts with the digestive juices, becoming an undigestible mucoprotein. If such a dietary process continues for long, the mucoprotein settles in various parts of the body: in the kidneys it can cause poor elimination of uric acid; in the gallbladder, partially halt the flow of bile or cause buildup of calculi, which in turn will create gallstones; or, in the lymph gland system cause congestion, thereby starving some parts of the body of protein. If a person is on a heavy milk diet (especially if he or she is a vegetarian), ½ glass of milk a day is certainly plenty. Any more will create an imbalance of mucus. (If a person wants to get rid of excess mucus, a three-day juice diet is recommended.)

Since today's milk is so bad, natural yogurt should be substituted in the diet. Natural yogurt is a good replacement because it is high in proteins, minerals and vitamins. It is also predigested, therefore assimilated by the body twice as quickly as milk. In addition, the lactobacillus bulgaricus in yogurt destroys putrefactive bacteria and helps the good bacteria manufacture B and K vitamins.

6. Do you take a bath or shower?

When a person takes a shower, only the skin is cleaned. But with a bath three important functions take place: first the blood pressure drops, then the heart slows, and then the muscles relax. And a bath gets the body clean.

So, a bath a couple of times a week will allow a person to relax in ways that a shower cannot. A person with a prominent water sign (Cancer, Scorpio or Pisces) in a natal chart will especially benefit from a bath because water is his or her natural environment, thereby conducive to health on more than just a physical level. A person who is tense, such as a Virgo or Gemini or someone with a prominent Mercury or Uranus, will also feel more revitalized with a bath instead of a shower.

7. Are you a meat, fruit or vegetable eater?

The average American diet consists of a lot of meat, a few well-boiled vegetables and a small amount of canned fruit. America by anyone's standards is overproteined and undermineralized. We eat more meat and protein than almost any other people in the world, the average citizen consuming 71 per cent animal protein and only 29 per cent vegetable products. We also lead the world in statistics for the highest rates of cancer, arthritis, heart disease, multiple sclerosis, high blood pressure, birth deformities, degenerative diseases and miscarriages. Heart disease is our number one killer.

Cooked animal protein causes many hazards to health. Meat is high in acidity, and many people cannot digest it properly because they have deficiencies in pancreatic enzymes, bile and/or hydrochloric acid. One pound of meat can generate as much as 18 grains of uric acid. Since the liver and kidneys combined can only excrete eight grains of uric acid in a given 24-hour period, problems such as gout, rheumatism or arthritis can occur. Cell destruction is also caused by high blood acidity from an excess of protein. And the acid-alkaline metabolism can be thrown out of balance, causing nervousness, tension and later disturbing the renal organs (the kidneys, ureter and bladder). Furthermore, meat produces a biochemical imbalance in the tissue, a deficiency of vitaimin B-6 (Jupiter), intestinal putrefaction that results in constipation and autotoxemia, arteriosclerosis, heart disease, kidney damage and arthritis. Edema and aching joints are other disorders brought on by heavy meat eating.

America's high protein fad is a killer. It is important to get protein, of course—but in moderation. And it is erroneous to assume that only animal products supply complete protein. The Max Plank Institute in Germany has shown that many vegetables, fruits, seeds and nuts are just as good sources of complete protein as meat. And vegetable proteins are higher in biological value than animal proteins, with raw proteins supplying better biological value than cooked proteins.

To lessen the instances of some of the killer diseases in America we should probably resort to a diet low in animal protein and high in natural carbohydrates. The Hunzas, Russians and Bulgarians hold world records for centenarians. The Hunzas eat grains, fruits (apricots, grapes and apples), mostly raw vegetables, a little goat's milk and very few eggs and meat—usually not more than once a month. The Russians derive 78.5 per cent of their protein needs from vegetables and only 21.5 per cent from animal sources. The Bulgarians, known to be among the healthiest people in the world, eat mainly black bread (whole rye and barley), vegetables, yogurt and kefir.

A person's answers to these questions, then, will help a medical astrologer determine what dietary habits may be causing disease and aid an astrologer in recommending a new diet. In general people with planets in Leo, Scorpio, Aries, Taurus or Capricorn tend to eat meat; individuals with planets in Saggittarius, Virgo or Aquarius usually prefer vegetables; those with planets in Gemini, Libra or Pisces normally like fruit; and people with planets in Cancer are prone to heavy ingestion of dairy products. If a person eats a great deal of meat and barely any fresh, raw fruit, a medical astrologer can advise him or her to have at least two meatless meals a week. And those meals should not be replaced with meals high in starch, such as potatoes or macaroni. The best substitute is a fresh fruit or vegetable salad. Raw fruits and vegetables are better than cooked ones, although partially steamed vegetables retain more vitamins and minerals than thoroughly cooked ones. And an intake of chicken and fish is preferable to eating heavier meats, such as beef, lamb and pork, which are harder for the digestive system to break down for use.

8.   Do you eat sweets and sugar products?

The average American now consumes 102 pounds of sugar a year. Nowadays even our newborn children are fed sugar in their formulas, which contain high amounts of dextromaltose or glucose.

Refined sugar overstimulates the production of insulin, disrupts the absorption of proteins, calcium and other minerals and retards the growth of beneficial intestinal bacteria. Although brown or Turbo sugar contains a few nutrients, it is just as damaging. And sucrose (cane sugar), a combination of one molecule of glucose and one of fructose is also not good. Although sucrose takes very little digestion to break down, it produces high energy associated with overstimulation and sensitizing of the isles of Langerhans, located above the pancreas: this cluster of cells manufactures insulin, and destruction or impairment of the isles through excess sugar intake will cause diabetes or hypoglycemia.

Sugar of any kind, ruled by Venus, also stimulates the production of alkaline digestive juices so that calcium becomes insoluble before it can reach the blood. In addition, excess sugar can lead to an imbalance in the calcium-phosphorus relationship: faulty bone formation may result. Sugar is also a factor in obesity, tooth decay, nervous disorders, pyorrhea and mental illness. And someone who craves sweet products is usually deficient in thiamine (Mercury).

A medical astrologer who finds a person with a high intake of sugar should advise the client to use some other source of sweetener. For instance, honey, a carbohydrate, is easily digested and does not cause a deficiency of calcium as does white sugar. Honey is also high in potassium, the brain food, and contains small amounts of minerals plus a trace of the vitamin B complex and vitamins C, D and E (Venus). It can be used in baked goods, coffee or anything that usually calls for sugar. A good replacement for chocolate is carob, a natural sweetener rich in B vitamins and minerals: it can be bought at any health food store. And molasses, for those who can tolerate the sulfur smell, is a good source of vitamins and minerals, especially rich in iron, copper (Venus) and

magnesium.

9.   What drug medications are you presently on?

I've often found that a doctor will prescribe a drug that a patient will have a reaction to. Using one of the three following books as references, a medical astrologer should crosscheck a drug with any reactions recorded by the client: *The People's Pharmacy*, by Joe Graedon; *The Essential Guide to Prescription Drugs*, by James W. Long, M. D.; and *Physician's Desk Reference* (PDR). If there are any warning signals, the astrologer should duly alert the client so that he or she may ask the doctor about the reaction and either get another medication or get off medication completely.

10.   What drug medications do you take that are over-the-counter?

The overuse of an over-the-counter drug frequently will alert a medical astrologer to a problem. For example, a person who takes aspirin (Neptune) all the time may have kidneys that are clogged or in a state of spasm, not fully emptying out the poisons and toxins accumulated from the body. Hence, the material is passed back into the bloodstream, triggering headaches. Even if a person has never had ailments of the kidney, excessive intake of aspirin could suggest that the kidneys are a possible root cause of a problem, and they should be checked out.

Moreover, over-the-counter drugs can usually be replaced by medical herbs, which will do just as good a job, are more inexpensive and kinder on the body. For instance, sleeping pills bought from a drug store can be substituted with herbs such as valerian root, skullcap, hops or blue vervain — if the doctor agrees.[1]

11.   Are you presently taking natural vitamin supplements?

People will often try to figure out what vitamin supplements they need and supply them through a hit-and-miss method. Although sometimes they are fairly accurate about the deficiencies that exist in their bodies, most of the time they are not. A medical astrologer should especially check clients' intakes of vitamins A and D (both ruled by the Sun), since too much of the synthetic variety of these vitamins is toxic to the body. Futhermore, people with heart problems may be overdosing themselves with too much vitamin E, possibly causing further heart palpitations

---

[1]Insomnia usually is a symptom pointing to a more severe disturbance. A calcium imbalance of the parathyroid gland (Saturn), known as tetany, can cause sleeplessness. Or a hypothyroid (Mercury and Taurus) may be suspect. A severe deficiency of zinc (Jupiter) can also cause sleepless nights. The reasons for sleeplessness may depend upon what a natal chart yields in the way of information.

or problems. Or they may be taking ferrous iron with vitamin E, automatically cancelling one nutrient out with the other. And people will frequently take one of the B vitamins by itself, thereby creating an imbalance of the entire B complex in the body.

12. Any side effects or benefits from 11?

It is not surprising that many people who take heavy dosages of vitamin supplements do not feel any change from their previous conditions, when they were not taking vitamins. This lack of change may be caused by some toxicity within the body. Other people on first taking vitamins may feel mildly uplifted and then sluggish once again. And some people benefit greatly, only because their bodies are relatively healthy to begin with.

13. How long have you been taking vitamins?

It's imperative to know the length of time a person has had the advantage of supplements. Over a year's time a body can make a comeback with this extra source of food that is not derived from our usual overprocessed, nonroughage foods.

14. Have you ever had any operations?

Knowing the operations a person has had can supply a medical astrologer with important information. For example, one of the most common operation is a tonsilectomy, which means that the body has been robbed of one of its defense systems against virus and bacteria. Or a woman may have had a hysterectomy for a variety of reasons, ranging from cancer of the cervix or uterus to cysts forming in that area of the uterus: a medical astrologer should pay attention to the reasons behind the operation. Furthermore, a person may have had a gallbladder taken out yet not be on a bile tablet of any kind: such a situation presents a detriment for the digestive process, inhibiting the breakdown of fat soluble foods and possibly giving the person intermittent constipation and/or diarrhea.

15. Have you ever had or do you presently have any of the following ailments?

heart problems	menstrual problems
sugar problems	digestive disturbances
constipation	endocrine problems
diarrhea	high blood pressure
nervous disorders	kidney ailments
dizziness	urinary disorders
blood problems	headaches

This is an essential check list that will steer a medical astrologer in the right direction of the root cause of the medical problems, even though many of the ailments listed above are symptoms and not the actual causes. For instance, dizziness may be attributed to high blood pressure, middle ear infection, toxicity of the colon or kidneys or several other causes. Headaches may point to digestive disturbances, kidney malfunction or a sluggish colon. Constipation is a good clue that the digestive system is not working properly: there may be a missing link that is not being formed somewhere in the chain; there may be too little bile being dispensed by a sluggish gallbladder that may be corroded with mucus or calculi; certain enzymes manufactured by the liver may be defunct; or there may be too little hydrochloric acid being manufactured in the stomach to break down food. Diarrhea can point to too much hydrochloric acid in the stomach or the lack of certain digestive juices in the duodenum to make chyme (partly digested food and gastric secretions) so that chyme literally does not run through the intestinal tract, or if it does, very few of the vitamins and minerals are absorbed through the lining for use by the body. This phenomenon, called diarrhea, can cause loss of electrolytes and dehydration—especially dangerous to babies and young children.

Height, weight and age

These figures will tell a medical astrologer if a person is at a comfortable weight for his or her age and height. Excess weight can point to possible endocrine problems, kidney elimination dysfunction or just plain overeating of sugars, sweets and carbohydrates.

THE NATAL AND PROGRESSED CHARTS

After a client has filled out the medical questionnaire, a medical astrologer examines the person's natal chart to locate possible areas of physical weakness.

Vitamins and Minerals

The first step involves determining potential vitamin and mineral deficiencies. If a person is on a good, natural diet, chances are that there will be minimal or nonexistent deficiencies; however, because most people live in cities, caught up in pressured lifestyles, they have diets containing nitrites, preprocessed and prepackaged foods that will create some deficiencies.

To ascertain the potential vitamin and mineral deficiencies, a medical astrologer looks at each of the planets to see how many hard aspects are present. A ten-degree orb is allowed for any hard aspect involving the Sun or Moon. The rest of the planets are allowed up to a seven-degree orb, although the smaller the orb the more likelihood of deficiencies. Tight orbs of three or fewer degrees strongly indicate "action" because of the strength inherent between the two planets and because of the amount of stress they are placing on the body.

The first question is: "What planets aspect the natal Sun?" In the chart reproduced in Figure 2 the Sun is square the Moon and conjunct Mercury.

The next question is: "How many hard aspects are there to the Moon?" In the chart in Figure 2 the Moon is inconjunct Pluto, Mars and Neptune, thus forming a double yod configuration, a very stressful pattern. Furthermore, both Mars and Pluto are in the Twelfth House, which rules health matters—a placement that should be noted.

Then the medical astrologer finds out the hard aspects of the other planets. In the sample chart Mercury is inconjunct Jupiter, Venus is square Neptune, Mars is conjunct Pluto, Jupiter is square Saturn, and there are no hard aspects between Uranus and Neptune and Uranus and Pluto.

Next, looking at all the planets represented, a medical astrologer counts the hard aspects in the following way, writing the information down on a work sheet such as that reproduced in Figure 3:

Su - 2 Ju - 2 Mo - 4 Sa - 1 Me - 2 Ur - 0 Ve - 1 Ne - 2 Ma - 1 Pl - 2

At this point the medical astrologer should take note of which planets have the most hard aspects to them. The planets with the highest number of hard aspects are suspect of creating deficiencies within the body if dietary needs are not adequately met. The planets with lower numbers of hard aspects usually hint at mild deficiencies that can be corrected with proper eating habits and do not necessarily require supplementation. And planets with no hard aspects must be scrutinized closely because they may be fully responsible for deficiencies. To know which planet rules what vitamins and minerals, see Figure 4.

Figure 2
FEMALE NATAL CHART

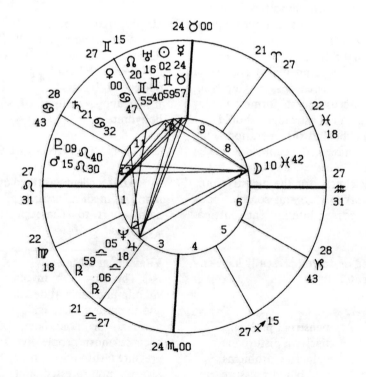

WORK SHEET

Height _____ Weight _____ Age _____

(If you have a copy of natal chart, please enclose copy)

ASPECTS   PLANETS

Birth data:

Date:_____

Time _____ a.m. or p.m. (circle one)

City/State _____

CROSS   CELL SALTS

_____

_____

_____

Dose: _____

_____

PARTS OF BODY INDICATED:

POSSIBLE TESTS INDICATED:

Cholecystography: _____

IVP (Kidney): _____

Upper GI: _____

Colon (Barium Enema): _____

Chem. Screening (SMA): _____

  (blood) 12-16-20

Five-Hour Glucose: _____

T-3, T-4, T-7: _____(Thyroid)

17-Ketosteroids: _____(Adrenals)

BUN: _____Serum Creatinine: _____

Liver Profile: _____

SGOT: _____(Cardiac)

Lipoprotein/electrophoresis: _____

Total Lipids:_____(Cholesterol)

CBC: _____(complete blood count)

Sodium/Potassium: _____

Thymus: _____

Other: _____

SUGGESTED SUPPLEMENTS:

SUGGESTED DIET:

HERBS:

HOMEOPATHIC REMEDIES:

JUICE THERAPY:

COMMENTS:

Detoxify _____

or Begin Vitamin Therapy _____

OTHER:

Bath _____

Foot Massage _____

Massotherapist _____

Nutrition Almanac _____

DRUGS TAKEN:

Overdose _____

Adverse Reaction _____

Test _____

Figure 3
MED-SCAN WORK SHEET

Figure 4
RULERSHIPS OF VITAMINS AND MINERALS

Sun:
Iodine
Magnesium
Vitamin A/D

Moon:
Potassium
Vitamin B-2
  (Riboflavin)

Mercury:
Vitamin B-1
  (Thiamine)

Venus:
Copper
Niacin
Vitamin E
  (d-alpha tocopherol)

Mars:
Cobalt
Chlorine
Folic Acid
Iron
Molybdenum
Phosphorus
Selenium
Sodium
Vitamin B-12
Vitamin F

Jupiter:
Biotin
Cholin
Chromium

Inositol
Manganese
Vitamin B-6
Vitamin B-15
Zinc

Saturn:
Calcium
Fluorine
PABA
Sulfur
Vanadium
Vitamin C
Vitamin K
Vitamin P
  (bioflavonoids)

Uranus:
No rulerships

Neptune:
Laetrile (B-17)
Pantothenic Acid

Pluto:
B-13 (Orotic Acid)

Poisonous Metals:
Aluminum — Neptune
Beryllium — Mars
Cadmium — Saturn
Lead — Saturn
Mercury — Saturn

In the chart example in Figure 2 the Moon has the most hard aspects to it. The planets with two hard aspects are also suspect of creating moderate deficiency potentials and should be included in the notations as well. The medical astrologer then puts the planets down in the following order:

Moon: potassium and riboflavin. Sun: vitamins A and D, magnesium and iodine. Mercury: thiamine. Jupiter: vitamin B-6, cholin, inositol, biotin, sulfur, manganese, chromium, zinc and pangamic acid. Neptune: pantothenic acid and laetrile. Pluto: orotic acid.

Thus there is the potential for this person to be deficient in one or more of these vitamins and minerals—but not all of them. To eliminate the weaker possibilities a medical astrologer should consult the chapters on vitamins and minerals and read the list of deficiency symptoms for each vitamin and mineral. If the person's symptoms fit one or more of the deficiency symptoms, the information should be written down for later reference.

Some of the potential deficiencies can be dismissed or assumed to be neglibible almost at once. For example, it is very rare that a person has a deficiency of laetrile or orotic acid. With such deficiencies a person would be suspect of contracting cancer or multiple sclerosis. And if an individual does not exhibit signs of either illness after proper testing by a doctor, these potential deficiencies can be overlooked because there is no proof for them to be considered.

Deficiencies of fluorine, cobalt, molybdenum, phosphorus, selenium and chlorine are also quite rare. And a person should first be tested for any such deficiencies before taking supplements because these minerals can have toxic side effects in many cases.

Next, a person's medical history should be examined. The medical history of the woman whose chart is reproduced in Figure 2 is as follows:

Age 5: Rheumatic fever that left a heart murmur until she was 12 years old. Age 6: Scarlet fever that left her kidneys weak. Age 9: Yellow jaundice that caused malfunction of her liver. Ages 21-23: Monthly bouts with cystitis or bladder infections plus kidney infections that resulted in "kidney ache" and her having to drink a lot of liquids. Ages 21-26: She took birth control pills. She finally quit taking them because they gave her a hyperthyroid and hypoglycemia. The thyroid and pancreas were affected by the pills but malfunction very slightly today because she watches her diet carefully.

Using the chapters on vitamins and minerals, a medical astrologer then matches the findings of potential nutritional deficiencies against a person's medical history. The example chart in Figure 2 indicates that this woman is potentially deficient in several vitamins and minerals:

Potassium: A person normally has a weight increase, edema, weakness in the female organs, low grade infections in the bladder or constriction of the urethra tube with a deficiency of potassium. Other, more serious signals are the inability to digest sugar, stomach distension and impaired kidney function. This woman's past medical history shows severe bouts with bladder and kidney infections. So, potassium should be noted as a needed mineral.

Riboflavin: Mild symptoms of insufficient riboflavin are cracks and sores at the corners of the mouth and skin problems. Hypoglycemia may also develop. Furthermore, without enough riboflavin and pantothenic acid yellow jaundice can occur. Since her past medical history shows both yellow jaundice and hypoglycemia, riboflavin should be marked down as a needed supplement.

Vitamins A and D: Night blindness and frequent bouts of respiratory ailments, such as chest colds and pneumonia, are often symptoms of deficiencies of vitamins A and D. Since her medical record shows very poor eyesight and an inability for her eyes to adjust quickly to darkness, a small supplement of these vitamins should be considered to aid in clearing up her visual problems.

Magnesium: Sensitivity to noise, a continual state of depression and heart palpitations are normal signals of a lack of magnesium. Since she has none of these symptoms, the possibility that this nutrient is deficient should be disregarded.

Iodine: A deficiency of iodine is usually felt in the thyroid: anyone with a hyper-or hypothyroid is suspect of a lack of iodine. After taking birth control pills this woman had poor thyroid function; subsequently, she received medication containing iodine in it to force the thyroid to work normally.

Vitamin B-6 and chromium: There are numerous symptoms of a deficiency of vitamin B-6, including hypoglycemia and diabetes. Chromium is also linked with sugar-related problems. Since this woman has a hypoglycemic condition, both the vitamin and mineral should be marked down as being needed.

Cholin, inositol and biotin: It is nearly impossible to get a deficiency of biotin unless one consumes a large number of raw eggs: then, hair will generally fall out, and skin problems will arise. Both cholin and inositol are connected with the making of lecithin within the body. Gallbladder problems, high cholesterol count and several other symptoms must be present to consider these vitamins deficient. The woman has no history of digestive problems, nor does she exhibit skin or hair problems; therefore, these three vitamins should not be considered lacking.

Pangamic acid: Symptoms of diminished oxygen in the body, causing heart strain or atherosclerosis, are normally associated with a deficiency of this vitamin. Although this woman has a heart murmur, it was the consequence of rheumatic fever at an early age and has nothing to do with the oxygenation process in her body. The vitamin should not be considered lacking.

Sulfur: Problems with the hair, skin and nails are the common signals for insufficient sulfur. Since this woman has no known history of these kind of health problems, sulfur should not be considered deficient.

Manganese: Mental gyrations, depression and diabetes can be signals that this nutrient is needed. Since this woman has hypoglycemia, the oppposite of diabetes, this mineral should not be considered deficient.

Pantothenic acid: Among numerous other symptoms adrenal exhaustion can occur when this vitamin is lacking, perhaps causing a hypoglycemic problem. Because this woman suffers from hypoglycemia, this vitamin should be marked down as needed to help the condition.

Laetrile: Laetrile is only linked with cancer. She has no past family hstory of cancer on either the mother's or the father's side; therefore, this vitamin should not be considered.

Orotic acid: Liver disorders, cell degeneration and premature aging are symptoms of a deficiency of this vitamin. Having contracted yellow jaundice, she may be suspect of needing this nutrient, and it should be marked down.

Physical Weak Spots

Once the vitamin and mineral deficiencies have been determined, a medical astrologer hunts for physical weak spots in the body—that is, possibilities of physical debility that are increased or modified depending upon hereditary, environment and dietary habits. The house and sign positions of Mars, Saturn, Uranus, Neptune and sometimes Pluto are especially important in ascertaining potential weak areas of the body. And if one of these planets is retrograde, a medical astrologer should pay special attention to it. A retrograde motion indicates that the planet and the sign it is in are probably more influential in terms of health than are the other planets that are direct. Moreover, if one of these planets goes retrograde during a person's lifetime, via secondary progressions, there is a chance that it will be implicated in the manifestation of a physical problem.

Following are the sign positions of the medical planets in the chart in Figure 2.

Mars in Leo: Ruling the heart, Leo can be implicated in such disorders as heart murmurs, rheumatic or scarlet fever, palpitations, a racing heart, pains in the chest and arms and a heart attack. Since this woman has had several of these ailments, the information should be written down. Moreover, the vitamins and minerals that Mars rules may play an important part in correcting some of these ailments. For instance, Mars rules iron, and too little iron can help produce anemia, which can cause the heart to work overtime to compensate. In the long run this situation could weaken the heart and perhaps shorten a life span.

Other factors in the chart can help pinpoint what this woman needs to aid her heart and keep it strong. For example, Mars conjunct Pluto hints that she has a larger-than-normal need for all Mars-ruled nutrients. Another mineral that helps the heart maintain its steady beat is potassium, and Mars is inconjunct the Moon, ruler of that nutrient. It is obvious at this point that the woman should undergo physician's tests to corroborate the findings that she probably needs such nutrients as vitamin B-12, iron and potassium.

Saturn in Cancer: Cancer rules the stomach and its numerous digestive phases plus the covering surrounding the liver. This woman had yellow jaundice (hepatitis, inflammation of the liver of a viral or toxic origin) at age nine. It took twelve years for the yellowish cast to disappear from her normally ruddy complexion. Thus this is probably an active health configuration in her chart.

Uranus in Gemini: This placement points toward possible spasms or constricture of the tubes of the body — i.e., the eustachian tubes of the ears, bronchial tubes of the lungs, ureter tubes that extend from the kidneys to the bladder, the fallopian tubes in a woman and the urethra tube from the bladder to the outside opening in the body and the cerebrospinal system. The lungs, arms and hands are also ruled by Gemini.

This is obviously an active health configuration in this chart. The woman suffered major ear infections as a child, had numerous lung and chest colds and had to have her tonsils removed at the age of one. Chest colds continued to plague her through young adulthood, and she had two bouts with pneumonia later in life. She also suffered constantly from cuts and bruises to her hands and arms. Later, when she had trouble with bladder infections, the urethra had to be stretched on four separate occasions to allow passage of the urine.

Neptune in Libra retrograde: Libra rules the eliminative organs, the kidneys. During her bout with scarlet fever, this woman sustained injury to the kidneys in the form of nephritis, an inflammatory condition. Thereafter, when under emotional stress, she would complain of lower back pain, particularly in the area of the right kidney. The bladder infections (cystitis) aggravated the kidneys, and at that time she

began herbal treatments for both problems. Within a month after treatment her troubles with her bladder and kidneys ceased. She now takes an herbal tincture to help the kidneys function to their capacity and has had no further complications.

Pluto in Leo: Mars conjnct Pluto in the Twelfth House indicates potential problems with the adrenal glands. And hypoglycemia, one of this woman's problems, is the result of the adrenal glands being placed under tremendous and sustained stress.

The Activated Cross

The next step in examining a natal chart is deciding which cross is activated according to the person's medical history and present symptomatology. Determining the cross helps corroborate the findings on the potential vitamin and mineral deficiencies and helps establish what ailments are most likely to occur from such deficiencies. For instance, a person who has hypoglycemia (usually a Mutable Cross occurrence) will probably have a high number of hard aspects of Jupiter, which rules vitamin B-6 and chromium, both necessary nutrients for the pancreas to function properly. Or a person with a hypothyroid condition (Taurus) may have several hard aspects to the Sun, which rules iodine: an iodine deficiency can cause the thyroid to fluctuate.

In the chart reproduced in Figure 2 there is a double-cross phenomenon—that is, two crosses are activated. The main cross centers on the mutable signs of Pisces, Gemini and Virgo. The bulk of this woman's ailments comes from these signs—specifically, the long bouts with colds, viruses and flu (Pisces); lung congestion as a child and later pneumonia (Gemini); and hypoglycemia, a pancreas ailment (Virgo). The second, less strongly activated cross consists of the cardinal signs. The planets in Libra have contributed towards such ailments as nephritis, cystitis and lower backaches caused by the kidneys. The woman has exhibited no other manifestations of diseases usually associated with the Cardinal Cross.

On the other hand, the Fixed Cross seems to be least activated in this woman's chart: it appears to be giving her the fewest number of continual problems. Granted, the heart murmur, caused by rheumatic fever, falls under the domain of Leo; however, her heart problems can be explained by other factors in the chart, such as the fact that Pluto is at a critical health degree in Leo. (See the next section.) And although she has also exhibited another symptom of this particular cross—thyroid problems—the thyroid condition resulted from her taking birth control pills, and within a year after she had stopped taking the pills her thyroid returned to normal.

A double-cross such as this usually means that an intricately balanced diet will be necessary. In this case a good diet would include fewer dairy products (Cardinal Cross) to keep the kidney tubules unplugged and functioning well plus a diet lower in meat and containing more fresh fruits and vegetables (Mutable Cross). The high vitamin and mineral content of such a diet would help the immunity system improve its defense of the body against foreign invaders as well as provide natural sugar to improve the functioning of the pancreas.

Critical Degrees

In addition, a medical astrologer should examine the natal chart to see if any planets are at certain critical degrees, thereby accentuating the possibilities of disease. Throughout the ages certain degrees have been thought to possess extraordinary sensitivity, making an individual either prone to greatness or problems, depending upon which planet is involved and the aspects to it. Although much more research needs to be conducted, there also seems to be a correlation between diseases and the critical degrees listed below:

Cardinal signs—13 and 26 degrees Fixed signs—9 and 21 degrees Mutable signs—4 and 17 degrees

To ascertain if a criticial degree is involved in a health problem, a medical astrologer should check each planet as well as the Ascendant and the Midheaven for critical degrees. If a planet, the Ascendant or the Midheaven is found in a critical degree, the position, the hard aspects involved and the eventual importance or weakness of the critical degree to the entire medical picture should be noted. For example, in the chart in Figure 2 Pluto is at 9 degrees Leo in the Twelfth House with a hard aspect to Mars. This is a pretty good indication that Leo, ruling the heart and the cardiovascular system, will be implicated in health situations. As we know, this woman has suffered from a heart murmur. And since the background information matches the potential problems indicated by the placement of the critical degree, a medical astrologer can be reasonably certain that Pluto at 9 Leo may someday reactivate if preventative health measures aren't taken to minimize its probable manifestation.

Progressions, Transits and Eclipses

Finally, a medical astrologer should look at the dates of all progressions, transits and eclipses. These dates can help indicate the time of a health crisis, thereby giving a medical astrologer lead time to get a person into a healthy state before the progression,

transit or eclipse worsens health. The dates of past progressions, transits and eclipses should also be examined to see if there is agreement between those dates and the onset of past illnesses.

A progressed chart, erected on the 90-degree dial, should be constructed to include the Uranian planets, which should then be progressed via solar arc. A medical astrologer should check to see if any progressed planets will conjunct natal planets. If so, the dates and appropriate comments should be noted. The dates that the progressions of the "malefic" planets will conjunct natal planets should be especially recorded. Then any progressed planets within six months of a 30-minute orb of a natal planet should be checked, with the dates recorded.

When examining transits in a 360-degree chart, a medical astrologer should especially scrutinize the transits of Saturn, Uranus, Neptune and Pluto to any natal planet or the First House cusp. Are they traversing the Sixth or Twelfth Houses? Are they conjunct or opposite natal planets in those houses? If so, the dates of the hard aspects should be noted: these times can be interpreted as periods of potential illness. And Saturn transiting over the Ascendant can indicate a time when a health problem may come to light.

In addition, the midpoint structures, otherwise known as "trees," should be checked out in the natal and progressed charts. Are there any health pictures? Are there any solar arc progressed planets hitting midpoints in any of these pictures? Transits over these midpoint structures should be examined and the times of conjunctions and oppositions for progressed and transiting planets recorded. The outer four planets as well as Mars are normally the most important in considering midpoint structures. (See Chapter Four.)

Then the eclipses should be checked. Do they hit malefic planets or occur in the Sixth or Twelfth Houses? Is so, the dates should be noted, with three months added to those times to get the fallout dates for when these eclipses will probably manifest into physical ailments.

PHYSICIAN'S TESTS

After cross-referencing a person's past and present symptoms against the potential nutritional deficiencies and physical weak spots indicated in natal and progressed charts, a medical astrologer must ask the client to go to a phsycian to get the proper tests to prove these assumptions.

There are several common tests that a person can ask for to check out the findings in a natal chart, but before describing these tests I would like to discuss the best approach for an individual to take with a doctor. How does a client go about getting the physician's help? Although nowadays the mood is shifting to more bilateral relationships between patients and doctors, and doctors are making more efforts to communicate with patients, some doctors still take great affront that patients will walk in and ask by name for certain tests. Such doctors get their pride hurt, still believing the old myth that patients are not supposed to know anything about medical terminology. But by taking certain tactful steps a person can get almost any doctor to acquiesce to the requests for tests.

First, a patient should be prepared when going in to see a doctor about tests. Before going to the doctor's office, a patient should tell the doctor he or she wants to take the time to discuss a condition. Unfortunately, many doctors run patients through like cattle in a livestock yard, flitting from one patient to another every five minutes and leaving very little time to discuss anything of consequence. A person should impress upon the receptionist that he or she wants at least 15 minutes or half an hour of the doctor's time. If the doctor says such time is impossible, the person should find another doctor by consulting the telephone directory, contacting the medical society and explaining the problem to the secretary, who may know of a doctor who takes time with patients: homeopathic doctors take up to two hours in the first session with a patient.

A patient should also have studied all aspects of his or her ailment before going to a doctor's office. Such knowledge shows a doctor that a patient cares about health and is willing to take the responsibility of learning more about bodily functions. A patient should have a list of all symptoms written down before going to the office, even symptoms that may seem silly or of no consequence: a sharp doctor will be able to use those clues to track down an ailment.

In addition, a patient should let a doctor know what kinds of vitamins, minerals, herbs, cell salts or homeopathic remedies he or she plans to try, discussing each of them with the doctor in detail and having a reason for taking each of them. A patient needs to listen to what a doctor feels about this contemplated program. If a doctor is steeped in nutritional knowledge, he or she may retailor the program slightly: the patient should take the doctor's advice.

It does no one any good to *tell* a doctor anything. He or she has spent at least eight years learning a specialty. To have a layperson tell a doctor what to do is akin to outright insult. It is best to let a doctor *think* it is his or her idea. A patient needs to be diplomatic, helpful and undefensive. If there is a specific problem involved, such as a thyroid disorder, a patient should bring a book on the subject along and

ask the doctor what he or she thinks about performing a test to see if the thyroid is, indeed, malfunctioning. Or a patient might try a white lie, saying that a friend who is a registered nurse had suggested a talk with a doctor about a thyroid test. Most doctors will respond to such diplomatic maneuvers. The patient has left the decisions in the doctor's hands.

If a doctor refuses to give a test, however, a patient has no alternative but to find another doctor. Many times a chiropracter or a doctor of osteopathy is the best choice. Both are licensed to give a wide array of laboratory tests.

A person will also stand a good chance of getting a test run with an orthmolecular doctor. To find such a doctor in a particular area, a person can write or telephone:

The Orthomolecular Society 2698 Pacific Avenue San Francisco, CA 94115 (415) 346-5692.

Such professionals deal in the holistic treatment of the body. They are much more open-minded than most doctors about drugless therapy. The definition of the brand of medicine they practice is that when nutritional needs are met, there will be the erradication of a disease through manipulation of bodily chemistry.

Following are some of the various tests that a medical astrologer might suggest be performed.

Cholecystography

This test is run when a gallstone or partial blockage of the bile duct is possible. An iodine dye is given orally for absorption and concentration of the dye to settle in the gallbladder. An X-ray of the organ is then taken the next morning to discern stones of either cholesterol or calcium. Since fewer than 50 per cent of gallstones are calcified, they are not easily picked up on X-ray. Another test, which would have to be decided upon by a doctor, is the intravenous cholangiography (IVC), given by feeding iodine intravenously. In most cases, though, the oral ingestion of iodine works.

Upper GI

This test checks out the gastrointestinal tract with the use of ingested barium. With this test the esophagus can be studied, ulcers in the stomach or duodenum can be discerned or a hiatal hernia discovered. The test may be conducted by having a patient swallow barium. The upper GI is not a test that should be done randomly: the dangers of taking barium are well-known to any doctor, and reaction to the dye is possible.

Barium Enema

Ulcers, a spastic colon or tumors in the large intestine are found through a barium enema. Other conditions, such as colitis, diverticular disease, unknown inflammation or bacterial infections, can also be spotted with this test.

IVP

The intravenous pyelogram (IVP) is taken when renal problems are suspected, including problems with the kidneys, ureters and the bladder. Dye is injected into the body, and then X-rays are taken of the abdomen to determine the health of the organs. Such ailments as kidney stones, cysts, obstruction in the ureter tube, tumors or other bladder abnormalities will show up.

SMA

This is a series of blood chemistry tests, usually consisting of 12, 16 or 20 various tests. A doctor may run an SMA as a matter of course to determine how the bodily functions are generally performing.

Five-Hour Glucose Test

This is a common test for anyone who suspects he or she may have hypoglycemia or low blood sugar. It is also used to determine diabetes mellitus and many other sugar-related ailments. An individual consumes a small amount of sugar in liquid form. A vial of blood is drawn once before this ingestion of sugar and five times on the hour thereafter. It's a boring test, and a patient will have to wait six hours in a hospital or doctor's office; so, he or she should take along plenty of reading material.

In the long run, though, the test is worth the time and effort. And it's important that an individual undergo the five-hour test. A doctor may try to talk a patient into a simple two- or three-hour blood test to determine the glucose level. But a hypoglycemic, in particular, may not start showing a problem until the fourth, fifth or even sixth hour.

A patient should also make sure that the test results are properly read. I've seen several five-hour glucose test results misread by lab people and doctors. Every once in a while the curve will vary, making a doctor think that a patient is "normal" My suggestion is that a person should get a couple of doctors or lab technicians to read the results. The head of a lab at a large hospital is frequently the best person to consult, since he or she will have had plenty of experience reading odd tolerance curves. If the test does come out "low normal," the person is slightly hypoglycemic and should get on a commensurate diet to relieve the symptoms.

T-3, T-4, T-7 Test

This is a standard thyroid test, a simple blood test to determine whether or not the thyroid gland is hyper, hypo or normal. Although this test is accurate, it may not give the full picture about an ailing thyroid. If a person registers "high normal," the thyroid is slightly hyper; if "low normal," the thyroid is slightly hypo. In many instances a person who is very sensitive to bodily functions doesn't need to be "out" completely to have all the symptoms and backlash of a malfunctioning gland.

This test, or one similar to it, should be given to all newborn infants. In Canada it's a law that such a test be performed to determine that an infant does not have a hypothyroid that could lead to cretinism. If a woman has just delivered a baby, she should request the test. No mother wants retardation of her child a year after birth because a simple blood test was not performed.

17-Ketosteroid Test

Anytime an adrenal gland malfunction is suspected, this 24-hour urine test is performed. It is a relatively common test that any doctor can run; however, for best results an endocrinologist should be seen for any other extensive lab work-ups involving this gland.[2]

BUN Test

The blood-urea nitrogen is raised in cases involving pre- or postrenal or kidney failure. With congestive heart failure the blood supply to the renal system may be adversely affected and reflected by a rise in the BUN test. It may be raised if the glomerulic filtering system of the kidneys are partially blocked. With prostrate gland obstructions the BUN may be raised. Borderline elevations sometimes accompany high protein intake.

Serum Creatinine Test

This is an index of renal function sensitive to early renal damage. The creatinine clearance test not only detects early kidney damage but is useful in monitoring the course of renal disease. Between the BUN and

[2]For a test on the endocrine glands, though, it might be best to consult an endocrinologist because most doctors have little knowledge in that area. That is not to say other doctors can't do the tests. A patient should ask a doctor if he or she is familiar with such tests as a 17-Ketosteroid test. If the doctor is and agrees to run it, the patient can have it done at that office.

the serum creatinine tests a doctor can have a good picture of how the entire renal system is operating.

Liver Profile Test

This is a test that encompasses many other tests. It is chiefly used to ascertain the levels of bilirubin in the circulation: in cases of jaundice the bilirubin leaves the blood and moves into the tissue, turning the skin yellow. The test can also determine if there is blockage within the ducts of the liver or if there is injury to that organ from viruses, toxins, drugs or alcohol. Enzyme functions can also be tested. The serum protein test, a part of the profile, is an excellent test to determine liver disease in general.

SGOT Test

Anyone with suspected heart ailments should have this test. The SGOT is elevated in certain heart, liver and skeletal diseases following myocardinal infarction, obstructive jaundice and muscular dystrophy.

Lipoprotein/Electrophoresis Tests

This particular group of tests helps determine some of the following conditions: tumor masses within the bone marrow (multiple myeloma), Hodgkin's disease, leukemic conditions, tuberculosis, brucellosis, collagen ailments such as rheumatoid athritis, hepatitis and liver diseases.

Total Lipid Test

This test determines the amount of cholesterol in the body. Elevated cholesterol levels, of course, contribute to coronary diseases. Other ailments, such as gallbladder obstruction and untreated diabetes mellitus, can also hike the amount of cholesterol in the blood. In addition, liver disease, kidney malfunction and thyroid and pancreatic dysfunction can raise the cholesterol levels. On the other hand, low cholesterol levels can be reflected in bad dietary habits, liver disease, hyperthyroidism, blood poisoning and anemia.

CBC Test

The complete blood count test (CBC) helps to discern anemia and polycythemia. In addition, the CBC may suggest inflammation, leukemia, bone marrow failure and platlet problems. The smears also show malaria parasites and other abnormalities.

Sodium/Potassium Test

This test is used to indicate the balance between sodium and potassium in the body. If sodium is high, a person is usually water-retentive or has edema in some part of the body. Although it's rare that a person has elevated levels of potassium, high levels are a signal that further testing should be undertaken.

Serum Calcium Test

This is a simple blood test that measures the amounts of calcium being circulated within the body. It is helpful in ascertaining whether or not the parathyroid gland is hyper- or hypofunctioning. Anyone who suspects such a condition should see an endocrinologist.

NUTRITIONAL SUPPLEMENTS

After physician's tests have confirmed which vitamins and minerals are indeed deficient, a medical astrologer in cooperation with the doctor must work out a program of suggested nutritional supplements that will be best for the person involved. And the medical astrologer must decide in what form the individual should take the nutrients.

As I've already indicated, not all people can absorb synthetic nutrients well. To see if a person can absorb nutrients properly, a medical astrologer should check the Jupiter-Saturn relationship in a natal chart. If these two planets are sextile or trine, a person can probably absorb synthetic nutrients with ease.

But if the planets are conjunct, inconjunct, square or opposite, a person probably has poor assimilation: a square or inconjunct, especially, may mean that anything synthetic will not be rapidly recovered by the body's mechanisms and will most likely be sloughed off in the urine or feces.

When such adverse aspects are present, a medical astrologer should determine if a person's stomach is functioning properly. If it is, then the person probably will absorb nutrients adequately, although the diet should be as natural as possible. If the stomach is showing signs of low levels of hydrochloric acid, enzyme deficiencies or problems with bile, an individual should have strictly natural supplementation and diet: absorption will probably be nill until the diet is straightened out over a six-month period. Moreover, whenever there is poor digestion, enzyme, bile or lecithin tablets should be considered, if the attending physician agrees. In this way vitamins and minerals can be broken down and utilized by the body instead of creating discomfort from gas.

In the example chart in Figure 2, Jupiter is square Saturn; so, this woman probably has difficulty assimilating any synthetic nutrients. Her chart matched against her history also indicates that she is deficient in several of the B vitamins as well as vitamins A and D. Therefore, it is necessary to find a natural way for her to get the needed vitamins instead of taking tablets.

Many people have problems taking a vitamin B

complex, multiple vitamin and mineral pills because they are poorly assimilated by the body. A good test to find out if someone is able to assimilate a synthetic vitamin B complex or multiple vitamin or mineral tablet is for the person to take the suggested dosage and wait four hours. At that time, if the urine is a bright, clear yellow (much more yellow than normal urine), the indication is that either the person doesn't need any of the vitamins or minerals or that the body did not assimilate them. Since with our food situation the way it is today we probably all need such vitamins and minerals, especially the vitamin B complex, the body probably did not absorb the nutrients—or very few of them. Then the individual should take one tablespoon of powdered brewer's yeast in a health drink and check the color of the urine four to six hours later. If it hasn't changed color, 100 per cent of the nutrients were absorbed by the body. If the urine is only slightly brighter, the body has used part of the nutrients and filtered off the rest because they were not needed.

One of the best ways to take the vitamin B complex in its natural state is brewer's yeast, which has all the B vitamins with the exception of pangamic acid and laetrile (B-17), neither of which this woman needs. Thus, providing she does not have an allergy to yeast, a medical astrologer should suggest that she take this form of the B vitamins, perhaps by placing one to two tablespoons of powdered brewer's yeast in a drink consisting of ½ cup natural apple juice, ½ cup natural grape juice and one banana. In this way, instead of having a handful of pills to take three times daily, the woman only needs to drink a health drink with brewer's yeast and take a vitamin A/D capsule of the fish liver oil perle type. Chances are she will more readily accept and assimilate this type of supplementation instead of numerous pills.

HOMEOPATHIC REMEDIES

A medical astrologer in cooperation with a homeopathic doctor may also recommend certain homeopathic remedies after tests have corroborated the findings in a natal chart. To determine the kinds and amounts of a remedy, a doctor examines a patient and carefully records all symptoms. Then, referring to the totality of symptoms, the doctor selects a remedy from the *Materia Medica*, a record of the effects of drugs upon healthy volunteers, embodying the knowledge of what drugs actually do when brought in contact with the functional activity of the body. The doctor then administers a single remedy, prescribing repetition of the dose as needed. Through experimentation and observation homeopaths have found that the smaller the dosage of a remedy, the

better its chances for effecting a cure. The reason is that the smaller the dose the less bodily resistance the drug must overcome before it can manifest its healing actions.

The theory of drugless dosage and therapy, of course, is in complete contradiction to the practices in allopathic medicine. In allopathy the remedy must first be high enough to overcome the natural defenses of the body and then still have enough strength left in it to fight the disease. Such a method of prescribing large doses of drugs can produce adverse side effects as well as bring on damage incurred to various parts of the body. But with a homeopathic prescription there can be no bodily resistance because the remedy being given is similar in makeup to the diseased environment that exists. The natural defenses are down since the disease has already begun work in the body. So, once the minute amount of the remedy enters the body, it can immediately begin to fight the disease and eventually get rid of it. Furthermore, the substances used by homeopaths are made of natural materials from the vegetable, animal and mineral kingdoms, rather than the synthetic materials employed by allopathic doctors.

Homeopathic remedies are made in a liquid, dry, soluble or insoluble state. Three different processes are used in the making of a remedy: trituration, solution and attenuation. The vehicles used for that purpose are sugar of milk or milk lactose, water and alcohol.

Milk lactose is used because its sharp, flinty crystals are especially useful in grinding down hard mineral substances. In addition, it is easily made into tablets, pellets or discs and can be made to absorb medicinal or alcoholic solutions as the case demands. Tablets made in a base of milk lactose melt instantly beneath the tongue and are absorbed through the tissue of the mouth with the help of saliva.

Alcohol is used in a wide array of medicines. Homeopathic pharmacies are especially careful to get only the finest and purest alcohol, usually containing 88 per cent ethyl alcohol. It is then used in the making of tinctures from substances that are completely or partially soluble in the liquid form. Fresh plants, barks, roots, seeds, gums and balsams are all placed in tincture form for use.

Distilled water is used as a solvent for many substances, especially solutions that contain acids. It is also used in converting triturations into liquid attenuations.

Aggravation may occur when a person takes a homeopathic dose. Such reaction can indicate one of two things: the dosage is either too potent (in which case other symptoms will probably appear) or it is the perfect remedy. There is frequently a backlash effect when the right remedy is used, but the aggravation is temporary. At that point the patient should do nothing further but wait for the disease to begin altering and eventually leave the body.

Here are a few rules that homeopaths follow during administration of a remedy:

1. Give one remedy at a time. Choose the one most identified with the recorded symptoms.

2. Choose a medium potency, such as 6X. If there are no results within six to twelve hours, move to a higher potency.

3. As long as improvement shows, do not change the remedy and do not repeat the dose. As long as the disease does not progress, there is no danger in waiting.

4. In sudden (acute) diseases, such as colds, flu and fever and hemorrhaging, repeat doses frequently, sometimes as often as every five or ten minutes until the symptoms cease and improvement in the condition is felt. Dosing once an hour is usually normal in most acute cases.

If other drugs have been used, it is advisable to wait a few days before trying to get a list of true symptoms. Then proper application of a homeopathic remedy can be pursued.

DIETS

The next step in the Med-Scan program is to determine a good diet for a client. One of the most important points that a medical astrologer should keep in mind is that every person has individual nutritional needs, and no one diet is going to be correct for everyone. Tailored diets are necessary, and they require the planning of a doctor or nutritionist who has a background in dietetics. Following are three of the possible diets a medical astrologer can suggest to a client.

Detoxification Diet

Many years ago Dr. John R. Christopher, M.H., wrote a small booklet entitled *Dr. Christopher's Three Day Cleansing Program and Mucousless Diet*. I tried the diet, and it worked. But trying to detoxify in three days puts a terrible strain on the body. Detoxification is like a jet that reverses its engines at full thrust: a lot of turbulence and backwash is created. But with detoxification the backwash occurs in the body, and toxins are violently stirred up, moving back into the bloodstream to be eliminated from the body. Since Dr. Christopher's method is so demanding on the body, I have substantially modified his program to make it easier on weakened individuals.

A person should begin this detoxification diet only if he or she is in relatively good health. And the diet should be initiated on a Friday, giving an individual a weekend to simply rest and sleep. When one detoxifies rapidly, the body is fighting an internal war and needs to slow down and rest a great deal so that it can do its duties. It's not uncommon to sleep several hours during the day plus all night with this diet.

The first step in my modified detoxification program is to have a person cut back on mucousproducing foods, which are a constant threat to the body. Mucus clogs everything: people who drink more than one cup of milk daily very often have either clogged sinuses or a continual sinus drip. Besides milk, cheese is the biggest problem for an adult. Over a month's time an individual must gradually cut back on the consumption of milk and cheese as well as white sugar, salt, starch foods and white flour products.

At the same time the person probably needs to cut down on the amounts of meat he or she eats. I'm an advocate of meat eating for some people: certain individuals don't fare well without it, whereas others do better without it or with a limited intake. But most Americans eat too much meat. Meat should be eaten sparingly. For instance, if a person is used to having meat every night, he or she should think about having two meatless meals a week. And heavy meats, such as beef and pork, should be avoided: for heavy meats to be truly digested, the gastric secretions of the stomach must be at optimum strength, and I have rarely encountered a healthy gastric system in any person today because our eating habits have deteriorated gastric secretions. If an individual is a heavy meat eater, he or she should limit the intake of such meat to one steak (six to eight ounces) every other week. Instead, he or she should eat chicken, Cornish game hens, turkey, fish and shell fish. The person should also eat more fresh vegetables and fruits, perhaps steaming the vegetables lightly so that they are semicooked.

As part of this detoxification diet, an individual should drink eight to sixteen ounces of a natural fruit juice three times a day, including the morning. Such drinks are good sources of vitamins and minerals. They also help the kidneys cleanse themselves. *Natural* means that the juice has not been strained, boiled or pasteurized: hand-squeezed juice is best. A natural fruit juice will be very murky or cloudy because of the unstrained or semistrained contents still left in the juice. Lime, lemon or orange juice may be used, providing the stomach can tolerate the citrus: some people's stomachs cannot take such diuretic juices because of a lack of gastric secretions.

Another important ingredient of this detoxification diet is apple cider vinegar. But not everyone can tolerate apple cider vinegar. Many people do not have enough gastric secretions to digest the vinegar readily. Some people (about 20 per cent) suffer from nausea, bloating, a burning sensation or other uncomfortable side effects from the consumption of vinegar.

But for those who can consume it apple cider vinegar is a marvelous food. When it has not been boiled, strained or pasteurized, it contains large amounts of malic acid and potassium. Upon hitting the stomach, malic acid turns alkaline. Thus for people with acidosis, vinegar can reestablish the acid-alkaline balance. In addition, the potassium value is extraordinary for people with a deficiency in that mineral. Potassium starved individuals usually have edema: many women with water weight problems are deficient in potassium. Drinking the vinegar will correct the metabolism between potassium and sodium.

The vinegar will also act as a diuretic, causing people to lose water weight. It's nature's diet pill. When beginning on the vinegar, some people will lose from ¼ to ½ pound a day, especially those with potassium-sodium imbalances. I've known some people to lose up to three pounds of water a day on vinegar alone. In one case a woman who weighed 300 pounds lost 150 pounds in six months just drinking vinegar.

Many people will have to gradually get used to vinegar, acquiring a taste for it as they would for beer or champagne. If people can tolerate it, vinegar is best plain in water—two tablespoons in an eight-ounce glass of warm or cold water. But for people who don't like the taste of vinegar, one tablespoon of honey may be added as sweetener.

Before beginning to drink vinegar a person should make sure that his or her kidneys are in good shape and then slowly move into the program. For the first week, to begin getting used to the vinegar, an individual should simply sip one eight-ounce glass throughout the day. This method usually gets that 20 per cent of people who have initial adverse reactions to vinegar over their aversions to the substance. After the body gets used to this valuable food, a person who is no more than 20 pounds overweight can drink up to three glasses daily for the first month.

After the kidneys are prepped an individual should drink one glass of vinegar daily for one to three months, depending upon the severity of edema and the doctor's discretion. Then for general maintenance he or she should probably consume only a glass every other day for another six months. As the body is cleansed, a person needs less and less of everything so that by the end of the year he or she may only be taking one glass of vinegar per week,

depending on each individual's needs and the doctor's suggestions. Drinking too much vinegar can render a body more alkaline than acidic, eventually causing just as many health problems as before.

In fact, an individual who is 30 to 150 pounds overweight should drink no more than one to one and a half glasses of vinegar daily, because more than that amount will put extreme demand and stress on the kidneys to get rid of the excess water. I will frequently ask the doctor monitoring the situation to place such a person on tincture of hydrangea for one month before the patient goes on the vinegar: since hydrangea is a poisonous herb, it must be dispensed with the recommendation of a doctor. Most herbalists normally recommend one to two teaspoons of hydrangea in some kind of juice once a day. This drink literally opens up partially clogged or plugged kidney tubules, preparing them for the excessive water that vinegar chases from the body. But, I repeat, any use of vinegar or hydrangea by an overweight person should be monitored by a doctor: if a person loses too much water weight too fast, it is dangerous to the heart and other organs of the body.

For those who have thyroid conditions taking kelp tablets during the detoxification diet is beneficial. Kelp is extremely high in iodine and other minerals. Dr. Christopher recommends 12 to 15 tablets of kelp daily, but I believe in underdosing instead of overdosing: I've not had a client have a bad reaction to taking that much kelp, but the dosage should be left to the discretion of the nutritionist or doctor involved. For those who don't like to take pills I suggest using kelp that has been ground up, sprinkling it on salads and other vegetables or meat as a seasoning and nutritional supplement.

Another important ingredient of the detoxification diet is blackstrap or sorghum molasses, suggested because of its high iron content. It is also somewhat of a substitute for sugar, although some people have problems taking it for that very reason. Hypoglycemic individuals should test it before taking one tablespoon three times daily: some of them have felt drained after ingesting it.

Not only are the kinds and amounts of foods a person eats important in my modified detoxification diet. It is also good to develop certain eating habits. If possible, an individual should fast until noon everyday. (Infants and children and people who work in physical occupations should *not* try this aspect of the diet. Nor should people who have diabetes or hypoglycemia: since for such people small, frequent meals are best, about every three hours they may nibble on some dried or fresh fruit until noon arrives.) The theory behind fasting until noon is that the digestive tract gets to rest approximately 18 hours, from 6 p.m. until 12 noon everyday. In the morning hours an individual may drink juices if desired. And vinegar will halt hunger pangs very nicely.

Lunch should ideally be the largest meal of the day: in this way a person will burn off what he or she has consumed during the rest of the working day. At this meal an individual may choose a salad, meat or fruit. Efforts should be made to insure that vegetables and fruit are raw or semisteamed for best absorption of nutrients. If a person gets the "nibbles" between lunch and dinner, he or she can eat a handful of sunflower seeds, dried fruit or nuts.

Dinner, on the other hand, should be a fairly light meal, perhaps soup broth, a salad and one course of a vegetable or fruit. It's important that a person does not consume coffee, tea, water or any other beverage with the meal. Adding extra liquid to the stomach dilutes the gastric juices, decreasing their ability to break the foods down properly. Liquids can be consumed 45 minutes to an hour after a meal or one hour before a meal.

After a person gets into the swing of this program he or she may expect certain reactions. When the body is given good, nutritious food, it is thrown into a tailspin for a day or two, maybe even weeks. Some very common symptoms are headaches, lethargy, sleepiness, mucus coming out of every orifice of the body (including the ears and eyes), irritability and tenseness. Approximately three to seven days after starting the program there will be days when a person will feel extremely clearheaded, energetic and positive; but the next day he or she may feel "down in the dumps." There is a reason for these up and down days. The body is urging toxins into the bloodstream. As the body is fed nutritious food, it sets up a cyclic disposal of the toxins on its own schedule; hence, about every seventh day a person will experience a down day.

A comment I've heard frequently from people just starting on this program is: "I felt better when I was eating junk food than I do now!" Yes, that's true—at first. But in time there will be more up days than down days. It is important to keep at the program for at least three months. And it normally takes one year to detoxify properly. But once a person is on a moderate, disciplined schedule, he or she will have more energy, a more positive outlook, need less sleep and generally feel better. And, most important, there will be fewer colds, flus and other aggravating illnesses.

An important adjunct to this detoxification diet is exercise. An individual should take a walk, go swimming, visit a spa, work in the garden, ride a horse, etc., for at least an hour a day. Sunshine and fresh air are also vital for health.

In addition, a person on this detoxification diet should cut back on the amount of vitamin, mineral and herbal supplements he or she takes. A heavy dosage of supplementary vitamins, minerals or herbs will slow the detoxification process down. With vitamins, minerals and herbs the body is getting solid nutrition so that it won't work hard to get rid of toxins. One usually must cut the intake of such supplements by ½ to effect a continuous detoxification. After about the sixth month an individual will need fewer supplements anyway, if he or she is eating raw, natural foods.

A person does not have to be absolutely strict with this detoxification diet. One should pay attention to the body's needs. If there is a time when a person craves a certain type of food, he or she should go ahead and eat it. Of course, I don't mean such substances as hot fudge sundaes but, rather, foods that satisfy a certain deficiency. For instance, I've known many people who become addicted to vinegar for a week or two after first trying it, thus satisfying certain nutritional needs within the body. After that time the craving goes away, and they return to their normal intake of vinegar.

A final note of caution about the detoxification diet: anyone who is presently ill or has a health condition should consult his or her physician first before attempting this program. A sick person usually should not detoxify: the diet drains the body too much and may make the individual more ill than before. If the body has to fight on two fronts (against the disease and the toxins stirred up from the diet), it is doing too much and eventually will break down. A person with cardiovascular problems or a heart condition must especially work with a doctor when getting on this program: when toxins are agitated in the body, the entire circulatory system and heart have to work almost twice as hard. Similarly, an individual with a kidney ailment must approach the diet very carefully, because further injury may occur to the renal system if detoxification is haphazardly approached without assistance from a physician.

High Calcium Diet

A diet high in calcium is especially helpful to arthritics, the elderly suffering from porus or brittle bones and younger children who have allergies to milk. Following is a list of foods high in calcium, with an asterisk (*) indicating those foods with extremely high calcium contents.

cream of wheat	*sockeye salmon
shrimp	soy
flour	dried apricots
macaroni and cheese	dried dates

farina
roasted liver
dried almonds
*Brazil nuts
peanuts
sesame seeds
sesame butter
club sandwich
*calcium
*baked custard
canned evaporated milk
greens
broccoli
garbanzos or chick peas
collards
dandelion greens
kale
mustard greens
raw parsley
raw or cooked soybeans
turnip greens

rolled oat flakes
buckwheat pancakes
cheddar cheese
roquefort cheese
brick cheese
cottage cheese
edam cheese
*Gruyere cheese
bonemeal tablets
tomato sauce
cooked beet
skim dry instant milk
fresh goat's milk
yogurt
blackstrap molasses
*custard pie
*lobster
*mackerel
cooked or raw oysters
*perch
*pink salmon

A person should not make meals out of just the foods listed above or a deficiency in other nutrients may result in the long run. Furthermore, many of these calcium-laden foods are either mucous-producing if taken in excess (e.g., dairy products) or high in acid (fish and seafood).

For best results with this diet a person should take a vitamin D supplement (of the fish liver oil variety) regularly to insure that the extra calcium is going to be absorbed by the body. In addition, he or she should eat no refined sugar but use natural honey sparingly as a substitute. A dieter should eat small meals, with no heaping portions, and chew the food thoroughly before swallowing.

I suggest a menu that includes a glass of freshly squeezed orange or grapefruit juice with ½ lemon added for breakfast. Lunch should be the biggest meal of the day, consisting of four ounces of meat (perferably fish or chicken), a fresh salad, cheese or cottage cheese and a dessert such as custard, nuts or cheese. Dinner should consist of a fresh fruit salad with a honey-baked yam or sweet potato. Acceptable desserts are baked apples, apple pie made with ¾ cups of honey and fresh fruits. Desserts should be eaten ½ hour after a meal. Moreover, no liquids should be drunk with meals but, instead, consumed at least ½ hour before or after a meal. All fish should be steamed or baked.

Acid-Alkaline Diets

Many people have acidosis, a condition that can result from eating too many acid-forming foods and that may alter gastric juice secretions from the stomach. People with arthritis are especially high in acid and need to eat more alkali-forming foods. But no one should eat entirely alkaline foods: they can eventually upset the acid-alkaline metabolism. Following is a list of foods categorized according to their acidic and alkaline properties.

ACID-FORMING FOODS
One-Ounce Portions (30 grams)

Acid No.		Acid No.	
egg yolk	7.5	goose	3.0
smoked herring	5.5	turkey	3.0
oysters	4.5	barley	3.0
crab	4.5	cereals	3.0
lobster	4.0	whole egg	3.0
oatmea	13.6	macaroni	3.0
sardines	3.4	spaghetti	3.0
veal	3.3	white or brown rice	2.8
salmon	3.3	haddock	2.5
perch	3.3	walnuts	2.4
swordfish	3.3	crackers	2.3
heart	3.3	whole wheat bread	2.2
kidney	3.2	white bread	2.2
chicken	3.2	egg white	1.7
rabbit	3.2	dry corn	1.7
liver	3.0	American cheese	1.6
beef	3.0	corn flakes	1.6
pork	3.0	corn meal	1.6
bacon	3.0	corn bread	1.6
mutton	3.0	zweiback	1.6
lamb	3.0	lentils	1.5
smoked ham	3.0	soda crackers	1.0
frog	3.0	peanuts	0.7
duck	3.0	green corn on the cob	0.5

ALKALI-FORMING FOODS
One-Ounce Portions (30 grams)

Alkali No.		Alkali No.	
dried figs	30.0	sweet or white potatoes	2.0
molasses	18.0	fresh apricots	2.0
green or ripe olives	16.0	fresh pineapple	2.0
dried lima beans	12.0	baked beans	2.0
soybeans	12.0	sweet cherries	1.8
dried apricots	9.5	nectarines	1.8
spinach	8.0	cabbage	1.8
mustard greens	8.0	dried currants	1.7
turnip greens	1.0	radishes	1.7
dandelion greens	8.0	grapefruit	1.7
beet greens	8.0	oranges	1.7
kale	7.0	sauerkraut	1.7

seeded raisins 7.0	tomatoes 1.7
Swiss chard 5.0	string beans 2.6
fresh lima beans 4.5	lemons 1.6
parsnips 3.6	cauliflower 1.6
almonds 3.6	peaches 1.5
carrots 3.5	mushrooms 1.2
beets 3.5	apples 1.1
dates 3.0	pears 1.1
rutabaga 2.5	bananas 1.1
rhubarb 2.5	grapes 1.0
celery 2.5	watermelon 1.0
cucumber with	
peel 2.5	squash 1.0
cantaloupe 2.2	buttermilk 6.7
lettuce 2.2	whole milk 6.5
parsley 2.2	onions 0.4
endive 2.2	green peas 6.3
pomegranates 2.0	asparagus 9.2
watercress 2.0	ice cream 9.1
coconut 2.0	

ALKALINITY OF JUICES
Per Pint (480 grams)

Alkali No.	*Alkali No.*
fig 200	pineapple 08
beet green 64	pomegranate 16
dandelion 64	watercress 16
spinach 64	cabbage 14
turnip leaf 64	grapefruit 13
parsnip 16	orange 13
carrot 16	radish 13
beet 28	sauerkraut 13
celery 20	tomato 13
cucumber 20	lemon 13
rhubarb 20	apple 9
parsley 17	pear 9
apricot 16	grape 8
coconut 16	watermelon 8
endive 16	asparagus 1.5

MASSOTHERAPY

Besides suggesting nutritional supplements, herbal and homeopathic remedies and specific diets, a medical astrologer may recommend that a client undergo some form of physical or mental therapy. One of the best forms of physical therapy I have found is massotherapy, the manipulation of the muscles to effect a cure. In more technical terms massotherapy is "a scientific method of treating disease by manipulating the tissue of the body by hand or modality to effect relaxation, relieve pain, increase range and mobility of joints and ligaments, reduce certain types of edemas, effect blood flow and nutrition, increase metabolism, promote absorption, stretch adhesions and beneficially affect the nervous system."

Massotherapy is an excellent adjunct to chiropractry. And it can be very pleasant compared to the roughness that sometimes accompanies chiropractic movements. I have been unable to understand why chiropractors simply adjust a bone or vertebra without first massaging the muscles in and around the area. Tense muscles can throw a vertebra out. And too often I've seen a back "pop" out two days after chiropractic adjustment because the muscles were as tense as before. Massotherapists effect such massage, thereby increasing the chances that the condition will not recur.

But massotherapy is not glorified massage. Massotherapists train for two years at colleges and then must pass state board exams given by AMA to practice their trade. They are graduates of schools licensed to teach anatomy, physiology, hydrotherapy, hygiene and therapeutic massage.

Massotherapy has many benefits. First, it has a profound effect on circulation. It acts as a tonic to the heart, increasing the flow of blood without raising arterial tension. It also moves the lymph and blood and by its mechanical and reflex action on the nervous system encourages the tissue to maintain a healthy condition.

In addition, massotherapy promotes a desirable effect upon the nervous system. It may produce relaxation, stimulation and metabolic balance. The massotherapist, by expert manipulation and massage of the tissue of the body, relieves pressure on the nervous system, thus allowing the inherent restorative and constructive powers of the body to be activated.

Massotherapy also increases respiratory activity. And it is one of the most effective ways of increasing tissue metabolism. Furthermore, it can be beneficial to nutrition, blood formation on the cellular level, elimination, heat regulatory functions, stimulation of the endocrine function and mobility of the joints and ligaments. Last but not least, massotherapy exerts a positive effect on mental well-being.

A list of the names and addresses of massotherapists found throughout the United States is presented in Appendix C.

CHAPTER SIX
Case Histories

The following case histories are all factual. The names of the individuals have been changed to protect them. Each person or the parents involved have given permission to have the cases discussed.

CASE HISTORY 1

Name

Todd.

Birth Data

March 19, 1975
6:48 p.m. EST
Dunedian, Florida

Ailments

Allergies, upper respiratory disorders, maldigestion and nutrient imbalance.

Background

I was called in on this case by my medical student, Susan Prigozen, in November of 1977. Todd's mother was frantic. Todd had been raised on breast milk for nearly a year. Then shortly after she had weaned him, he became croupy, allergic and susceptible to numerous colds and upper respiratory ailments. The baby was beginning to lose weight rapidly because he could not properly digest or

Figure 5
TODD'S NATAL CHART

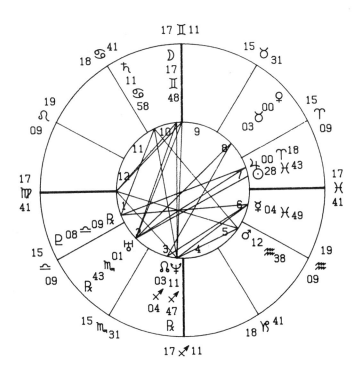

```
            Todd
   3 19 1975 18h48m  0s EDT
   PLACIDUS  28N 1  82W47
```

assimilate food to get the nutrients necessary for life. His mother had taken him to three different pediatricians, and none could help her child. After hearing Susan deliver a talk on child education, she called Susan on the verge of tearful hysteria, frustrated with the medical establishment. We were her last hope.

The Natal Chart (Tropical/Placidian).
(Figure 5)

My eyes went immediately to Virgo rising. A Virgo Ascendant potentially means a highly sensitive metabolism. I next noticed Pluto retrograde in Libra in the First House, and I wondered if this placement meant endocrine imbalance. Furthermore, Pluto has *four* hard aspects—quite an impressive number. Since Pluto rules the endocrine system, I felt there might be a problem with a gland. But which one? With Saturn inconjunct Neptune I felt that either the parathyroid gland (Saturn) or the thymus gland (Neptune) was involved. So, on my Med-Scan worksheet I checked off tests for the parathyroid and thymus to be run by the doctor. I also reasoned that since Pluto was playing such a strong part in this chart I should first carefully check any other aspects from it to other planets.

Pluto inconjunct Mercury: With Mercury ruling the thyroid and the hormones this configuration could indicate either a possible thyroid malfunction or a hormonal imbalance in general. I had already checked off the thyroid test to be run.

Pluto inconjunct Venus: This hard aspect could mean sugar disruption or pancreatic disorders.

Pluto opposition Jupiter: This configuration could indicate an endocrine disorder on a large scale.

Pluto square Saturn: This hard aspect could mean a potentially severe deficiency of vitamin C (Saturn) as well as potentially malfunctioning endocrine glands, particularly the thymus, adrenals, pancreas or parathyroid.

My overall analysis of Pluto was that there was definite endocrine involvement, enzymic or hormonal disruption, chronic, long-term problems and allergies or blood disorders.

Next I looked at Saturn, which with three hard aspects to it I felt was strongly involved in Todd's ailments. In fact, I believed that Saturn and Pluto were the bases for most of the complaints.

Saturn inconjunct Mars: Mars rules the adrenal glands. I placed a question mark by this hard aspect, not sure how to analyze it at that point except that I felt intuitively that the adrenals were involved, perhaps in a secondary way. Later my theory would prove correct.

Saturn inconjunct Neptune: This hard aspect could mean a sluggish thymus gland, a body prone to infections in general or the possibility of poisoning. I wrote *poisoning* down because Neptune rules this phenomenon in general, whether from drugs or other sources. But I wasn't sure poisoning had taken place. Later, when I got into the progressed chart, I found this to be one of the *main* reasons for Todd's ailments.

Saturn square Pluto: See *Pluto square Saturn* above.

My overall analysis of Saturn was that it might be implicated in sluggish endocrine activity. And possible poisoning of an undetected nature might be taking place.

Then I examined Jupiter, which also has three hard aspects to it. In Todd's natal chart Jupiter is in Aries. This placement usually indicates excess blood in the head, causing stress on the vessels and suggesting the potential for aneurysms if the veins or arteries do not remain flexible and elastic. But these possibilities did not fit the baby's symptoms.

From long experience I decided to consider the opposite polarity, Jupiter in Libra, which indicates changes in blood circulation from the fluctuation of kidney regulation, cholesterol deposits in the kidney tubules and sugar-related problems. These potential ailments, especially sugar-related problems, did fit. For the problems to be active, the sign Virgo or Pisces had to be in evidence: Mercury and the Sun are in Pisces in Todd's chart, with Virgo on the Ascendant. I wrote down, "Oversensitive to sugars, hyperactive?" I found out later that the mother could barely control him and that pediatricians had already dubbed him a hyperactive child.

Jupiter conjunct the Sun: This configuration could indicate overdose of something, since Jupiter expands and overdosage is common when the planet is highly aspected in a chart. I had to find out what was overdosing and where the symptoms were manifesting.

Jupiter inconjunct Uranus: This hard aspect can mean a spasm occurring somewhere that might influence health on a large scale.

Jupiter opposition Pluto: See *Pluto opposition Jupiter* above.

My overall analysis of Jupiter in this case was pancreatic spasm and uncontrolled insulin release under stress. In the "Diet" section of my worksheet I suggested no sugars in any form to see if Todd's behavior would change under such circumstances.

After examining the hard aspects in Todd's chart I looked at the sign positions of the outer planets to determine their possible effect on the child's health.

Saturn in Cancer: With this placement the gastric secretions in the stomach may be below normal standards, perhaps producing gastric complaints, bloating, croup in babies and poor digestion that prohibits nutrients from getting back in the body.

Uranus in Scorpio (retrograde): This placement could indicate a spastic colon, sporadic peristalsis and with reflex action from Taurus a potential spastic thyroid condition that could manifest under stress.

Neptune in Sagittarius (retrograde): This placement might mean poor oxygenation in general and, with reflex action from Gemini weak lungs and respiratory infections.

Pluto in Libra (retrograde): This placement could mean either malfunctioning kidneys or a metabolic imbalance. In Todd's case the metabolism was imbalanced. His kidneys were working fine, and he had no signs of edema or other kidney dysfunction symptoms.

The Cross: Todd had three planets in cardinal signs. He was also exhibiting ailments of the Cardinal Cross, such as gastric and digestive upsets and metabolic imbalance. However, he had other ailments implicating the Mutable Cross—sugar problems, respiratory infections and lymph gland impairment. In addition, he had four planets plus the angles in mutable signs. Although determining the cross helps a medical astrologer decide on the best diet, in Todd's case I had to weigh carefully the dietary considerations because of his allergies: he could hardly eat any food without a reaction. I decided to look at Todd's progressions and transits before setting forth a diet.

Other Information: The fixed star Fomalhaut is conjunct Todd's natal Mercury.

Figure 6
TODD'S PROGRESSED CHART

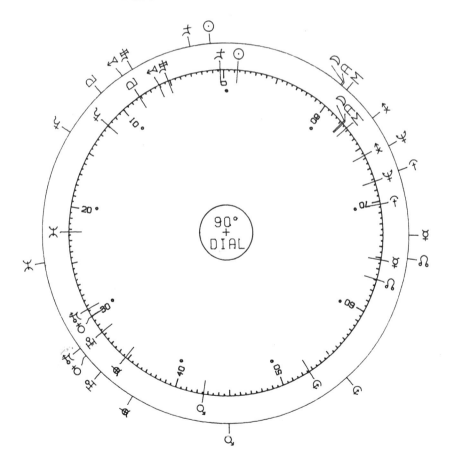

The Progressed Chart (Figure 6)

I set up Todd's progressed chart for December 19, 1977, when he would be 2.43 years of age by mean solar arc. (I normally make up a progressed chart for the time when a client comes to me.) By looking back on the dial I could immediately see when Todd's medical conditions were triggered.

When Todd was one year and one month of age, progressed Apollon reached the midpoint of natal Vulcanus and Pluto. This midpoint structure is a primary indication of an illness or the beginning of a sickness that may develop complications later. It was at this time that his mother weaned him off breast-feeding. Once denied the nutrients from his mother's milk, Todd became croupy and allergic and seemingly developed several ailments at once—a typical trait of an activated Apollon.

Pluto is in opposition to Hades in Todd's natal 90-degree chart. This configuration will always be a fostering point for potential illness. Case in point: in November of 1977 progressed Apollon conjuncted natal Pluto, triggering the Pluto/Hades structure and thus indicating a transformative illness that would multiply rapidly and threaten health. In fact, the baby was dying inch by inch from lack of food. Moreover, there were multiple symptoms that had confused three different doctors, and the transformation (Pluto) involved a life or death situation.

In the future any other medical planet progressing over this Pluto-Hades axis could stir up other health-related problems: e.g., the progressed Sun conjuncting it when Todd is 9.25 years; progressed Neptune, 26; progressed Hades, 45.25; and progressed Mars, 55.30 years of age. One of my duties as a medical astrologer was to inform Todd's mother of the potential danger of these dates, and within six months of each conjunction she should know how her child is doing. If Todd were to begin developing problems at those times, a doctor would have six months to right the situation so that the effects could be moderated.

Any planet progressing across the Hades part of this axis would also trigger similar symptoms: progressed Mars conjunct natal Hades when Todd is 10: progressed Admetos, 18; progressed Uranus, 20.75; and progressed Pluto, 44.30.

As of December 1977 several midpoint pictures were activated, leading to Todd's major health crisis and the contacting of a medical astrologer.

P. Ap conjunct N. Pl + P. Ha-N. Ur: This midpoint structure can indicate a crisis or a health situation that may deteriorate rapidly.

P. Pl + N. Ma-N. Ne: This configuration can mean an endocrine disorder that goes undetected or misdiagnosed. In addition, energy levels may be low. A person may be unable to sustain a physical effort to throw off infection.

N. Ve + P. Ha-N. Ma: Although I had no information on this midpoint structure, I felt it could mean a poisoning in the blood or a blood disorder, since Venus and Mars rule such functions.

N. Ur/P. Ne-P. Ap conjunct N. Pl: The occurrence of this configuration reinforced the fact that the crisis occurred suddenly, with possible accompanying misdiagnosis. The seriousness of the crisis is indicated by Pluto and Hades both being in the picture.

N. Ap/P. Tr-N. Ne: This configuration can indicate a chronic, hidden illness with multiple complications. In this case Neptune was the triggering factor of the midpoint structure, indicating misdiagnosis or difficult determination of the root cause of the illness.

P. Ma conjunct N. Tr: Transpluto here shows the potential activation of an acute illness that gets totally out of control.

After examining the progressed chart and seeing how often Neptune was involved I was convinced that Todd had been misdiagnosed and that there was poison in his body. At first I thought the lymph system was affected because it handles poisons in the body: with so much Pisces in the natal chart this was a logical assumption. Another possibility was that the thymus was not manufacturing lymphocytes to help ward off infection and was badly backlogged from fighting allergies. Thus the thymus could also be implicated in a type of poisoning.

With Pluto, Hades and Apollon all prominent in various midpoint structures I also felt that this boy's life was in question. (Repetition of planets in midpoint structures usually reaffirms their strength in the progressed chart: they must be scrutinized closely for their possible involvement in the health of the in-

Figure 7

MIDPOINTS ARRANGED IN 90-DEGREE SEQUENCE

♃ 00 18	♂/♆ 12 12	☿/♆ 23 18	♅ 31 43	☽/♃ 39 03	♃/♄ 51 08	☿ 64 49	♆ 71 47	☿/♇ 81 29	
☿/♀ 02 26	☉/♀ 14 23	A/☊ 25 22	A/M 32 26	♆/♇ 39 58	♅/♆ 51 45	☉/♂ 65 40	♆/M 74 29	♂/♅ 82 10	
☿/♅ 03 16	♂/M 14 54	☿/M 26 00	☽/A 32 45	♂ 42 38	♀/M 53 37	♀/♄ 66 01	☽/♆ 74 48	♄/☊ 82 31	
☉/♇ 03 26	♀/♃ 15 11	☽/☿ 26 19	☉/♆ 35 15	♇/M 42 40	☿/♂ 53 43	♂/♃ 66 28	☉/☿ 76 46	☉/A 83 12	
♃/♇ 04 14	☽/♂ 15 13	♂/♄ 27 18	♇/☊ 35 37	☽/♇ 42 59	☽/♀ 53 56	♄/♅ 66 51	M 77 11	♃/A 84 00	
♂/☊ 07 51	☉/♅ 15 13	♆/A 29 44	♃/♆ 36 03	♄/A 44 50	♅/M 54 27	♆/☊ 67 26	☽/M 77 30	♄/♆ 86 53	
♇ 08 09	♃/♅ 16 01	♀ 30 03	☉/M 37 57	♀/☊ 46 34	☽/♅ 54 46	M/☊ 70 07	☿/♃ 77 34	♇/A 87 55	
♀/A 08 52	☿/☊ 18 57	♀/♅ 30 53	☉/☽ 38 15	♅/☊ 47 24	♄/♇ 55 04	♂/♇ 70 23	A 77 41	☉ 88 43	
♅/A 09 42	♀/♇ 19 06	☉/☊ 30 53	☿/♄ 38 24	☉/♄ 50 20	♂/A 60 09	☽/☊ 70 26	☽ 77 48	☉/♃ 89 30	
♄ 11 58	♅/♇ 19 56	♃/☊ 31 41	♃/M 38 45	♀/♆ 50 55	☊ 63 04	☿/A 71 15	♀/♂ 81 20	♄/M 89 35	
								☽/♄ 89 53	

dividual.) However, since progressed Saturn wasn't in any of the midpoint pictures to indicate that he would die, I felt confident that we could avert a crisis with swift action and clean diagnosis for his mother to take to a sympathetic doctor.

Transits

My next step was to check Todd's transits to see if they were adding anything to the overall health picture.

Saturn: This planet is in the Twelfth House of Todd's natal chart at 0 Virgo. It went retrograde on December 12, setting up a vibration, or warning. I've many times seen an outer planet enter the Twelfth House and activate a chronic medical condition that has been mildly active but has not really gone into the crisis stage. In Todd's case transiting Saturn did exactly that. Saturn was at 29 Leo in November 1977 with only one degree separating it from the natal Sun in an inconjunct aspect. I'm sure that in late October of 1977 his condition became worse when this aspect was exact.

Uranus: At 12 and 13 Scorpio in November 1977 Uranus made an exact square to natal Mars. This aspect can indicate an acute condition suddenly manifesting or a worsening of an already deteriorating condition, which, of course, was exactly what took place in Todd's case.

Neptune: At 14 and 15 Sagittarius in November 1977 Neptune seemingly had little to do with the crisis. Only the progressed chart indicated how deeply involved the planet was, because in the long run Neptune provided the answer to the problem.

Pluto: At 15 Libra for the entire month of November 1977 Pluto remained on the Second House cusp, seemingly uninvolved.

Eclipses

On April 18, 1977, there was an eclipse of the new Moon at 28 Aries in Todd's Eighth House. I ordinarily would not pay attention to such an eclipse because it hit no planet and did not occur in the Sixth or Twelfth Houses of health and hospitalization. But, since astrologers have traditionally said that the Eighth House indicates death, I did note the date. (Although I've seen some eclipses activate in the Eighth House of a person's chart, usually they involved the death of someone the person knew and not the individual.) The fallout date for the eclipse was July 18, 1977, with the effects lasting for six months—that is, to October 18, 1977, a time when Todd's ailments began to enter a crisis.

On September 27, 1977, an eclipse of the full Moon took place at 4 Aries within four degrees opposition to Todd's natal Pluto. And this eclipse, I

feel, had an influence on the overall health picture. The fallout date was December 27, 1977. By that time Todd's health was just beginning to stabilize after his mother had found an orthomolecular physician to give the tests I had suggested.

Final Analysis

From experience I hated having to deal with a strong progressed Neptune in anyone's chart: it meant that I could be just as wrong as the three other doctors who had already been involved in Todd's case. But I was fairly sure that the endocrine glands were implicated, and I strongly suspected a poison in his system.

I still hadn't determined, however, what substance was causing the poisoning. I had Susan call to ask if the child had a high salt intake, what kind of water he drank and if he ate fish, cabbage or nuts. I was trying to find out if a poison in the food or water could be disturbing his entire metabolism—for instance, cyanide in the water or food. Afterwards I reexamined the Saturn-Pluto square for a long, long time. Finally, I focused on metal, specifically Saturn-ruled lead, as the probable cause of poisoning. This time I called Todd's mother direct. She told me that Todd chewed on a lot of plastic toys. I told her to get those toys tested and to get him in for a heavy metals test as well as the other tests I had suggested for the parathyroid, thymus and adrenal glands.

Because Todd was allergic to 90 per cent of the foods a child normally eats, I decided not to suggest that he get on a diet I usually recommend for people with strong Mutable Crosses in their charts—one rich in fruits and vegetables, very light in meat and without refined sugar. But I informed Todd's mother of the diet in hopes that after the allergies were under control Todd could eat such foods.

Outcome

Todd's mother took her child to an orthomolecular physician, who ran a hair analysis, blood and heavy metals tests on him, as well as endocrine tests. In the toxic metals test lead was 13 parts per million, with the upper limit 15: Todd definitely had lead poisoning. Furthermore, he was deficient in manganese, zinc, iron and calcium. And he was high in copper, magnesium, potassium and chromium.

Todd had allergies to rye, wheat and oat cereals, cow's milk, oranges, tangerines, tomatoes, pork, almonds, peanuts, garlic, onions, potatoes, soybeans, tea, squash and string beans. He also had severe reactions to chocolate, egg whites, refined sugar, brewer's yeast, baker's yeast and malt. He was considered a nutritional allergic.

The physician felt the allergies were related to

the minerals, which affect the enzymes, which in turn affect the hormones. So, the endocrine functions would restabilize with proper intake and absorption of nutrition. Todd's lymph system was all right, but because his body was in such a compromised state from the allergies the lymph system wasn't working properly. The doctor also discovered that Todd had small red blood cells (Mars) from nutritional deficiencies: there were four per cent allergy cells.

The thyroid test came out low-normal, which is to say that Todd had a mild hypothyroid condition. With his Sun in Pisces low- or high-normal would be just as good as having the ailment.

Other problems Todd had were acidosis (Libra and hard aspects to Mars), deficiency in stomach acid (Saturn in Cancer) and liver dysfunction (Jupiter and Virgo). The BUN was low, meaning a block in protein metabolism. He will have a tendency toward gout in later age if he doesn't watch his intake of acid-forming foods. And mucus was found in the urine.

The doctor prescribed the following regimin to get Todd healthy: enzymes with each meal, multivitamin tablets, one gram of vitamin C daily, chelated magnesium, apple pectin, chelated calcium, manganese, selenium, calcium pantothenate, vitamin B-6, zinc, thymotrophic concentrate (a thymus stimulant from natural sources) and adrenatrophin (an adrenal gland stimulant from natural sources).

In the months that followed Todd's mother wrote me several letters describing the child's progress.

December 30, 1977:"There are two reasons that I am especially glad that I had Todd's chart done at the same time of the physical. First, as a good mother it is easy to feel guilt when your child has a physical problem. Knowing that, somehow, these problems are influenced by the planets relieves me of the feeling of responsibility. Next, it helped me evaluate the prescribed treatment. This doctor prescribed two hormones. I have omitted these... All other nutrients are being taken. I have added a little of some of the allergic foods as a matter of necessity. He has to eat something!"

January 16, 1978:"You were so kind in helping, I thought you would like to have a complete set of the results of Todd's tests. Your results and recommendations ran so closely to this specialist's that I thought you would like to make your own comparisons."

April 15, 1979:"We stick very closely to Todd's diet and vitamins and mineral supplements. He is in optimum health as long as we adhere to this program. If we don't, he gets congestion, a cold or, perhaps, the croup. His body is built up and can tolerate an occasional allergic food. We get hair analysis every six months, and his doctor changes his prescription accordingly. Todd is in vibrant health."

January 29, 1980: In a phone call Todd's mother reported on Todd's continued health. Furthermore, his Jekyll-Hyde personality had halted the day she took him off sugars. He is a pleasant, happy child growing up normally.

What Astrology Missed

At the time I did Todd's chart I still thought Uranus ruled zinc. Later, after further investigation and research I realized I was wrong. But at the time, because I suspected metal poisoning, I researched and found that zinc is a good antidote when the body is undergoing poisoning. Hence I suggested a zinc supplement. In 1979 I awarded Jupiter rulership of zinc. Interestingly, Todd's chart now bears out the need for zinc.

At the time I had not entertained the thought of a deficiency in selenium—a case of ignorance since there was very little available on that mineral in 1977. Fortunately, the doctor recommended selenium, emphasizing to me how important it is to work with a physician, since my lack of medical background might jeopardize a client. Nor had I suggested manganese. (I had suggested vitamins A and D—the vitamin A to strengthen the lungs and nasal tissue to fight off infections and the vitamin D to help assimilate the calcium properly.)

Furthermore, I had not thought about magnesium being high, although its ruler, Jupiter, is under stress by three hard aspects in Todd's natal chart. I believe the Jupiter-Pluto opposition precipitated this overdose. When Jupiter or Pluto is involved, one should usually check toxic symptoms for those vitamins or minerals that are affected by this aspect.

Nor had I detected copper being high. But Pluto is inconjunct to Venus, copper's ruler. I've found since then that the inconjunct is probably the aspect most suspect of producing conditions of either too much or too little nutrients in the body: it should never be assumed that the inconjunct always represents a deficiency.

I had not recommended any glandular supplements either. In 1977 natural gland-stimulants were just hitting the market, and I knew little about them. Furthermore, I didn't feel I should suggest anything until the test results on the glandular functions came back. In my opinion, the thymus and adrenal supplements the doctor suggested were excellent.

CASE HISTORY 2

Name
Ray.

Birth Data
July 8, 1914
2:38 a.m. CST
Mercer City, Ohio

Ailment
Heart attack.

Background
I met Ray in March 1978 through his wife, Meg, who is a very good astrologer. At 10:30 a.m., on February 4, 1978, in Dayton, Ohio, Ray had suffered a heart attack, probably caused by a clot in the artery. Meg asked me to do a Med-Scan because she had progressed Ray's chart to July of 1978 and did not like what she saw: in fact, she saw his potential death at that time.

Ray suffered from arterial sclerosis (clogging of the arteries with plaque buildup). At first his condition had been misdiagnosed as arthritis. Since Ray had been complaining of shoulder and arm pains, the doctor thought Ray had bursitis or arthritis and in 1976 prescribed water pills to reduce the high blood pressure. Ray faithfully took the pills for six to seven months and then began to feel terribly dehydrated, while the pain in the arms and shoulders increased. So, he quit taking the pills without informing the doctor. Since he felt the doctor had not helped his situation but worsened it, Ray unfortunately never went to another doctor about the continuing pain, which was actually the sign of an impending heart attack: especially in the left side pain very frequently occurs under the shoulder blade (the scapula) and down the arm when a heart attack is imminent; sometimes shooting pains run down the arm, or there is a tingling sensation or numbness occurring for a few seconds to minutes in the hands and then disappearing.

Ray's arterial sclerosis was finally diagnosed after the first heart attack in 1978. His diet aggravated the disease: he was strictly a meat and potatoes man; he also enjoyed fat, eating it from meat, eggs fried in grease, etc. At the time I met him he was 5'9" tall and weighed 148 pounds.

An interesting note: Ray had four kidneys.

The Natal Chart(Figure 8)
In Ray's natal chart Gemini is rising with Saturn conjunct the Ascendant. This configuration may have something to do with Ray's having four kidneys: data is too scanty at this time to make

generalized conjecture.

The chart shows some very highly aspected planets. The Moon and Jupiter both have four hard aspects, a high number that needed to be examined closely to determine any probable deficiencies of vitamins and minerals. For instance, potassium (Moon) has a great deal to do with the heart and the regularity of its beat; and Jupiter rules cholesterol, normally the substance that clogs up the arteries in arterial sclerosis. The Moon plays an especially prominent part in Ray's chart, which contains a yod consisting of the Moon inconjunct Venus and Saturn. I would say that in this case the Moon made Ray too much a creature of habit in terms of food.

Moreover, Ray's Venus is in Leo, in direct opposition to Jupiter in Aquarius — a configuration that also probably influenced his tastes in food: he liked fats, and although he did not normally eat a lot of sweets, according to Meg, he put sugar on some strange combinations—such as vegetable stew. A high starch diet coupled with fat is bound to cause trouble. Meg had tried to change Ray's unhealthy diet in the past but to no avail: Ray liked what he liked (Venus and Moon), and he wasn't too crazy about trying new dishes (Saturn).

In addition, Mercury has three hard aspects to it in Ray's natal chart. Mercury conjunct Neptune, although not prominent on an angle, warns the medical astrologer that misdiagnosis is possible. And this configuration plus the other hard aspects of Mercury indicates deficiencies in much of the vitamin B complex. So, I was not surprised that Ray had had Bell's palsy, which, according to most health sources, can be erradicated with thiamine (Mercury) and the rest of the B complex.

Next I examined the lineup of outer planets in relation to his ailments.

Saturn in Gemini: This placement can mean that nerves may tremble from lack of calcium to feed the nervous system. It can also signify lung congestion: at an early age Ray had had many bouts with colds and sniffles, up until the time his tonsils were removed at age 23. Finally, Saturn in Gemini can indicate constriction of some tube in the body or partial blockage by either a stone or other sedimentary waste such as cholesterol, of a small opening. The key to Ray's condition was the arterial blockage by plaque. Jupiter with four aspects indicates problems with the arteries instead of the veins (Venus).

Uranus in Aquarius (retrograde): This configuration may indicate neural degeneration related to diseases of the muscles, nerves and spinal column. Ray, of course, had had Bell's palsy, a neural inflammation. But in this case I decided to also check out the opposite polarity, Uranus in Leo, to make sure there was no crossover of symptoms. Uranus in Leo can mean arrhythmia of the heart, spasmodic palpitations and sudden attacks of angina pectoris. Here was the crux of the problem: angina pectoris is caused by an insufficient supply of blood to the heart, and, if the arteries are constricted or clogged (Saturn in Gemini), a heart attack can take place.

Neptune in Cancer: This placement can signify weak peristalsis of the stomach during the digestion phase or diluted gastric juices. I decided that Neptune in Cancer was a contributing factor to Ray's condition because of the amount of fat he had consumed over 40 to 50 years: the gastric secretions or bile just couldn't break down and emulsify the amount of fat Ray consumed.

The Cross: I chose the Fixed Cross as the root of Ray's problems, partly because of his heart ailment and also because he had suffered hemorrhoid prob-

lems (Scorpio) and sore throats (Taurus) as well as had his tonsils removed.

Thus I recommended a diet considered best for individuals with strong Fixed Crosses in their charts—one high in fiber and roughage to make sure the colon creates strong, regular peristalsis, to discourage fecal buildup on the inner walls and to discourage toxicity in the bloodstream that might stress other organs or systems in the body. I also suggested that Ray consume meats in moderate amounts, eating very little beef, pork and lamb, instead substituting those meats with chicken, turkey, Cornish game hen and fish.

Other Information: Two critical degrees are in Ray's natal chart—Venus and Jupiter at 21 degrees of a fixed sign—and they were intrinsically involved with his ailments.

Figure 8
RAY'S NATAL CHART

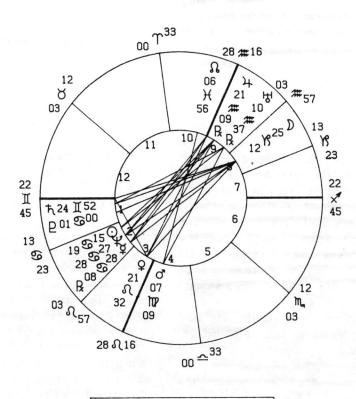

```
                    Ray
        7  8 1914   2h38m 0s CST
        PLACIDUS   40N40  84W31
```

The Progressed Chart(Figure 9)

When Ray had his tonsils removed at age 23, progressed Mars was conjunct natal Admetos in his 90-degree chart. I'm sure he was feeling quite miserable during the six months leading up to this operation because Admetos hints at a condition that gradually builds to an intolerable level.

At age 41 Ray had a hemorrhoid operation. At that time progressed Zeus was quite active—conjunct his natal Mars. Zeus can sometimes pinpoint the time of an operation. With Mars and Vulcanus involved I don't believe there was any choice other than to operate. Progressed Vulcanus conjunct the natal Sun lends an air of cosmic inevitability: probably only an operation could have brought Ray's condition back to normalcy.

In February of 1978 at the time of Ray's first heart attack progressed Uranus sat at the midpoint between Zeus, Admetos and Pluto. This powerful configuration probably helped to make the attack a severe one.

The chart also showed that progressed Saturn was going to conjunct the midpoint of the natal Midheaven in August of 1978. I've frequently seen the Midheaven involved in many serious injuries and/or deaths. In Uranian astrology it is considered the "I" or ego for this lifetime.

When Meg contacted me in March of 1978 to do the Med-Scan, she confided that she felt Ray was going to die within the year. After studying the progressed chart I concurred with her findings. This was one of the rare times that I gave a date for the death of an individual. Almost 100 per cent of the time I do not believe it is wise to predict a date. But Meg is a thoroughly accomplished astrologer, who knows her craft as well as I do. To lie and say Ray would not die would have offended her professionalism. I told her that his death would occur by December of 1978. At that time progressed Mars would conjunct natal Uranus, and I've seen that configuration active many times during heart attacks, when an individual suddenly has a seizure and is dead within a matter of moments.

Transits

As usual, the transits weren't too prominent in

Figure 9
RAY'S PROGRESSED CHART

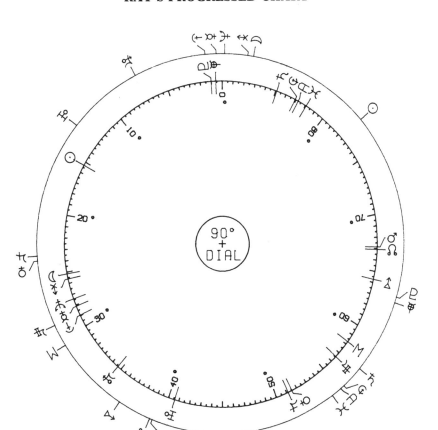

the overall picture. Transiting Saturn, however, did go retrograde on February 2, 1978, and Ray suffered his first heart attack on the fourth. I've found many heart attacks take place shortly after Saturn turns retrograde. At that time Saturn was at 28 Leo retrograde, exactly conjunct his Fourth House cusp. Interestingly, it was opposite the Midheaven, which, we have seen, was very actively involved in Ray's health problems in 1978.

Eclipses

There were no eclipses activated that directly affected Ray's health on any of the crucial dates, either by aspect or via fallout.

Final Analysis

In a way I felt like a stranger intruding upon designed plans for Ray. That he would probably die no matter what I suggested was fairly obvious to me. Yet I knew that I could not walk away from the case. I felt like a midget trying to beat off a giant, knowing I couldn't succeed but must try. I did not want to interfere with the cosmos, but I felt I should try to save Ray with whatever knowledge I had.

I saw Ray in person on March 18, 1978, and outlined a program to help his heart, so long as his cardiologist agreed with the suggestions. Since Ray's doctor would not cooperate with the program I had recommended, Meg found another doctor willing to try my suggested nutritional supplements. From March through July Ray faithfully took multivitamin tablets plus supplements of vitamins E, A, D, C and B-12, riboflavin, pantothenic acid and zinc.

Outcome

In July 1978, sometime around his birthday or solar return, Ray suffered his second heart attack. At that time progressed Neptune conjuncted Admetos, hinting that a hidden condition still lingered and that a weakening was taking place. In addition, transiting Uranus was at 12 Scorpio retrograde and conjunct within 30 minutes applying from his Sixth House cusp, meaning a sudden hospitalization. Transiting Saturn was also moving back across his Fourth House cusp.

According to Meg, the second attack was severe. The doctors were astounded that he had survived such a seizure and lived to tell about it. They all agreed that the program of nutrients and his new diet were responsible for his survival. I had always had the utmost faith in vitamins and minerals, but Ray's condition showed me in dramatic terms what three months of supplements can do in a deadly chronic condition. It was a great insight that vitamins and minerals can effectively fight off anything—even a crippling heart attack.

Around August 5, 1978, Ray had his last, devastating heart attack and died. Meg told me that his heart literally ruptured that time. And I was convinced that it would have to be such an attack to kill him since he was getting nutrients that his body needed to shore up against the weaknesses.

The progressions at that time are an eloquent testimony to the higher forces at work. Although there was no clearly defined death axis, the most suspect was progressed Saturn conjunct the natal Midheaven. Another strong axis was progressed Transpluto at the midpoint of his natal Hades and Poseidon. This unlikely combination to me is symbolic of the rebirth of Ray's soul into another dimensional realm, a leaving of the earthly plane for another: in Uranian terms Poseidon represents the spirituality of humankind, the tie between people and the God force; Hades symbolizes the return of our physical beings to dust. In addition, progressed Saturn conjunct the Midheaven was surrounded by Zeus and Pluto, a signature that indicates forces beyond our control will be at work: whenever I see Zeus and Pluto in combination, I know I might as well back off and let the energies do what must be done. There was so much power in the progressions that for Ray not to have died this third time, I believe, was almost impossible.

As far as the transits were concerned, in early August of 1978 Uranus had turned direct and was about 20 minutes separating from the Sixth House cusp again, and Saturn was at 0 Virgo, sextiling Ray's natal Pluto in the First House.

Figure 10
MIDPOINTS ARRANGED IN 90-DEGREE SEQUENCE

♇ 01 00	☽/♇ 13 06	♃/A 21 57	☽/☿ 26 40	☽/♅ 32 55	♃/♆ 39 19	♃/♅ 45 53	♀/♃ 51 21	♀/♂ 59 21
☉/A 04 02	♆/♇ 14 14	♀/A 22 08	♆ 27 28	☉/♃ 33 14	♀/♆ 39 30	♀/♅ 46 04	♀ 51 32	M/☊ 62 36
☉/♄ 05 06	☿/♇ 14 34	♃/♄ 23 01	☿/♆ 27 48	☉/♀ 33 26	☿/♃ 39 39	☽/☊ 46 04	♅/☊ 53 46	♂/M 62 43
☉/♇ 08 10	☉ 15 19	♀/♄ 23 12	☉/♅ 27 58	♇/☊ 33 58	☿/♀ 39 50	☽/♂ 46 11	♂/♅ 53 53	☊ 66 56
☽/A 08 59	♅/A 16 41	☽ 25 12	☿ 28 08	♅/♆ 34 02	♅ 40 37	♆/☊ 47 12	♃/M 54 43	♂/☊ 67 03
☽/♄ 10 02	♄/♅ 17 45	A/M 25 31	♇/M 29 38	♂/♇ 34 05	☉/☊ 41 08	♂/♆ 47 18	♀/M 54 54	♂ 67 09
♆/A 10 06	☉/☽ 20 16	♃/♇ 26 05	A/☊ 29 50	☿/♅ 34 23	☉/♂ 41 14	☿/☊ 47 32	M 58 16	A 82 45
☿/A 10 27	♅/♇ 20 49	♀/♇ 26 16	♂/A 29 57	☉/M 36 48	☽/M 41 44	☿/♂ 47 39	♃/☊ 59 03	♄/A 83 49
♄/♆ 11 10	☉/♆ 21 24	☽/♆ 26 20	♄/☊ 30 54	☽/♃ 38 11	♆/M 42 52	♅/M 49 27	♂/♃ 59 09	♄ 84 52
☿/♄ 11 30	☉/☿ 21 44	♄/M 26 34	♂/♄ 31 01	☽/♀ 38 22	☿/M 43 12	♃ 51 09	♀/☊ 59 14	♇/A 86 53
								♄/♇ 87 56

What Astrology Missed

I was wrong about the date of Ray's death, being fairly sure that it would be in December of 1978 when progressed Mars conjuncted natal Uranus. After Ray's case I learned to pay more attention to solar returns and have since noted that many important changes in medical conditions take place at those times.

I still placed zinc under the rulership of Uranus, which in Ray's chart has only two hard aspects. But I recommended a zinc supplement anyway, and after I had changed the rulership to Jupiter (with four hard aspects in Ray's chart), the reasons for his need of zinc became clearer.

I still don't know why Ray had four kidneys. I know it's a hereditary trait, and with Saturn on the Ascendant, hereditary traits were perhaps stronger in Ray than in other people. Furthermore, as I've suggested, Gemini, meaning two of everything, might signify two more kidneys in this instance. I had thought Libra, ruling the kidneys, would have been involved more than it was; the fact that it wasn't just points out to me how far we have yet to go to make medical astrology a precision tool.

CASE HISTORY 3

Name

Bonnie.

Birth Data

January 4, 1941
4:24 a.m. CST
Delphos, Ohio

Ailments

Leukopenia, heart murmur and cancer of the uterus.

Background

Bonnie represents a typical case that I may receive at any given time: she had several ailments and a history of progressive deterioration of health. Besides the ailments listed above, she suffered from headaches, low blood pressure, low white blood cell count, nerve-related problems, constipation and thyroid complications. When I met her she was extremely pale, overweight and lethargic.

I had encountered many different types of anemia but never leukopenia. At the time Bonnie was having severe reactions to this disease: it had not gone into a state of remission for quite some time, and she was showing the ravaged effects of it. At this point her doctors (who were many and some of the best in the United States) were totally stymied as to what to do to bring the leukopenia into a state of remission. She had been a guinea pig for new drug therapy and different experiments, but her body was not responding. In the medical world her case was being monitored; later on it would be written up.

Leukopenia is characterized by an abnormal decrease of white blood corpuscles—not to be confused with anemia, caused by a decrease in red blood cells, or leukemia, distinguished by an increase in white blood cells. White blood cells are formed in the bone marrow or in the lymphatic tissue. They may form in the lymph glands, spleen or lymph nodes. With leukopenia the spleen, which manufactures several types of white blood cells, is sometimes surgically removed to try to rebalance the white count. Fortunately, Bonnie still had her spleen.

Bonnie's heart murmur was a result of rheumatic fever as a child. The hole in her heart had repaired itself as she grew into adulthood, and she had had no further trouble with it. She had had all the other normal childhood diseases. In 1948 her tonsils and adenoids were removed. In 1971 she had had a complete hysterectomy because cancer was found: she has had no more cancer since that date. She had three children, born in 1959, 1962 and 1963. In 1961 she suffered a miscarriage at three months of pregnancy.

I noted on the questionnaire she filled out for me that she was drinking five to six glasses of milk a week. She ate meat, fruit and vegetables. She was on drug medication for her thyroid (two grains), Premarin (an estrogen drug), iron pills and a multivitamin tablet.

The Natal Chart (Figure 11)

Since Bonnie had an abnormal white blood cell count, I first checked out Pluto, which rules any type of abnormality, especially of the blood. Pluto has three hard aspects, the highest number of any of the planets in her natal chart. With Pluto in Leo with those hard aspects her heart murmur was no surprise. Neither was it a surprise that she had had cancer: the few charts I have on this disease usually show fixed signs on the angles plus strongly accented Pluto and Saturn in the chart to characterize long-term, abnormal changes taking place in the body. Bonnie's chart shows Pluto square Saturn, a hard aspect that often signifies a potential ailment.

I did not feel that the spleen, ruled by Neptune, was the root cause of Bonnie's leukopenia: Neptune seemed minimally involved with only one hard aspect to Venus in Sagittarius. Instead, after doing hours of research on this ailment I became convinced that the problem involved the bone marrow, ruled by Cancer. Although she has no planets in that sign, by polarity she has the Sun and Mercury in Capricorn. Furthermore, bone is ruled by Saturn, and Saturn is conjunct Jupiter and square Pluto in Bonnie's natal chart. If at any time Bonnie had told me that the doctors were going to remove her spleen, I would have argued strongly against the operation, instead urging her doctors to check out the bone marrow as the cause first: fortunately, I never had to argue my case.

Next, because of all her throat and thyroid problems, I examined the planets in Taurus and Scorpio, feeling those signs were probably involved. Bonnie's chart shows three planets in Taurus in the Sixth House, the house of health. Probably contributing most heavily to her thyroid problems is Uranus in Taurus retrograde, a configuration that indicates a spasm in the thyroid gland that causes the thyroid to go from normal to either hyper or hypo: stress may cause it to malfunction; colon stasis can also contribute to the problem. The Jupiter-Saturn conjunction in Taurus also indicates that the thyroid will hypofunction, especially with Saturn also retrograde. In addition, Bonnie has Mars in Scorpio on the Ascendant in opposition to Uranus, a configuration contributing to her throat and thyroid problems as well as involving the female organs, which had been cancerous.

Bonnie's natal Moon in Aries has no hard aspects to it. But through the years I have found that a planet with no aspects can be implicated in health problems. So, I felt the Moon was also involved in her female complaints.

All four of Bonnie's outer planets are retrograde, an unusual number for one chart. And each of those retrograde planets had played major parts in Bonnie's ailments. As I've indicated, Saturn and Uranus both contributed to her thyroid problems. In addition, she has Neptune in Virgo retrograde, signifying weak intestinal peristalsis: in other words, food stays longer in the intestinal tract, causing toxins to be reabsorbed through the walls, poisoning an individual and producing toxemia.

The Cross: There was no question in my mind that the Fixed Cross was the root of Bonnie's problems. She had fixed signs on the angles and five planets in Taurus, Leo and Scorpio. But it was not the number of planets in fixed signs that convinced me to choose the Fixed Cross; rather, heart, thyroid,

Figure 11
BONNIE'S NATAL CHART

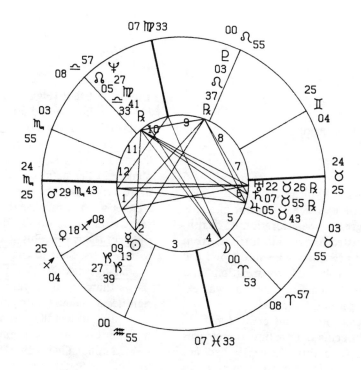

Bonnie
1 4 1941   4h20m 0s EST
PLACIDUS 40N51 84W21

throat, uterine and constipation problems are all indicative of illnesses implicating the Fixed Cross.

Other Information: The fixed star Zanrak is conjunct Bonnie's natal Uranus: Zanrak is said to represent long, draining illnesses and a difficult life.

The Progressed Chart (Figure 12)

In Bonnie's natal chart Hades sits at the midpoint of Saturn and Neptune, a powerful configuration representing wasting diseases of the body, poor immunity against viral and bacterial complaints and a potentially malfunctioning thymus. This midpoint structure had been very crucial in Bonnie's life. For intance, when Bonnie was four years old, Admetos and then nine months later the progressed Sun went over this position. At that time the leukopenia state began—an insidious ailment that was not detected until many years later.

Another important midpoint structure in Bonnie's chart is Neptune + Transpluto-Mars. This picture also hints at an unknown disease inflicting damage. In fact, Transpluto has appeared on a continual basis in Bonnie's chart over the years.

Moreover, natal Mars is opposite Admetos and the Sun on the 90-degree dial, a configuration that indicates subtle conditions of great seriousness remaining hidden for quite some time.

In 1959 when Bonnie was 18, she had her first child. At that time progressed Mars was conjunct natal Vulcanus/Venus—a birth configuration. Progressed Vulcanus/Venus was conjunct the natal Node/Poseidon, a picture that indicates that the birth will go smoothly. The progressed Sun was conjunct natal Transpluto: having this baby apparently changed the entire course of Bonnie's life. Progressed Hades was conjunct natal Jupiter, a configuration that would normally hint at birth complications, except that Poseidon was being activated at the same time. And progressed Jupiter was conjunct the natal Ascendant, another picture suggesting an easy birth, one that Bonnie was very happy about.

In 1962 when Bonnie was 21, she had her second child. At that time progressed Vulcanus/Venus was conjunct natal Mercury, a configuration indicating possible news about the birth. Progressed Admetos was conjunct natal Jupiter, a picture that suggests

Figure 12
BONNIE'S PROGRESSED CHART

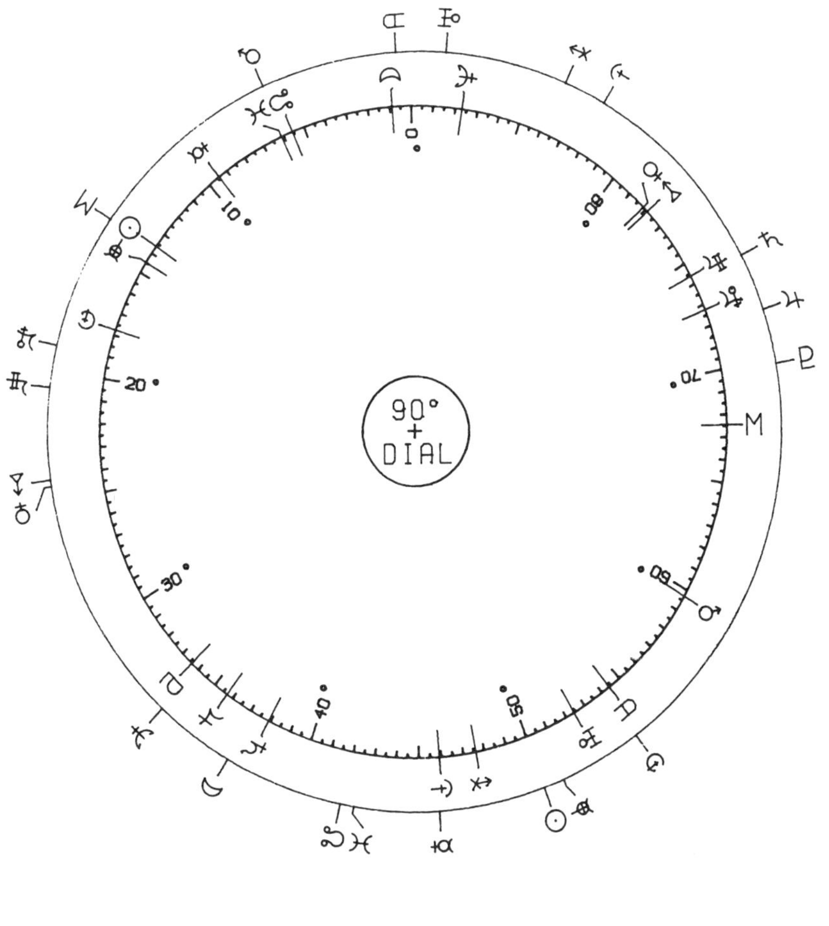

Bonnie would get pregnant shortly after the birth of her second child: I've seen this configuration active in many surprise pregnancies that no one was aware of until too late. Progressed Transpluto was conjunct natal Uranus, indicating an operation or birth of a child. And progressed Kronos was conjunct the natal Midheaven, perhaps signifying the competency of the doctor involved.

In 1963 at 22, Bonnie had her last child. At that time progressed Mercury was conjunct Transpluto, suggesting news of a transforming nature on a psychological level: Bonnie was emotionally affected by this third birth since she had lost a baby in 1961 from miscarriage. The progressed Sun was conjunct natal Jupiter, an excellent sign for an easy birth and delivery. Progressed Transpluto was conjunct the natal Ascendant: there must have been a great deal of activity in Bonnie's immediate environment with three children, two of whom were one year old or less. And progressed Uranus was conjunct natal Apollon, indicating possible operation and with Apollon involved suggesting that Bonnie had her hands full—literally and figuratively speaking.

Then in 1971 Bonnie had a hysterectomy because of cancer. At that time progressed Apllon was conjunct natal Admetos, progressed Vulcanus was conjunct natal Hades, and the progressed Node and Poseidon were conjunct natal Jupiter. This last picture indicated that Bonnie would come out of the operation free of cancer, and since 1971 she has had no indications of the disease returning: Poseidon acts like a guardian angel, suggesting successful operations.

Bonnie's one other operation, a tonsilectomy performed in 1948, occurred when transiting Uranus was conjunct natal Mars—a classic signature for operation.

At the time I saw Bonnie she was very sick. Her progressed Admetos and Sun would conjunct natal Uranus in approximately one to one and a half years from June of 1978. Thus I knew I had that much lead time to get her on the road to recovery.

The Transits

In June of 1978 transiting Saturn was applying to a square to Bonnie's natal Mars in the First House, implying that it was time for her to renew efforts to implement her serious, Saturnian ideas and goals. At the same time transiting Pluto was making a square to her natal Sun in the Second House, indicating that it was time for some serious transformation of self, e.g. getting better nutrition to make herself into a new kind of person.

Although transiting Uranus in her Twelfth House was making no major aspects at the time, such a transit can often mean that hidden knowledge may suddenly become available through an astrologer or other unusual source, as in fact happened. Finally, transiting Neptune was in her First House retrograde and separating from her natal Venus, hinting tht some unforeseen forces were at work to help her.

The Eclipses

An eclipse opposite Bonnie's natal Moon on March 24, 1978, implied that Bonnie was gaining an awareness of herself; it also marked a good time for her to take action on her desires 'o get well. An eclipse on September 16, 1978, was o posite her natal Neptune, indicating that by the allout date of December 16, 1978, she would either be very much better or chroncially and inexplicably worse: as her letters indicate, through a good nutritional plan Bonnie was rapidly returning to health by the fallout date.

Final Analysis

Besides having leukopenia Bonnie was overweight and tired. In addition, her thyroid was chronically hypofunctioning. To help her with her weight I recommended she daily take raw apple cider vinegar, which is high in potassium and acts as a natural diuretic. I also wanted her to form a diet around foods that would increase peristalsis; so, I suggested that she begin to eat more roughage and fibrous foods to stimulate the small intestines. And I recom-

Figure 13
MIDPOINTS ARRANGED IN 90-DEGREE SEQUENCE

☽ 00 53	☉/☿ 11 33	☿/♇ 21 32	A/☊ 29 59	☉/M 40 36	♇/M 50 35	♂/A 57 04	☿/♄ 68 41	☽/M 79 13
☉/♀ 00 54	☉ 13 39	♄/☊ 21 44	☽/♂ 30 18	♀/☊ 41 51	☉/♆ 50 40	♀/♄ 58 02	♀/♂ 68 55	☿/♂ 79 35
♆/☊ 01 37	♅/M 15 00	☉/♇ 23 38	♂/☊ 32 38	♃/♅ 44 04	☉/☽ 52 16	♂ 59 43	☉/♃ 69 41	♃/♇ 79 40
♂/♇ 01 40	A/M 15 59	♅/♆ 25 04	♇ 33 37	♃/A 45 04	♅ 52 26	♆/♇ 60 39	☉/♄ 70 47	♄/♇ 80 46
☽/☊ 03 13	♃/♆ 16 42	♆/A 26 03	♃ 35 43	♄/♅ 45 11	☿/☊ 52 30	☽/♇ 62 15	☿/♅ 75 56	M/☊ 81 33
☊ 05 33	♄/♆ 17 48	☽/♅ 26 39	♃/♄ 36 49	♄/A 46 10	♅/A 53 25	♇/☊ 64 35	☿/A 76 56	☉/♂ 81 41
♃/M 06 38	☽/♃ 18 18	☽/A 27 39	♀/♆ 37 55	♂/♃ 47 43	A 54 25	♀/♅ 65 17	♆/M 77 37	♆ 87 41
♄/M 07 44	♂/M 18 38	♀/M 27 51	♄ 37 55	☿/♆ 48 34	☉/☊ 54 36	♀/A 66 17	☉/♅ 78 03	♅/♇ 88 02
☿ 09 27	☽/♄ 19 24	♂/♆ 28 42	☿/M 38 30	♂/♄ 48 49	♂/♅ 56 04	M 67 33	♀ 78 08	☿/♀ 88 47
♀/♇ 10 53	♃/☊ 20 38	♅/☊ 29 00	☽/♀ 39 30	☽/☿ 50 10	♀/♃ 56 55	☿/♃ 67 35	☉/A 79 02	♇/A 89 01
								☽/♆ 89 17

mended that she get off milk: the excess mucus was not needed with her already toxic condition. Since two grams of thyroid medication is quite a bit, I suggested she substitute kelp tablets for part of that medication, providing her doctor agreed. I also recommended she take supplements of vitamins A, D, B-6, C and thiamine. I talked over the comprehensive diet and supplement plan with her and told her to get in touch with her doctors before initiating it, which she did.

Outcome

In October 1978 I got an update on Bonnie's condition: "By following your diet of vinegar and honey mixture, etc., everything is on the way up. (The blood) is on the border. It's not now critical. I still am not feeling up to par, but the doctor said it would take a while. I need more iron and vitamin C. I also have phlebitis in the large veins. He said that, unfortunately, they couldn't do anything for that except for me to stay off my legs. I remembered you saying you had a cure for it; wasn't that right? My blood pressure is extremely low, but he said as long as the blood keeps improving, that's the main thing. I have been losing weight slowly but surely. If I get really hungry, I just fix honey and vinegar and that cuts my appetite quickly. And the diet does help to clean my system out. At first, I had some cramps with it, but it seems to have just regulated me more than anything else.

"If I could just get these pains from the legs, I'd be on my way. I'm sure the only reason everything's improving now is because of your help. The doctors have done nothing for months because they didn't know what to do—and now they don't have a cure for phlebitis! HELP!"

I was satisfied that Bonnie's blood was stabilizing, and I had warned her ahead of time that no program based on a healthy diet plus herbs and supplements was going to cure her overnight: it had taken three months of continuous discipline to get her this far. Then the phlebitis developed. I called her the day I received her letter and told her to talk to her doctors about getting on vitamin E and on higher doses of vitamin C: both administered in high dosages can get rid of phlebitis quickly and easily. Since Bonnie had had a previous heart condition, I warned her to get one of her doctors to dispense the d-alpha tocopherol (vitamin E) to her in small dosages, eventually working up to a high amount: too much vitamin E taken suddenly can sometimes create heart palpitations.

Her second letter came in December of 1978: "I'm coming along pretty well. Actually, I'm 110 per cent better, if that's possible. I'm on 3,000 mgs. of vitamin C pretty steadily, occasionally upwards to 5,000. But I find I have diarrhea then, so I stay around 3,000 to 4,000. I'm also on 1,600 I.U. of vitamin E. I can feel that my blood pressure is up. Every so often, I have a 'backslide' day, and it seems things start dropping. But then, next day or so, I'm back at it. The iron content is pretty steady; my stool is pretty dark so I know I'm getting enough now. My energy, on the whole, has greatly increased. I do have my lazy days and some stinging of the veins in the legs—but all in all, it's going great."

This is the kind of report that makes medical astrology worthwhile. The leukopenia was in a state of remission. And, as a matter of fact, it still is at the printing of this book.

I received Bonnie's last update on her condition in April 1979: "As you know, when you did my Med-Scan I was in terrible shape—lots of blood problems, vein problems, blood clots, anemia! I started right away on your suggestions.... It's been slow, but my blood is straightening up very well. I take honey and vinegar twice a day (in grape juice mostly—water at times, but grape juice gives it a smoother flow until I get myself convinced it's good). I have lost 15 pounds, and that has been slow also. I feel good about that, though, because I know it's gone forever. I'd like to lose about eight more pounds. In general, I feel much better. I am learning this body is the only one I have, and it's time I respect it a little."

Bonnie is progressing nicely, although when she gets off her program her body punishes her immediately: people who have chronic ailments cannot afford to stray from diets that work for their bodies, something Bonnie found out the hard way. Bonnie still takes a thyroid supplement in lieu of the kelp tablets.

What Astrology Missed

I did not suggest the use of vitamin E until the phlebitis developed. I made the mistake of thinking that since Venus has only two hard aspects to it and Bonnie hadn't really had any symptoms of a deficiency in that vitamin, she didn't need it. But her natal Venus is in Sagittarius, indicating the possibility of blood clots and ensuing leg problems. Furthermore, Neptune is square Venus, and Neptune is frequently involved in phlebitis because clots form without the knowledge of the recipient until it is too late. If left unattended, phlebitis can kill a person. But, fortunately, the oversight on my part, attributable to my lack of a medical background, was easily corrected and the phlebitis disappeared.

CASE HISTORY 4

Name
> Anne.

Birth Data
> June 10, 1925
> 5:00 a.m. EST
> Vandergrift, Pennsylvania

Ailment
> Raynaud's disease.

Background

Anne contacted me in November 1978. She had Raynaud's disease, an ailment that affects the circulation in the fingers. The disease may remain dormant for years. Then an attack may be brought on by infection, fatigue or nervous exhaustion; therefore, rest is essential. During an attack the fingers become cold and numb, deeply blue or white and blue. There may be perspiration around the four fingers (rarely the thumb). Warm rooms or warm water can help ease an attack. Tingling, throbbing and swelling are the after effects of an attack. The arteries eventually continue to constrict until all circulation has halted to the fingers, making them cold, painful and deformed. Gangrene may set in, necessitating amputation.

Raynaud's disease is sometimes blamed on nervousness, an individual's inability to relax and give the body downtime. Strong emotions constitute another reason for the disease. Smoking aggravates the condition because smoking causes vasoconstriction.

Besides Raynaud's disease Anne experienced a great deal of pain in the chest area: she wasn't sure whether she had heart problems or not. Menopause was making the Raynaud's disease worse. She had borne four children—in 1957, 1958, 1961 and 1964. As a youngster she had suffered from bouts with pneumonia and bronchitis. Chronic sinus infections have plagued her most of her life. In 1937 she had a tonsilectomy and in 1966 had surgery performed on the varicose veins of her left leg. She is a vegetarian and at one point in her life used to drink much milk. Today she does not smoke.

The Natal Chart (Figure 14)

After doing extensive research on Raynaud's disease I compared the symptoms with Anne's chart. I felt that nerves were the main reason for Anne's bouts with the disease. Gemini on the Ascendant and both her Sun and Mercury in Gemini in the Twelfth House give ample cause for Raynaud's disease. Moreover, Anne's natal Moon has four hard aspects, all of which certainly help heighten her emotions,

which if repressed could manifest in the form of nervous irritation. Probably the most significant of these aspects is the Moon square Saturn, suggesting blocked emotions and subsequent constriction of the arteries. Although with the Moon in Aquarius and Saturn in Scorpio Anne is emotionally strong, able to withstand emotional duress for many years, her stored-up emotions needed to be released—in this instance in a negative way in the form of disease.

I do not usually include Mars in my final analysis because many times that planet is not implicated in the ailment, even though I check it out as a matter of habit. But in Anne's case I felt that the placement of Mars was a contributing factor to her problem. Her natal chart has Mars in Cancer, a combination that can indicate ulcers or a sensitive stomach: the walls of the stomach may be irritable or prone to inflammation from spicy foods, and vomiting may occur from emotional stress. Mars in Cancer normally means the stomach holds large amounts of acidity or excess hydrochloric acid, which can make an individual very nervous and jumpy. With Venus and Pluto also in Cancer, by polarity implicating the gallbladder, I wanted to make sure Anne was getting enough bile into the duodenum to emulsify fats to insure no plaque buildup occurring in the veins or arteries to aggravate her condition.

Next I examined the placements of the outer planets.

Saturn in Scorpio (retrograde): This placement can mean poor peristalsis, resulting in constipation; caking of fecal matter on the walls of the large intestine; and toxemia, potentially affecting the thyroid, heart, throat and back. For many years Anne had suffered from constipation before she had had the good sense to straighten out her diet. And she was still experiencing pains in the chest, had had a tonsilectomy and suffered from dizziness—all of which can be by-products of a sluggish colon.

Neptune in Leo: This configuration can signify a weak heart, low blood pressure from sluggish activity of the heart, a weak back and commensurate problems. Anne had the chest pains. She also had had some cervical vertabrae problems involving her neck and back earlier in life.

Uranus in Pisces: This placement can indicate spasmodic release of insulin from the pancreas because of emotional states, unpredictable sugar problems, foot deformity, cramping and spasm of the muscles in the feet. This description did not fit Anne's state of health: she did not appear to have any sugar problems—either through testing or symptoms. So, I looked at the opposite polarity, Uranus in Virgo, to double check. This placement can mean spasms and cramping in the intestinal tract, twisting and telescoping of the bowels. This, I felt, was a better description of Anne's particular case, especially since she had had diarrhea and constipation earlier in life.

The Cross: I chose the Fixed Cross as the root of Anne's problems because her past medical conditions involved fixed signs for the most part.

Other Information: There are no critical degrees in Anne's chart. She has several fixed stars, but none that pertain to medical conditions.

The Progressed Chart (Figure 15)

In 1937 when Anne was 12, she had her tonsils removed. All of her childhood she had suffered from continual attacks of bronchitis and pneumonia as well as sinus drainage. Her doctor decided that perhaps these attacks could best be brought under control by removal of the tonsils. At that time progressed Uranus was conjunct natal Admetos, progressed Pluto was conjunct natal Transpluto and progressed Saturn was conjunct natal Neptune. These configurations indicate that Anne had been suffering from a long-term condition—with Saturn

and Neptune involved probably a poisoning but a poisoning in terms of continued viral and bacterial infections.

In 1966 when Anne was 41, an operation was performed on her left leg to alleviate a problem with varicose veins. At that time progressed Uranus was conjunct natal Kronos, progressed Poseidon was conjunct natal Saturn, progressed Saturn was conjunct the natal Sun and progressed Vulcanus was conjunct natal Jupiter. Although none of these is a traditional operation axis, the presence of Saturn in these configurations indicates a chronic condition; the Vulcanus-Jupiter conjunction implies extensive and complete renovation; the Uranus-Kronos conjunction suggests a very competent surgeon made the operation a success; and Poseidon and Jupiter in these configurations hints that all will go well, as it did.

Anne had four children. At the first birth in 1957, when she was 32, the progressed Sun was conjunct natal Jupiter, the progressed Moon was conjunct natal Vulcanus and progressed Cupido was conjunct the natal Ascendant: these are all fairly

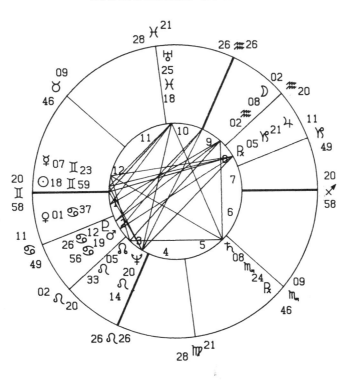

Figure 14
ANNE'S NATAL CHART

Anne
6 10 1925   5h 0m 0s EST
PLACIDUS   40N36   79W34

common midpoint structures suggesting the birth of a child. Then at the second birth in 1958, when Anne was 33, the progressed Ascendant was conjunct natal Transpluto and progressed Zeus was conjunct natal Mercury: Zeus is very often present in birth situations, as is Transpluto, which embodies the psychological ramifications of the birth. At the third birth in 1961, when Anne was 36, progressed Pluto was conjunct natal Cupido, progressed Mars was conjunct the natal Midheaven and progressed Cupido was conjunct natal Uranus: Mars conjunct the Midheaven can mean many things, including a birth. Then at the fourth birth in 1964, when Anne was 37, progressed Poseidon was conjunct natal Zeus, progressed Venus was conjunct natal Saturn and progressed Neptune was conjunct natal Poseidon: the Uranian planets involved indicate an easy, uncomplicated birth.

The progressed chart also shows that Anne has three natal midpoint structures that could potentially affect her health at various times in her life.

Admetos/Hades-Neptune: This configuration can mean a chronic, hidden illness that may manifest. A disease is often hidden because of repressed emotions, such as anxiety, anger or frustration—emotions that need to be released to insure continued health. A planet progressing to Neptune could signal a release of such a backlog of emotions: a person could "blow up" verbally, take appropriate actions or manifest a physical illness.

Uranus/Pluto-Hades: Activation of this midpoint structure can indicate the sudden manifestation of an illness. Chronic disorders, such as anemia, and with a strongly aspected Pluto irregularly shaped red or white blood cells are also fairly common with this configuration, especially for Fixed Cross individuals. As far as I knew, Anne did not have such problems; however, a sudden flare-up of a condition was possible if a progressed planet conjuncted the Hades midpoint.

Jupiter/Hades-Pluto: Although there is no specific information available on this combination, I felt it could mean a chronic condition that might run rampant (Jupiter) or spread quickly, with the body unable to check its rapid progress. I felt that this configuration could be a secondary factor in making a

Figure 15
ANNE'S PROGRESSED CHART

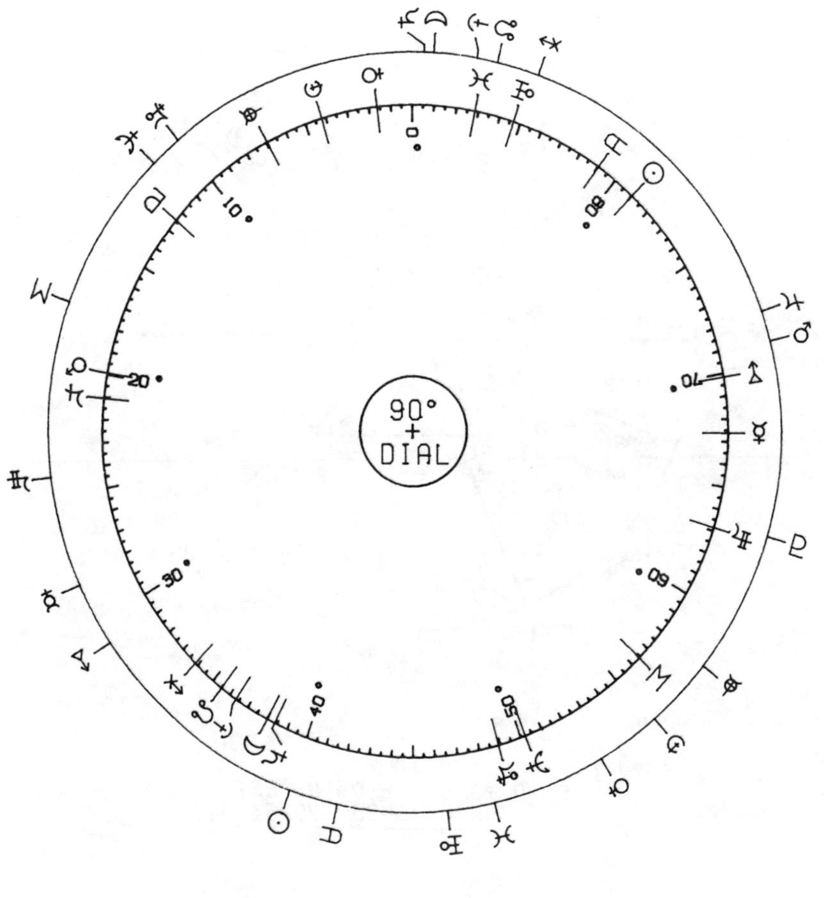

festering condition worse when it finally surfaced. Progressed Neptune had crossed this midpoint in August, about 3 ½ months before Anne consulted me, and I suspect that at the time her condition worsened she decided to give medical astrology a try.

The Transits

At the time I worked up Anne's Med-Scan she had already passed a crisis that had taken place in late July and early August of 1978. There were no pressing transits in November—at least from a health standpoint.

Eclipses

An eclipse occurred on September 16, within two degrees of Anne's natal Uranus in the Tenth House. The fallout date for it was December 16, 1978, indicating that an unusual event might take place. In this case, around the time of the fallout date Anne contacted me, and I was to play an important part in her career: Anne is a massotherapist and without the kind of help medical astrology afforded her she would have been unable to use her fingers and thus unable to earn an income.

Final Analysis

I recommended that Anne take moderate exercise to strengthen her heart muscle, I suggested a diet high in roughage and raw or nearly raw foods to get her intestines into a better working state, and I provided a list of supplements to be approved by her doctor—vitamins B-6, E and D, riboflavin and pantothenic acid to help her adrenal glands handle stress more efficiently and potassium to help alleviate her heart pain. Although I knew that an improved diet and supplementation could do much to alleviate Raynaud's disease, I indicated to Anne that the true cure lay in how she handled her emotional energies.

Outcome

In February of 1979 I received a call from Anne. No matter what supplements she took they gave her gas. It appeared that her gastric juices were weak (Mars in Cancer). I suggested she talk to her doctor about some enzyme tablets to help digestion: whenever there is poor digestion, the medical astrologer with the approval of the attending physician should consider hydrochloric acid, pancreatic enzymes or bile or lecithin tablets to break down the food.

Anne also had gas from the yogurt she had been eating; so, at my suggestion she switched to acidophilus tablets, which seemed to help a great deal. She needed the good bacteria that yogurt or acidophilus tablets provide for various vitamins to be synthesized in her large intestines.

In April of 1979 she wrote: "I feel better following the diet, even though there are times I go off the diet (only occasionally). I've lost five to ten pounds of weight and generally have more energy, less depression and fewer pains around the heart. I'm greatly improved."

I felt the pains around the heart were from a deficiency of potassium. Since any type of synthetic potassium can cause problems in the gastric system for many people, we worked up a program whereby she was able to get more natural potassium from food instead of supplements. If potassium is deficient, the intestines can be immobilized, halting peristalsis and resulting in constipation.

The Raynaud's disease continues in a state of remission. She now takes an herbal formula containing ginger, golden seal and capsicum, as well as a supplement of vitamin E—all of which helps increase the circulation throughout her body. Since she has Mars in Cancer, indicating an ultrasensitive stomach lining, I was hesitant about suggesting the capsicum (red pepper). But Anne began by taking small amounts with her food, gradually increasing the amount until the problem was overcome: capsicum is extremely helpful in increasing circulation.

What Astrology Missed

Although my diagnosis was adequate, providing Anne with a comprehensive diet was more difficult. In addition to reacting adversely to synthetic sup-

Figure 16
MIDPOINTS ARRANGED IN 90-DEGREE SEQUENCE

☉/♇ 00 43	☽/☿ 07 42	♃/♇ 16 45	☉/M 22 43	♆/♇ 31 20	♂/M 38 11	♂/♅ 52 37	☿ 67 23	☉/A 79 58
♀ 01 37	♀/♂ 10 46	♄/♅ 16 51	A/M 23 42	☿/♅ 31 21	♄ 38 24	☿/♄ 52 54	♅/♆ 67 46	A 80 58
♇/A 01 42	♀/♃ 11 21	☿/M 16 55	♇/☊ 23 59	♇/M 34 26	♃/M 38 45	♃/♅ 53 12	♄/♇ 70 25	♄/☊ 81 58
♄/M 02 25	☉/☊ 12 16	♀/☊ 18 35	☽/♇ 25 14	♂/♆ 35 05	♆/☊ 42 53	♆/M 53 20	♅/M 70 52	☽/♄ 83 13
☉/♂ 04 27	♇ 12 26	☉/♆ 19 36	♀/♆ 25 55	☊ 35 33	♀/♅ 43 28	M 56 26	☉/☿ 73 11	☿/♇ 84 55
☉/♃ 05 02	A/☊ 13 15	☽/♀ 19 50	♂/☊ 27 44	♃/♆ 35 39	☽/♆ 44 08	☉/♄ 58 42	♂/♄ 74 10	☉/♀ 85 18
♂/A 05 27	☉/☽ 13 30	♂ 19 56	♃/☊ 28 19	☽/☊ 36 47	M/☊ 45 59	♄/A 59 41	☿/A 74 10	♅ 85 18
♃/A 06 01	☿/♆ 13 48	♂/♃ 20 30	☽/♂ 28 59	☉/♅ 37 09	☽/M 47 14	♅/☊ 60 26	♃/♄ 74 44	♀/A 86 17
☿/☊ 06 28	☽/A 14 30	♆/A 20 36	♀/M 29 02	☽ 38 02	♅/♇ 48 52	☽/♅ 61 40	☉ 78 59	☿/♂ 88 39
♀/♇ 07 02	♂/♇ 16 11	♃ 21 05	☽/♃ 29 33	♅/A 38 08	♆ 50 14	♀/♄ 65 01	☿/♀ 79 30	☿/♃ 89 14
								♄/♆ 89 19

plements and yogurt, Anne could not properly digest raw fruits and vegetables, which caused gas and bloating. So, it was necessary to straighten out Anne's digestion before anything else.

CASE HISTORY 5

Name

Jessica.

Birth Data

November 2, 1951
1:48 p.m. EST
Buffalo, New York

Ailments

Infertility, abdominal pains, exploratory abdominal surgery (laparotomy), overweight and severe menstrual cycle problems.

Background

I met Jessica when I was on the road giving lectures. She told me that in two days she had to go in for another laparotomy, medical terminology for exploratory surgery in the abdomen. Jessica had gone through a laparoscopy in early 1976 as part of diagnostic procedures to find out why she could not have children: her ovaries were checked to see if they were capable of producing eggs. Then in September 1976 she went through a laparotomy. The surgeon found tumorlike tissue on the left ovary and extensive adhesion, which he felt contributed to her inability to conceive.

In August 1977 Jessica told her specialist she was experiencing a feeling like a pulled abdominal muscle. Without examining her the infertility specialist said he assumed she was finally pregnant and feeling that way because of the cyst on her left ovary. Then a few weeks later Jessica felt extremely uncomfortable: the pain was barely tolerable. She went to the ermegency ward. Her specialist assumed either that the cyst had ruptured and was bleeding internally or that the suspected pregnancy had ruptured in the Fallopian tube. The emergency room nurse, the only person to diagnose the symptoms accurately, said Jessica had a ruptured appendix. Jessica could have died from peritonitis if the nurse hadn't insisted on her diagnosis and finally persuaded the doctor to perform an appendectomy.

In February 1978 Jesica had another diagnostic laparoscopy. Because of the ruptured appendix, her pelvic and abdominal cavity was a mass of adhesions. Her left ovary was still not in good shape, and her specialist said that he might want to yet remove it. At this point he gave Jessica only a 10 per cent potential of becoming pregnant.

That is when I met her—two days before she was to go in for that laparotomy. She described her symptoms to me: she had horrible pain and cramping during her period, and she still experienced pain in the region of the ovaries when not on her period.

Jessica had several other problems as well. She was overweight, weighing 160 pounds at 5'7": at age 18 she had weighed 200 pounds. She continually battled borderline anemia and was treated with iron supplements off and on throughout her life. She had had an ear infection at age two, which had resulted in a weakness of both ears for the rest of her life. Since her family had a history of diabetes, she annually took glucose tolerance tests to make sure her sugar levels were remaining normal: at the time I saw her she did not seem predisposed to diabetes. Another irritating problem Jessica had was chronic vaginal yeast infections that never totally cleared up. She was also susceptible to severe headaches, eyestrain and tension. And she had worn glasses since 1959.

In May 1973 she had had a tonsilectomy because her tonsils were enlarged, not infected. In 1976 she had had impacted wisdom teeth extracted. And in 1975 she had had a D & C to get rid of cervical polyps.

At the time I first saw her Jessica was on several drugs to try to get pregnant. She was on a three to four month's suppression therapy with Enovid following the laparotomy. Then she took Clomid and Premarin for four months: the Clomid induced cysts twice. Moreover, both she and her husband took Minocin to try to reduce any possible micro-organisms that might have been present in the vaginal secretions, thereby inhibiting conception. And she had taken Ovral regularly before 1975 for contraceptive purposes. Such drug treatment had obviously been unsuccessful. And many estrogentype drugs will do more than simply produce cysts: they can create gallbladder disease, blood clots, liver problems, high blood pressure and hypoglycemia—just to mention a few of their side effects.

The Natal Chart (Figure 17)

None of Jessica's planets has more than one or two hard aspects. So few aspects to the planets does not necessarily mean there is no vitamin or mineral deficiency; instead, a medical astrologer needs to examine which planets are in aspect. For instance, in Jessica's chart Jupiter opposite Saturn is far more likely to indicate a nutritional problem than Uranus square Neptune because Jupiter and Saturn help control assimilation of nutrients into the body. The fact that she had suffered from anemia further enhances the probability that she assimilates nutrients poorly. Jessica's chart also has the Sun inconjunct Jupiter.

Jupiter in hard aspect usually indicates a severe deficiency, as does an inconjunct, and with the Sun ruling vitamins A and D, vital to good eysight, and Jessica's past history of eye trouble, this hard aspect strongly indicates deficiencies of vitamins A and D.

Because of Jessica's problems with childbearing, I also looked at the hard aspects of her natal Moon, which is square both Venus and Mars, poor configurations for someone who wants to become pregnant. Next I noticed that Uranus is in Cancer retrograde in her Fifth House: from other cases I've noted that such a placement can indicate tubal pregnancies or other abnormal pregnancies.

After looking at Jessica's chart I felt she might get hypoglycemia at some time in her life if she didn't continue to deal positively with her emotions. Both Venus and Mars are in the sign Virgo, which rules the pancreas. And the Moon square Venus and Mars suggests the potential for disease to occur: hypoglycemia is often brought on by severe stress. Fortunately, Jessica is extremely intelligent and knows the value of venting her feelings.

I next examined the outer planets, especially anxious to find out the reasons for the pain that crisscrossed Jessica's abdomen before and after her period. Two of these planets are in Libra, a hint that metabolic problems may have been partly responsible for her reproductive ailments.

Saturn in Libra: This placement can indicate thickening of the tubule walls of the kidneys, creating poor filtering conditions to remove urea from the blood, renal or urine retention or toxemia. I felt that this configuration represented the root cause of Jessica's problems: her blood, improperly filtered, moved back into her circulatory system, poisoning everything in general. Furthermore, her weight problem probably stemmed from water retention, which also pointed to sluggish kidneys.

Uranus in Cancer (retrograde): This configuration can mean spasms in the stomach, stomach cramps brought on by emotional duress, spasmodic release of gastric juices and a "nervous" stomach. Since Jessica did not seem to have any of these problems, I checked the opposite polarity, Uranus in Capricorn, which suggests spasms or calculi stones in the gallbladder. I wondered if it was possible to have

Figure 17
JESSICA'S NATAL CHART

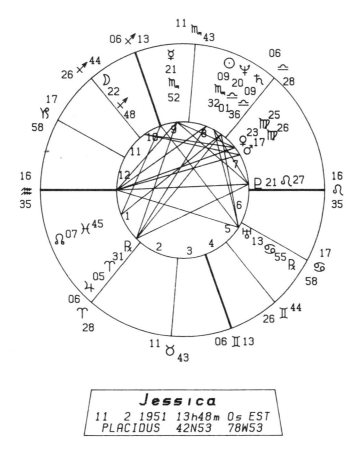

Jessica
11 2 1951 13h48m 0s EST
PLACIDUS 42N53 78W53

a gallstone and have the pains originating in the area of the abdomen. Although I had seen several cases of gallstones involving pains shooting down the arms, under either shoulder blade or in the region of the heart, I had not encountered a reflex action to the abdomen. But Jessica did have bloating shortly after eating—another sign of a sluggish gallbladder. I put "gallstones" down on her Med-Scan sheet, intending to suggest that she get a cholecystography test to determine whether or not the gallbladder was affected.

Neptune in Libra: This placement can mean weak or poor kidney function, weakened kidneys from illness or heredity and poor filtering of urea from the blood, causing anemia. It suggested to me that some of Jessica's anemia could possibly be cleared up by cleaning out her kidneys, although I knew such a cleansing alone would not cure the anemia: there were other deficiencies contributing to the disease.

The Progressed Chart (See Figures 18 and 19)

In 1975 when Jessica was 24, she had a D and C.

At that time progressed Jupiter was conjunct natal Hades.

In 1976 when Jessica was 25, she had a laparotomy. At that time progressed Uranus was conjunct the natal Sun, a well-known operation axis; progressed Admetos was conjunct the natal Ascendant, mirroring the frustration and fears she was experiencing; progressed Mercury was conjunct natal Mars; and progressed Vulcanus was conjunct natal Neptune, suggesting misdiagnosis or confusion.

When Jessica had her ruptured appendix in 1977 at the age of 26, progressed Neptune was conjunct the Ascendant, signifying possible misdiagnosis in a woman; the progressed Sun was conjunct the natal Midheaven, showing the seriousness of the risk to her life; progressed Pluto was conjunct natal Mars, a dangerous configuration that can at times spell the death of an individual; progressed Kronos was conjunct natal Apollon, a picture that can indicate misdiagnosis on the part of a doctor; progressed Mars was conjunct natal Uranus, a common operation axis; progressed Venus was conjunct natal Neptune, hinting that she could have died of poisoning;

Figure 18
JESSICA'S PROGRESSED CHART

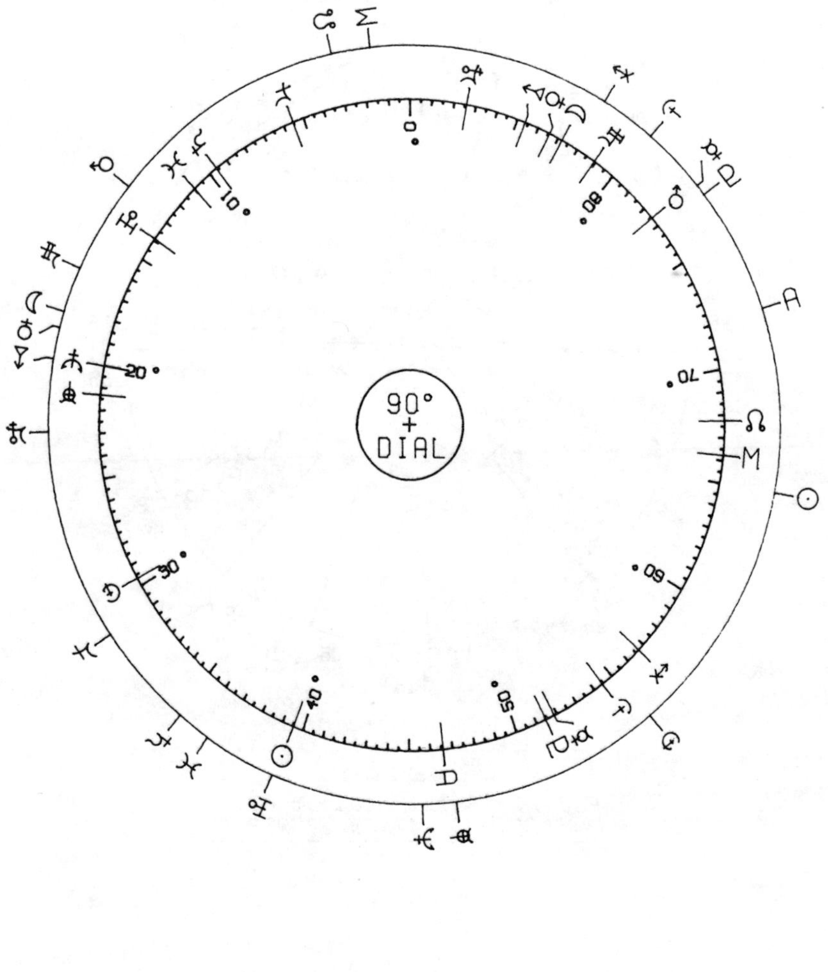

and progressed Vulcanus was conjunct natal Admetos, suggesting the presence of a major, hidden illness.

When Jessica had her second diagnostic laparoscopy in 1978 at the age of 27, progressed Hades was conjunct natal Zeus and progressed Zeus was conjunct natal Venus. These two configurations can indicate the worsening of reproductive problems, which was the case when Jessica underwent the surgery.

Examination of the progressed chart revealed several potentially relevant midpoint structures.

Mo/Ne-Pl: In the charts of women this configuration suggests a possible endocrine disorder that goes undetected as well as edema or water-weight problems. Jessica certainly had those problems. But what I felt was more important was that this structure probably affected her ability to conceive with ease. It can represent inherent weakness in the female reproductive system. In addition, Pluto can stand for tumors and cysts, which she had on her left ovary.

Ne/Ze-Ve: Although I had no specific information for this midpoint structure, I surmised that with Neptune in the picture once again, and with the presence of Zeus, representing the seed of life, conception was going to be difficult. I also felt Venus, ruling vitamin E, might be partly responsible for Jessica's inability to conceive because she suffered from a deficiency in that vitamin.

Me/Ne-Ap: This configuration can indicate a person who is highly strung, with sensitive nerves. Despite Aquarius rising and the Sun in Scorpio, Jessica is very sensitive.

Ne/Pl-Ap: Having no specific information on this structure, I conjectured that it hinted at multiple weaknesses, perhaps endocrine disorders plus problems with tumors.

Su/Ne-Ha: Ailments involving water retention of the body, edema, drug overdose or drug side effects, weakening of the physical body and susceptibility to infections or viral strains are all suggested by this configuration. Jessica had water retention, repeated and chronic yeast infections and drug-induced tumors. Note that once again Neptune is involved. Any time one planet recurs in midpoint structures, the medical astrologer can surmise that it wields great power over all. Neptune rules misdiagnosis, drug sensitivity, infections and atonic conditions.

Ve/Ha-Ze: This configuration suggests an inability to conceive because of a disease of the reproductive system. This midpoint structure, then, reaffirms others. Whenever two or three pictures indicate essentially the same problem, the chances are strongly increased that the problem exists.

Ur/Pl-Ma: A severe, sudden and debilitating accident may occur with this midpoint picture. When Jessica's appendix ruptured, progressed Pluto conjuncted Mars, indicating the seriousness of the situation and the potential for death.

Ha/Tr-Ma: Although I had no information for this configuration, since it is on the same tree as Ur/Pl-Ma, I felt it indicated big trouble. In my opinion this particular tree is a very dangerous one for Jessica and must be closely watched. Hades could worsen the situation, and Transpluto could mean a matter of life or death.

Su-Vu: These two planets are in opposition in Jessica's natal chart. With Vulcanus representing easily mishandled cosmic force, I wanted to keep an eye on this combination because it could mean an operation in the right circumstances. For instance, Jessica had her laporotomy when progressed Uranus conjuncted the Sun in September 1976.

Me/Ap-Ad: With no information about this picture I was somewhat mystified about its meaning. Since Mercury rules the nerves in general, I surmised that it simply pointed to Jessica's innate sensitivity and her ability to react under duress. Later on I was to be proven very wrong.

Transits

Transiting Neptune had been hovering around Jessica's natal Moon since late in 1977, helping to create a cloud of confusion and misdiagnosis, In February 1980 it conjuncted her Moon, then

Figure 19
MIDPOINTS ARRANGED IN 90-DEGREE SEQUENCE

☉/♇ 00 30	♄ 09 36	☽/A 19 41	♀/M 29 49	☉ 39 32	☽/♆ 51 24	♅/♆ 61 58	♂/☊ 72 35	♆/♇ [illegible]
♀/♄ 01 30	A/M 11 24	♆ 20 01	♅/A 30 15	♅/☊ 40 50	♇ 51 27	♂/A 62 01	♄/A 73 05	♃/☊ 81 [illegible]
☽/♅ 03 21	♃/♆ 12 46	M/☊ 21 59	☽/☊ 30 16	♆/M 43 07	☿ 51 52	♂/♇ 64 26	♃/♇ 73 29	☽ 82 48
♂/♆ 03 44	☉/♂ 13 29	☽/♇ 22 07	☿/♄ 30 44	☽/♃ 44 09	☉/M 52 53	♀/A 65 00	☽/M 74 31	♀ 83 25
☿/A 04 14	♇/M 13 50	☉/♃ 22 32	♅/♇ 32 41	♂/♅ 45 41	♃/♅ 54 43	M 66 13	♄/♇ 75 31	♄/☊ 83 40
♃ 05 31	♅ 13 55	☿/♀ 22 39	☽/♂ 35 07	☉/☿ 45 42	♄/♅ 56 45	☽/☿ 67 20	♀/☊ 75 35	♅/M 85 04
☿/♇ 06 39	♄/♆ 14 48	☉/♄ 24 34	♃/M 35 52	☽/♄ 46 12	A/☊ 57 10	♀/♇ 67 26	♂ 77 26	♂/♃ 86 28
♀/♆ 06 43	☿/☊ 14 48	♂/M 26 50	☿/♆ 35 57	A 46 35	☿/M 59 03	☊ 67 45	☿/♅ 77 54	☉/A 88 04
♃/♄ 07 33	☉/♀ 16 29	☿/♃ 28 41	♄/M 37 55	♀/♅ 48 40	♇/☊ 59 36	♃/A 71 03	♆/A 78 18	♂/♄ 88 31
☉/☊ 08 39	☿/♂ 19 39	☉/♆ 29 47	☽/♀ 38 07	♇/A 49 01	☉/☽ 61 10	☉/♅ 71 44	♀/♂ 80 26	♆/☊ 88 53
								♀/♃ 89 28

retrograded back over the luminary in April and crossed it a third time in December 1980. I noticed that from July through October of 1980 it would hit the Moon again. After that I felt many of her problems concerning childbirth would disappear.

Eclipses

Jessica's chart was activated by eclipses with great regularity in 1975 and 1976. On September 17, 1977, an eclipse occurred at 4 Aries in opposition to Jessica's natal Saturn in the Eighth House, one month after her appendectomy. The next eclipse, on October 12, 1977, conjuncted her Neptune, emphasizing the misdiagnosis that she was undergoing. On March 4, 1978, an eclipse conjuncted her Saturn, one month after her February 1978 laparoscopy. Then in April 1978 an eclipse occurred in opposition to her Neptune. At that time I began working on her case, hoping to clear up the confusion and chronic misdiagnosis and get her on a road back to health: I've found that eclipses in opposition to planets or angles usually clarify a situation, whereas eclipses in conjunction with planets or angles tend to aggravate or induce a problem or illness.

Final Analysis

When I saw Jessica after going over her chart, the first thing I told her was not to go in for the laparotomy until she could get a cholecystography to determine if she had gallstones. She looked at me strangely and confided with relief that she just didn't feel good about going in for the exploratory surgery. She agreed to postpone it and ask her specialist for the gallbladder test.

I then listed the nutritional supplements I felt she needed, telling her to have the list approved by a physician. I suggested she start taking vitamin E and zinc, both extremely helpful in restoring fertility. I also recommended vitamin A, riboflavin, vitamin B-6, vitamin B-12 and pantothenic acid, all good for getting rid of vaginal yeast infections. I wrote down potassium as essential for her water-weight problem: I felt she was water-retentive because her sodium-potassium exchange was out of balance. And I suggested an oiltype lecithin because two capsules with each meal work wonders for people who have no gallbladder or poor bile secretion or are susceptible to cholesterol type stones in their gallbladders: oil-perle lecithin helps reduce bloating and gas during and after meals.

Since one of the best and safest ways to open up the kidneys is vinegar, I recommended that Jessica ask her doctor if she could have two glasses of vinegar a day to start losing weight. I also cautioned her against eating a lot of fried foods because the gallbladder has problems producing adequate amounts of lecithin to emulsify the fats.

When Jessica requested a cholecystography, the doctor refused to perform it, saying that she didn't have any gallstones. She then sought out a woman doctor who agreed to give her the test. Here are the results sent to me from her doctor: "Oral Telepaque study revealed satisfactory concentrating function. Within the gallbladder, there was a radiolucent filling defect that measured 1 cm. in diameter, and which was basically radiolucent or cholesterol type. Cholelith within functioning gallbladder."

Needless to say, her specialist was shocked. So was Jessica. And frankly so was I. Medical astrology had worked. The doctor suggested surgery, but I quickly vetoed the idea, saying there was a good chance we could melt the stone down with lecithin. Jessica agreed to try the lecithin, since she didn't want any more operations at that point: she was tired of getting cut on. Furthermore, her belief in her doctors was fairly tarnished.

Outcome

Jessica faithfully stuck to her diet after her new doctor okayed it. In April she wrote: "I started the program of vitamin therapy on the 27th of March, haven't noticed anything too distressing in terms of reactions, though, as you warned, I've been spending a lot more time in the bathroom.... Aside from that, I feel all right—just a bit draggy."

Jessica's frequent trips to the bathroom were caused by the vinegar, which is a diuretic. But the vinegar was also cleaning her kidneys, rebalancing the potassium-sodium metabolism and working toward getting rid of the excess water in her body. Her "draggy" feeling was simply detoxification taking place.

Following are excerpts from further letters she sent me.

August 1978:"I've been following the diet off and on since May 21 and have gone from 170½ pounds to 150—the least I've ever weighed in my adult life. In general, I'm feeling much better now than I did back in March! The menstrual cramps have lessened a great deal, which is a blessing! I have noticed, though, that I now experience mild nausea on the first day. *That* I can cope with!"

April 1979: "I stayed on your program between May and late September of 1978. During that time, I lost 24 pounds. I'm presently trying to maintain 147 pounds. More importantly, during that time, I noticed that the vicious menstrual cramps I'd had almost all my adult life steadily lessened in severity! From feeling *rotten* the first three days of the cycle, I went to experiencing just mild discomfort. . . . on the first day—some nausea and slight cramping that could be ignored for the most part.

"My energy level also seemed to increase.... After the detoxification blahs were over, I found that I just didn't feel as burned out and draggy by the end of the day.

"One other thing: you know, I just didn't believe that the vinegar-honey regimen would do *anything* for water retention. In fact, I *tried* to make it not work, maintaining or increasing fluid intake on the days I skipped the vinegar-honey just to prove that it was the amount of liquid taken rather than any property of the vinegar that increased the quantity voided. As you know, that scheme failed. Volume increased on days that I drank the vinegar/honey mix and dropped on days I didn't, even though fluid intake on those days was the same or greater! I used to pick up four to seven pounds during the last week or so of my menstrual cycle, all of it due to fluid retention. With the vinegar-honey, I'm able to keep that under control—no more preperiod bloat!"

When I contacted Jessica in February 1980, she reported no more discomfort with her gallbladder. Although she had not undergone another test to prove conclusively that the lecithin had melted down the gallstone, the symptoms had all been alleviated. Instead of trying to get pregnant Jessica and her husband are adopting a baby, which they were to receive in December 1980.

What Astrology Missed

When I called Jessica in early 1980 to see how she was coming along, she informed me that she had had three epileptic seizures of a grand mal variety—on July 1, October 8 and October 9, 1979.

I was slightly shocked, to say the least. I had never dealt with a case of epilepsy before. And because I had had no idea of what to look for in a chart, I had missed the diagnosis.

As I looked back over Jessica's charts in light of these new developments, I noticed several interesting features:

1. Unuk, a fixed star, is conjunct Jessica's natal Mercury.

2. At the time of the October seizures transiting Uranus was applying toward a conjunction of Mercury and Unuk.

3. Mercury is in a critical degree; several other planets—Pluto, the Sun, Uranus and Mars—are also in special degrees in Jessica's chart.

4. At the time of the seizures the progressed Moon was conjunct Neptune, a planet that represents a weakness—in this case a weakness in the brain.

Jessica has no family history of this ailment, thought to be hereditary in large part. With no

research to back up my idea I believed that epilepsy (perhaps changes in the electrical brain potentials during seizures) was probably a Mercury or Uranus phenomenon. At that point one of the puzzling midpoint structures in Jessica's chart — Me/Ap-Ad — finally made sense: a multiple condition (Apollon) relating to the nerves (Mercury) remained hidden (Admetos). (I am not inferring, however, that everyone with this midpoint structure in a chart will contract epilepsy.) After transiting Uranus left her natal Mercury Jessica had no further trouble with epilepsy.

CASE HISTORY 6

Name

Steve.

Birth Data

March 17, 1969
12:07 a.m. EST
Dayton, Ohio

Ailments

Supposedly mentally retarded and autistic, with possible brain damage.

Background

I met with Steve and his mother, Joyce, in early 1978. Steve was 11 years old at the time and had been pronounced mentally retarded, autistic or brain-damaged by several specialists. Joyce did not believe them. She felt sure that Steve would talk and thought that the medical establishment had overlooked something.

Since the doctors felt Steve was hyperactive, they had put him on Mellaril, a tranquilizer, to calm him down. And he was certainly a handful. He would be up and running around early each morning, finally falling into an exhausted sleep sometime between 1 and 2 a.m. This behavior had started when he was two. According to his mother, at age two he "just went haywire": one moment he had been a calm and happy child; the next, he turned into a Jekyll-Hyde personality. He was almost uncontrollable, a nervous, jumpy child given to fits and starts. He was also underweight for his age. His diet consisted of no fruits or vegetables, a little meat, plenty of milk, orange juice and other sweetened juices and starch foods, such as casseroles. He craved sweets most of the time. He got allergies in the spring and fall of each year.

The Natal Chart (Figure 20)

Steve's chart has Neptune on the Ascendant. This placement always makes me suspicious that misdiagnosis has occurred. I did not feel that Steve was retarded: he appeared to be an exceptionally bright and alert child. And his case had certainly fooled the entourage of specialists—psychologists, pediatricians, psychiatrists and other doctors—who had seen Steve over the years.

I checked the aspects to Neptune out carefully. Neptune is inconjunct Saturn, a classic configuration in medical astrology, indicating a bodily weakness or viral or bacterial infections: he had yearly allergies. Venus is also inconjunct Neptune, but I did not feel he was suffering from a blood problem as much as a sugar problem: a craving for sweets usually indicates a deficiency of thiamine, and that vitamin's ruler, Mercury, has four hard aspects to it in Steve's natal chart.

With Pluto on the Midheaven opposite Steve's natal Sun I wanted to check out the endocrine functions against Steve's symptomology. I felt the thyroid could be in question since Mercury is conjunct the Moon, meaning that emotional stress might throw the gland out of normal functioning. I also considered the adrenal glands because Mars has it—square Mercury and the Moon: unrelieved tension can eventually cause adrenal exhaustion. And because he seemed small for his age I thought perhaps he should get a parathyroid test to check his assimilation of calcium: Saturn has three hard aspects to it—conjunct Venus, inconjunct Neptune and inconjunct Pluto.

Since Steve has a strong polarity between Aries and Libra, I felt that perhaps blood was not circulating within his brain as it should. With Mars in the First House and two planets in Libra I also thought there might be acidosis: people freqently get high strung when they are overacidic.

Next I examined the sign placements of the outer planets.

Saturn in Aries This placement can mean constriction or lack of blood to the head; it suggests apparent apathy, listlessness or dullness from a lack of blood supply to the brain. Although I did not feel Steve was retarded, I thought that there might be some problem originating in the brain. I just didn't know what.

Uranus in Libra (retrograde): This placement

Figure 20
STEVE'S NATAL CHART

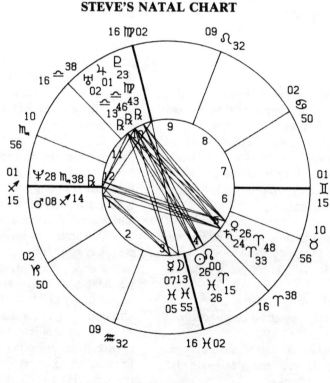

Steve
3 17 1969   0h 7m 0s EST
PLACIDUS   39N45   84W12

can mean the kidneys work intermittently or urea is not completely filtered out of the blood. Although Steve exhibited no bladder or kidney infections, I had worked on cases before where infections were not in evidence but toxins affected the body in different areas and ways. I wondered how toxins could affect the brain.

Neptune in Scorpio (retrograde): This placement can signify a weakened colon, a toxic condition or a hypothyroid condition. As several factors in Steve's chart show, he had a toxin or toxins in his body. But where and in what way were they manifesting to help bring on Steve's behavior?

The Cross: The bulk of Steve's problems were connected with the Mutable Cross. For instance, the planets in Pisces indicate an extreme sensitivity to any products with chemicals in them. Furthermore, sugar consumption in any form would not help the pancreas, ruled by Virgo, do a proper job of utilizing carbohydrates. Although with planets in Aries and Scorpio and Mars in the First House Steve would always need some meat, the best diet for him is one rich in fruits and vegetables that can be eaten raw or

lightly steamed. Also good for him are whole grains, such as hot oatmeal or wheat cereals and whole-grain breads, perhaps placed in soups to entice him to eat them. In other words, I realized he needed a diet just the opposite of what he was used to. By eating almost a solely meat and starch diet, a diet for Fixed and Cardinal Cross individuals, Steve was going against the dictates of his bodily requirements. As a result he had acidosis and was extremely nervous and tense.

The Progressed Chart (Figures 21 and 22)

When Steve was between the ages of two and two and a half, his chart was hit with several progressed aspects.

The progressed Node conjunct natal Uranus: Although nodal connections are still a mystery to most medical astrologers, I felt this configuration could have meant the sudden loss or addition of something.

Progressed Jupiter conjunct natal Vulcanus: In this configuration the expansive sweep of Jupiter and the almost cosmic, catalytic intervention of Vulcanus are coupled. This overwhelming duo obviously had

Figure 21
STEVE'S PROGRESSED CHART

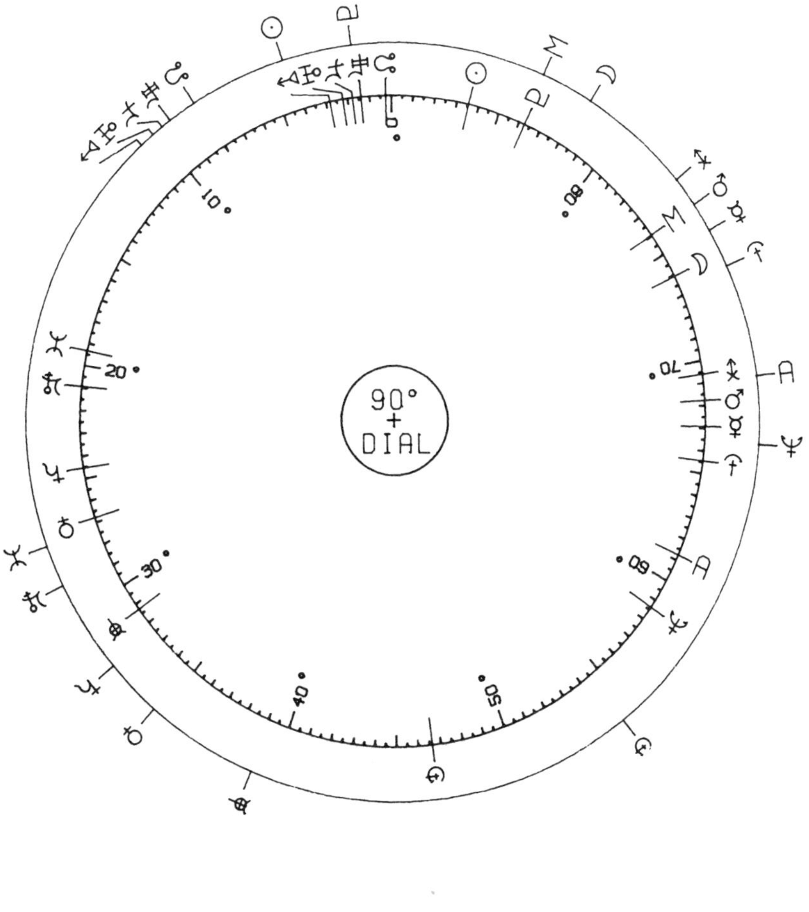

affected Steve on some mental, emotional or psychological level, causing some kind of buildup of negative emotions that had done damage to his psyche.

Progressed Saturn conjunct natal Venus: I wondered if there had been some traumatic emotional experience that had occurred simultaneously with this progression. Had affection or love been denied?

The progressed Moon conjunct the natal Midheaven: This was a strong medical configuration but one that still indicated an emotional trauma.

Progressed Neptune conjunct the natal Ascendant: Once again Neptune was in the picture, clouding the facts concerning this case.

The progressed Midheaven conjunct natal Mars: This configuration indicated that Steve was the target of the trauma, so to speak.

Progressed Pluto conjunct the natal Sun: This configuration indicated an endocrine imbalance as well as a shattering transformation on the physical and emotional levels.

Progressed Kronos conjunct natal Mercury: This progression suggested that adult intervention or an authoritarian method had to be initiated to keep Steve from totally losing control.

All of these progressions occurring within a six-month period indicated that Steve had experienced a great phsyical change plus a change in personality and behavior.

Next I looked at the midpoint structures, noticing that one of the stronger trees involved Uranus.

Vu/Ap-Ur: This configuration can point to a possible "short-circuiting," perhaps an accident, taking place on two or more levels at once, such as the physical and emotional levels.

Sa/Ze-Ur: This picture can indicate that damage may have occurred at delivery time. Uranus is opposite Hades. Therefore, anytime a planet progressed to this midpoint structure, Steve would probably react explosively.

Sa/Ne-Su: This is a classic medical tree, suggesting a tendency to bodily weakness, poor health and viral or bacterial infections.

Transits

Steve's transits are most interesting for the time he was two years old. Transiting Saturn was in opposition to his natal Uranus in June 1971, indicating something may have developed in his body to trigger his hyperactive behavior. Transiting Neptune was conjunct his Ascendant in retrograde motion, indicating further confusion or perhaps an infection or bacterial problem. And transiting Jupiter was conjunct his Neptune in the Twelfth House. Jupiter in the Twelfth House normally has the effect of a kind of guardian angel but not in this case: it only compounded the problem.

Eclipses

In February 1971 when Steve's crisis began, an eclipse conjuncted his natal Mercury within one degree, indicating that perhaps there was a functional brain disturbance or something affecting his speech development. When I saw him, there was an eclipse conjunct his natal Jupiter within three degrees of orb, perhaps indicating that progress was going to be made.

Final Analysis

There was no doubt in my mind that a toxic condition existed in Steve's body, but I was not well enough acquainted with viral ailments to make a clear-cut decision on what was causing the poison. I suggested the following supplements to Joyce so that she could discuss their implementation with her doctor: thiamine, vitamin E, vitamin C, riboflavin, vitamin B-12, vitamin A, vitamin D, pantothenic acid and zinc. I felt Steve should get the B vitamins through brewer's yeast so that he would not have to take a handful of pills everyday. And I told Joyce to mix all of the nutrients in a blender with orange juice and a banana to mask the taste. I also urged Joyce to talk over an alkaline diet with her doctor to try to rebalance Steve's metabolism. In addition, we discussed Dr. Feingold's diet for hyperactive

Figure 22
MIDPOINTS ARRANGED IN 90-DEGREE SEQUENCE

☊ 00 15	☽/♀ 05 21	♀/♃ 14 17	♀/♄ 25 40	♅/♆ 30 26	♀/♆ 42 43	☿ 67 05	☽/♇ 78 49	♇ 83 43
☿/♄ 00 49	♀/M 06 25	♀/♅ 14 30	☽/♂ 26 04	A/☊ 30 45	♄/A 42 54	♂ 68 14	☿/♃ 79 25	♃/M 83 54
♃/☊ 01 00	♄/♇ 09 08	☿/♆ 17 52	♆/♇ 26 11	♂/♇ 30 58	♀/A 44 01	☽/☿ 70 30	☿/♅ 79 39	♅/M 84 08
♅/☊ 01 14	♀/♇ 10 15	☿/A 19 10	♀ 26 48	♃/A 31 30	♂/♄ 46 23	☿/M 71 34	♇/M 79 53	☉/♇ 85 04
♃ 01 46	☉/♄ 10 29	☽/♆ 21 17	♂/M 27 08	♅/A 31 44	♀/♂ 47 31	☽ 73 55	☉/☽ 80 11	☉ 86 26
☿/♀ 01 56	☉/♀ 11 37	♆/M 22 20	♇/A 27 29	☉/♂ 32 20	♆ 58 38	☽/M 74 59	☉/M 81 14	♇/☊ 86 59
♃/♅ 01 59	♄/☊ 12 24	☽/A 22 35	☉/♆ 27 32	♂/☊ 34 14	♆/A 59 57	☿/♇ 75 24	☽/☊ 82 05	♃/♇ 87 44
♅ 02 13	♃/♄ 13 09	☿/♂ 22 39	☉/A 28 51	♂/♃ 35 00	A 61 15	M 76 02	☽/♃ 82 50	♅/♇ 87 58
☽/♄ 04 14	♄/♅ 13 23	A/M 23 39	♆/☊ 29 26	♂/♅ 35 13	♂/♆ 63 26	☉/☿ 76 46	☽/♅ 83 04	☉/☊ 88 20
♄/M 05 18	♀/☊ 13 31	♄ 24 33	♃/♆ 30 12	♄/♆ 41 35	♂/A 64 44	☿/☊ 78 40	M/☊ 83 09	☉/♃ 89 06
								☉/♅ 89 20

children, a highly successful diet that eliminates all foods with chemicals, instead substituting wholesome, natural foods. And I recommended that Joyce take Steven to see a homeopathic doctor who lives in Chicago.

Outcome

In October 1978 Joyce took her son to see the homeopathic doctor, who after carefully recording the symptomology diagnosed the following: Steve must have had some viral infection around the age of two that either began or did not finish its cyclic work. The infection apparently did not leave the body but remained dormant, swelling the membrane between the brain and the skull. Since that time it had caused problems because of the pressure being brought to bear on the brain against the skull.

The doctor prescribed a homeopathic remedy. Then I got a call from Joyce shortly after she had given Steve the medicine. Her son had suddenly contracted a very high fever of 102 to 103 degrees and had reverted to his state of hyperactivity. Joyce's main fear was that her previous successful efforts to improve his behavior would have to begin all over again. I felt that once the virus was killed she would not have to start over again but, rather, pick up where she had left off. And I knew it was important for the treatment to continue. Scientists are now aware that when a body is invaded with a foreign organism it will raise its temperature to kill it. Joyce believed me enough to allow the raging fever to continue.

The treatment worked. Steve's mother reports that he is no longer hyperactive because of his diet: whereas he used to be till 1 or 2 in the morning, now he regularly goes to bed at 11 p.m. Although Steve is still not talking much, he is talking more than before. His general attitude is good, and he's learning at a normal, expected level. Joyce writes: "All in all, I am very encouraged, and I will keep plugging away."

What Astrology Missed

This case had me stymied from the start. I felt incompetent to a great degree. What was most frustrating was my lack of knowledge about virulent strains: I had not known that infections could remain dormant for so long, causing continual problems. Neptune fooled me to an extent but not the doctor, who was able to complete the work I had started. This case illustrates how important it is for a medical astrologer to develop a close, working relationship with a doctor.

CASE HISTORY 7

Name

Bobby.

Birth Data

April 28, 1969
12:04 p.m. EST
Dayton, Ohio

Ailments

Hyperactivity, bladder deformity, migraine headaches and constant pneumonia for one year.

Background

Bobby was nine years old when I met him. He raced around the house, seemingly unable to sit still for one minute. His case history was long and involved.

During pregnancy Tara had suffered from severe hemorrhaging complications. She was hospitalized on and off throughout her pregnancy. The labor was long. When Bobby finally arrived, he was two months overdue and weighed five pounds.

By the age of 2½ Bobby had all the symptoms of hyperactivity. The neurologist put him on Ritalin, a commonly used drug for this ailment. The drug only made Bobby worse, and it was stopped after six weeks. Between the ages of three and four Bobby spent many months in the hospital with frequent attacks of pneumonia. For a year he was on V-cillin, a drug to combat pneumonia. During that time he had an electroencephalogram (EEG) to record the electrical activity of his brain: the EEG was irregular but with no definable pattern. On psychological tests he had a very high I.Q.

At this point the physician felt Bobby was emotionally disturbed and not hyperactive. Tara agreed. His emotional disturbance was the result of an alcoholic father who abused both the mother and son. By the time Bobby was five Tara had gotten a divorce and placed both herself and her son under psychoanalysis.

The psychiatrist who headed up the program became concerned that Bobby was experiencing constant bed-wetting (enuresis). Through testing it was found that Bobby's bladder had not grown since birth: it could hold only 75 cc of fluid, as opposed to 250 cc for most children his age. As Bobby got older his lack of control worsened. An urologist informed Tara that by the onset of puberty the hormonal change would hopefully encourage the growth of the bladder. Meanwhile, Bobby had constant bladder infections, and the doctor recommended that if the bladder did not grow it should be surgically removed or an operation should be performed on the bladder muscles: Tara was undecided at that point. Bobby had to wear diapers and urinate every one to two hours to keep from contracting another infection.

At age six Bobby developed severe migraine

headaches. He also experienced loss of balance and eyesight, accompanied by prolonged bouts with vomiting. When these migraines continued for more than a week, he was hospitalized for the vomiting. The doctors found nothing but the same old strange EEG pattern and nothing on the brain scan. The psychiatrist called the problems emotional, and the chiropractor said they were caused by subluxation of vertebrae: at times the chiropractor was able to relieve the headaches. During his last hospitalization Bobby had an I.Q. test score of 145 but a motor-sensory level of 75. He was then classified as motor-sensory brain damaged. Although he communicated and read very well, when he entered the third grade he was unable to write legibly and had problems learning cursive writing. He also lost his balance often, could not skip and ran with difficulty.

From ages six to eight Bobby went to a psychiatrist who helped him to understand his emotional nature and comprehend his father's alcoholism. By age nine Bobby had few behavioral problems left and was becoming well-adjusted. At that age he weighed 42 pounds. His bouts with

vomiting had not stopped: he was either nauseated or throwing up 50 per cent of the time. The GI series had revealed nothing. Tara had to give him only foods that would not upset his stomach, such as fruit juices and cheese. He could not drink milk or eat breads, cereals or vegetables. He ate a great deal of meat, especially beef.

Another problem contributing to his poor digestion is a birth defect involving a third degree malocclusion. The teeth of his upper and lower jaws do not meet to allow him to chew food properly. This lack of mastication and a consequent habit of swallowing food whole contributed greatly to his vomiting: if Tara had allowed him, he would have subsisted on a liquid diet. She finally found an orthodontist who would reform the teeth and jaws by removing all Bobby's baby teeth and realigning his permanent teeth as they were coming in to establish a bite. Tara was pleased with the results.

The Natal Chart (Figure 23)

Bobby's problems were obviously emotional as well as physical. The Moon is very prominent in his

Figure 23
BOBBY'S NATAL CHART

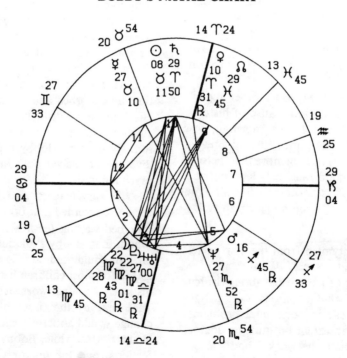

Bobby
4 28 1969 12h 4m 0s EDT
PLACIDUS   39N45   84W12

chart, with five hard aspects to it. The strongest configuration is a stellium in the Third House—the Moon, Pluto and Jupiter all conjunct, with a wide conjunction to Uranus. The Moon is also square Mars and inconjunct Saturn. The vulnerability to hurt implied by this Third House stellium is intensified by the fact that the Moon rules Bobby's Ascendant, Cancer. And although the Moon/Pluto conjunction indicates that Bobby has a strong heart with which to undergo his worst trials, it also suggests a great intensity of emotion: since the boy's emotional pyche had been badly damaged, it was fortunate that his mother had found a sensitive and patient psychiatrist to deal with Bobby's emotional problems.

Because the stellium is in Virgo, I also decided it was at least partially responsible for Bobby's supposed hyperactive behavior: after observing Bobby I became convinced that he was not hyperactive but probably hypoglycemic. The involvement of Pluto, ruling over the endocrine system, further convinced me that some of his behavorial problems were organic in nature.

Saturn also plays a very important part in Bobby's chart. It has hard aspects to the Sun, Moon, Jupiter and Neptune. The Sun-Saturn conjunction indicates that the father image could greatly influence and/or damage Bobby, as it had. This same conjunction also indicates a potential slowing down of the thyroid, a possibility strengthened by the fact that both Saturn and Mercury are in Taurus, with Mercury opposite Neptune, indicating a general weakness of the thyroid. Saturn inconjunct Jupiter, of course, is one of the worst signals that assimilation of nutrients will be difficult. Moreover, all of the four hard aspects to Saturn suggest that the boy was deficient in calcium: and a later bone test showed that he was two years behind in growth from malnutrition, mostly caused by his malocclusion.

With Pluto heavily aspected in Bobby's chart I felt his thymus might be malfunctioing, causing his immunity system to perform poorly and inducing his frequent bouts of pneumonia.

Next I looked at the outer planets.

Saturn in Aries: This placement can mean constriction or lack of blood to the head, perhaps causing strokes. It also suggests mucous build-up in the ears, causing earaches or deafness. And there may be apparent apathy, listlessness or dullness from lack of blood supply to the brain. Although I felt that this configuration might explain part of Bobby's problems, I also checked the opposite polarity, Saturn in Libra. This placement can indicate thickening of the tubule walls of the kidneys, renal or urine retention and toxic waste being unfiltered by the organs.

Uranus in Libra: This placement can mean that the kidneys are working intermittently, perhaps undergoing spasms. The opposite polarity, Uranus in Aries, suggests sharp, shooting pains in the head, sudden headaches and pain in the eyes. I was getting a recurrence of symptoms: renal problems and headaches.

Neptune in Scorpio (retrograde): This placement can indicate a weakened colon, poor peristalsis and a hypothyroid condition—all of which seemed to fit Bobby's case.

The Cross: I felt Bobby's root problem stemmed from the Cardinal Cross. I believed the kidneys should be cleaned out. Clogged kidneys will often create toxic conditions in the body: in Bobby's case those conditions affected his head, giving him migraines; they also affected the acidity of his digestive tract. Venus and Saturn in Aries opposite Uranus in Libra triggered migraines, bladder infections, dizziness and loss of balance—all from toxemia because the kidneys poorly filtered toxins from the blood. I had seen similar situations many times before.

The best diet for a Cardinal Cross individual is what is generally considered a balanced diet. Bobby needed some meat, although I suggested he eat the white meat of turkey, chicken and Cornish game hen, as well as sea food, instead of heavy meats that would be less assimilable with his digestive problems. He also needed some dairy products, and I suggested that some cheese on a weekly basis would help him get part of his protein and calcium needs. Since Bobby's malocclusion problem complicated matters, I suggested blending his fruits and vegetables into palatable drinks to get the nutritive ingredients into his body at that point and worry about roughage and fiber at a later date.

Other Information: Although there are no fixed stars concerned with medical astrology or critical degrees in Bobby's chart, the Ascendant, North Node and Saturn are all at 29 degrees. According to traditional astrology, people with planets at 29 degrees in their charts will have tough, demanding lives. Bobby certainly fit that pattern.

The Progressed Chart (Figures 24 and 25)

When Bobby's supposed hyperactivity began at 2½, two powerful progressions took place.

Progressed Uranus conjunct natal Vulcanus: Bobbly's natal Vulcanus is opposite Hades, a configuration that suggests Bobby must learn to channel his vast reservoir of energy, or his body will suffer the consequences. When the progression activated this opposition, Bobby's energy was unleashed, and he was barely able to control his own body or actions. With Hades involved I believed an environmental situation triggered this kind of reaction.

Progressed Ascendant conjunct natal Admetos: This configuration can indicate the sudden coming to light of an environmental situation that has remained hidden, such as an alcoholic father who abuses his son.

Two other progressions occurred when Bobby suffered his bouts of pneumonia between the ages of three and four.

Progressed Pluto conjunct natal Jupiter: Since the Jupiter tree is bracketed by Pluto and Apollon, I believed this was the time when Bobby's problems with the thymus gland began. Apollon always seems to mean two or more of something—in Bobby's case multiple trips to the hospital.

Progressed Jupiter conjunct natal Uranus/ Apollon: With both Jupiter and Apollon involved this progression indicates a multiple expansion on some level—such as the lungs. Uranus suggests the sudden appearance of this ailment.

When Bobby suffered migraines, loss of balance and vomiting at the age of six, three progressions

took place.

Progressed Jupiter conjunct natal Vulcanus: The expansiveness of Jupiter appears to contribute to the problems by setting off tremendous energy.

Progressed Admetos conjunct the natal Sun: This configuration can indicate the culmination of hidden emotional problems—in Bobby's case manifested as migraine headaches.

Progressed Mars conjunct the natal Moon/ Pluto This progression reinforces the idea that the migraines were emotional, not organic, in origin.

As Bobby underwent successful psychotherapy between the ages of six and eight, three progressions occurred.

Progressed Mars conjunct the natal Moon/ Pluto: The occurrrence of this progression suggests that Bobby's emotional turmoil had to surface at that time.

Progressed Jupiter conjunct natal Vulcanus: The occurrence of this configuration probably helped the therapist to make Bobby understand the reasons for his raging, unchecked emotions and to learn how to channel those emotions effectively in the future.

Figure 24
BOBBY'S PROGRESSED CHART

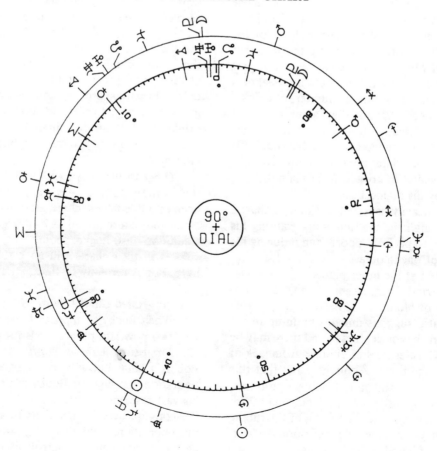

Progressed Zeus conjunct natal Mars: This configuration represents a kind of rebirth—in Bobby's case his enlightenment through his visits to the therapist.

At the time I saw Bobby his progressed Sun was going to conjunct his natal Hades in approximately three months—not much lead time for helping the boy. And within the next 1½ years progressed Hades was going to conjunct natal Mercury and Neptune. So, I didn't expect great results from his program for about two years.

Looking at the Uranian planets and midpoint structures in the 90-degree wheel, I was to understand the nature of Bobby's disturbed brain-wave patterns a little better. I also discovered that Mercury was quite active in the various structures.

Mo/Ad-Me: This midpoint structure can indicate a negative or pessimistic outlook on life.

Pl/Ad-Me: Progressed Saturn to this configuration may trigger a long-term, hidden endocrine problem.

Me/Ne-Su/Ma: Although I had no information on this picture, I felt perhaps it represented a weakening of the electrical currents in the brain. The Sun, life-giver, and Mars, the engine, in such a configuration could be partially responsible for Bobby's motor nerve damage.

Su/Me-Ha: Although I had no information on this structure either, to me it suggested that Bobby's mental processes might be interfered with at some time, causing him great distress.

These pictures involving Mercury show some mental disturbance but nothing debilitating as far as his intelligence is concerned. That there was physical damage to the brain, though, is indicated by the involvement of Mars. The Moon/Pluto and Admetos picture also indicates harbored emotional dross that must be dug up and dealt with positively before he can be emotionally well.

Su/Ne-Vu: This configuration can mean a terrific weakening of the body, susceptibility to a wide range of viral or bacterial infections, allergies and tremendous reaction to drugs. Although Bobby didn't have allergies, he did have a severe reaction to the Ritalin. And his continual bouts with pneumonia and constant trips to the hospital indicated that this picture is an extremely important one that has been active throughout his life.

Ur/Ha-Ze: Although I had no information on this midpoint structure, I believed it indicated problems during the birthing process.

Su/Mo-Vu: This configuration can indicate a person with tremendous reserves of energy or strength, who may overdo things. This midpoint structure was triggered when Bobby was 2½ and progressed Uranus conjuncted natal Vulcanus.

Ma-Ad: These two planets are in opposition. They are an explosive pair, and, when they are triggered, a situation may come to light and have to be dealt with.

Ma/No-Su: I find that Nodal connections can mean a separation or an addition. For example, a person may literally lose an organ, or he or she may add a certain emotion. Admetos in opposition to the Sun in this picture perhaps hints that hidden emotions must be surfaced and dealt with, but first a loss must occur before the emotional cleansing.

Transits

When I saw Bobby, Saturn was transiting Leo retrograde in his Second House. Saturn in the Second House usually means concrete results will eventually come about: in other words, it was the right time to begin work with Bobby, although some stops and starts could be expected before a health plan could be instituted with any degree of success because Saturn was retrograde. At the same time Uranus was at 16 Scorpio retrograde in his Fourth House, a placement that had been immensely important earlier in Bobby's successful therapy. In addition, Neptune was at 18 Sagittarius, going retrograde in Bobby's Fifth House. That meant Neptune was hovering around Bobby's natal Mars, a transit that indicates confusion, mistakes and weakening of the body in some way. I felt I had to be extracareful in my diagnosis because of this transit, and I went over all

Figure 25
MIDPOINTS ARRANGED IN 90-DEGREE SEQUENCE

♅/☊ 00 08	M/☊ 07 04	♄/♅ 15 11	☿/♇ 24 57	♅/♆ 29 12	☉ 38 11	☽/A 55 46	A/M 66 44	♃/♇ 84 52
♅ 00 31	♅/M 07 27	☉/☽ 15 19	☽/♆ 25 10	♄ 29 50	♂/☊ 38 15	♇/A 55 54	☿/♂ 66 58	☽/☊ 86 06
☽/♀ 01 29	♂/A 07 55	☉/♇ 15 27	♆/♇ 25 18	☿/♀ 33 51	♂/♅ 38 38	☿ 57 10	♂/♆ 67 19	♇/☊ 86 14
♀/♇ 01 37	♀ 10 31	☉/♃ 17 36	☉/M 26 17	☉/♄ 34 01	☿/♄ 43 30	☉/♂ 57 28	♄/A 74 27	☽/♅ 86 29
☽/M 03 26	☽/♄ 11 09	☉/☊ 18 58	☿/♃ 27 05	♀/♆ 34 12	♀/♂ 43 38	☿/♆ 57 31	♂ 76 45	♅/♇ 86 37
♇/M 03 33	♄/♇ 11 17	☉/♅ 19 21	♃/♆ 27 27	☽/♂ 34 36	♄/♆ 43 51	♆ 57 52	☉/A 78 38	♃ 87 01
♀/♃ 03 46	♀/M 12 27	♀/♄ 20 11	☿/☊ 28 28	♂/♇ 34 44	♂/M 45 34	♃/A 58 03	☽ 82 28	☿/A 88 07
♀/☊ 05 08	♃/♄ 13 26	♄/M 22 07	♆/☊ 28 49	☿/M 35 47	☉/☿ 47 40	A/☊ 59 25	☽/♇ 82 35	♃/☊ 88 23
♀/♅ 05 31	M 14 24	☉/♀ 24 21	☿/♅ 28 51	♆/M 36 08	☉/♆ 48 01	♅/A 59 48	♇ 82 43	♆/A 88 28
♃/M 05 42	♄/☊ 14 48	☽/☿ 24 49	A 29 04	♂/♃ 36 53	♂/♄ 53 18	♀/A 64 48	☽/♃ 84 44	♃/♅ 88 46
								☊ 89 45

my findings three times to make sure I wasn't going to make mistakes.

Eclipses

In 1972 when Bobby had his severe bouts with pneumonia, two eclipses took place in his Sixth House and one in his Twelfth. Eclipses to either of these houses can often trigger health ailments.

In 1975 when he started the migraines and simultaneously the therapy, an eclipse occurred opposite his Mercury: although wide in orb (seven degrees), this eclipse could still influence established attitudes that were going to be changed.

In November there was an eclipse within two degrees of Bobby's natal Sun and another in opposition within one degree of his natal Mercury. That was a time when he was focusing upon his thought processes and internal mental structure.

In 1976 the eclipses continued to hit his Sun and Mercury respectively: one was conjunct within a degree of his Sun; another was in opposition to Mercury by four degrees; the last was in opposition to Saturn within one degree, perhaps indicating the crystalization of the problem.

In 1977 an eclipse occurred within one degree of a conjunction with Bobby's Saturn, indicating the solid improvement he was making in therapy. In September an eclipse conjuncted his Venus by a wide conjunction of seven degrees, perhaps indicating the new-found love of self Bobby was developing because of his therapist. An eclipse in October was in opposition to his Midheaven and conjunct his Nadir within five degrees, indicating a change in his habits and a new image.

When I came on the scene in March 1978, an eclipse took place opposite his Venus by six degrees, showing hope for future improvements.

Final Analysis

Bobby's was a tough case, but in my opinion Tara was an excellent mother, who would follow everything to the letter to get improvement in her son. I felt sure she would give Bobby all the foods and supplements I suggested.

Both Tara and I were concerned about Bobby's ability to absorb supplements, especially with Jupiter inconjunct Saturn; therefore, I devised a diet of natural foods rather than supplements. We also had our doubts that Bobby could keep all the foods down; so, I recommended he drink vinegar to help soothe the acidic condition of his stomach, especially since he has Uranus in Libra, a placement indicating acidosis. As another measure to lower his acidity I suggested that he not eat as much meat, high in acid, and, instead, adhere to a more alkaline diet. I also wanted to

get Bobby off his high-protein diet because it could eventually cause problems with the kidneys. Tara agreed to talk to her doctor about such changes in his eating habits.

In addition, I suggested a diet high in potassium (Moon) to increase Bobby's attention span and cut down on his forgetfulness. With the Moon also ruling over riboflavin I recommended that vitamin, which has a great deal to do with the carbohydrate metabolism and fats in general, to help Bobby digest food better plus get the pancreas back into functioning order. I also advised that he eat foods high in calcium and take calcium lactate tablets to help devlop his muscles and, perhaps, his coordination. Other vitamins and minerals I discussed with Tara were vitamins C and B-6, pantothenic acid and chelated zinc.

The tests I recommended Bobby undergo were for the thymus, the thyroid, the parathyroid and the adrenal glands. I wanted the parathyroid gland checked to make sure it was dispensing enough calcium so that Bobby's bones could grow and his teeth form properly. With a wide inconjunct between the Sun and Mars in Bobby's chart, I suspected the adrenals might be malfunctioning.

Finally, I suggested that Tara take Bobby to see my massotherapist friend, Dave Schneider.

Outcome

In late March 1978, not long after I had met with Tara and Bobby, I received a letter from Tara. She informed me that she had taken Bobby to the massotherapist, and after the treatment Bobby did not wet his bed for the first night in several nights. Furthermore, the boy calmed down immediately after the massotherapy and was a joy to be around for about 12 hours.

In her letter she also added two items of Bobby's medical history she had not told me before. She wrote that he was not always "with it": "He can't remember anything, even when he tries; you can say something to him and it does not register. It really sounds like a potassium problem." She added that during bladder X-rays taken two years previously the technician had found several staples lodged in Bobby's lower left large intestinal wall: the boy had eaten them in school one day when he was bored. "They are still there," Tara wrote. "We have been to three surgeons who will not remove them, and they say that they are so imbedded that about six inches of the bowel would have to be removed. Until they have signs of infection, they will not put him through the surgery." With all the Virgo in Bobby's chart, this information did not surprise me: Virgo usually means potential intestinal disorders. My hope was that no infection would develop, necessitating surgery.

During the next two years Tara had great difficulty finding a physician who would consider the vitamin therapy, diet and lab tests I had recommended. Finally, after she had moved to another state, Tara located a chiropractor who ran the tests. The hair analysis paralleled my findings from the natal chart. In addition, the doctor agreed there was thyroid, parathyroid and adrenal malfunctioning. Bobby was also found to have hypoglycemia.

Bobby's been on the program since 1979, and Tara reports that he has no more migraines, he's eating better and is growing. Right now he's four feet tall and weighs 50 pounds. The vitamin and mineral therapy plus the diets have done nothing but make him stronger: he has no dizziness, and he has much more vitality. A dentist works on Bobby's malocclusion, and the chiropractor has stimulated growth of the jaw through massotherapy and kinesiology (another holistic concept that deals with the study of muscles and muscular movement). Perhaps best of all, Bobby's digestion is good. Bobby's chiropractor told Tara that there is a reflex between the jaw and the bladder: he's presently stimulating the jaw area; once it is in tune, he'll work on the bladder.

The bed-wetting continues, and Bobby's bladder has not started to grow as yet. But Bobby is only 11 and probably has another year before hormonal changes really begin to take place. Meanwhile, all concerned deal with Bobby's wetting problems so that the boy does not feel guilty. And I feel sure the chiropractor will get the bladder growth stimulated.

What Astrology Missed

This case presented such a diverse and complicated number of problems that I questioned my ability to get to the root cause of everything. But by methodically following the steps I had set up for the Med-Scan I was able to do so. I was accurate in my diagnosis, and I prescribed the right program. I would have had limited success with this case, however, if Bobby had not been undergoing successful psychotherapy. Getting Bobby's emotions straightened out was 50 per cent of the battle, and we can thank a talented and insightful psychiatrist for most of the healing.

Part Two
GUIDE TO NUTRITION

CHAPTER SEVEN
Vitamins

In 1911 Casimir Funk, a Polish chemist, undertook a study of why widespread diseases such as scurvy, beriberi, pellagra and rickets occurred. He became convinced that these diseases were caused by the lack of something in the daily diets of those people who contracted the ailments. After more research he proposed the theory of vitamins, arguing that if certain vitamins were left out of diets, the diseases would occur. Funk named the vitamins after the ailments each cured. For instance, vitamin B was so-named because it was the antiberiberi vitamin.

During the 1930's and 1940's chemists discovered many more vitamins needed daily to keep us healthy. As these vitamins were discovered, they were dubbed with letter names derived from some aspect of their properties: for example, the letter *K* was given to a coagulation-promoting chemical, since *K* is the first letter in the Scandinavian word *koagulation*. The vitamins were named out of order. In addition, some received chemical names as well, resulting in a general confusion about the names of vitamins: most people call the vitamins by their chemical names, such as thiamine or riboflavin. By now the alphabet has all been used, and there are approximately 41 kinds of vitamins. (The importance of some of these vitamins to human nutrition has yet to be established.)

Vitamins are among six nutrients essential for the human body to function properly: carbohydrates, fats, proteins, vitamins, minerals and water. All these nutrients are in the foods we eat, and all contain chemical substances that help our bodies in one or more of three ways: they give our bodies heat and energy, provide material for the repair of tissue and for growth and aid in the regulation of the bodily processes. Although each nutrient has its own specific function in the body, no single one is able to act independently of the others: all the nutrients must be present in the food we consume for our bodies to maintain good health.

Many vitamins are used as part of the body's enzymes. An enzyme, a large protein molecule, is a complicated chemical considered a special tool inside the cell structure: it may have just one job to do in a cell, such as joining two molecules, thus helping to build a chemical composition that can aid the body in some way. When an enzyme is joined by two smaller molecules, it is called a coenzyme. Many vitamins are coenzymes. And when a vitamin is absent, cellular health begins to decline until a disease caused by vitamin deficiency crops up. Since the body is a marvelously adaptive piece of equipment, a synthetic vitamin substituted for a natural one can still be broken down and utilized to some extent.

Two standards of measurement are used for vitamins and minerals: activity-based and quantity-based. Activity-based measurements—the International Unit (I.U.) and the United States Pharmacopeia unit (U.S.P.)—are used for vitamins A, D and E because there may be variations in the types of materials and sources used in these vitamins that can alter how much of the vitamin the body absorbs or how active it becomes in the system. Quantity-based measurements, such as *microgram* (mcg.), *milligram* (mg.) and *grain* (gr.) are used for the other vitamins, all of which have standard strengths. One microgram equals 1/1,000,000 gram, one milligram equals 1/1,000 gram, and one grain equals about 65 milligrams. Liquids or capsules, such as wheat germ oil or lecithin in an oil base, may be measured in *minims* (M), equaling about one drop of water: 60 minims equals one teaspoonful of liquid.

The amount of each vitamin a person needs daily is a subject of some controversy. The Minimum Daily Requirement (MDR), the smallest amount of a particular vitamin that the average person must consume daily to prevent a vitamin-deficiency disease, is based on a table compiled by the Federal Drug Administration in 1941. The table has since grown obsolete and has been replaced with a more up-to-date table known as the Recommended Dietary Allowance (U.S.RDA OR RDA), which is broken down into four segments of age: infants (0-12 months), children (under 4 years), adults and children (4 or more years) and pregnant and/or lactating women.

The trouble with both of these tables is that they are designed for the needs of a mythical, *average* person. Although each person needs the same nutrients, factors such as age, environment, sex, body size and activity level influence how much of each nutrient a person needs. Therefore, these tables, especially the one for the MDR, are of little value to most people because most of us are not average. For instance, an individual may be the right height and weight to receive the MDR of vitamin C (45 milligrams); however, if he or she lives in Los Angeles, Chicago, New York City or any other high pollutant area, many doctors believe that doses should be higher to combat the effects of carbon monoxide. Dr. Linus Pauling even asserts that a person should take between 250 and 10,000 milligrams of vitamin C for optimum health.

Dr. Roger Williams, Ph.D., of the University of Texas, for the last 25 years has repeatedly stressed the connection between susceptibility to disease and an individual's unique nutritional pattern. Dr. Williams calculates that there are only a few people who have "average" needs for each of the 40-odd known vitamins. And Dr. Williams' experiments have shown that we inherit a far-from-average need for at least one or two of each of the nutrients. If these needs are not satisfied, body cells will fail to act properly and diseases may eventually take over.

Unfortunately, it is presently expensive to test a person's unique nutritional needs. And the medical establishment has never entertained the possibility of computerized feedouts containing information about individual needs.

In fact, for the past 200 years the medical establishment has not really been interested in the relationships between vitamin and mineral deficiencies and disease. Instead, doctors have tended to blame all of humankind's diseases on microorganisms, such as microbes and viruses, and have felt that cures depended on the administration of drugs to kill invading agents. Hence, more and more drugs have been developed to cover over the symptoms of diseases and to poison our bodies, producing side effects that injure our organs and other bodily functions. Let us hope that we are soon to see what Dr. Williams terms a "renaissance of nutritional science," when more and more doctors will realize that nutrients—not drugs—are the best antidotes to disease.

VITAMIN A

Astrological Ruler
The Sun.

Synthetic Forms
Acetate and palmitate.

Synonyms
Antikeratinizing vitamin, antiophthalmia vitamin, antiinfective vitamin and fat-soluble vitamin.

Sources
Vegetables: Alfalfa meal, asparagus, broccoli, carrots, celery, chard, dandelion leaves, escarole, green lettuce, okra, green peppers, red peppers, sweet potatoes, spinach, hubbard squash, turnip greens and watercress.

Fruits and Nuts: Dried apricots, fresh apricots, cherries, nectarines, yellow peaches, dried prunes and figs.

Fish and Meat: Veal kidney, mutton kidney, lamb, beef liver, calf liver, pig liver, oysters, tuna, sardines and salmon.

Grains: Unknown.

Dairy Products: Butter, cream cheese, whole eggs, egg yolks, whole dried milk and malted milk.

Herbs: Lemon grass, annotto seed, horseradish, lamb's-quarters, paprika and parsley.

Natural Supplements: Fish liver oil and yeast.

Unit of Potency
The International Unit (I.U.) is most frequently used. One I.U. of vitamin A is equivalent in biological potency to 0.6 gamma of beta-carotene. (Gamma is a unit of weight equaling 0.0001 milligrams.)

History and Characteristics
Vitamin A is soluble in fats and oils and insoluble in water. It is not affected by dilute alkalies and acids. It is stable to heat with little loss of activity, even at boiling point (212 degrees Fahrenheit) if air is kept away from it. But it is unstable in air, even at room temperature. Any jar containing vitamin A should be tightly sealed.

There are two types of vitamin A: preformed and provitamin. Preformed vitamin A is concentrated in certain tissue of animal products in which the carotene contained in the food has metabolized into vitamin A. Fish-liver oil is a rich source of preformed vitamin A: vitamin A-1 (retinol) is found in sea water fish only; vitamin A-2 (3-dehydroretinal) is found in fresh and salt water fish. Provitamin A is carotene, a substance found in fruits and vegetables that must be converted into vitamin A before it can be utilized by the body. Carotene is especially abundant in carrots.

People unable to synthesize vitamin A from carotene will need a vitamin A supplement. In ailments of the abdominal region of the body loss of vitamin A can bring on ulcerative colitis, obstruction of the bile duct or cirrhosis of the liver. In such cases unhealthy flora is retained in the intestines and can prohibit the conversion of carotene to vitamin A.

Vitamin A is used for promoting healthy tissue formation both inside and outside the body and increasing blood platelets (round or oval disks in the blood that aid in blood coagulation after an injury). It gives strength to the cell walls, aids in good digestion and helps prevent senility.

Vitamin A is especially important to people who live in high pollution areas. Those individuals may have their respiratory tracts taxed to the limits because of poisons; hence frequent colds, bronchitis and even pneumonia develop easily and seem to hang on. Once bodily defenses are broken down, these people cannot repel the invaders until the necessary vitamin A has been supplied. The vitamin also aids in the relief of bronchial asthma, chronic rhinitis and dermatitis.

Vitamin A has been used successfully in treating many types of eye disorders—such as blurred vision, night blindness, Bitot's spots (white patches on the whites of eyeballs), cataracts, glaucoma and conjunctivitis (inflammation of the mucous membrane that lines the eyelids).

Communicable diseases—such as measles, colds and scarlet fever—as well as infections of the intestines, ovaries, uterus and vagina, have been halted with dosages of vitamin A. In addition, high cholesterol and atheroma (fatty deposits in the arterial walls) have been controlled with the vitamin. And people who suffer from hyperthyroidism, nephritis (inflammation of the kidney), tinnitus (a ringing sound in the ear) and migraine headaches have also benefited from adding more of this vitamin to their diets.

Allies: Vitamin A's primary allies are protein and vitamins D and E. It is also more effective when taken with the vitamin B complex (especially cholin), vitamin C, vitamin D, vitamin E, fatty acids, calcium (bonemeal, gluconate or lactate), phosphorus and zinc.

Antagonists: Vitamin A's effectiveness is diminished by mineral oil, fertilizers with high nitrogen content, ozone and nitrogen dioxide, found in air pollutants.

Dosages

Recommended Dietary Allowance:
Infants 0-1 yrs. 1,500 I.U.
Children1-6 yrs. 2,000 I:U.6-10 yrs. 3,500 I.U.
Men 10-12 yrs. 4,500 I.U. 12-75+ yrs. 5,000 I.U.
Women 10-12 yrs. 4,500 I.U. 12-75+ yrs. 5,000 I.U.
Pregnant Women 6,000 I.U.
Lactating Women 8,000 I.U.

Therapeutic Dose: With a physician's guidance 25,000 I.U. to 50,000 I.U. daily in case of deficiency are recommended.

Megadose: With a physician's guidance 125,000 I.U. to 200,000 I.U. daily are recommended.

Toxicity

Vitamin A is one of only two known vitamins (the other is vitamin D) that in its synthetic form can cause harm if the dosages are too large. It has been suggested that 50,000 I.U. daily for six months can cause toxicity. Dosages of 18,500 I.U. given daily for one to three months have been reported toxic for infants.

Common symptoms of a mild vitamin A poisoning are nausea, dizziness, vomiting, diarrhea, dry skin, loss of hair, headaches, loss of appetite and sore lips. Deep bone pain, thickening of long bones, blurred vision, skin rashes, enlargement of the liver and spleen, reduced thyroid activities and abnor-

malities of the mucous membrane, skin and eyes are more severe symptoms.

In cases of vitamin A toxicity a person should refrain from taking any more vitamin A, and within a few days to weeks, depending upon the severity of the overdosing, the symptoms will disappear. Vitamin C has also been known to help prevent the harmful side effects of vitamin A toxicity.

Fish liver oil does not seem to incur toxic side effects. Instead, the synthetic varieties of vitamin A build up in the body and produce toxicity.

Deficiency Symptoms

Sinus trouble, catarrh (inflammation of mucous membranes), ear abcesses, eyelids glued shut in the mornings upon waking and "sleepy sand" in abundance around the upper eyelids upon waking are warnings that there may be a slight deficiency of vitamin A. Clues of a moderate deficiency are the appearance of skin blemishes—such as acne, pimples and boils —as well as increased susceptibility to infections, especially psoriasis and chest colds. Other common signs are night blindness, xerosis (when the eyeball loses luster, becomes dry and inflamed and visual ability is altered), rough, dry skin, prematurely wrinkled skin, a poor sense of smell and/or taste and poor appetite. Pneumonia, softening of bones and teeth, defective gums, sties in the eye, corneal ulcers, formation of gallstones or kidney stones, retarded growth in children, diarrhea, lack of stamina and vigor and sterility in both male and female are signals of a severe deficiency.

Recent Clinical Developments

Vitamin A is valuable in the correction of various skin problems. External application of the vitamin (fish liver oil perles), for instance, can aid in rapid healing of skin conditions and open wounds and can prevent scarring in much the same fashion as vitamin E. Injections of vitamin A have also helped remove Plantar's warts. Moreover, premature aging, liver spots (brown dots appearing first on the hands and arms then all over the rest of the body), dry and wrinkled skin, flabby muscles and poor resistance to disease are all found to be caused by malfunctioning of a very small but important genetic linkup, which can only be maintained with sufficient vitamin A.

As this information indicates, sufficient vitamin A on a regular basis insures younger bodies for many years for most people. In a test performed at the University of Oklahoma in 1968 Drs. Johnson, Kennedy and Chiba found that 10 milligrams of potassium retinoate (vitamin A) increased the incorporation of uridine into total ribonucleic acid (RNA) in the liver up to 30 hours after administration. RNA contains the proper code of instructions for individual cells to know how to perform so that life, health and metabolic functions may be evenly maintained. RNA must reproduce itself; otherwise, as it becomes old its computer patterns blur, the physical body distorts more and more, and liver spots and other signs of aging appear.

Vitamin A also helps overcome certain reproductive problems. For example, the vitamin has been effective in relief of premenstrual cramping and tenderness of the breasts. Furthermore, the problem of sterility in men and women in some cases may be nothing more than a deficiency of vitamin A.

Proper glandular functioning is linked to vitamin A as well. The vitamin fortifies and strengthens the thymus so that the gland does its job. Part of the lymphatic system that alerts the body to invasion by foreign viruses and bacteria, the thymus sends hormonal messengers (white blood cells) to fight the intruders. These cells (lymphocytes) stay on duty because of a good, regular supply of vitamin A. Especially during childhood the thymus is large and extremely active: if it is functioning properly, there are few childhood ailments; if it is hypofunctioning, a child runs the risk of continued colds, allergies, flu and other viral ailments.

Those who have hyperthyroids or diabetes mellitus (a pancreatic disease, characterized by a deficiency of insulin) are seemingly incapable of storing vitamin A in their bodies. Such individuals are advised to take recommended allowances of vitamin A suggested by their physicians to insure against deficiency.

VITAMIN D

Astrological Ruler
The Sun.

Synthetic Forms
Irradiated ergosterol and calciferol D-2.

Synonyms
Antirachitic vitamin, fat-soluble D, sunshine vitamin, irradiated 7-dehydrocholesterol (D-3) and calciferol (D-2).

Sources
Vegetables: Watercress.
Fruits and Nuts: Sunflower seeds.
Fish and Meat: Chicken liver and salmon.
Grains: Wheat germ.
Dairy Products: Yogurt, egg yolks and butter.
Herbs: Annotto seed.
Natural Supplements: Yeast, fish oils

(cholecalciferol), cod liver oil, D-3 and viosterol, a solution of irradiated ergosterol in vegetable oil. (Unlike cod liver oil, viosterol does not contain vitamin A.)

Unit of Potency
One I.U. is equal to 0.025 gamma of calciferol (D-2).

History and Characteristics
The exact composition of vitamin D is unknown. There is no vitamin D-1 because the substance originally designated as vitamin D-1 was later discovered to be the same molecular compound as vitamin D-2, referred to as ergosterol or ergocalciferol.

Calciferol (vitamin D-2), a synthetic product with antirachitic (antirickets) properties, is made by irradiating ergosterol (a substance derived from yeast, ergot and other fungi and resembling cholesterol in composition) with ultraviolet light. Calciferol is a colorless, odorless crystalline vitamin, insoluble in water and soluble in fats and oils. It is estimated that one square centimeter of white human skin can synthesize 18 I.U. of the vitamin in three hours. Calciferol is stable to oxidation, heat and light and retains its potency very well. In foodstuffs its stability is short-lived and not good.

Natural vitamin D is formed by the Sun's ultraviolet rays striking the skin. This process begins the synthesis reaction of the provitamin 7-dehydrocholesterol (a derivative of cholesterol), which is turned into natural vitamin D and easily ingested for use within the body. This action is a precursor of the transformation of the vitamin in the skin to cholecalciferol (vitamin D-3), the same substance found in fish liver oils. Because of this process vitamin D is called the sunshine vitamin.

A provitamin form of vitamin D is found in fish, which are able to manufacture the vitamin without the aid of ultraviolet rays and store the substance in their livers. Hence fish liver oil perles are another source of natural vitamins D, D-2 or D-3 rather than direct sunlight on our skins.

Vitamin D is absorbed with fats through the intestinal walls with the aid of bile from the gallbladder. Natural vitamin D-3 is formed on the skin as ergosterol and absorbed into the circulatory system. Vitamin D is then transported to the liver for storage. It can also be found in the skin, brain, spleen and bones.

Allies: Vitamin D's primary allies are calcium (bonemeal, gluconate or lactate), vitamin A (ten parts vitamin A to one part vitamin D) and vitamin C. It is also more effective taken with cholin, fatty acids and phosphorus.

Antagonists: Vitamin D stored in the intestinal walls can be destroyed by the use of mineral oil.

Dosages

Recommended Dietary Allowance:
Infants 0-1 yrs. 400 I.U.
Children 1-6 yrs 400 I.U. 6-10 yrs. 400 I.U.
Men 10-12 yrs. 400 I.U. 12-75+ yrs. 400 I.U.
Women 10-12 yrs 400 I.U. 12-75+ yrs. 400 I.U.
Pregnant Women 400 I.U.
Lactating Women 400 I.U.

Therapeutic Dose: For adults 4,000 to 5,000 I.U. daily are recommended; half the amount is recommended for children if taken for not longer than one month.

Megadose: Under a physician's guidance 50,000 to 100,000 I.U. daily are recommended.

Toxicity

Vitamin D-2 can be toxic if taken in excessive doses, especially infants. The nutritionist Adelle Davis feels a toxic dose of vitamin D-2 for adults is 300,000 to 800,000 I.U. daily for many months; 30,000 and 50,000 I.U. daily for infants and children appears dangerous. In the 1940s there was a rash of vitamin D-hypervitaminosis in the United States and Great Britain. Officials were worried about the rise of rickets in children, they began to fortify milk powders, infant cereals and other foods with synthetic vitamin D (calciferol D-2). At that time the average baby in Great Britain was ingesting about 2,000 I.U. of vitamin D-2 daily. Although the rate of rickets fell, symptoms of hypercalcemia (excess calcium in the blood) began to appear. In 1947 a reduction was made of vitamin D-2 in baby food and supplements, and the hypercalcemia began to disappear.

The toxicity of vitamin D-3, the natural form found in fish liver oils, however, has not been proven. According to Dr. Jennings of Cambridge University, vitamin D-2 (calciferol) has an unsaturated side chain in its chemical makeup that makes it more toxic than the natural animal vitamin. For this reason it is best to take the natural form. And anyone who is receiving megadoses of vitamin D under a doctor's guidance should have frequent serum calcium blood tests to keep a check on the levels of calcium in the blood. At the first suggestion of hypercalcemia the dosage should be reduced.

The symptoms of acute overdose of vitamin D are frequent urination, loss of appetite, vomiting, diarrhea, dizziness, muscular weakness, nausea, weariness and calcification of the soft tissue of the lungs, heart and blood vessels. General malaise or depression may also appear. And calcium deposits in the liver, lungs, kidneys and stomach may occur. Sunstrokes are thought to be toxic effects from too much vitamin D as well.

To halt hypervitaminosis an individual should stop taking the vitamin D supplement. If the poisoning is severe, he or she should avoid all foods that tend to increase the blood calcium for a length of time decided upon by the physician—that is, until the toxicity has subsided and calcium has returned to normal levels.

Deficiency Symptoms

Each winter vitamin D shortages appear in people who live in the higher northern latitudes, since their main, natural supply is cut off: the ultraviolet rays of the Sun cannot penetrate clothes. Too little vitamin D in the intestinal tract leads to inadequate absorption of calcium and in turn creates a retention of phosphorus in the kidneys, triggering faulty mineralization of bone structures.

One of the most severe diseases caused by insufficient vitamin D is rickets, which affects children all over the world, especially in the Third World. This disease, resulting from a lack of calcium, unassimilable without vitamin D, produces soft bones. Softening of the skull, bowing of the legs, spinal curvature and enlargement of the ankles, knees and wrist joints are also common with the disease. Poorly developed muscles and nervous irritability are part of the same symptomology.

In adults this ailment is referred to as osteomalacia; in older adults it is called osteoporosis and marked by mineral depletion of the bones. The bones become pitted with holes and look like sponges. They become weak and brittle. A small bump can cause a broken hip or pelvic bone and incapacitate an elderly person up to six months in a hospital or cast because the bones knit so slowly from the deficiency of vitamin D.

The endocrine system also suffers badly with insufficient vitamin D. The parathyroid gland may be particularly affected. This gland, which sends out hormones to regulate the transport of calcium to parts of the body, may begin to place too little calcium in the system, thereby accelerating tetany: the symptoms include muscular numbness of the limbs, tingling and spasm. The thyroid may also be affected by too little vitamin D, resulting in flabbiness, poor metabolism of ingested food and diabetic distress.

As I've indicated, calcium cannot be properly absorbed without vitamin D. And if the level of calcium becomes dangerously low, the heart can be adversely affected. Thus, heart racing, flutters or fibrillation (twitching) suddenly and without warning can result from lack of vitamin D.

Eye problems may also occur. For example, myopia (nearsightedness) is known to manifest from an imbalance of calcium.

Other ailments that can result from insufficient vitamin D are faulty tooth development, constipation, potbelly (especially in children), pyorrhea, faulty jaw development and perspiration at the back of the head when a baby sleeps.

Recent Clinical Developments[1]

Studies have shown that the present treatments for osteoporosis, the vitamin D-related disease that strikes hundred of thousands of the elderly each winter, actually do more harm than good by depleting the body even further of calcium, phosphorus and vitamin D. Nowadays, to relieve arthritic and rheumatoid symptoms, doctors give corticosteroid therapy: the relief doesn't last, but the treatment does reduce the inflammation and swelling of the affected joints. Cortisone, a hormone manufactured by the adrenal glands, is released into the body, and the blood vessels dilate to allow passage of sluggish blood through the smaller capillaries and help relieve the aches and pains. But cortisone side effects cause urinary losses of calcium and phosphorus, in turn leading to demineralization of the bones.

Such steroid therapy has also been known to cause ulcers and adrenal exhaustion. In addition, it instills poor recuperative powers: it breaks down the body's defense mechanisms and impedes the healing of wounds, thus increasing the risk of infection and prolonging postsurgery recovery periods. Furthermore, steroid therapy blocks intestinal absorption of calcium and can trigger hyperparathyroidism. Patients frequently suffer from compression fractures of the spine—perhaps induced by a mere sneeze. The steroids also cause the loss of trabecular bone (strands of connective tissue), a loss that can be controlled by adequate intakes of natural vitamin D.

Recent studies have linked cigarette smoking to a loss of vitamin D, too. Cigarette smoking affects the bones, made mostly of calcium and phosphorus. These minerals are responsible for the hardness of bones, and they become more soluble in acidic solutions: smoking is known to increase the acidity of bone tissue. Moreover, bone minerals dissolve and are absorbed into the blood much more quickly when a person smokes. Smoking makes calcium leave the bones to move into the blood. Thus the bones become brittle, and a person can develop symptoms of hypercalcemia.

Another new theory is that the color of one's skin automatically controls how much vitamin D is ingested into the body. Anthropologists hypothesize that dark skin evolved as a protection against sunburn in the equatorial latitudes: black skin allows only 3 to 36 per cent of the ultraviolet rays to penetrate, whereas white skin allows 53 to 72 per cent. On the other hand, Dr. W. Farnsworth Loomis, a biochemistry professor at Brandeis University, feels that dark skin came first with white skin evolving later: as humankind moved northward, Dr. Loomis suggests, skin became lighter to take in added amounts of vitamin D; today, black children who live on or above the 40th parallel are much more susceptible to rickets because the color of their skin effectively blocks out the needed ultraviolet rays to supply adequate amounts of vitamin D to their bodies.

Sunlight is a health aid for ailments related to deficiencies in vitamin D. The sunlight helps restore good mineral assimilation and has been known to cure psoriasis, nervous disorders, respiratory disorders, arthritic conditions, rheumatism and anemia. The best time to sunbathe is before 11 a.m. and after 3 p.m., when the rays are not too strong and apt to burn. A person should ideally sunbathe 15 minutes the first day, adding 15 minutes each subsequent day to avoid burning while providing the body with needed vitamin D.

Algae (sea plants) have also been discovered to have large amounts of vitamin D as well as vitamin A and zinc. They are often used in treating thyroid conditions and could prove helpful in aiding problems caused by a deficiency of vitamin D.

In addition, women going through menopause may benefit from increased amounts of vitamin D, perhaps received through a mixture of powdered calcium bone meal, cod liver oil and raw vegetable juice. As the ovaries cease production of eggs, estrogen declines, creating metabolic havoc for some women whose metabolisms have already been imbalanced by the earlier child-bearing process. Vitamin D acts as an expediter of calcium into the bones, and the pituitary and adrenal glands use vitamin D as an energizer. The vitamin helps to metabolize the calcium through the hormones to strengthen the bone-building cells—a function previously performed by the estrogen hormone.

Finally, it has been discovered that osteitis fibrosa cystica generalisata is caused by a deficiency

---

[1]In the sections entitled "Recent Clinical Developments" in this and the succeeding chapter I am speaking about experiments taking place in laboratories or in double-blind studies or about information passed on from doctors about their patient therapy. These sections are designed to provide the latest knowledge about the vitamins and minerals and their application, although the information has not been "proven" to the satisfaction of those in the medical establishment.

of vitamin D. With this disease the bone mass is decreased because of an increase in the rate of bone destruction. No bone is spared, and the serum alkaline phosphatase is invariably elevated. Two conditions are apparent because of the disease: hyperparathyroidism and chronic nephritis (inflammation of the clusters of capillary blood vessels in the kidneys). Renal (kidney) calcification can also become a serious problem with osteitis fibrosa. And with osteitis fibrosa of a renal type acidosis can become an acute problem. The acid-alkaline metabolism is a ratio of 4 alkali to 1 acid in the human body: if the ratio drops to 3 to 1, health is seriously menaced; if it drops to 2½ to 1, death occurs. If the acidosis is arrested, the bone disease may be controlled. Doctors have suggested treatment with calcium gluconate, lactate and vitamin D (50,000 I.U. daily) to help this condition.

THE VITAMIN B COMPLEX

The vitamin B complex is a generic term assigned to a large group of chemically nonrelated compounds. The known B vitamins are B-1 (thiamine), B-2 (riboflavin), B-3 (niacin), B-6 (pyridoxine), B-12 (cyanocobalamin), B-13 (orotic acid), B-15 (pangamic acid), B-17 (laetrile), biotin (vitamin H), cholin, folic acid, inositol (hexahydroxycyclohexane) and PABA (para-aminobenzoic acid)

These vitamins are referred to as the B complex because they share certain characteristics in common. All are water-soluble. All are concerned with the biochemical processes of the body's metabolism. They constitute part of the enzyme system used for release of energy from foods. Their biochemical actions help in the metabolism of carbohydrates, proteins and fats. And an inadequate amount of one B vitamin in needed relationship to others in the complex constitutes an imperfect biochemical reaction in the metabolism or complete failure, depending on how severe the deficiency has become.

The richest source of a natural B complex is brewer's or Torula yeast (which, however, does not contain pangamic acid or laetrile). Some other natural sources of the complex are all legumes, unrefined grains, nuts and seeds. Synthetic sources of the complex are often difficult to assimilate because of poor digestion. And if unassimilated, synthetic sources will wash out of the body within six hours, turning urine a bright yellow. The vitamin B complex is assimilated more easily if it is taken with vitamins C and E, calcium and phosphorus.

Among the worst enemies of the complex are coffee, alcohol and sugar. Since alcoholics tend to consume large amounts of carbohydrates, they have an especially great need for the complex. Birth con-

trol pills (estrogen), insecticides, sleeping pills and sulfatype drugs will also destroy the B complex in the digestive tract. And because of their water solubility the vitamins must be replaced daily through proper diet.

The vitamin B complex is very important to the health of the nervous system. It also affects muscle tone as well as the digestive process. The vitamin B complex has been used successfully in treating hyperactive children plus people with addictions to drugs or alcohol.

THIAMINE

Astrological Ruler
Mercury.

Synthetic Forms
Thiamine hydrochloride (sometimes thiamine HCl), thiamine chloride and thiamine mononitrate.

Synonyms
Thermolabile B, torulin, antiberiberi vitamin, antineuritic vitamin, appetite-stimulant and vitamin B-1.

Sources
Vegetables: Artichokes, green asparagus, dried pinto beans, kidney beans, lima beans, chick peas (garbanzos), sweet corn, lentils, watercress, okra, cabbage, radishes, turnip leaf juices and soybeans.

Fruits and Nuts: Coconut, grapefruit, lemons, pineapple, pomegranates, almonds, filberts, hazel nuts and peanuts.

Fish and Meat: Bacon, ham, beef heart, lamb, beef liver, lamb liver, pork and bologna.

Grains: White cornmeal, whole-wheat flour, rye germ and wheat germ.

Dairy Products: Egg yolks.

Herbs: Bladderwrack, fenugreek and parsley.

Natural Supplements: Yeast, rice polish, rice bran, dulse and kelp.

Unit of Potency
The Chase-Sherman Unit is usually standard; however, the I.U. is most widely known and is equivalent to two Chase-Sherman Units. One I.U. of crystalline thiamine equals 0.0005 milligrams.

History and Characteristics
Thiamine, or vitamin B-1, is not affected by dilute acids. It is destroyed by alkalies and sulfites, is water-soluble and is insoluble in oil. Thiamine is not stable in boiling of slightly acidic solution or ultraviolet rays. Heating in an alkaline solution results in complete loss of the vitamin; in pasteuriza-

tion partial destruction is incurred. Cooking processes destroy most of it, as do blanching and freezing.

Thiamine is involved with the dehydrogenase system and the intermediary metabolism of carbohydrates. It is rapidly absorbed through the walls of the upper and lower small intestine. It is then carried through the circulatory system to the major organs, where it combines with manganese and certain proteins. It also combines with pyruvic acid to form a coenzyme necessary for the breakdown of carbohydrates into glucose, which will be oxidized by the body to produce energy.

Thiamine must be renewed on a daily basis through a healthy diet. Small amounts may be stored in the liver fats, but a high intake of carbohydrates will rapidly deplete the supply.

Thiamine hydrochloride, also known as thiamine HCl or thiamine chloride, is a synthetic derivative obtained from rice polishings through extraction or crystallization.

Allies: The entire vitamin B complex is best taken all together rather than in separate dosages, since all the vitamins play an important part in the metabolic processes of the body. In addition, vitamins C and E are very effective in the utilization of thiamine. The vitamin is also more effective when taken with manganese and sulfur.

Antagonists: Excessive sugar intake, smoking and drinking alcohol contribute to the depletion of thiamine. Moreover, some people on poor diets have intestinal bacteria that can produce an antivitamin, the enzyme thiaminase, which destroys thiamine. People suffering from constipation are especially likely to have this antivitamin. People who eat a great deal of raw fish or shell fish also bring this enzyme into their bodies, thereby producing a deficiency of thiamine. In addition, antibiotics can cause a deficiency of thiamine, as can any severe, stressful situation, such as pregnancy, lactation, fever or surgery.

Dosages

Recommended Dietary Allowance:
Infants 0-1/6 yrs. 0.2 mg. 1/6-1/2 yrs. 0.4 mg. 1/2-1 yrs. 0.5 mg.
Children 1-3 yrs 0.6 mg. 3-4 yrs. 0.7 mg. 4-6 yrs. 0.8 mg. 6-8 yrs. 1.0 mg. 8-10 yrs. 1.1 mg.
Men 10-12 yrs. 1.3 mg. 12-14 yrs. 1.4 mg. 14-18 yrs. 1.5 mg. 18-35 yrs. 1.4 mg. 35-55 yrs. 1.3 mg. 55-75 + yrs. 1.2 mg.
Women 10-12 yrs. 1.1 mg. 12-18 yrs. 1.2 mg. 18-75 + yrs. 1.0 mg.
Pregnant Women +.1 mg.
Lactating Women +.5 mg.
Therapeutic Dose: Under a physician's guidance

50 milligrams for a limited time are recommended.
Megadose: Under a physician's guidance 100 milligrams are recommended.

Toxicity

There is no known toxicity level for thiamine, although large doses of the vitamin alone can cause high urinary excretion of other vitamins in the B-complex, thereby inducing deficiencies of other B vitamins.

Deficiency Symptoms

The first signs of a deficiency of thiamine are usually tiredness, loss of appetite, emotional instability and unexplained irritability. These symptoms may be brought on by the consumption of too many sweets that wash the vitamin out of the body.

More severe symptoms of a deficiency are loss of mental alertness, labored breathing and, eventually, cardiac damage. Thiamine keeps pyruvic acid in the blood—an intermediate product in the metabolism of carbohydrates, fats and amino acids. If thiamine is not available, the pyruvic acid increases in the blood and tissue, resulting in oxygen deprivation and the symptoms listed above.

Among the heart problems that can be caused by insufficient thiamine are an erratic heart beat, bradycardia (an abnormally slow heart rate) and cardiomegaly (an enlarged heart). The two enzymes necessary to carry on energy metabolism for the heart are PDH and 2-KGDH: if not enough thiamine is ingested, these enzymes cannot use the coenzyme containing thiamine properly to keep the heart rate regular.

The gastrointestinal tract may also be disturbed, producing such symptoms as indigestion, anorexia (loss of appetite), severe and continuous constipation and gastric atony (flabbiness of the muscle tone of the stomach). There may be vague abdominal pains, and by a reflex action the chest area may be bothered. Since thiamine is essential in the formation of hydrochloric acid, which aids in digestion, loss of stomach acidity will bring on improper digestion: undigested food may stagnate for hours or days, and gas will form, producing flatulence, heartburn or a seeming attack of gastroenteritis (inflammation of the mucous membrane of the stomach and intestine). The deficiency may even lead to erosions and ulcers of the stomach.

Neural problems occur from lack of thiamine in the diet as well, because the vitamin is the catalyst to the enzymatic reactions that supply energy to the nerves of the body and brain: it forms acetylcholine, a compound that transmits nerve impulses. Polyneuritis (beriberi), literally meaning "many types of nerve disease,'' is a problem primarily related to a deficiency of thiamine. The first effects of the disease are the loss of muscle tone and waste of tissue, beginning in the legs and then moving throughout the body. In later stages there is swelling in the arms and legs, moving to the trunk of the body. Another nerve-related ailment is neuritis (inflammation of a nerve or nerves, usually associated with a degenerative process such as polyneuritis or multiple sclerosis). Symptoms of the disease include numbness and tingling of the hands and feet. Along with other vitamins in the B complex thiamine plays a part in eradicating this condition.

Although few skin problems normally develop with a deficiency of thiamine, herpes zoster (shingles), characterized by a cluster of small, painful blisters that can erupt anywhere on the body, may occur. Caused by a virus that produces vesicular eruptions, these cold sores or fever blisters can be helped by thiamine. In one test 25 patients suffering from the disease were given intramuscular injections of 200 milligrams of thiamine hydrochloride daily, and all were successfully treated. And during World War II captured soldiers living mainly on raw or poorly cooked fish and ocean produce, such as clams, complained that it was impossible to walk because their feet burned and itched painfully: the antivitamin enzyme thiaminase was responsible for destroying thiamine in the body and creating the condition.

Finally, iron-related anemia (a condition in which there is a reduction in the number of circulating red blood cells or hemoglobin) takes place when the diet is high in iron but deficient in thiamine and other B complex vitamins. Since the hydrochloride in the stomach is not secreted in sufficient quantity to break down and dissolve the iron, the mineral is not absorbed, and anemia can result.

Recent Clinical Developments

There is a definite link between alcoholism and a deficiency of thiamine. Although a thiamine deficiency by itself does not create alcoholism, if there are low levels of the vitamin in the body, alcohol is oxidized less rapidly, and the blood sugar levels become erratic, causing a continual "thirst" for alcohol. Thiamine in sufficient amounts tends to cut down on the craving for sugar found in alcohol, thereby blunting the craving that causes an alcoholic to consume large quantities of beer, wine or other spirits. Thiamine chloride in doses of 50 to 100 milligrams has been used successfully to restore an alcoholic's blood sugar level. If an alcoholic has the delirium tremens, 1,500 milligrams of nicotinic acid and 500 milligrams of thiamine chloride stabilize the withdrawal symptoms.

Other studies have shown that the use of diuretics causes the loss of many essential nutrients, including the vitamin B complex. Loss of thiamine as well as pantothenic acid can result in decreased circulation, conducive to blood clotting and degeneration of the heart muscles. Furthermore, the loss of iodine with diuretics can be excessive, eventually causing thyroid malfunction.

In addition, infants who fail to gain at normal rates of growth may be suspect of a low intake of thiamine. Loss of appetite, indicative of a deficiency of thiamine, may contribute to a slow growth rate in the beginning, eventually slowing a child's entire growth process. In a test group the vitamin B complex was administered over a period of seven months, and children in the control group who took it gained 1.6 times more weight than those who did not.

Supplements of thiamine can help relieve dental pain as well. For instance, postoperative dental pain has been reduced with prompt doses of thiamine, since the vitamin lowers the levels of sensitivity to pain. Thiamine has also been administered before operations to reduce pain. And whenever a tooth is extracted thiamine helps quicken the healing time of the dry socket. Several other problems can be helped with adequate doses of thiamine. Sugar-related ailments, such as diabetes, have been helped with the use of thiamine to increase insulin production. Bell's palsy, an acute and inflammatory reaction in or around the seventh facial nerve marked by paralysis of the muscle that controls facial expression, has also been successfully treated with thiamine. Moreover, degeneration of the spinal cord, associated with pernicious anemia (a destructive form of blood disease marked by a decrease in red blood cells, muscular weakness and gastrointestinal and neural disturbances), may be helped with doses of thiamine and vitamin A.

RIBOFLAVIN

Astrological Ruler
The Moon.

Synthetic Forms
Riboflavin (synthesized from ribose, a pentose sugar).

Synonyms
Antidermatitis vitamin, antipellagra vitamin, vitamin P-P, vitamin G, lactoflavin, flavin, water-soluble vitamin, heat-stable B, old yellow vitamin and vitamin B-2.

Sources
Vegetables: Lima beans, beet greens, broccoli,

chick peas (garbanzos), escarole, cabbage, mustard greens, soybeans, spinach, turnip greens and water-cress.

Fruits and Nuts: Dried apricots, blueberries, mangoes, dried prunes, tangerines and peanuts.

Fish and Meat: Beef, beef heart, beef kidney, veal kidney, mutton kidney, beef, calf, lamb liver and pork.

Grains: Rye germ and wheat germ.

Dairy Products: Cheese, whole eggs, egg yolks, whole milk, dried milk and malted milk.

Herbs: Bladderwrack, fenugreek and saffron.

Natural Supplements: Yeast, rice bran, dulse and kelp.

Unit of Potency

Riboflavin is measured in three forms: the Sherman-Bourquin Unit, U.S.P. and milligram. It is commonly sold by milligram dosage.

History and Characteristics

An orange-yellow crystalline powder, riboflavin, or vitamin B-2, is referred to as the "old yellow enzyme" because it was discovered as the pigment in milk. It is not affected by dilute acids or air, but alkalies will bring about its destruction. It is water-soluble. Ordinary light makes it unstable, and ultraviolet radiation will cause its decomposition. It is stable to heat except in alkaline compounds or solutions.

Riboflavin forms a reaction with protein to create flavoprotein, essential in cellular respiration. The vitamin is converted into two coenzymes—flavin mononucleotide (FMN) and flavin adenine dinucleotide (FAD), both found in the liver. Riboflavin is a coferment (coenzyme) to phosphorus. It also regulates the sodium-potassium exchange of cells and helps break down and assimilate carbohydrates, proteins and fats. It is needed for proper assimilation of iron into the body as well.

Riboflavin is easily assimilated through the walls of the small intestine. It is carried through the circulatory system and then excreted in the urine. Small amounts are stored in the heart, liver and kidneys, but the vitamin must be resupplied on a daily basis through a sound diet.

Allies: Riboflavin is more effective when taken with all the vitamin B complex, especially vitamin B-6, niacin, biotin and folic acid, as well as vitamin C, which helps protect against oxidation.

Antagonists: Any glass or plastic container for milk will produce a loss of riboflavin because the container is irradiated to give the milk vitamin D, and the ultraviolet light kills riboflavin. The clearness of a milk container also helps destroy riboflavin because of the normal light reaching the milk. Moreover, cooking, blanching and freezing foods that contain riboflavin will destroy the vitamin's beneficial effects. Riboflavin also loses potency when antibiotics or alcohol is placed in the body. And oral contraceptives may lower the levels of the vitamin in the body.

Dosages

Recommended Daily Allowance:
Infants 0-1/6 yrs. 0.4 mg. 1/6-1/2 yrs. 0.5 mg. 1/2-1 yrs. 0.6 mg.
Children 1-2 yrs. 0.6 mg. 2-3 yrs. 0.7 mg. 3-4 yrs. 0.8 mg. 4-6 yrs. 0.9 mg. 6-8 yrs. 1.1 mg. 8-10 yrs. 1.2 mg.
Men 10-12 yrs. 1.3 mg. 12-14 yrs. 1.4 mg. 14-18 yrs. 1.5 mg. 18-22 yrs. 1.6 mg. 22-75+ yrs. 1.7 mg.
Women 10-12 yrs. 1.3 mg. 12-16 yrs. 1.4 mg. 16-75+ yrs. 1.5 mg.
Pregnant Women 1.8 mg.
Lactating Women 2.0 mg.

Therapeutic Dose: Dr. Tom Spies of the Nutrition Clinic of the Hillman Hospital, Birmingham, Alabama, has treated more than 5,000 people with deficiencies of riboflavin. His figures indicate that a daily intake of the vitamin should be around 3.5 milligrams daily. Other doctors have used 25 milligrams.

Megadose: Under a physician's guidance 25 to 50 milligrams are recommended.

Toxicity

There is no known level of toxicity of riboflavin; however, prolonged use of a a dosage of 25 milligrams or more can induce high urinary loss of other B vitamins, especially vitamin B-6.

Deficiency Symptoms

Some of the most common signs of a deficiency of riboflavin are cracks and sores at the corners of the mouth—in medical terms, angular stomatitis associated with transverse fissures. The lips will have an abnormal shiny redness of the mucous membrane. There will also be a scaling or "sharkskin" appearance of the skin around the nose and eyes and occasionally over the ears. The tongue may be a purplish or magenta, swollen, painful and bright. A mild deficiency may produce whiteheads on the skin, and the hair and skin may become oily: a dosage of from five to fifteen milligrams daily has been used to clear up such conditions.

Although the flaking off of skin usually occurs on the facial area, the scrotum or vulva may also be affected. Many women who suffer several times a year from pain during intercourse plus inflammation and itching in the vaginal area have contracted an ailment known as trichomonas (vaginitis) caused by a deficiency of riboflavin. This annoying ailment responds dramatically to as few as six milligrams a day of riboflavin.

A deficiency of riboflavin can also produce probblems with the eyes. The eyes may show abnormal reaction to light, have bulbar conjunctivitis, burn, feel as though grit or sand is beneath the lids or undergo changes in the cornea. Most noticeable are bloodshot eyes because the riboflavin, necessary to carry oxygen to the small vessels, is missing. Other eye symptoms include watering, the accumulation of bits of mucus at the base of the lashes (especially during sleep) and splitting at the outer corners of the skin around the eyes. As few as five milligrams daily has helped clear up a variety of the above problems.

Finally, a deficiency of riboflavin is associated with hypoglycemia (low blood sugar). This disease occurs when the liver is unable to produce the enzymes to inactivate insulin. The excess insulin remains in the blood, causing fat to be formed and the blood sugar to fall. Without adequate riboflavin symptoms of trembling, dizziness or sluggishness will occur three to five hours after a meal. If protein is not ingested immediately, the symptoms will continue until fainting or a comatose state may occur, which if severe enough can bring on death. This condition is fortunately highly correctable through proper diet and a good, continuing supply of riboflavin and pantothenic acid.

Recent Clinical Developments

There has been considerable speculation that riboflavin helps prevent damage to the fetus. In tests rats deficient in riboflavin had offspring with foreshortened limbs. Since the vitamin is essential in the utilization of oxygen to produce energy, fetal activity may be impaired and deformities may develop with insufficient amounts. A lack of riboflavin can also increase the teratogenicity (fetal-damage potential) of certain drugs. If drugs must be used during pregnancy, a physician should make sure the patient is on an optimum diet to insure proper amounts of riboflavin and a healthy fetus.

Although anemia is usually associated with a lack of folic acid or iron in the body, a deficiency of riboflavin can also create the condition. A lack of riboflavin halts the coenzymes from joining and fewer red blood cells are produced for use. Furthermore, with a diet high in iron but lacking in vitamin B-12 and other vitamins of the B complex, the stomach is unable to secrete hydrochloric acid to dissolve the iron. Anemia then becomes a potential disease.

High blood pressure can also be related to a lack of riboflavin. One of the vitamins instrumental in lowering sodium to acceptable levels is riboflavin. One of the reasons for high blood pressure is an imbalance of sodium and potassium: too much sodium in the body will cause potassium to be expelled through the urine.

In addition, experiments with rats have shown that deficiencies of riboflavin can bring about cancer in the lymph glands or liver. When the rats were given sufficient amounts of the vitamin, cancer was delayed from further development. The experiments have also indicated a close relationship between cancer and the balance of riboflavin and vitamin B-6 in the body. Cancers developed when vitamin B-6 was missing. When the rats were given vitamin B-6 in megadoses, they excreted riboflavin, increasing cancer growth. Similarly, megadoses of riboflavin induced deficiencies of vitamin B-6 and allowed tumors to grow rapidly.

A deficiency of riboflavin can indirectly add to the sluggish output of the adrenal glands, too. With decreased activity of the adrenal cortex, a person may not be able to handle stress well.

Unlike many of the other B complex vitamins, extra riboflavin is not needed if a person increases the amount of carbohydrate consumption.

NIACIN

Astrological Ruler
Venus.

Synthetic Forms
Niacin and niacinamide.

Synonyms
Antipellagra vitamin, niacinamide, nicotinic acid, nicotinamide and vitamin B-3.

Sources
Vegetables: Green peas, mushrooms and watercress.
Fruits and Nuts: Fresh apricots, avocados, fresh elderberries, dried dates, cooked rhubarb, carob, peanuts and sunflower seeds.
Fish and Meat: Beef liver, beef heart, beef kidney, beef, rabbit, white turkey meat, white chicken meat, ham, halibut and tuna.
Grains: Whole-wheat flour, brown rice and wheat germ.
Dairy Products: Unknown.
Herbs: Alfalfa leaves, blueberry leaves, burdock seed, fenugreek and parsley.
Natural Supplements: Yeast, rice polishings and rice bran.

Unit of Potency
Milligram.

History and Characteristics

Niacin, or vitamin B-3, is resistant to heat, light, air, acids and alkalies.

Although the terms *niacin* and *niacinamide* are used interchangeably, both forms of vitamin B-3 are different. First, niacin, not niacinamide, can be produced in the body with the aid of one of the essential amino acids, tryptophan: with other necessary vitamins and proteins present to act as catalysts, it takes 60 milligrams of tryptophan to create 1 milligram of niacin in the body. Second, the effects of the two types of vitamin B-3 are different: niacin (nicotinic acid) is a vasodilator (what opens or enlarges the blood vessels) and was first isolated from yeast and rice bran; niacinamide (nicotinamide) lacks the vasodilator ability and was first isolated from liver concentrates. Third, niacinamide, known as the pellagra-preventive factor, or PP, is used to treat certain diseases when the flush created by nicotinic acid is not needed nor desired.

Niacin, a white crystal or powder, is used orally or parenterally to treat such diseases as pellagra, caused by a deficiency of niacin. Niacin is also instrumental as a coenzyme in breaking down and utilizing carbohydrates, fats and proteins. It is necessary in the synthesis of the sex hormones as well as the continued health of the nervous system, the digestive system and the skin.

Niacin is primarily absorbed in the intestines and stored in the liver, heart and muscles in small amounts. Excess is sloughed off in the urine. Niacin can also be synthesized in the colon, providing that thiamine, riboflavin and vitamin B-6 are present to make the catalytic exchange.

Allies: Niacin is most effective when taken with the other vitamins of the vitamin B complex. Vitamin C, which helps protect niacin against the oxidation processes, is also a primary ally.

Antagonists: Excessive sugar consumption, cooking and the use of the antibiotic penicillin will eliminate niacin from the body. The antibiotic chloramphenicol, used primarily for the treatment of typhoid fever, salmonella (food poisoning by bacteria) and rickettsial infections (diseases transmitted by lice, fleas, ticks or mites) is also an antagonist. Alcohol as well as any long-term illness will decrease niacin's effectiveness by inhibiting its assimilation in the intestinal tract.

Dosages

Recommended Dietary Allowance:
Infants 0-1/6 yrs. 5 mg. 1/6-1/2 yrs. 7 mg. 1/2-1 yrs. 5 mg.

Children 1-3 yrs. 8 mg. 3-4 yrs. 9 mg. 4-6 yrs. 11 mg. 6-8 yrs. 13 mg. 8-10 yrs. 15 mg.
Men 10-12 yrs. 17 mg. 12-14 yrs. 18 mg. 14-18 yrs. 20 mg. 18-35 yrs. 18 mg. 35-55 yrs. 17 mg. 55-75+ yrs. 14 mg.
Women 10-14 yrs. 15 mg. 14-16 yrs. 16 mg. 16-18 yrs. 15 mg. 18-75+ yrs. 13 mg.
Pregnant Women 15 mg.
Lactating Women 20 mg.

Therapeutic Dose: One hundred milligrams or more with each meal are recommended. If niacin (nicotinic acid) is taken at this dosage, temporary side effects may occur: the body will "blush," turning red; there will be a prickly, tingling sensation; and the body will itch and throb as the vitamin dilates the lumen (the space within an artery, vein, intestine or tube) in the blood vessels. As few as 25 milligrams of niacin will bring on similar reactions, but lasting only moments. To avoid the side effects (except for migraine headaches and acne), many doctors suggest taking niacinamide (nicotinamide).

Megadose: Under a physician's guidance up to 25,000 milligrams is used to treat certain conditions. (See **Recent Clinical Developments**.) But massive doses will put stress on the stomach, liver, sex hormones and intestines.

Toxicity

No toxicity level has been indicated. Since niacin is a water-soluble vitamin, the body eliminates excesses through the urine.

As I've indicated, however, with massive doses there can be permanent damage to the liver, digestive tract or sex hormones: that is why the strict guidance of a physician and follow-up tests are necessary for administering megadoses. Overdosing will frequently happen to patients who need to have their blood cholesterol reduced to lessen what appears to be symptoms of schizophrenia but are really symptoms of subclinical pellagra, misdiagnosed as schizophrenia.

Deficiency Symptoms

There are many symptoms associated with deficiencies of niacin. Among the first to appear are skin eruptions (such as canker sores in the mouth), trench mouth, fissures in the tongue, swelling or tenderness of the tongue, splotches on the skin, bad breath, gum problems, continual headaches, skin lesions, diarrhea, forgetfulness and irritability.

Besides skin lesions, sores or tumorlike pustules, there can be a change in pigmentation, particularly in exposed areas of the skin. Darkening of the skin can indicate adrenal exhaustion: a white person may become dark brown within a matter of weeks because of deficiencies of niacin, folic acid and pantothenic acid. Undernourished women who are pregnant often have a pigmentation change, usually on the forehead: it's called a "pregnancy cap." Pantothenic acid normally clears up this phenomenon.

Moderate deficiencies of niacin can bring on a flurry of nervous disorders known as subclinical pellagra. They include depression, mental dullness, confusion, forgetfulness, disorientation, hallucination, insomnia, nausea and vomiting. Fear and anxiety can make a person think that he or she is "going crazy," and if the deficiency is severe enough mental breakdown can occur.

In fact, people have been committed to mental institutions and diagnosed as schizophrenic because of a deficiency of niacin. Dr. Glen Green, M.D., in a 1970 publication of *Schizophrenia* outlines six basic questions that a physician should ask a patient to distinguish the difference between the symptoms of pellagra and schizophrenia:
1. Does your face seem to change when you look in a mirror?
2. Do words move when you try to read?
3. Does the ground move when you walk?
4. Do you feel you walk on the ground or off the ground?
5. Do pictures move when you look at them?
6. Do you hear someone calling your name when you're alone?

A person who has experienced some or all of these symptoms is probably suffering from a moderate deficiency of niacin and should seek help from a doctor of medicine instead of a psychologist or psychiatrist.

Finally, severe deficiencies of niacin can cause pellagra, a disease that affects the skin, gastrointestinal system and nervous system. It is characterized by the "three Ds"—dermatitis, diarrhea and dementia. And the disease can be fatal if the niacin deficiency, usually caused by a poor diet consisting mainly of corn or maize, is allowed to continue.

Recent Clinical Developments

People who have bouts with diarrhea on an almost constant basis could be deficient in niacin. Two days on a natural source of B vitamins plus 100 milligrams of niacinamide has been known to clear up the problem.

Niacin taken in megadose proportions under a doctor's guidance has also been known to heal a sore or fissured tongue in approximately 24 hours. If the liver is the source of the niacin deficiency, it will take about three days to correct the problem. Yeast with

some niacin will correct the condition in five or six days.

In addition, high blood pressure is often treated with niacin, although in cases of overdoses the vitamin can worsen the condition. Doses of niacin can also increase circulation in the entire body, particularly the hands and feet. And painful leg cramps in middle-aged and elderly people can be relieved through sufficient dosages.

Niacin has also been known to help children suffering from subclinical pellagra, who seemingly lack any sort of attention span in a classroom situation, are unable to sit still and are nervous, restless and sometimes even destructive.

A great deal of success has been noted in the use of niacin to reduce or end migraine headaches, too. Unlike normal headaches, migraines are thought in some cases to be caused by vasodilation of extracerebral cranial arteries in the head. The contraction of the blood vessels diminishes the blood supply to the brain, causing many symptoms: lights flashing before the eyes, nausea, vomiting, stabbing pains in the head, sweating and several other uncomfortable side effects. If at the first suspicion of a migraine coming on a person takes between 50 and 150 milligrams of niacin, in about ten minutes a flush will occur, signifying that the vessels are opening up, and the migraine will cease.

In many of our foods, particularly cereals, niacin becomes bound. The bound form of niacin is not released from the food so that it can be used properly by the body. Tests with animals also show that such foods are ineffective in curing diseases caused by deficiencies of niacin.

VITAMIN B-6
Astrological Ruler
Jupiter.

Synthetic Forms
Pyridoxine hydrochloride and pyridoxine.

Synonyms
Antiedema vitamin, pyridoxal, pyridoxamine, pyridoxine and the female vitamin.

Sources
Vegetables: Raw soybeans, raw white beans, lima beans, lentils and green peas.
Fruits and Nuts: Bananas, walnuts, sunflower seeds, avocados, prunes and peanuts.
Fish and Meat: Tuna, mackerel, salmon, beef liver, chicken liver, white chicken meat and lamb.
Grains: Wheat germ.
Dairy Products: Skim milk.

Herbs: Alfalfa and bladderwrack.

Natural Supplements: Dulse, kelp, yeast, rice bran, pyridoxal-5-phosphate, pyridoxol-5-phosphate p-s-p and pyridoxamine-p.

Unit of Potency
Milligram.

History and Characteristics
Several terms are used for vitamin B-6, which consists of three related compounds: pyridoxine, pyridoxinal and pyridoxamine. Pyridoxamine is a 4-aminoethyl analog of pyridoxine. Pyridoxal 5-phosphate is a derivative of pyridoxine and pridotanune: it serves as a coenzyme of certain amino acids (decarboxylases) in bacteria, and it is also found in animal tissue of 3.4-dihydroxyphenylalanine (dopa) decarboxylase. The principal end product of pyridoxine metabolism is 4-pyridoxic acid.

Vitamin B-6 is water- and alcohol-soluble, very sensitive to light but not so much to heat. It is rapidly inactivated in the presence of heat, sunlight or air. Modern refining and processing techniques drain the reserves of the vitamin in the food we consume. A recent study concludes that 57 to 77 per cent of vitamin B-6 is lost in canned vegetables, 37 to 56 per cent in frozen vegetables, 15.4 per cent in frozen fruit juices, 37.6 per cent in canned juices, 42.6 per cent in canned meat, 93 per cent in precooked rice and 80 per cent in white flour.

Upon entering the body and with the aid of riboflavin vitamin B-6 is transformed into the coenzyme pyridoxal 5-phosphate. At that stage the vitamin is primarily concerned with the metabolism of fats, carbohydrates, potassium, iron, insulin and the adrenal hormones. It is extremely important in maintaining the protein metabolism. As a coferment it influences the amino acid metabolism and regulates the proper utilization of fats. It is also needed in the anabolism processes in the tissue of the skin and organs. It is essential for the absorption of vitamin B-12. It aids the activity of the central nervous system. And it helps in the formation of antibodies.

After vitamin B-6 is ingested it moves through the circulatory system. If not utilized, the vitamin will be excreted about eight hours afterward. Unlike many other nutrients, it is not stored in the liver. It can be synthesized by healthy intestinal flora. Fasting and reduction diets will cause a loss of vitamin B-6 if proper safeguards are not taken.

Allies: Vitamin B-6 is most effective when taken with the entire vitamin B complex, especially thiamine, riboflavin and pantothenic acid. Vitamin C and magnesium are also primary allies. And potassium, linoleic acid and sodium greatly aid in the assimilation of vitamin B-6.

Antagonists: Steroid and semicarbazide hormones, such as cortisone and estrogen, as well as isoniazid (an antibacterial drug used in the treatment of tuberculosis) penicillin and streptomycin will destroy vitamin B-6 in the body. Diets high in protein, such as the kind many hypoglycemics must adhere to for proper sugar levels, will also cause a depletion of vitamin B-6 unless enough of the vitamin is taken to compensate for the added protein in the diet. In addition, there is a 30 to 45 per cent loss of vitamin B-6 during working.

Dosages
Recommended Dietary Allowance:
Infants 0-1/6 yrs. 0.2 mg. 1/6-1/2 yrs. 0.3 mg. 1/2-1 yrs. 0.4 mg.
Children 1-2 yrs. 0.5 mg. 2-3 yrs. 0.6 mg. 3-4 yrs. 0.7 mg. 4-6 yrs. 0.9 mg. 6-8 yrs. 1.0 mg. 8-10 yrs. 1.2 mg.
Men 10-12 yrs. 1.4 mg. 12-14 yrs. 1.6 mg. 14-18 yrs. 1.8 mg. 18-75 + yrs. 2.0 mg.
Women 10-12 yrs. 1.4 mg. 12-14 yrs. 1.6 mg. 14-16 yrs. 1.8 mg. 16-75 + yrs. 2.0 mg.
Pregnant Women 2.5 mg.
Lactating Women 2.5 mg.

Therapeutic Dose: Under a physician's guidance 100 milligrams daily are recommended, preferably with the rest of the vitamin B complex to prevent deficiencies.

Megadose: Doctors have administered from 50 to 450 milligrams daily and 1,000 milligrams for short intervals in some cases. Especially in pregnancy there seems to be a higher need for vitamin B-6 to combat side effects such as edema, swelling of ankles and hands and nausea. There have been claims that excessive vitamin B-6 is responsible for cleft palates in infants. Megadoses should always be administered with a physician's guidance to prevent other deficiencies.

Toxicity
No toxicity level is indicated. Since vitamin B-6 is a water-soluble vitamin, the body will excrete what is not needed through the urine. But too much vitamin B-6 can cause deficiencies in the other B complex vitamins if a proper relationship between the vitamins of the complex is not maintained.

Deficiency Symptoms
When vitamin B-6 is deficient, the amino acid tryptophan is changed into xanthurenic acid. If this condition occurs, the pancreas can become damaged within a short amount of time: the blood sugar will rise and excessive glucose will spill into the blood, creating the onset of diabetes. Glucose spilled into

the blood spurs the body to take water from the cells and form urine to get rid of the water—hence the great thirst that accompanies diabetes.

Another sugar-related disease associated with insufficient vitamin B-6 is hypoglycemia, the opposite of diabetes. Among the numerous symptoms of the disease are tremors, dizziness, fainting, irritability and other forms of mental illness. Its victims may think they are treading the thin line of insanity, and, indeed, people with undiagnosed hypoglycemia have ended up in mental hospitals and sanitariums. Vitamin B-6 and proper diet can help control and in some cases eradicate the ailment.

Vitamin B-6 is also known as the female vitamin because the symptoms of many pregnancies—edema of the hands and legs, morning sickness, depression and uremic toxemia—are actually symptoms of a deficiency of the vitamin. The edema is caused by toxemia (poisonous products of bacteria within the body). Although many doctors blame this swelling on too much salt or sodium in the diet, high sodium content is not the only reason for the swelling. In one test a doctor treated 225 pregnant women without restricting their salt intake or prescribing diuretics but instead prescribing 10 milligrams of vitamin B-6 daily. Many women lost their edema, whereas others had to take higher doses of the vitamin to stay free of the swelling. Vitamin B-6 is also essential during pregnancy because it plays a significant part in the release of hormones in a woman's body. When more estrogen is needed, vitamin B-6 will increase the supply.

Adequate amounts of vitamin B-6 are also important for women who are not pregnant. Without enough of the vitamin depression can become a frequent problem, particularly five days before a menstrual cycle begins. And with insufficient vitamin B-6 women on birth control pills may suffer symptoms of edema, weight gain and menopausal arthritis on a monthly basis.

Hypochromic anemia (a condition in which the red blood cells have a reduced amount of hemoglobin) may be caused by a deficiency of vitamin B-6 as well. It appears that iron is necessary for hemoglobin synthesis. When vitamin B-6 is not plentiful, iron is not used properly and granular deposits will form in the blood cells. (Some doctors feel that once this type of anemia is contracted even vitamin B-6 cannot completely undo the damage.)

Furthermore, certain skin disorders are linked to a lack of vitamin B-6. For instance, seborrhea (an inflammatory skin condition manifesting in scaling, redness and crusted patches on the face, scalp and ears) can be cured with vitamin B-6: in one test, when 10 milligrams of pyridoxine were put in a vanishing cream base and applied to skin lesions, all ailments disappeared within five to twenty-one days with daily application. And acne associated with the premenstrual cycle can be curbed 50 to 75 per cent when vitamin B-6 is taken internally.

Swelling of the hands and feet, the extremities going to sleep and cramps or painful neural disturbances in the fingers and hands can also signal a need for vitamin B-6.

Finally, although deficiencies of vitamin B-6 are not as clearly identifiable as those of certain other vitamins and minerals, lack of the vitamin can bring on other deficiencies because vitamin B-6 plays such an integral part in the overall functioning of the body's metabolism. Without vitamin B-6 thiamine, riboflavin and vitamin B-12 cannot effectively function or be assimilated properly. The best laboratory test to determine a deficiency of vitamin B-6 is to check the level of xanthurenic acid excreted in the urine.

Recent Clinical Developments

Some heart problems can indirectly be traced to insufficient amounts of vitamin B-6. This vitamin, along with its partner, magnesium, helps keep the cholesterol levels of the body in balance. If vitamin B-6 is not present in sufficient quantities, lecithin (a phospholipid created in the liver to help cells remove fats and cholesterol) cannot be synthesized. The end product is atherosclerosis (clogging of the arteries with fat and cholesterol), which results in heart ailments.

Deficiencies in vitamin B-6 are also responsible for a kind of anemia that usually shows up in pregnancy and is treated with iron supplements. Without enough vitamin B-6 the body becomes poisoned with iron and can eventually form scars that can calcify, a condition similar to a fatal iron-storage disease called siderosis or hemosiderosis. But if vitamin B-6 is plentiful, the body only absorbs the iron it needs, and the rest is harmlessly excreted. In this case vitamin B-6 acts as a police officer directing the traffic of other vitamins and minerals in the body and ordering any excesses out so that no damage is incurred.

Another blood condition that has been known to respond favorably to extra vitamin B-6 in the diet is leukopenia, occurring when the white blood corpuscles decrease below 5,000 per cubic millimeter.

Vitamin B-6 can also help alleviate the pains and complications of surgery. Given to a patient before surgery, vitamin B-6 can give the adrenals a boost and help increase the antibodies to fight off any potential postsurgical infections. It can also alleviate vomiting that often occurs during postsurgical recovery. Usually a 50-milligram injection is used.

In addition, vitamin B-6 can help stop the vomiting associated with labyrinthitis (Meniere's syndrome) an infection of the inner ear. A person deficient in vitamin B-6 and pantothenic acid may lose so much salt in the urine that the adrenals become exhausted, and excessive fluid may enter the tissue—in this case, the ears. Vomiting is a side effect.

Along with insufficient vitamin C and pantothenic acid, too little vitamin B-6 can also be responsible for certain allergies. All of these vitamins have special antihistaminic action, and lack of any one may allow the eosinophil blood cells to increase abnormally, causing an allergy.

Moreover, a deficiency of vitamin B-6 can be implicated in malfunctioning of the pancreas (a gland responsible for secreting insulin into the blood and digestive enzymes). A diet lacking in protein, certain amino acids and vitamin B-6 can bring on pancreatitis (inflammation of the pancreas). This condition can also occur if persons have been given ACTH or cortisone therapy. With this ailment the pancreas absorbs large amounts of iron, pointing to a shortage of vitamin B-6. Without the vitamin the pancreas will eventually be damaged and scarred, causing loss of enzymes associated with the digestive process.

Some cases of hair loss can also be attributed to deficiencies of vitamin B-6 and folic acid.

Vitamin B-6 can be beneficial in alleviating certain tics, tremors, spasms or twitching, too. Other kinds of muscle cramping caused by a deficiency of calcium can be induced if not enough vitamin B-6 and magnesium are in the body to prevent loss of calcium through the urine.

Finally, vitamin B-6 is a natural diuretic, and under a doctor's guidance it should be used instead of drug-diuretics whenever possible.

VITAMIN B-12

Astrological Ruler
Mars.

Synthetic Forms
Vitamin B-12 cannot be made synthetically but is grown in bacteria or molds like penicillin.

Synonyms
cyanocobalamin, cobalamin and the red vitamin.

Sources
Vegetables: Green peas.
Fruits and Nuts: Unsweetened prunes.
Fish and Meat: Raw beef liver, chicken, raw beef kidney, raw beef heart, raw clams, raw oysters, crayfish, trout, herring, sardines and cooked crab.
Grains: Bran flakes and wheat flakes.
Dairy Products: Yogurt, cottage cheese, eggs, Swiss cheese and skim milk.
Herbs: Alfalfa and bladderwrack.
Natural Supplements: Yeast, desiccated liver tablets, dulse and kelp.

Unit of Potency
Microgram.

History and Characteristics
Vitamin B-12 is a crystalline red substance referred to as the red vitamin. It is unique in that cobalt, essential for longevity, is found in the vitamin: it is the only vitamin that contains essential mineral elements. Vitamin B-12 is water- and alcohol-soluble. It is unstable in hot alkaline or acidic solutions, heat, light and oxidation.

Vitamin B-12 is made by bacteria in the oceans and lakes and is found in the intestines of mammals. A small amount is manufactured in the human intestinal tract but is immediately used in that part of the body and is not dispensed to other needed areas.

Vitamin B-12 is probably one of the least assimilable vitamins because it is dependent upon two gastric secretions found in the stomach—hydrochloric acid and the intrinsic factor. The intrinsic factor, especially, is of the utmost importance in the absorption of vitamin B-12. The intrinsic factor (a mucoprotein enzyme) is essential to bind vitamin B-12 with calcium to make the vitamin assimilable: it coats and protects the vitamin B-12 until it reaches the small intestine, from where it goes to the liver and bloodstream.

But many people's diets are so lacking that the intrinsic factor may be only partially available. Furthermore, people who have had stomach surgery or prolonged deficiencies of iron may damage or atrophy the secretion glands of this mucoprotein, thereby making any vitamin B-12 supplement given orally unassimilable. Ninety per cent of patients with pernicious anemia have also been found to have antibodies against the stomach cells that produce the intrinsic factor. In such cases oral administration of vitamin B-12 will do little good: instead, injections of vitamin B-12 directly into the bloodstream must be given.

After being absorbed through the intricate balance of the stomach juices and other needed vitamins, vitamin B-12 is bound to serum protein known as globulins and moved through the bloodstream to various bodily tissue. It is needed for normal metabolism of nerve tissue, carbohydrates, proteins and fats. It is related in activity to four amino acids, vitamin C and pantothenic acid. Small amounts of vitamin B-12 are found in the liver, kidneys, heart, pancreas, testes, brain, blood and bone marrow. What is not used is excreted in the urine.

Allies: Vitamin B-12 is most effective taken with the entire vitamin B complex, especially cholin, folic acid and inositol. There is a close relationship between vitamin B-12 and folic acid. If one of those vitamins is lacking, ailments may ensue. Together the two vitamins aid in synthesis of cholin. Vitamin B-12 also converts folic acid to folinic acid. Another primary ally is vitamin C. And vitamin A, potassium and sodium increase the effectiveness of vitamin B-12.

Antagonists: Vitamin B's effectiveness is diminished by a prolonged deficiency of iron, oral contraceptives, stress situations (such as pregnancy) and vegetarianism, if all animal and dairy products are avoided.

Dosages

Recommended Dietary Allowance:
Infants 0-1/6 yrs. 1.0 mcg. 1/6-1/2 yrs. 1.5 mcg. 1/2-2 yrs. 2.0 mcg.
Children 2-3 yrs. 2.5 mcg. 3-4 yrs. 3.0 mcg. 4-8 yrs. 4.0 mcg. 8-10 yrs. 5.0 mcg.
Men 10-55 yrs. 5.0 mcg. 55-75+ yrs 6.0 mcg.
Women 10-55 yrs. 5.0 mcg. 55-75+ yrs. 6.0 mcg.
Pregnant Women 8.0 mcg.
Lactating Women 6.0 mcg.

Therapeutic Dose: Under a physician's guidance 50 to 100 micrograms are recommended. Because of the difficulties involved with assimilating vitamin B-12, such dosages are usually given by injection rather than by mouth.

Megadose: Pernicious anemia patients have been given vitamin B-12 orally in amounts of from 250 to 400 micrograms daily to keep the disease in remission.

Toxicity

No toxicity level is indicated. Vitamin B-12 is water-soluble; therefore, any unwanted vitamin is excreted through the urine. No cases of vitamin B-12 toxicity have ever been recorded.

Deficiency Symptoms

A loss of this vitamin in the body's mechanism is long in coming, but once the vitamin is missed the body has a long and arduous return to health. Some of the first signals of a deficiency can come from the sensitive nervous system in the form of sore or weak extremities and poor reflex action. In addition, there

are some general symptoms, such as exhaustion, diminished mental energy, loss of concentration and lethargy: nothing seems to stimulate interest or desire. Later there can be difficulties with walking, stammering or twitching of the limbs. The tongue may become smooth and shiny. And there may be a tingling sensation in the fingers, a stiffness throughout the body and arm and shoulder pain.

The end product of all these symptoms is pernicious anemia. Red blood cells are developed within the marrow of the bones. As vitamin B-12 becomes severely deficient, megalocytes (large red cells) are produced, whose life spans are only half those of the red blood cells. There is arrested maturation and quick destruction of these cells; many never get into the bloodstream. Hence anemia develops. The normal red blood cell count is 5,000,000; white, 5,000 to 10,000. Without vitamin B-12 these levels drop to 1,000,000 or fewer red cells and 3,000 to 5,000 white cells—obviously a very dangerous and potentially fatal loss.

Parallel damage may also occur in the nervous system, making a person shuffle along and lose the sense of position of his or her feet. Complete paralysis may result.

The best way to detect a vitamin B-12 deficiency is with the Schilling test, which measures the absorption of the vitamin.

Recent Clinical Developments

Vegetarians who restrict their diets to exclude meats and dairy products will sooner or later probably acquire deficiencies of vitamin B-12. If the soils were not so depleted and chemical-laden, vegetarians might not develop such deficiencies. But our soils today are extremely barren of needed minerals to make them rich and provide healthful nutrition to vegetables and fruits. Therefore, we must rely on meats and dairy products to acquire the necessary vitamin B-12: egg whites, for example, are very high in vitamin B-12, and yogurt contains two hard-to-get vitamins—vitamins D and B-12. After about five years of their diets strict vegetarians may have sore mouths and tongues, menstrual problems and various nervous complaints—warning signals indicating that they should be taking 50 micrograms of vitamin B-12 each week.

Female problems may manifest with a deficiency of vitamin B-12 as well. For instance, there may be irregular, decreased or halted menstrual flow, correctable with vitamins B-12 or E. There may be an odiferous vaginal discharge, too, especially in women who do not eat meat: this condition is also easily remedied with proper amounts of vitamin B-12. In addition, tests have shown that during pregnancy vitamin B-12 is used up at a faster rate and should therefore be regularly replenished. Women on birth control pills also need higher doses of vitamin B-12.

Allergies related to deficiencies of vitamin B-12 include asthma, hives and eczema. Children with allergies particularly respond to daily supplements of liver or vitamin B-12.

Dropsy (water retention having to do with kidney damage) and Bright's disease (a kidney ailment) can also be corrected with vitamin B-12 and folic acid. The addition of cholin will stop hemorrhaging.

As I mentioned previously, vitamin B-12 and folic acid are a working team. When one but not the other is deficient, anemia may go undetected; when both are deficient, the disease comes to light.

Getting vitamin B-12 into the body when the intrinsic factor is not operative in the stomach is achieved through intermuscular injections, making it unnecessary for the vitamin to be absorbed in the digestive tract; instead, the vitamin B-12 rushes through the circulatory system to where it is most needed. Although oral supplements are sometimes combined with the intrinsic factor taken from animal stomachs, a shot is faster and more economical.

Finally, an ample amount of vitamin B-12 in the body will promote fast production of bile, containing lecithin, to decrease the levels of cholesterol in the blood.

BIOTIN

Astrological Ruler
Jupiter.

Synthetic Forms
D-biotin.

Synonyms
Vitamin H, coenzyme R and protective factor X.

Sources
Vegetables: Unknown.
Fruits and Nuts: Nuts in general, red grapefruit, orange juice, raisins, fresh strawberries and watermelon.
Fish and meat: Lamb, veal, beef, kidney, chicken, liver, pork, herring, mackerel, sardines, sockeye salmon and tuna.
Grains: Brown rice, rolled oats and bulgar wheat.
Dairy Products: Milk, cooked eggs and cheese.
Herbs: Unknown, but since the vitamin is part of the B complex, herbs such as bladderwrack and alfalfa might contain quantities of the vitamin.
Natural Supplements: Yeast and desiccated liver.

Unit of Potency
Milligram.

History and Characteristics
In its pure form biotin is a crystalline white powder that comes from liver or egg yolks: the two types differ slightly in chemical makeup. A component of the vitamin B complex, biotin is a water-soluble vitamin. It is also soluble in alkali and sparingly in dilute mineral acids. It crystallizes in water and is heat-sensitive. It is stable in heat and light and unstable in oxidation.

Although its effects have not been clearly determined, biotin is active throughout the body and may be found in trace amounts in almost every type of food, indicating its importance to many bodily functions. To be effective the vitamin must be broken down by acid hydrolysis and gastric enzymes to the free form. It acts as a coenzyme factor in the making of fatty acids and in the oxidation of fatty acids and carbohydrates. It also affects the metabolism of carbohydrates, proteins and lipids. And recent findings indicate biotin reduces high cholesterol levels and hyperglycemia (diabetes, or excessive sugar in the blood).

Synthesized by intestinal bacteria, biotin is not stored in any particular area of the body, although some is found in the liver. Instead, it is found in minute trace amounts in the cells.

Allies: Biotin is most effective when taken with the entire vitamin B complex, especially vitamin B-12, folic acid and pantothenic acid as well as vitamin C and sulfur.

Antagonists: Nothing destroys biotin more quickly than sulfa drugs and antibiotics because they destroy the intestinal flora and bacteria necessary to synthesize biotin successfully. A protein in raw eggs, avidin, binds with the biotin so that the vitamin cannot be broken down as it passes through the intestines and is therefore excreted unused.

Dosages
Recommended Dietary Allowance:
Infants 0-1 yrs. 0.05 mg.
Children 1-4 yrs. 0.15 mg.
4+ yrs. 0.30 mg.
Men 10+ yrs. 0.30 mg.
Women 10+ yrs. 0.30 mg.
Pregnant Women 0.30 mg.
Lactating Women 0.30 mg.
Therapeutic Dose: Two to five milligrams are recommended.
Megadose: Two hundred and fifty milligrams are recommended.

Toxicity

There are no known toxic effects.

Deficiency Symptoms

It's almost impossible to get a deficiency of biotin unless a person is on a diet high in raw eggs, causing avidin to bind the biotin and make the vitamin unassimilable. In one reported case a doctor placed a patient with a liver ailment on a high-protein diet, which included six raw eggs daily and two quarts of milk with her regular meals. After maintaining the diet for 18 months, the woman manifested a deficiency of biotin. Another way a slight or moderate deficiency of biotin may develop is by taking sulfa drugs or other antibiotics that kill the bacterial flora in the intestines needed to synthesize the vitamin.

If a deficiency does occur, dermatitis (a skin condition) may appear, and the flesh will take on a grayish cast. In addition, hair may start falling out. There may be dry skin, lack of appetite or energy, insomnia, depression and a disturbed nervous system. A dry, scaly, itching type of eczema may occur if oral antibiotics are being taken.

Recent Clinical Developments

Some infants have been reported to have a biotin-related ailment, seborrheic dermatitis, early in their first few months after birth. Their digestive systems may be defective at the beginning and not producing gastric enzymes for hydrolysis of biotin. If a mother is breast-feeding an infant, her own body will be able to convert bound to unbound biotin, carried in the breast milk. The mother can add liver and cooked eggs to her diet to help her infant with this problem. Injections of biotin are also known to clear up the disorder.

Sudden Death Syndrome (SIDS) in children may be attributed to a deficiency of biotin as well. This disease, usually fatal, strikes babies two to four months old. Research scientists in Australia and England working with baby chicks found that the chicks died without warning from a deficiency of biotin plus mild stress. Subsequently, the bodies of 35 infants who had died from SIDS were checked: their levels of biotin were found to be very low. Moreover, many of the babies who died of SIDS were found to be heavily clothed at the time of death. The theory now is that SIDS develops from a lack of biotin, prompted by some event such as a missed meal, plus too much warmth or coldness from blankets or clothes or a change in environment.

If a woman finds her hair falling out during pregnancy, one of the vitamins needed may be biotin. The deficiency may be caused by stress factors involved in adjustment within the body.

It's also just now becoming understood that biotin has something to do with the carbohydrate metabolism process. Diabetics who take insulin have a higher requirement for biotin, thiamine and pantothenic acid. But further research is needed to understand biotin's complete role in the process.

Of great interest and much controversy, too, is a study reported by Adelle Davis. She found that cancer patients who had been fed 36 to 42 raw egg whites daily for a year showed a trend toward general health improvement and no deficiency of biotin.

CHOLIN

Astrological Ruler

Jupiter.

Synthetic Forms

Choline bitartrate.

Synonyms

Choline, B complex member and lipotropic factor.

Sources

Vegetables: Lima beans, mung bean sprouts, carrots, chick peas (garbanzos), cooked lentils, mushrooms, green peas and raw soybeans.

Fruits and Nuts: Fresh orange juice, peanuts and pecans.

Fish and Meat: Fried liver, beef and lamb.

Grains: Wheat germ.

Dairy Products: Eggs.

Herbs: Unknown, but because cholin is part of the vitamin B complex and closely associated with vitamin B-12, herbs such as alfalfa and bladderwrack may be beneficial.

Natural Supplements: Yeast.

Unit of Potency

Milligram.

History and Characteristics

Cholin is a colorless, strongly alkaline, trimethylated hydroxide compound. It can be crystallized only with difficulty because of its hygroscopic nature. It is usually a viscid liquid, soluble in water and alcohol and insoluble in ether. It is relatively stable to heat but can be decomposed by hot alkali.

Cholin can be made in the intestinal tract providing certain of the B vitamins are present so that the amino acid methionine can synthesize it properly. Cholin can also be synthesized in the stomach if vitamin B-12 and folic acid are present.

Cholin is one of the four nutrients classified as lipotropes, needed to synthesize nucleic acids in the formation of new cells. The vitamin's chief duty is binding with inositol to make lecithin, which in turn burns up excess fat. Cholin is also necessary for the continued health of the myelin sheaths surrounding the nerves plus the nerve synapses. The vitamin is part of the ingredients referred to as the nerve fluid acetylcholine, which is responsible for the synapses, or jumps, taking place; otherwise, paralysis, cardiac arrest or death can take place.

Allies: Cholin is most effective when taken with vitamin A and the rest of the vitamin B complex, especially vitamin B-12, folic acid and inositol. Linoleic acid also helps its assimilation and effectiveness.

Antagonists: Choline's effectiveness is diminished by alcohol and high-sugar consumption.

Dosages

Recommended Dietary Allowance: No RDA has been established; however, some sources assert that many species need a relatively large quantity—about 300 times the amount of riboflavin needed. Depending upon age and sex, that would be a dosage of approximately 250 to 600 milligrams for a human.

Therapeutic Dose: Under a physician's guidance 500 to 1,000 milligrams are recommended. Since abnormal doses can cause a deficiency in vitamin B-6, cholin should be taken with the entire vitamin B complex.

Megadose: Dr. Paavo Airola feels that up to 6,000 milligrams can be administered without toxic effects. In one case 50,000 milligrams were given orally daily for one week under a physician's guidance without any toxicity.

Toxicity

No level of toxicity has been established, and symptoms of toxicity are unknown.

Deficiency Symptoms

Deficiencies of cholin can adversely affect the liver. Because the liver is linked with the proper use and assimilation of fats in the body, it may develop fatty deposits, causing the liver cells to become inflamed, swollen or enlarged so that the flow of blood and lymph is partially or completely halted. This condition, known as cirrhosis, produces scars and can damage or block certain liver functions. Without cholin to bind with inositol to create lecithin in the liver to burn up fatty deposits properly, there may be a bloated feeling in the liver area after the person eats a meal. In addition, a person may not desire meat products. He or she may also feel hungry but then

full after only a few bites. But the liver is a regenerative organ, and with proper cholin and a diet high in protein it can recover.

The kidneys may also suffer damage from lack of cholin. The kidneys may hemorrhage, although when they are medically tested no pathological reason for the bleeding will be apparent. And fatty deposits may block the tubules within the kidneys, causing blood to be passed into the urine. Other symptoms can be atherosclerosis or hardening of the arteries. High blood pressure associated with malfunctioning kidneys may also develop: characterized by headaches, dizziness, heart palpitations and constipation, such high blood pressure can be alleviated in some cases with proper amounts of cholin. Moreover, kidney stones or gallstones may form with a lack of cholin: oral doses of lecithin have been known to prevent formation of such stones.

Nerve-related problems, such as myasthenia gravis (a disease characterized by great muscular weakness and fatigue in general), have shown positive responses when cholin was administered, too. With such conditions nerve impulses fail to induce normal muscle contractions: acetylcholine is responsible for the nerve impulses making contact so that the muscles respond quickly and fluidly.

In addition, glaucoma (a disease of the eye characterized by an increase in intraocular pressure and resulting in atrophy of the optic nerve and eventual blindness) may be indirectly related to a deficiency of cholin, which has been known to help such a condition.

Recent Clinical Developments

The importance of cholin to the correct and continued function of the liver cannot be overemphasized. Without the vitamin there can be an almost instant overaccumulation of lipids in the liver. Without cholin the fats do not leave the liver as phospholipids, such as lecithin, and they begin to plug up the systems of the liver and the kidneys. In time the body could become diseased by its own toxins, which cannot be properly eliminated through the necessary channels because of fat build-up. Cholin as well as vitamin A may also protect the liver whenever drugs or other chemicals are in the body.

It is also very important for pregnant women to have sufficient amounts of cholin in their systems. Research indicates that cholin-deficient women can produce children with smaller-than-normal thymus glands. The research indicates that children with malfunctioning thymuses have continual problems with infections from infancy on through late childhood because the thymus is responsible for keeping the immunity system functioning at peak efficiency. Pregnant women can help insure that their children will have healthy thymus glands by breast-feeding their babies: breast milk contains lecithin, whereas cow's milk does not.

Another reason that pregnant women need adequate amounts of cholin is that since cholin is one of the lipotropes (the nutrients involved with a metabolic transfer of methyl groups) and therefore directly concerned with the formation of new cells, a deficiency of cholin could theoretically interfere in the rapid growth of the fetus.

Furthermore, cholin can be indirectly responsible for iron-deficiency anemia. If a diet is high in iron but lacking in thiamine, riboflavin, niacin, pantothenic acid and cholin, the stomach is unable to secrete enough hydrochloric acid to dissolve the iron, thereby inducing anemia.

Hypertension (or high blood pressure) may also be partially caused by insufficient cholin. When a deficiency of cholin exists, the chances of hemorrhaging in the brain, eyes and many other parts of the body are increased. Dosages of cholin have proven effective in strengthening the capillary walls, dilating blood vessels and accelerating blood flow so that the work of the heart decreases.

Cholin may also help in curing kidney ailments. In experimental tests the kidney ailment nephritis was induced in animals. Cholin was then administered and quickly corrected the situation. Kept on 1,000 milligrams of cholin, the animals improved and hemorrhaging was arrested.

Adequate cholin is needed to prevent myasthenia gravis, too. The nervous disorder occurs because production of acetylcholine is deficient and the nerve cells are not provided with the synapses or impulses needed for proper muscle movement. A lack of cholin cuts down production of acetylcholine, although other nutrients, such as thiamine, pantothenic acid and potassium, are also required for its important formation.

Finally, cholin is essential to the thyroid, which releases the hormone thyroxine. Too little thyroxine will make a person sluggish; too much, nervous and irritable. Cholin as well as vitamins B-6 and C must be available to make the hormone.

PABA

Astrological Ruler
Saturn.

Synthetic Forms
Unknown.

Synonyms
Para-aminobenzoic acid (PABA) and vitamin B-x.

Sources
Vegetables: Soybeans.
Fruits and Nuts: Peanuts.
Fish and Meat: Fish in general and beef liver.
Grains: All whole grain products and wheat germ.
Dairy Products: Eggs.
Herbs: Unknown.
Natural Supplements: Yeast and lecithin.

Unit of Potency
Milligram.

History and Characteristics
PABA, a necessary component of the vitamin B complex, is a vitamin within a vitamin, and there is still some question as to whether or not it should be considered a vitamin. It is water-soluble.

PABA was discovered because it is antagonistic to sulfa drugs. Sulfa in the body links up with the same bacteria in the intestinal tract that PABA does. Consequently, if PABA is present first, sulfa drugs are rendered harmless; conversely, if the sulfa arrives first in the intestinal tract, PABA is crowded out and not created. Because of this problem, PABA cannot be purchased for internal or oral ingestion without a prescription, but it can be found in over-the-counter external cream applications for skin or sunburn problems.

PABA stimulates the intestinal flora to make folic acid, which in turn creates pantothenic acid. PABA is a coenzyme that uses proteins. It helps in the formation of red blood cells. It also helps to determine the health of the skin, hair and flora of the intestinal tract.

PABA is synthesized within the intestinal tract by healthy and friendly bacteria. It is also stored in the body tissue.

Allies: PABA is most effective when taken with the rest of the vitamin B complex, especially folic acid as well as vitamin C.

Antagonists: PABA's effectiveness is diminished by sulfa drugs.

Dosages
Recommended Dietary Allowance: The need for PABA in the diet has not been established by the FDA. Adelle Davis suggests that supplements be sold without prescription and that 100 milligrams be added as a daily supplement. It does seem safe to make PABA available over-the-counter, since there is little use of sulfa drugs today in lieu of more sophisticated and synthetic derivatives on the market.

Therapeutic Dose: Under a physician's guidance 100 to 300 milligrams are recommended.

Megadose: Dosages of up to 20,000 milligrams have been reported, but such megadoses should not be attempted without the strict guidance of an attending physician.

Toxicity

No toxicity level has been established; however, continued oral consumption of PABA is felt by some researchers to have negative effects on the heart, kidneys and liver. Symptoms of toxicity are nausea and vomiting.

Deficiency Symptoms

Because PABA is sold by prescription only, not much valuable research has been done on it; however, fatigue, general irritableness, headaches and depression may develop from a deficiency. Digestive disorders in general or constipation may also manifest. It has also been found that skin disorders (such as eczema or aging of the skin) and pigmentation discoloration (such as vitiligo) common among black people or people in the tropics, respond to treatment with PABA.

Recent Clinical Developments

PABA is a curious component of the vitamin B complex. It seems most important for producing folic acid and then joining with folic acid to create pantothenic acid. Although clear symptoms of a deficiency of PABA do not appear, symptoms do surface if folic acid and pantothenic acid aren't synthesized.

PABA is used externally to treat a variety of skin problems. It's needed for healthy skin, and it provides a screen against sunburn. People who have received severe sunburns have also found that PABA ointment can relieve the pain of the burn. In addition, Adelle Davis feels that 300 milligrams of PABA, along with vitamin E, should be taken orally after each meal for sunburn.

Skin disorders such as eczema and lupus erythematous (any chronic, progressive, usually ulcerative skin disease that may or may not be fatal) also respond favorably to external applications of the vitamin in a cream form. In animal experiments a lack of PABA has caused dermatitis.

FOLIC ACID

Astrological Ruler
Mars.

Synthetic Forms
Pteroylglutamic acid.

Synonyms
Folacin, folate, antianemia factor, L. Casei fac-

tor, vitamin M and PGA.

Sources
Vegetables: Spinach, asparagus, beet greens, kale, endive, turnips, potatoes, broccoli, chard, black-eyed peas and lima beans.
Fruits and Nuts: Avocados, dried dates and plums.
Fish and Meat: Liver, kidney and lamb.
Grains: Wheat bran.
Dairy Products: Cottage cheese.
Herbs: Unknown.
Natural Supplements: Yeast.

Unit of Potency
Microgram and milligram.

History and Characteristics

Folic acid is a collective term used to include several types of folates and their various derivatives, with the lactobacillus casei factor, commonly referred to as L. Casei, the folate that seems to have the most significance to humans.

Folic acid is a dull, yellow substance found in crystal form. Part of the vitamin B complex, it is slightly soluble in water. It is unstable to heat, acid, oxidation and light and stable in alkali and water. It decreases in potency when food is stored at room temperature.

Folic acid's main job is to be a carbon carrier in the formation of heme (an iron-containing nonprotein portion of the hemoglobin molecule), necessary for the creation of healthy red blood cells. Folic acid's other diverse functions include helping form nucleic acid for the growth and reproduction of body cells and working as a coenzyme with vitamins B-12 and C in the breakdown and use of protein. Wherever there is a rapid turnover of cells and bodily repair going on, folic acid is vital for quick recuperation.

Folic acid may be made in the intestinal tract, providing PABA is present. Ingested through food stuffs, the vitamin will be absorbed by the gastrointestinal tract and diffused throughout the body for use. Small amounts are stored in the liver.

Allies: Folic acid is most effective when taken with the rest of the vitamin B complex, especially vitamin B-12, biotin and pantothenic acid, as well as vitamin C.

Antagonists: Persons undergoing chemotherapy to destroy or put their cancers into remission may be administered amethopterin, used in the treatment of leukemia, methotrexate (MTX) or a drug that contains diaminodichlorophenyl pyrimidines, used against tumors. All of these drugs are antimetabolites and will inhibit folacin activity by binding folic acid to an enzyme and preventing formation of THRA, a key reaction in the metabolism of folic acid. Other sulfa drugs as well as streptomycin will also destroy folic acid.

In addition, oral contraceptives will create deficiencies of folic acid and more incidence of megaloblastic anemia. Severe stress situations, such as surgery, will also bring on a need for larger doses of folic acid, as will the consumption of alcohol.

Dosages
Infants 0-1/2 yrs. .05 mg. 1/2-1 yrs. 0.1 mg.
Children 1-2 yrs. 0.1 mg. 2-8 yrs. 0.2 mg. 8-10 yrs. 0.3 mg.
Men 10-75+ yrs 0.4 mg.
Women 10-75+ yrs. 0.4 mg.
Pregnant Women 0.8 mg.
Lactating Women 0.5 mg.

Therapeutic Dose: Under a physician's guidance five to ten milligrams are recommended. Although folic acid is available in small amounts across-the-counter, a prescription is needed for dosages higher than 400 micrograms per tablet. Epileptics taking anticonvulsant drugs have found that large doses of folic acid interfere with the drugs' effectiveness.

Megadose: Fifteen milligrams are recommended. When 450 milligrams of folic acid were given to adults, no side effects were reported.

Toxicity
There is no known toxicity level at this time, nor are there any known symptoms of toxicity. But a high intake of folic acid can mask a deficiency of vitamin B-12.

Deficiency Symptoms
Anemia of the megaloblastic variety can be induced by a deficiency of folic acid. Such symptoms as fatigue, bodily weakness, irritable behavior, insomnia and forgetfulness can be forerunners of this ailment. Furthermore, sore mouths and tongues and sometimes a grayish-brown pigmentation of the skin may also accompany this type of anemia. (Folic acid is not responsible for pernicious types of anemia, which are treated with vitamin B-12 instead.)

It is also very important for pregnant women to have adequate supplies of folic acid in their bodies. Pregnant women deficient in folic acid have been known to give premature birth, to hemorrhage after birth and to incur toxemia. Abruptio placentae (premature separation of the placenta from the uterine wall) is known to be contributed to by a lack of folic acid, too. And since, like vitamin B-12, folic acid plays an important role in cell growth and is related to the synthesis of DNA and other nucleic acids, a deficiency can affect the fetus. Moreover, after birth a child may exhibit low resistance to minor ailments because the thymus gland was not given enough folic acid via the mother's body. A severe deficiency has even been shown to play a part in mental retardation of a child. And a child's growth may be abnormal or delayed because of a deficiency. In Britain (not America) pregnant women receive folic acid from their physicians to insure their fetuses healthy starts.

Intestinal disorders may manifest with a deficiency of folic acid as well. Sprue, for instance, characterized by anemia, diarrhea, sore mouth and tongue and large amounts of fat in the stool, has been corrected with daily injections of 25 micrograms of folic acid. And gastrointestinal disorders, such as diverticulosis (a condition wherein bulging sacs line the intestinal tract and bacteria collect, causing inflammation, diarrhea and discomfort), have responded well to folic acid and acidophilus milk. But sometimes when the deficiency is severe enough, the mucous lining of the intestinal tract is damaged so much that even oral ingestion of folic acid will not correct the condition.

Other symptoms of a deficiency of folic acid are a smooth, shiny, red tongue, poor hair growth, lackluster hair, balding or premature graying. Mental depression sometimes bordering on schizophrenia has also been noted.

Recent Clinical Developments
Folic acid's relationship with leukemia is one of continuing mystery. In some tests folic acid has sent the blood cancer into remission; at other times, according to some sources, the folic acid has precipitated a condition until it turned into leukemia. The vitamin has caused other types of cancer either to regress or to accelerate, too.

Other recent developments indicate that some cases of diarrhea can be overcome by administration of folic acid, vitamin B-6 or magnesium. Folic acid is also known to help victims of atherosclerosis in that it helps circulation of blood through the arteries, increasing the surface body temperature. And researchers have discovered that folic acid, found in concentrated amounts in the spinal fluid, increases the threshold of pain.

OROTIC ACID
Astrological Ruler
Pluto.

Synthetic Forms
Calcium orotate.

Synonyms

Vitamin B-13, uracil-L-carboxylic acid and Oro.

Sources

Vegetables: Root vegetables organically grown.
Fruits and Nuts: Unknown.
Fish and Meat: Unknown.
Grains: Unknown.
Dairy Products: Curdled or soured cow's milk, sheep's milk, goat's milk, pig's milk and horse's milk.
Herbs: Unknown.
Natural Supplements: Whey.

Unit of Potency

Unknown.

History and Characteristics

Little information is available about orotic acid at this time because it is not used here in the United States. In 1905 two scientists, Biscaro and Belloni, discovered it in whey, a byproduct of cottage cheese. Its name derived from the Greek word *oros-whey*, orotic acid was also found in the milk of sheep and goats and in smaller amounts in the milk of humans, pigs and horses. It is not found in cow's milk until the milk undergoes the process of curdling: the whey is then skimmed off the top.

Part of the vitamin B complex, orotic acid is unique in that it is soluble in many different solutions—water, acetone, ethanol, ether, chloroform and benzene.

Orotic acid plays a small but important step in the formation and biosynthesis of nucleic acid, which in turn aids in creating RNA, one of the main components of genetic makeup in the human body. Orotic acid, then, is vital in the regeneration of cell processing.

The absorption and storage of orotic acid is not known at this time, except that it has special importance in certain tissue, especially in the brain.

Allies: Based upon available information, speculation is that orotic acid is more effective when taken with folic acid and vitamin B-12, both of which also play important roles in cell growth and the synthesis of DNA and other nucleic acids.

Antagonists: Unknown at this time.

Dosages

Recommended Dietary Allowance: Since the FDA has not recognized orotic acid as a vitamin yet, no RDA has been set. Nor is the vitamin sold in the United States. It is available, though, in a supplemental form known as calcium orotate.

Therapeutic Dose: Unknown.

Megadose: Unknown.

Toxicity

There is no known level of toxicity; however, too much orotic acid may cause megaloblastic anemia or leukopenia. (See Recent Clinical Developments.)

Deficiency Symptoms

Little is known at this time about the results of a deficiency in orotic acid, although several sources have suggested that lack of the vitamin may lead to liver disorders, cell degeneration and premature aging. Multiple sclerosis (MS, a chronic, slowly progressing disease of the central nervous system), is also thought to stem from a deficiency of orotic acid: Dr. J. Evers of West Germany has been using the vitamin to treat the disease. And some experts believe that any degeneration that takes place in the body, such as MS, may have its origin from a lack of orotic acid.

Recent Clinical Developments

Too little orotic acid in the body breaks down the RNA mechanism so that cell degeneration ensues, and a person can contract a chronic, long-term ailment. On other other hand, too much orotic acid stunts growth and causes the formation of large red blood cells that have short life spans, inducing megaloblastic anemia or a severe decrease in the white blood cell count—usually below 5,000 per cubic millimeters.

An inherited disease related to an overabundance of orotic acid in the body is orotic aciduria, a disorder caused by the accumulation of the pyrimidine metabolism (a group of compounds, some of which are found in nucleic acid, one of the building blocks of RNA). Children with the ailment fail to grow and develop megaloblastic anemia or leukopenia (abnormal decrease of white blood cells). Apparently what happens is that somewhere in the chain of chemical interaction orotic acid is not chemically changed so that it may help create uridine and cytidine, products concerned with the cycle of urea in the body. The administration of either uridine or cytidine apparently fulfills the chain, the body rids itself of excess orotic acid, and the disease responds favorably.

In experiments on rats a disturbed orotic acid metabolism has also caused acute ammonemia (too much ammonia in the blood). Ammonia is normally found in only minute trace amounts in the blood, and the liver converts the ammonia into urea. Without enough orotic acid, a key ingredient in the cyclic urea production and in the riddance of urea with the help of the liver, ammonia will poison the body. And the liver function may be impaired and eventually fail.

Researchers have not settled the question of whether or not orotic acid is a true vitamin or a vitamin within a vitamin, much like PABA; however, I feel it is probably a vitamin within a vitamin, found in very minute amounts in the body but nevertheless playing a vital role in the formation of our genetic coding. Its importance cannot be diminished nor ignored. Still, its consumption should best be administered by physicians until we can find out more about the vitamin.

INOSITOL

Astrological Ruler
Jupiter.

Synthetic Forms
Unknown.

Synonyms
There is some conflict about how this vitamin should be referred to. Some sources call it meso-inositol. The term favored most recently, however, is myo-inositol. It is also known as inontal, bios I, i-inositol, mouse antilopecia factor and inosite.

Sources
Vegetables: Red kidney beans, mung bean sprouts, green peas, corn and soybeans.
Fruits and Nuts: All nuts, boysenberries, grapefruit, orange juice and apricot juice.
Meat and Fish: Beef brain, beef heart and beef liver.
Grains: Bulgar wheat, wheat germ and brown rice.
Dairy Products: Unknown.
Natural Supplements: Yeast and molasses.

Unit of Potency
Milligram.

History and Characteristics
Part of the vitamin B complex, inositol is a white, crystalline substance that is water-soluble and has a sweet taste. There are nine basic types of inositol found in plant or animal tissue. It is found in seeds and whole grains as phytic acid. Phytic acid seems to interfere with the absorption of calcium and iron; however, inositol found in animal tissue acts as a helpmate to these minerals.

Inositol was discovered in Europe in the 1850's. And in 1871 Leibig postulated its existence as a growth requirement of yeast. But it was more than ten years before inositol was referred to as a vitamin and not until 1956 as a "true" vitamin: until the

1950's it was regarded as an interesting substance, but little research was conducted to understand its true nature. Even today researchers know little of inositol's vast abilities. And scientists have come up with varying results from their experiments. There is even disagreement about whether or not inositol is manufactured by intestinal flora or within the cell structure itself.

Inositol is felt to have three diverse functions within the body: the oxidation of carbon dioxide, synthesis of phospholipids, such as lecithin, and use in gluconeogenesis (the formation of glycogen from protein or fat sources). About seven per cent of the vitamin is used to make glucose. It is found in free and combined forms in the liver, lungs, muscles and most tissue and fluids. And the brain is an especially rich source of inositol. The vitamin is excreted daily through the urine in fairly large amounts (about 35 milligrams).

Allies: Inositol is most effective when taken with the rest of the vitamin B complex, especially cholin and biotin. It works very closely with cholin and biotin to form lecithin within the body. Other primary allies are vitamins C and E and linoleic acid.

Antagonists: Several types of antibiotics, especially streptomycin, streptidine and streptamine, seem to lower production of inositol by killing intestinal flora—an occurrence that suggests that inositol is manufactured within the intestines. Coffee drunk in large quantities will also deplete the vitamin from the body.

Dosages
Recommended Dietary Allowance: The need for inositol has not been established by the FDA. Single doses are available up to 500 milligrams without a prescription; however, Adelle Davis recommends a B complex vitamin that contains 1,000 milligrams each of inositol and cholin. Since so little is truly understood about this vitamin, care should be taken in consuming oral supplements, and supplements should be administered only under a physician's guidance.
Therapeutic Dose: Under a physician's guidance 500 to 1,000 milligrams of inositol with cholin are recommended.
Megadose: Drs. Leinwand and Moore have used 3,000 milligrams to help patients with atherosclerotic symptoms.

Toxicity
There is no known level of toxicity nor symptoms of toxicity.

Deficiency Symptoms
All deficiencies of inositol are related to defi-

ciencies of other vitamins, particularly cholin,. In unison with cholin inositol is primarily concerned with the breaking down of fats throughout the body. The two vitamins join in the liver to create lecithin. If lecithin is not available to break down fats into bile salts, fatty deposits will clog the arteries, the tubules of the kidneys and liver. And heart ailments, swelling and inflammation of the liver and Bright's disease in the kidneys may occur later.

There is also a relationship between diabetes and a lack of inositol, although scientists don't know the exact connection. People who have diabetes insipidus (a disease caused by the posterior pituitary gland not secreting enough vasopressin, the antidiuretic hormone) tend to excrete far more inositol than average: it has been suggested that the renal tubular mechanisms for the transport of glucose and inositol may be closely related. Tests have also shown that inositol can lower the levels of cholesterol in diabetic cases.

Loss of hair, abnormalities of the eyes and high blood cholesterol are other symptoms that may result from a deficiency of inositol

Recent Clinical Developments

Under the direction of nutritionists some people have lowered their serum blood cholesterol markedly by taking vitamins A, D, E and B. A few took 250 milligrams each of cholin and inositol six times daily for a short period. The outcome was lowered levels of cholesterol, more energy and a sense of general well-being.

In addition, inositol can break up deposits of fat in cirrhosis of the liver.

PANTOTHENIC ACID

Astrological Ruler
Neptune.

Synthetic Forms
Calcium pantothenate or D-Ca pantothenate.

Synonyms
Antistress vitamin, biolla, antigray-hair factor, coenzyme-A, vitamin B-5.

Sources
Vegetables: Lima beans, broccoli, raw cauliflower, chick peas (garbanzos), cooked lentils, mushrooms and soybeans.

Fruits and Nuts: Avocados, raw elderberries, orange juice, pineapple juice and watermelon.

Fish and Meat: Beef liver, beef kidney, beef heart, chicken heart, chicken liver and lobster.

Grains: Dark buckwheat flour, wheat bran and

sesame-seed flour.

Dairy Products: Eggs and skim milk.

Herbs: Unknown.

Natural Supplements: Yeast.

Unit of Potency
Milligram.

History and Characteristics

First obtained in a pure state from yeast and liver extracts, pantothenic acid is a pale yellow, unstable viscous oil. Because it is so unstable as an oil, it is stabilized in the calcium or sodium form. And it is available commercially as a stable, white crystalline calcium or sodium salt (both synthetic). It takes 1.087 parts of calcium pantothenate to be equivalent to 1 part of pantothenic acid. A component of the vitamin B complex, pantothenic acid is readily soluble in water. It is sensitive to acid, alkali and heat. Up to 44 per cent of the vitamin is lost in cooking.

Pantothenic acid, or pantothen (derived from the Greek work meaning "from everywhere"), is found in all kinds of animal and plant tissue. It may occur free but is usually chemically bound.

Although it occurs in all living cells, pantothenic acid is especially important in the adrenal cortex (the outer layers of tissue surrounding the adrenal glands located atop each kidney), where it stimulates production of cortisone and many other hormones responsible for healthy nerves and skin. Because of its importance to adrenal functions, this vitamin is involved in all the vital bodily functions.

One of its most important tasks is keeping the body free from infection. Pantothenic acid has been identified as essential to the production of antibodies. It increases energy and speeds recovery. And pantothenic acid, which protects all membranes from possible infection, is necessary to keep the endocrine system functioningproperly.

Furthermore, as a coenzyme (A) pantothenic acid synthesizes cholin into acetylcholine in the area of the brain responsible for the synapses taking place between nerve endings. Pantothenic acid also helps to synthesize cholesterol, steroids (fat-soluble compounds) and fatty acids. And it keeps the intestinal flora healthy.

Pantothenic acid is found in the plasma of the blood. Small amounts of it are found in the liver, heart and kidneys. Since it is water-soluble, it is excreted in the urine on a daily basis.

Allies: Pantothenic acid is most effective when taken with the rest of the vitamin B complex, especially vitamin B-6, vitamin B-12, biotin and folic acid. Vitamin C, calcium and sulfur are also primary allies.

Antagonists: Pantothenic acid's effectiveness is diminished by methyl bromide (an insecticide fumigant for foods), W-methyl pantothenic acid (a compound usually used in laboratories to trigger deficiencies of pantothenic acid for further study), homopantothenic acid and N-substituted pantothenamides.

Dosages

Recommended Dietary Allowance:
Infants 0-1 yrs. 3 mg.
Children 1-4 yrs. 5 mg. 4-10 yrs. 10 mg.
Men 10+ yrs. 10 mg.
Women 10+ yrs. 10 mg.
Pregnant Women 10 mg.
Lactating Women 10 mg.

Therapeutic Dose: Under a physician's guidance 50 to 1,000 milligrams daily for six months are recommended.

Megadose: Ten thousand milligrams of calcium pantothenate has been administered daily for six weeks. But one source cautions that 10,000 to 20,000 milligrams of pantothenic acid given as a calcium salt may have side effects in some people.

Toxicity

There are no known side effects from pantothenic acid; however, folic acid is believed to be needed to assimilate pantothenic acid.

Deficiency Symptoms

Because pantothenic acid is found in most cells of the body, the vitamin is not usually lacking; however, deficiencies can exist. Some of the early symptoms are fatigue, depression, irritability and dizziness — all related to a lack of the release of proper amounts of adrenal hormones that rely on pantothenic acid for their production. If the deficiency continues, muscular weakness can develop; moreover stomach distress and constipation will begin.

In a severe state of depletion there will be adrenal exhaustion. For example, a lack of pantothenic acid will hinder production of an adrenal hormone that saves nitrogen from the worn body cells and redistributes it for building amino acids vital to tissue repair. Thus in the phase of adrenal exhaustion the muscles will lose their strength, inducing cramping and lack of coordination. Another hormone, aldosterone, retains sodium in the cell structures: without enough pantothenic acid the sodium is not produced, potassium leaves the cells, and muscular problems, including weakness and partial or complete paralysis, may occur.

A secondary ailment of exhausted adrenal production is low blood pressure, brought on when large amounts of sodium and water are excreted and the blood volume within the body decreases because the hormones are not there to stabilize the condition. A person may also easily develop infections with the body unable to throw them off for a long time.

Other symptoms of a severe deficiency of pantothenic acid are hypoglycemia and insomnia. Burning, itching or painful feet also seem to be caused by a lack of pantothenic acid and/or vitamin B-6: fat deposits plug the smaller arteries of the feet, shutting off the oxygen supply and inducing pain and itching.

Stomach and intestinal disorders are associated with a deficiency of pantothenic acid as well. For instance, pantothenic acid aids in the production of hydrochloric acid. Without enough of the vitamin and with sustained emotional stress an ulcer may form. In addition, gastrointestinal disturbances, ranging from a strange itching and burning sensation, in the area to balky bowels and constipation may occur. Loss of appetite is not uncommon, and digestive enzymes and stomach acid may become markedly reduced, causing many types of intestinal problems.

Since our ability to withstand stress is closely tied in with pantothenic acid, certain types of ailments (such as allergies and asthma) thought to be brought on by emotional duress have responded well to dosages of pantothenic acid. And without adequate amounts of the vitamin to make cortisone from the adrenals, allergies such as hay fever, rose fever, hives, eczema and asthma can worsen because eosinophils (types of white blood cells) will increase abnormally.

Recent Clinical Developments

A disease known as subacute myelo-optic neuropathy has symptoms similar to those produced when the body is lacking in pantothenic acid. This ailment is brought on by the consumption of methyl bromide, an insecticide fumigant. It has been successfully shown that the insecticide changes pantothenic acid into another, unknown compound, thereby making pantothenic acid leave the body.

Some scientists also blame the loss of pantothenic acid as well as the overuse of preprocessed foods for the growing incidence of rheumatoid arthritis and osteoarthritis. The adrenal glands produce cortisone, which controls inflammation, and a lack of pantothenic acid causes a high sedimentation rate. Tests have proven that doses of the vitamin help alleviate the symptoms of arthritis.

As I've indicated, pantothenic acid as well as vitamins B-6 and C can alleviate the symptoms of various allergies, too, because it has an antihistaminic action and quality. Therefore, it is a valuable substitute for antihistamines, which in excess, as Adelle Davis points out, can harm the liver, impairing that organ's ability to create its own enzyme to form histaminase and forcing the already lagging adrenal glands to produce more cortisone.

In addition, bruxism (the grinding of one's teeth during sleep) has been found to be helped by supplements of pantothenic acid and calcium. Stress situations use up the pantothenic acid plus its coenzyme (A), responsible for making acetylcholine. Nerve transmission then falters and bruxism can occur.

Brittle diabetes (a disease wherein blood sugar falls from high to low levels in a phenomenally short time) seems to respond dramatically to supplements of pantothenic acid, too. Adelle Davis mentions that people with brittle diabetes have very high requirements for potassium, protein, vitamin B-12, vitamin C, niacinamide and lecithin—but mostly for pantothenic acid.

Gout (an accumulation of uric acid in certain parts of the body) can also be aided by pantothenic acid. If the vitamin is lacking, uric acid cannot change into urea, and the deposits occur. Vitamin A is also helpful in preventing this ailment.

Finally, the pituitary, adrenal and sex hormones are all made from cholesterol. Without pantothenic acid to help make the biochemical change, cholesterol cannot be made to resupply the glands with the necessary hormones.

PANGAMIC ACID

Astrological Ruler
Jupiter.

Synthetic Forms
Calcium pangamate and sodium pangamate.

Synonyms
Vitamin B-15.

Sources
Vegetables: Unknown.
Fruits and Nuts: Apricot kernels (sparingly, since they contain cyanide), nuts in general, sunflower seeds, pumpkin seeds and sesame seeds.
Fish and Meat: *Horse liver and beef.*
Grains: *Rice bran, whole-grain cereals and whole brown rice.*
Dairy Products: *Unknown.*
Herbs: *Unknown.*
Natural Supplements: *Yeast and rice polish.*

Unit of Potency
Milligram.

History and Characteristics
Relatively little is known about pangamic acid. It is a water-soluble vitamin, orginally extracted from apricot kernels. A crystalline form was later obtained from rice bran, yeast, rice polish and whole-grain cereals.

Pangamic acid, a member of the vitamin B complex, was discovered in the United States in 1952 by one of the great vitamin explorers of our time, Dr. E.T. Krebs. The word *pangamic* was derived from *pan*, meaning "everywhere," and *gami*, "family." The vitamin is found in many seeds. Krebs made a synthetic version of it, called sodium pangamate, but it had some toxic side effects. Later, in 1964, the Russians produced a second synthetic, calcium pangamate, which seems to avoid some of the toxic reactions found with the other type.

Pangamic acid is a powerful methylating agent of glucuronic acid and is concerned with the oxidation process and cell enzyme respiration. It has been particularly helpful in treating hypoxia (poor supply of oxygen to the tissue of the body). It plays a role in the metabolism of protein, especially of the heart muscles. It is a needed vitamin in helping to stimulate the endocrine and nervous systems. It breaks down and metabolizes fat and has been found helpful in alleviating high levels of cholesterol.

At this time little information is available on the absorption or storage of this vitamin; however, it is known that large amounts of pangamic acid are excreted through the kidneys, bowels and the pores in perspiration.

Allies: Pangamic acid is most effective when taken with the rest of the vitamin B complex, vitamin C, vitamin E and vitamin A.
Antagonists: Unknown.

Dosages
Recommended Dietary Allowance: Since the FDA has not recognized pangamic acid as a needed nutrient for daily health maintenance, there is as yet no RDA.
Therapeutic Dose: Dr. Paavo Airola recommends 100 milligrams daily—50 in the morning before breakfast and 50 at night. Injections of 2.5 to 10 milligrams have caused some patients to experience flushing similar to the effects of niacin.
Megadose: It has been reported that 500 milligrams is tolerated on a daily basis without side effects. Some authorities suggest 150 milligrams, but the Russians, who have done the most experimenting with the vitamin, say 50 milligrams daily.

Toxicity
Dr. E.T. Krebs, Jr., states that pangamic acid's

toxic level is 100,000 times the therapeutic dose (50 to 100 milligrams) and that its value is in its lack of toxicity to humans. The symptoms of toxicity are unknown at this time, and more research is needed.

Deficiency Symptoms

According to Dr. Airola, lack of pangamic acid may diminish oxygenation to the cells, thereby creating hypoxia. Disorders of the endocrine and nervous system are also possible.

Furthermore, heart disease associated with atherosclerosis may occur. In Russia even very serious heart problems have been successfully treated with the vitamin. And symptoms associated with atherosclerosis—such as headaches, tension, shortness of breath, insomnia and chest pains—have been aided with the addition of pangamic acid to the diet.

Recent Clinical Developments

Under the leadership of Professor Yakov Shpirt the Russians have conducted years of tests on pangamic acid. More than 1,000 patients have taken pangamic acid in experiments to test its validity. And the Russians have had stunning results in helping heart patients and autistic or minimally brain-damaged children. Pangamic acid appears to help in a wide array of heart ailments, including angina (a disease characterized by attacks of choking and/or suffocation), coronary sclerosis (hardening of the coronary arteries), circulatory problems and cardiopulmonary insufficiencies.

As for the lungs, emphysema, cyanosis (discoloring of the skin from lack of oxygen) and bronchial asthma have all responded to dosages of from 120 to 160 milligrams in test cases.

Pangamic acid has also proved valuable in relieving disorders associated with alcoholism. For example, sufficient dosages of the vitamin have helped some alcoholics lose their cravings for liquor. And pangamic acid has aided certain liver ailments, such as cirrhosis and hepatitis, when they were discovered in their early stages of development.

Pangamic acid may become another alternative for treating some kinds of cancer as well. Dr. Felix Warburg suggests that when cells lose their oxygen because of a lack of pangamic acid they can metabolize differently and perhaps become malignant: one theory is that healthy cells need oxygen and those that are cancerous do not.

Damaged or injured muscles have also responded well to the administration of 300 milligrams of pangamic acid on successive days, and the vitamin has assisted in early healing of the muscles: when oxygen is plentiful, cells can carry on in their assigned tasks and speed up the healing process.

Finally—an interesting note—the United States equestrian team supplies pangamic acid to its jumpers.

VITAMIN C

Astrological Ruler

Saturn.

Synthetic Forms

Cevitamic acid, ascorbic acid and sodium ascorbate.

Synonyms

Antiscorbutic acid, cevitamic acid, hexuronic acid and water-soluble C.[2]

Sources

Vegetables: Alfalfa tablets, asparagus, brussel sprouts, carrots, celery, chard, collards, tomatoes, turnip greens and watercress.

Fruits and Nuts: Oranges, orange juice, lemon juice, tangerines, strawberries, almonds, bananas, blueberries, currants, cranberries, grapefruit, pineapple, cantaloupe and apple juice.

Fish and Meat: Chicken liver, rabbit heart and liver.

Grains: Unknown.

Dairy Products: Skim milk.

Herbs: Buffalo berries, burdock seed, capsicum, coltsfoot, elderberries, marigold, oregano, paprika, parsley and rose hips.

Natural Supplements: Acerola and rose hips.

Unit of Potency

Milligram.

History and Characteristics

Vitamin C is a white powder. It is soluble in water and insoluble in oils. It is destroyed by light and oxidation and is stable in acid. Because of a chemical reaction, copper pans cause great loss of vitamin C. Cooking, but not steaming, also destroys most of the vitamin.

Since vitamin C is quite unstable, a more reliable synthetic form, often referred to as ascorbic acid, is frequently used in medicine. Dry crystals of ascorbic acid are stable on exposure to air and daylight at room temperature for long periods of time. They also retain much of their strength in frozen foods if no air is present.

[2]Anyone buying synthetic vitamin C should check the labels carefully. Some brands may contain sodium, and we get enough sodium daily as it is. In addition, bioflavonoids will not be contained in the supplements unless stated on the labels.

Humans are one of the few species, along with guinea pigs, apes, monkeys, certain birds and fish, that cannot internally synthesize vitamin C. Irwin Stone, a biochemist, asserts that the reason humans do not have the ability to create our own vitamin C is because of a genetic flaw that he calls a "biochemical catastrophe." Stone states that vitamin C was once a substance normally made in the body until a mutation of a gene occurred, destroying a liver enzyme necessary for synthesis of ascorbic acid in the body. Consequently, we have all contracted a genetic disease Stone calls hypoascorbemia. From this disease resulted such problems as scurvy, which killed hundreds of thousands of people over the centuries before it was discovered that fresh citrus fruit would stop the ailment from developing.

And, indeed, ascorbic acid's numerous functions seem to give weight to Stone's theory. It has even been hypothesized that vitamin C's metabolism may be an index of the total bodily metabolism: in other words, vitamin C helps in all known metabolisms within the human body.

One of vitamin C's greatest contributions is helping to form collagen, a substance that constitutes about 40 per cent of the bodily protein. Collagen is a fiberlike substance that holds the cells in their natural formations in the tissue and keeps them healthy. If collagen is strong and vital, the cells resist any invading infections; if collagen is weak from lack of ascorbic acid in the body, the cells lose their supportive strength, causing weakening of the protein of the skin, tendons, bones, cartilage and other connective tissue.

Vitamin C is also extremely important in the formation of red blood cells by keeping the capillaries, veins and arteries elastic and preventing hemorrhaging. Moreover, it's necessary for halting allergies and fighting bacterial infections: phagocytes (kinds of white blood cells) are the body's defense against invading bacteria, and ascorbic acid aids the biochemical reactions taking place in these cells to increase their activity and strength in killing off bacteria. Furthermore, one of vitamin C's most important functions is helping in the transfer of plasma iron to the liver and incorporation into the iron storage compound called ferritin: without proper levels of iron, anemia results.

Vitamin C reaches blood in two to three hours after ingestion, and what is not used is excreted daily in the urine. Vitamin C is absorbed in the gastrointestinal tract and then moves through the bloodstream to where it is needed by the body. It is stored in the adrenal glands and in high amounts in the pituitary gland. About 200 milligrams of vitamin C are found in the cellular fluids.

Allies: Vitamin C is most effective when taken with the vitamin B complex, bioflavonoids, calcium and magnesium.

Antagonists: Many substances and circumstances can either diminish vitamin C's full effects or stop it from helping other vitamins and minerals in their particular synthesization processes. Following is a brief discussion of some of the worst antagonists.

Deoxycorticosterone depresses the action of vitamin C, consequently affecting the growth of the skeletal tissue. D-glucoascorbic acid, aspirin, barbituates, adrenaline, stilbestrol, estrogen, sulfonamides, ammonium chloride, antihistamines, thiouracil, thyroid medication and indomethacin either destroy vitamin C or inhibit uptake. Vitamin C also has an adverse chemical reaction to iron and copper, hemochromogens (compounds of hemeiron, part of hemoglobin with nitrogen-containing substances such as protein) and quinones (a product of quinic acid). Stress situations (including surgery), fatigue, smoking, consumption of alcohol, a diet high in nitrite-laden foods and diabetes will use up large amounts of the vitamin. And copper pots, pans, bowls or knives will destroy vitamin C.

Dosages

Recommended Dietary Allowance:
Infants 0-1 yrs. 35 mg.
Children 1-4 yrs. 40 mg. 4-10 yrs. 60 mg.
Men 10 + yrs. 60 mg.
Women 10 + yrs. 60 mg.
Pregnant Women 60 mg.
Lactating Women 60 mg.

Ever since vitamin C's importance to so many of the bodily functions was discovered, there has been controversy about the minimum daily needs for the vitamin. Taking into account individual needs, Dr. Linus Pauling feels the optimum amount is between 250 and 10,000 milligrams daily: he takes 2,000 milligrams daily.

Therapeutic Dose: Dr. Paavo Airola suggests between 100 and 10,000 milligrams daily.

Megadose: Dr. Fred R. Klenner, M.D., has used massive doses with astounding and positive results. He gave up to 140,000 milligrams (nearly five ounces) to a woman suffering from pneumonia: she recovered from the ailment in three days as a result. On the average it is felt that anything more than 15,000 milligrams constitutes a megadose for some individuals, whereas others may need more.

Toxicity

The level of toxicity is unknown. Since vitamin C is excreted on a daily basis, there is no fear of build-up or excessive storage in the body: however, when some people take 10,000 to 15,000 milligrams at one dose, symptoms such as a burning sensation during urination, diarrhea or skin rash may occur. A skin rash reaction is probably caused by the filler holding the vitamin together. Diarrhea or a burning sensation during urination is an indication that the body has ample amounts of vitamin C, and the excess is being sloughed off through the urine or intestinal tract.

Deficiency Symptoms

Many of the symptoms of scurvy that Americans share in common are spongy gums, bleeding gums (especially during brushing), pyorrhea (a disorder of the gums) and loose teeth. More advanced signs of scurvy include capillary hemorrhaging, easy bruising with the bruises disappearing only after many days or weeks, swollen joints and continual susceptibility to infections. In the later stages of the disease there can be fractured bones, anemia and respiratory and intestinal infections.

Other signals of a deficiency of vitamin C are wounds or broken bones that take an inordinate amount of time to heal, nosebleeds, peptic and duodenal ulcers, reduction of hemoglobin that causes secondary anemia and impaired adrenal functions that bring about fatigue, irritability and exhaustion.

Recent Clinical Developments

Vitamin C is a powerful friend to many other vitamins. Taken in sufficient doses, for example, it decreases symptoms of a deficiency of folic acid by stimulating formation of the citrovorum factor or folinic acid. In addition, it protects thiamine, riboflavin, panthothenic acid, folic acid, vitamin A and vitamin E against the oxidation process. And vitamin B-12 can be replaced or potentiated by ascorbic acid in lactic acid bacterial.

One of the best vitamin teams is vitamin C and pantothenic acid. Vitamin C has been known to stimulate the growth of intestinal flora that produce the body's needed amounts of the vitamin B complex, including pantothenic acid. Together the vitamins also help in healing ulcerous tissue, particularly in the stomach and duodenal area: without enough pantothenic acid ulcers can develop; and without enough vitamin C ulcers cannot heal.

Moreover, vitamin C can partially compensate for a deficiency of pantothenic acid, especially in preventing adrenal exhaustion. Pantothenic acid is responsible for hormonal output to keep the body stable during duress. Although the hormones can be supplied without vitamin C, if not enough vitamin C is available, the glands may hemorrhage and the out-

put of hormones will decrease substantially, leaving the body inwardly ravaged by the stress. Ascorbic acid accelerates the production of cortisone and helps improve use of cortisone within the body. When pantothenic acid is deficient, enough vitamin C can delay damage to the adrenal glands.

Vitamin C is also necessary for vitamin E to function at full effectiveness as an antiaging agent. In the aging process free radicals (peroxidation of essential fatty acids) go about the body destroying tissue and changing the shape of cell organization: as a result, sagging skin occurs. When the diet contains too many fats that overbalance the vitamin E in the body, damage is done. Furthermore, when collagen fiber gets old, it chokes off tissue and becomes anoxic (lacking in oxygen), thereby causing wrinkles. Vitamin C is very important to healthy collagen and, if taken in sufficient amounts, will help hold off the aging process considerably.

In addition, iron will not be broken down and used properly unless sufficient vitamin C is available. Women suffering from a shortage of iron from menstrual problems are often placed on supplements of iron by their attending physicians. Without enough vitamin C to help assimilate the iron, the women can become constipated when the iron is excreted through the intestinal tract unused. And with vitamin C lacking to utilize iron anemia may result.

Vitamin C is also a useful antidote against poisons (such as mercury, cadmium and lead) found in our environment from automobile emissions, factory discharges and other pollution, including cigarette and cigar smoking. High levels of ascorbic acid can effectively throw these inorganic substances out of the body so that they do not become sedimentary and cause a wide array of symptoms and/or diseases. Other poisons of an organic variety, such as insect bites, stings and snakebites, are lessened or controlled by injections of massive doses of vitamin C.

All in all, vitamin C can be a powerful killing agent. It is a strong antibiotic. Tests with hydrogen peroxide and ferrous sulfate have proven that vitamin C is equal in power with other germ fighters and if faster. Moreover, vitamin C fights nitrites used as preservatives and flavoring in such food as hot dogs, bacon, luncheon meats and many other products). Laboratory tests have shown that nitrites combine in the stomach with secondary amines to create a compound known as nitrosamines, a known, powerful cancer-causing chemical: enough vitamin C in the system can effectively block the transformation of nitrite into that deadly new compound.

Vitamin C can also fight the effects of drugs. For instance, corticosteroid (a drug prescribed for a number of ailments, including acne, eczema, allergies, rheumatic fever, bronchial asthma, gastrointestinal diseases and myasthenia gravis) has a wide range of toxic side effects that can induce hypertension, hyperglycemia, heart problems, skin ailments, slow healing of wounds, glaucoma and menstrual problems: by taking vitamin C with the drug, though, a person has a better chance of avoiding these complications. Another drug, alcohol, consumed in immoderate amounts, can tax the liver, impeding that organ's ability to make enough of the enzyme alcohol dehydrogenase to get rid of the liquor effectively: with enough vitamin C the enzyme is able to function more rapidly.

Women who are pregnant seemingly benefit from added vitamin C in their diets. Dr. Klenner has observed that in more than 300 obstetric cases women given between 4,000 and 15,000 milligrams of vitamin C daily suffered fewer leg cramps and had more stabilized hemoglobin levels than those women who did not take supplements. Furthermore, labor was shorter and less painful, and there were fewer postpartum hemorrhaging cases.

Vitamin C can also help alleviate the phlebitis that may occur after childbirth or surgery. Phlebitis (a disease of thrombi, or blood clots) begins as an inflammation in a vein, usually a vein in the legs. This inflammation may destroy the smaller capillaries or a larger vein, or it may migrate and lodge in the lungs or heart, causing heart failure or obstructing the vein completely. Vitamin C is believed to be able to maintain the wall strength of the veins and arteries, keeping them elastic and repairing weak spots where fibrinogen (a blood protein) might snag and begin building up into a clot. Dr. Constance Leslie of England has run a series of tests administering approximately 250 milligrams of vitamin C daily to thrombi patients with very successful results.

Stress situations (especially hospitilizations requiring X-rays, radiation treatment, drugs, surgery, IVs, injections or immobilization) can take enormous tolls on the body's reserves of vitamin C. And stress without daily administration of ample doses of the vitamin can produce slow healing time with the adrenals becoming tired and perhaps exhausted, thereby inducing many new and unnecessary complications.

Among the people under enormous, continual stress are schizophrenics, who have huge needs for vitamin C. Ascorbic acid converts the substance adrenochrome to leucoadrenochrome, a nontoxic substance. In schizophrenia adrenochrome is converted to the toxic substance adrenolutin. Dr. Allan Cott, psychiatrist, points out that vitamin C given in megadose portions of from 10,000 to 30,000

milligrams retards the oxidation of adrenaline and reduces the amount of adrenochrome within the body. It's also felt that vitamin C may be the missing link in the chain that provides brain cells enough adrenaline to function properly. In some tests too little vitamin C has caused biochemical changes in the brain, such as mental listlessness, confusion and depression.

Vitamin C is also helpful in the treatment of diseases caused by fatty deposits. Coronary atherosclerosis (a disease characterized by fatty deposits in the arteries leading directly to the heart) has been successfully controlled when the body compound chondroitin-4-sulfate (CSA) is plentiful enough to keep the lining of the arteries protected from build-up of fat deposits; when CSA is missing or deficient, plaque builds up on the walls of the arteries, causing atherosclerosis: vitamin C stimulates production of CSA. And recent research in Czechoslovakia shows that vitamin C can help prevent the formation of gallstones, usually 60 to 100 per cent cholesterol. Gallstones indicate that the gallbladder is not supplying enough bile, made in the liver, to break down cholesterol properly, and vitamin C aids in the production of bile acid.

Finally, people taking medication for arthritis deplete their supplies of vitamin C. Arthritics often take aspirin to alleviate some of the minor symptoms of the disease, little realizing that aspirin immediately blocks vitamin C from being absorbed into the blood cells. In addition, a group of researchers has found that prednisone (a steroid drug used by arthritics) can damage the the bones of children unless vitamin C is administered in large doses.

VITAMIN E

Astrological Ruler
   Venus.

Synthetic Forms
   D-alpha tocopherol, d-alpha tocopherol acetate, d-alpha tocopherol succinate and d-alpha tocopherol phosphate.

Synonyms
   Alpha tocopherol, beta tocopherol, gamma tocopherol, delta tocopherol, epsilon tocopherol, zeta (1) tocopherol, zeta (2) tocopherol, eta tocopherol, delta tocopherol, 1-tocopherol, antisterility vitamin, 5, 7, 8-trimethyltocal, epsitan, ephynal, tokopharen and factor X.

Sources
   Vegetables: Alfalfa, dandelion leaves, nasturtium leaves, soybeans and watercress.

Fruits and Nuts: Whole raw seeds, nuts and avocados.

Fish and Meat: Haddock, kidney, ham and chicken.

Grains: Wheat germ.

Dairy Products: Unknown.

Herbs: Avena sativa, bladderwrack and nettle leaves.

Natural Supplements: Dulse, kelp, cold-pressed safflower oil, peanut oil, cottonseed oil, bran oil, wheat oil, soybean oil, tocopherols and d-alpha tocopherol.

Unit of Potency

International Unit.

History and Characteristics

Vitamin E is a pale, yellow viscous oil. It is fat-soluble and insoluble in water. It oxidizes rapidly in the presence of alkali and is stable in acid. It is also stable in heat and alkali, providing there are no oxidizing agents. It is stable to light but destroyed by the ultraviolet light of the sun. It is easily oxidized by a variety of chemical agents, including ferric, auric, ceric and nitrate ions. Rancid oils will reduce its potency.

There are nine known types of tocopherols, and each type is slightly different in chemical makeup. The various types of natural tocopherols can be gotten from wheat, bran, palm, rice, cotton and soy oils. The one most often used in therapeutic administrations, especially for heart and circulatory problems, is d-alpha tocopherol.

Vitamin E was discovered in 1922 by Evans and Bishop. The name *tocopherol* comes from the Greek words *tokos*, "childbirth," and *phero*, "to bear."

Vitamin E's most important function is as an antioxidant: that is, it keeps oxygen from forming with toxic peroxide, instead giving red blood cells pure oxygen. It also protects other nutrients, such as vitamin A and polyunsaturated fatty acids, from the damage caused by oxidation. And it keeps linoleic acid functioning to feed the pituitary and adrenal glands so that they can secrete hormones.

Erroneously called the antiaging vitamin, vitamin E, according to the latest research, does not prolong life; rather, it improves health by promoting the life of cells. It keeps the free radicals from doing maximum damage to the cells, which without adequate vitamin E produce wrinkles and the aging process. Cell respiration in muscles, bones and the cardiac system all function better with adequate vitamin E available in the body. It will dissolve blood clots, dilate blood vessels to promote better flow of blood to all parts of the body, stimulate secretion of urine

for those people who have edema, lower blood pressure and protect lungs from pollutants.

Vitamin E also has an effect on the tissue concerned with the reproductive organs in women and can prevent sterility in some cases, providing scar tissue or irreparable damage has not previously taken place in the reproductive tract.

Being fat-soluble, vitamin E is absorbed with bile salts and fats. In the intestinal tract it is absorbed into the lymph to the bloodstream, where it is turned into tocopherol and stored, mainly in the liver. It is stored in smaller amounts in the pituitary and adrenal glands and in the muscles of the body, including the heart. Since it is not manufactured internally, we must rely on outside sources to supply necessary amounts of vitamin E to keep our bodies healthy.

Allies: Vitamin E is most effective when taken with vitamin A, the vitamin B complex, vitamin C, fatty acids and manganese. It also works in concert with the microtrace element selenium: together vitamin E and selenium seem to destroy toxic peroxides that form within capillary cells; they also help produce antibodies.

Antagonists: Iron supplements, such as inorganic ferric iron, ferrous sulfate or gluconate compounds, interfere directly with the assimilation of vitamin E. Some doctors suggest that these two antagonists be taken at least eight to twelve hours apart. But organic iron derived from such sources as brewer's yeast is not antagonistic toward vitamin E; only the synthetic varieties are.

The consumption of mineral oil, usually ingested for constipation, will also interfere with vitamin E by dissolving it. Only *cold-pressed* vegetable oils will release their inherent vitamin E.

Other antagonists to vitamin E are estrogens found in birth control pills, long known as destroyers of vitamin E, synthetically derived cholin and thyroxine, a compound usually made from crushed sheep's thyroid and administered to people with impaired thyroids or who react to high amounts of chlorine in the water. In addition, cod liver oil, oxidants, rancid fats and oils and a-tocopherol quinone all destroy vitamin E. It is also destroyed by chlorine found in water.

Dosages

Recommended Dietary Allowance
Infants 0-1 yrs. 5 I.U.
Children 1-4 yrs. 10 I.U. 4-10 yrs. 30 I.U.
Men 10 + yrs. 30 I.U.
Women 10 + yrs. 30 I.U.
Pregnant Women 30 I.U.
Lactating Women 30 I.U.

Adelle Davis feels the RDA is too low and recommends 30 I.U. daily for infants and children and 100 I.U. for adolescents and adults.

Therapeutic Dose: One hundred to six hundred I.U. are recommended, but people with high blood pressure or chronic rheumatic heart ailments cannot tolerate large dosages of vitamin E: they should consult physicians before taking any vitamin E. And anyone taking the vitamin should start at very small amounts, building up to a therapeutic range under the guidance of a doctor.

Megadose: Under a physician's guidance from 600 to 2,000 or more I.U. daily are recommended.

Toxicity

Vitamin E is essentially nontoxic; however, some people taking 4,000 to 30,000 I.U. for long periods may experience some side effects, such as heart palpitations, shortness of breath and dizziness. Only when taken in large doses by a person who has high blood pressure or a rheumatic heart condition can vitamin E become deadly.

Deficiency Symptoms

Very rarely is there a deficiency of vitamin E. Deficiencies related to vitamin E actually develop because the vitamin is not available in sufficient quantities to synthesize properly with other substances, such as polyunsaturated fatty acids (PUFA), nonspecific antioxidants, selenium or sulfur-containing amino acids. For example, if vitamin E is insufficient to halt the oxidation of fatty acids, hemolytic anemia may occur because the hemoglobin is not kept within the cells.

When a deficiency of vitamin E does occur, however, there may be degeneration of the cardiopulmonary region, the formation of clots, decreased circulation and strokes. Problems with sterility related to cell regeneration and other reproductive disorders in women, such as miscarriages, resorption of the fetus and menopausal ailments, can also be brought on by lack of vitamin E.

Severe deficiencies of vitamin E can damage the kidneys, liver and pancreas. A lack of the vitamin is implicated in nephritis (kidney tubules blocked by dead cells, halting the flow of urine out of the body), pancreatic inflammation and gastrointestinal upsets from faulty absorption of fats and fat-soluble vitamins.

Recent Clinical Developments

The best type of vitamin E to take appears to be d-alpha tocopherol, derived from natural sources —i.e., oils. This is the kind that Adelle Davis recom-

mends. Although there has been minor success reported with d-alpha tocopherol acetate, a synthetic, it does not seem to have the wide-ranging healing powers of the natural vitamin. Furthermore, several sources indicate that the mixed tocopherols are unstable and, therefore, produce fewer results than does the pure vitamin E. This difference may be why some doctors see no improvement in patients after they have recommended vitamin E in the treatment of an ailment: it appears that only d-alpha tocopherol possesses the broadest curative measures, whereas the rest of the tocopherol family has limited healing potential.

Doctors, for example, have used d-alpha tocopherol repeatedly with great success for victims of heart attacks. Once such preventive therapy is undertaken, patients notice a difference within five to ten days, although the complete healing process usually takes up to four to six weeks.

Diabetics who eventually suffer the irreversible symptoms of gangrene in their toes, feet or legs have also been helped by massive doses of vitamin E —between 600 and 1,600 I.U. daily. The vitamin dilates the blood vessels, allowing blood to circulate freely and giving new life to the affected limbs.

In addition, vitamin E appears to have miraculous healing powers for scars caused by burns, accidents or surgery. Vitamin E applied directly to the damaged tissue and taken orally will literally dissolve the scar tissue, replenishing the skin so that it acquires elasticity and flexibility. At the same time as it works on the exterior skin, it heals inner scar tissue.

With vitamin E patrolling the body capillaries, veins and arteries also remain elastic and smooth so that no plaque or fiber can build up on the walls and produce atherosclerosis. Moreover, free radicals are kept in place to prevent premature aging and wrinkling. And people with varicose veins and phlebitis have been helped with supplements of vitamin E.

Many kinds of muscle damage or disease, such as muscular dystrophy, cystic fibrosis or deterioration, have been helped with supplements of vitamin E as well. According to Russian experiments, when vitamin E is added to the high-protein diets of athletes, they have more wind and stamina and their muscles withstand hardships better than before. They are thus able to increase the times, lengths or distances in their particular events. Vitamin E gets oxygen to the cells in a pure state so that they can carry it around the body to the needed areas: as a result, stamina and athletic potential can be increased.

Women who suffer from menstrual pain, irregular cycles, spotting and/or hemorrhaging have also been helped when vitamin E was added to their diets.

VITAMIN K

Astrological Ruler

Saturn.

Synthetic Forms

Menadione (K-3) and menadiol (K-4).

Synonyms

K-1 (phylloquinone and phytonadione), K-2 (farnoquinone and menaquinone), antihemorrhagic vitamin, prothrombin factor and koagulations-vitamin.

Sources

Vegetables: Alfalfa, chestnut leaves, spinach, soybeans, tomatoes, cauliflower, cabbage, peas, carrots and potatoes.

Fruits and Nuts: Prunes.

Meat and Fish: Pork liver, lean meats and kidney.

Grains: Unknown.

Dairy Products: Yogurt and egg yolks.

Herbs: Shepherd's purse.

Natural Supplements: Kelp.

Unit of Potency

Milligram or microgram.

History and Characteristics

Vitamin K-1 is found in pure form in alfalfa, and vitamin K-2 is found in putrefied fish meal and a number of other bacterial sources. Vitamin K-1 is a yellow oil, and vitamin K-2 is a yellow crystalline solid. Both are fat-soluble and insoluble in water. They are stable to heat and oxidation. Cooking won't easily destroy vitamin K, although frozen foods are found to be deficient in it. Four synthetic varieties (K-3 through K-7) are used by doctors in treating hemorrhaging when natural vitamin K cannot be utilized by the body.

Vitamin K was discovered in 1935 by Henrik Dam, a Danish scientist. He named it *koagulation* because of its blood-clotting abilities. Once hemorrhaging takes place within or outside the body, a factor called prothrombin is changed by enzymatic action into thrombin, which then converts fibrinogen in the blood into fibrin. Fibrin literally becomes a protein net that halts the flow of red corpuscles until the flow ceases—in other words, what is known as coagulation. To date, it has been discovered that four out of five blood coagulation factors are proteins that need vitamin K to start the coagulation process.

Vitamin K is also involved with the conversion of glucose into glycogen, which is stored in the liver. And the vitamin is partly responsible for the normal functioning of the liver.

Since vitamin K is fat-soluble, if natural foods containing it are ingested, the intestinal bacteria will produce it. From the intestines it is transported to the liver, where it becomes available to synthesize prothrombin to trigger the clotting process. Bile or bile salts are necessary to break vitamin K down so that it can be used to its full potential.

Allies: Although no one has suggested it, I believe that vitamins A, E, C and K are all synergists: that is, they are all agents working in cooperation with each other. Moreover, there is some evidence that vitamin K is linked with coenzyme Q or vitamin Q as well as vitamin E, since the structures of these substances are very similar. Cevitamic acid (vitamin C) may also be related because hemorrhaging can take place from weak intercellular fibers, causing capillary fragility and then bleeding.

antagonists: The list of substances that can slow down the clotting mechanism is long. At the top of the list are drugs such as dicoumerol (a blood-thinner, often given to patients with phlebitis), sulfonamides and antibiotics; poisons such as warfarin and iodinin; and other chemicals, specifically A-tocopherol quinone, dihydroxystearic acid glycide and salicylates. All of the above substances can destroy intestinal flora so that vitamin K cannot be manufactured within the body. And any continued use of an antibiotic will kill the flora.

In addition, mineral oil will cause excretion of vitamin K. Rancid fats, radiation and X-rays also destroy it. Damage to the liver itself, where vitamin K works, may result in the body's inability to synthesize prothrombin. And biliary obstruction of either the liver or gallbladder or impaired lipid absorption from lack of bile or bile salts can stop vitamin K from being synthesized.

Any ailments having to do with the intestinal tract, such as diarrhea or colitis, will affect the amount of vitamin K in the body. The ingestion of too many aspirins or sedatives will also reduce synthesis of the vitamin.

Dosages

Recommended Dietary Allowance: Vitamin K has not been established by the FDA as being necessary to human nutrition; however, some sources consider 300 to 500 micrograms daily adequate.

Therapeutic Dose: In some instances one milligram is given to infants shortly after birth to prevent hemorrhaging. Mothers in labor are sometimes given 10 to 20 milligrams. Vitamin K, administered through injection, should be dispensed by physicians who have had experience with it.

Megadose: Any megadose should be administered only with a physician's discretion.

Toxicity

Ten milligrams or more of vitamin K can be toxic to infants. Although natural vitamin K has no toxic effects in adults, the synthetic variety can be toxic if administered in doses of 30 milligrams or more. Pregnant mothers injected with synthetic vitamin K have experienced flushing, sweating and chest constrictions. In infants the vitamin has produced kernicterus (a disease wherein a yellow pigment invades the brain and spinal cord between the second and eighth day after birth): the prognosis for recovery from this disease is poor.

Deficiency Symptoms

The most noticeable symptoms of a deficiency of vitamin K are decreased clotting time of the blood, excessive bleeding in the muscles, colon or other organs, susceptibility to bruising, nosebleeds, miscarriages and anemia. A deficiency can also manifest in intestinal disorders, such as diarrhea and colitis.

Recent Clinical Developments

The uses of vitamin K are well-known to most physicians, particularly those in obstetrics and surgery. Patients are given injections of the vitamin before and/or during labor to prevent excess bleeding. Vitamin K is also used to prevent the hemorrhaging that many infants suffer shortly after birth.

Adelle Davis recommends that when a person has been on antibiotics for a long time, he or she should eat yogurt or acidophilus daily to keep the intestinal bacteria alive to manufacture vitamin D. It should also be remembered that the clotting process doesn't depend solely on vitamin K. Vitamins C and E and calcium are also necessary.

LAETRILE

Astrological Ruler
Neptune

Synthetic Forms
Amygdalin and nitrilosides.

Synonyms
Antineoplastic vitamin and vitamin B-17.

Sources
Vegetables: Mung beans, lima beans, kidney beans, chick peas (garbanzos), black-eyed peas, alfalfa sprouts, mung bean sprouts and garbanzo sprouts.

Fruits and Nuts: Apricot seeds, apple seeds, cherry seeds, nectarine seeds, peach seeds, pear seeds, plum seeds, prune seeds, bitter almonds (not sold in this country), macadamias, cashews, wild blackberries, elderberries, choke cherries and wild cranapples.

Fish and Meat: Unknown.
Dairy Products: Unknown.
Herbs: Unknown.
Natural Supplements: Apricot pits.

Unit of Potency
Milligram and gram.

History and Characteristics

Laetrile is a collective name for a group of chemically related compounds called nitrilosides; therefore, no specific, chemical formula can be given for the substance. And since it is not a pure essence but rather a chain of metabolized events, laetrile's stability cannot be ascertained.

Laetrile was discovered by Dr. E.T. Krebs of San Francisco, who has advocated its use as a cancer cure in the United States. Amygdalin, from the Greek word *amygdale*, meaning "almonds", was found to be the only active substance in apricot pits. After being chemically broken down amygdalin was found to release one molecule of hydrogen cyanide, a very quick and killing poison. So, hydrogen cyanide was called amygdalin. It was later referred to within the medical establishment as nitrilosides and by the lay public as either laetrile or vitamin B-17.

Once ingested, with the help of the enzyme B-glycosidase laetrile is hydrolyzed (a chemical decomposition in which a substance is split into simpler compounds by the addition of and the taking up of the elements of water) to free one molecule of hydrogen cyanide, one molecule of benzaldehyde or acetone and two molecules of sugar. The substances are then absorbed into the lymph and portal systems and circulated throughout the body.

Allies: For treating people with cancer several clinics outside the United States use the following nutrients in concert with laetrile: pancreatic enzyme preparations, bromelain, calcium supplements and calcium di-orotate. Others used but not routinely are vitamins C, E and A and pangamic acid.

Antagonists: Unknown at this time. More research is needed.

Dosages

Recommended Dietary Allowance: Laetrile is not recognized by the FDA as necessary for human nutrition. It was not until April 1977 that it was to be imported into the country without threat of law suit or imprisonment. And since 1980 it has once again been banned for import.

Some sources suggest one apricot kernel per each ten pounds of body weight a day as an aid in the prevention of cancer. The seeds should be eaten and *should not be placed in a liquid left to sit for any amount of time.* Because this is a poisonous substance, great caution is advised. A physician should be consulted before anyone embarks upon any planned program of cancer-prevention.

Therapeutic Dose: Laetrile should only be taken under a physician's guidance. For controlling moderate cancer crises 300 grams is average. Another recommended range is 300 milligrams per kilogram (2.2 pounds) of body weight, or about 140 milligrams per pound.

Megadose: Only under a physician's guidance laetrile has been given orally or injected into the body in such amounts as 10 to 20 grams daily. Injections of up to five grams per kilogram of patient weight per day have also been suggested.

Toxicity

The level of toxicity has not been established. Opinion is divided about the toxicity of laetrile: its proponents stress its nontoxic properties; other people believe laetrile can be extremely deadly. On test mice and rats injections of 25,000 milligrams of laetrile proved lethal. And some authorities feel that two to three tablets taken orally can be lethal to children. More research is necessary to prove whether or not laetrile is relatively nontoxic to humans. A physician should always be consulted before anyone takes any kind of dosage of laetrile.

Certain side effects have been noted when laetrile is injected into a cancer patient. There seems to be a fall in blood pressure, with the decrease proportionate to how much of the compound is given. Upon the first injection blood pressure can drop anywhere from 5 to 68 millimeters within the first five minutes. If the blood pressure drops too far and too quickly, shock can set in — a dangerous condition. According to one doctor, this side effect can be avoided by using .3 to 1 milligram of phenylephrine hydrochloride in the same syringe with the laetrile solution.

Deficiency Symptoms

Laetrile's only area of strength appears to be in fighting cancer. With a deficiency of the substance there may be diminished resistance to all forms of cancerous ailments.

Recent Clinical Developments

Until 1977 the FDA considered laetrile a drug and a poison and threatened legal action and im-

prisonment against anyone using the compound. While the FDA banned laetrile in the United States, cancer patients flocked out of the country, usually to Tijuana, Mexico, where two laetrile clinics were established. Then in April 1977 a judge in Oklahoma declared that laetrile could be used legally in this country; however, in 1980 it was again banned.

Because of the ban on laetrile, research on the substance is in its infancy, and I cannot stress too strongly that anyone seeking treatment with laetrile must have guidance from a doctor.

There are many myths about the miraculous healing powers of laetrile. One of the myths is that laetrile can cure cancer, but evidence is proving that it cannot cure cancer per se. Instead, it can relieve some of the discomforts.

The most striking feature of laetrile is that it can provide relief from pain. And with the easement of pain cancer patients have been able to diminish dosages or stop administration of drugs such as pain killers and sleeping pills over a period of time. Within days after laetrile treatment cancer patients also regain their appetites and body weight in some cases. The psychological effects accompanying such reductions in pain are the emergence of more positive thinking, interest in living once again and involvement in simple routines once put aside because of the disease.

It also appears that laetrile can prolong the life of cancer patients. At one clinic there was a 40 per cent remission rate among patients after laetrile therapy—an unheard of remission rate with normal means of cancer therapy, such as chemotherapy or radiation. Thus although laetrile does not cure a person completely of cancer, it does seem to either contain or reverse the process up to a point.

Laetrile appears to be more effective with some kinds of cancers rather than others. In one clinic laetrile was successful in treating cancer of the ovaries, lungs, colon and prostate, as well as leukemia, but it was unsuccessful in treating cancer of the pancreas. In addition, women with some types of breast cancer are given five years more survival with laetrile treatment. And although much more research is needed, evidence suggests that laetrile may inhibit growth of tumors or induce premature aging of tumors.

For those types of cancer accompanied by nauseous odors laetrile is effective in eliminating the fetid smells linked with the decay of flesh.

BIOFLAVONOIDS

Astrological Ruler
Saturn.

Synthetic Forms
Unknown.

Synonyms
Vitamin P, bioflavonoid complex, citrin, hesperidin, quercitrin, rutin, flavone, vitamin C-2, flavonols and flavonones.

Sources
Vegetables: Cabbage and green peppers.
Fruits and Nuts: Lemons, oranges, tangerines, white grapes, plums, grapefruit, apricots, cherries, blackberries, plums, black currants and prunes.
Meat and Fish: Unknown.
Grains: Buckwheat.
Dairy Products: Unknown.
Herbs: German rue (*Ruta graveolens*, unsuitable for pregnant women because it induces abortion), paprika and rose hips.
Natural Supplements: Citrus bioflavonoids, rutin (a source of bioflavonoids from buckwheat leaves), hesperidin and citrin.

Unit of Potency
Milligram.

History and Characteristics
Bioflavonoids are a water-soluble group composed of many brightly colored nutrients found in fruits and vegetables. Bioflavonoids are insoluble in oils and stable in acid. They are partially lost in frozen fruit juices. Boiling will destroy bioflavonoids but steaming will not.

Bioflavonoids are not sold as an individual supplement but instead are added to vitamin C. The best source of natural bioflavonoids is the white rind of any citrus fruit, especially lemons, oranges and tangerines. Frozen orange juice is not a good source of bioflavonoids because the pulp that contains the complex is squeezed off by processors.

Bioflavonoids were discovered by Dr. Albert Szent-Gyorgyi as an offshoot of vitamin C. Discovered in the white pulp surrounding citrus fruit, the group of compounds was named vitamin P because it is concerned with the permeability of the capillaries. Composed of citrin, hesperidin, rutin, flavones and flavonals, bioflavonoids are sometimes called by the names of individual components.

The main function of bioflavonoids is to assist vitamin C in its work. Their first specific task is to keep the collagen healthy and the capillaries elastic and permeable to diffuse and absorb nutrients. Afterwards the bioflavonoids travel through the circulatory system to parts of the body where they are needed. Bioflavonoids also act as anticoagulant fac-

tors, stopping capillaries from breaking and causing bruising.

Bioflavonoids are easily absorbed in the intestinal tract, from there going into the circulatory system. Any excessive amount is sloughed off through urination or perspiration.
Allies: Vitamin C.
Antagonists: Since bioflavonoids are synergists with vitamin C, some of the same antagonists of vitamin C may affect the bioflavonoid complex. (See section on vitamin C.) But further research needs to be done to prove this theory.

Dosages
Recommended Dietary Allowance: None has been established by the FDA.
Therapeutic Dose: Fifty to two hundred milligrams are recommended.
Megadose: Two hundred or more milligrams are recommended.

Toxicity
Bioflavonoids are completely nontoxic.

Deficiency Symptoms
One of the first signs of a potential deficiency of bioflavonoids is bruising of the skin. Such bruising means that the capillaries are fragile and are breaking with the slightest amount of pressure placed against the skin. Where the capillaries are damaged the skin may be pale pink, splotchy red or purplish. Furthermore, there is general swelling in the area from excess fluids beneath the skin.

A deficiency of bioflavonoids will also bring on problems with bleeding, especially for a person who tends to bleed easily. A bleeding wound may take longer than usual to heal. And there may be an irregular menstrual flow or pain associated with the loss of blood.

Recent Clinical Developments
Bioflavonoids are effective in treating varicose veins and hemorrhoids. Since bioflavonoids help keep the walls of the capillaries elastic and permeable to needed nutrients, doses can supply relief from the pain and swelling of varicose veins. And the pain, bleeding and itching that accompany hemorrhoids may stop between two and five days after treatment with bioflavonoids.

For women who abort easily dosages of vitamin C and bioflavonoids together help improve conditions so that mothers can carry their babies full-term.

Since bioflavonoids are antithrombosis agents that do not allow blood clot and form barriers within the circulatory system, they have proven helpful in alleviating blood clots, especially in tandem with vitamin C. The bioflavonoids discourage build-up of plaque on the walls of the veins or arteries. (Bioflavonoids are not effective against clots collecting in one area.)

FATTY ACIDS

Astrological Ruler

Mars.

Synthetic Forms

Any oil not cold-pressed.

Synonyms

Linoleic acid, linolenic acid, arachidonic acid, polyunsaturated fats, vitamin F, unsaturated fatty acids and essential fatty acids.

Sources

Vegetables: Unknown.

Fruits and Nuts: Avocados and sunflower seeds.

Fish and Meat: Chicken, pork sausage, pork, canned sardines and tuna.

Grains: Unknown.

Dairy Products: Eggs and mayonnaise.

Herbs: Unknown.

Natural Supplements: Unsaturated fatty or polyunsaturated acids, cold-pressed corn oil, flax-seed oil, sunflower oil, peanut oil rich in arachidonic acid, safflower oil rich in linoleic acid and soy oil rich in linolenic acid.

Unit of Potency

Gram or milligram.

History and Characteristics

Vitamin F is a group of fatty acids—linoleic, linolenic and arachidonic acids—rather than a individual component; therefore, it has no single chemical compound equivalent. It is soluble in fats and insoluble in water. Long cooking destroys its properties. It is unstable to air and easily destroyed, becoming rancid.

Fatty acids, commonly referred to either as unsaturated fats or polyunsaturates, are gotten from fish or vegetable oils. They should not be confused with saturated fats, such as margarines, cooking fats, tallow, lard or the fats from meat products. The body cannot manufacture its own unsaturated fatty acids and must rely on outer sources.

Fatty acids play a continual part in the respiration and oxygen processes to all cells, tissue and organs. They are similar to vitamin C in that they maintain the structure of the cells. They also keep the endocrine glands healthy, particularly the adrenal glands.

Fatty acids help maintain an overall blood coagulation rate. And perhaps their most important job is breaking up cholesterol deposits in the arteries to prevent atherosclerosis.

Fatty acids are also responsible for keeping the skin, hair and nails in health. They aid vitamin D by helping to make calcium available. They also convert carotene into vitamin A, assimilate phosphorus and generally keep the reproductive system operating efficiently.

Digestive enzymes covert fatty acids into glycerin so that the glycerin can enter the blood. If the enzymes do not break down the fatty acids properly, the fatty acids cannot aid in the absorption of vitamins A, D, E and K. Fatty acids are also needed by the body to stimulate the flow of bile.

Fat is broken down by enzymatic action in the stomach and intestinal tract and then converted into fatty acids and glycerols. They are then absorbed through the walls of the intestines and carried to the liver, where they are used as a source of energy as needed. Other parts may be taken into the lymph system to act as collectors of bodily fluids and to make sure the fluids return to the circulatory system.

Allies: Fatty acids are most effective taken with vitamins E, C and D.

Antagonists: Unless generous amounts of vitamin E are taken, X-ray treatment will diminish the effectiveness of fatty acids. Other antagonists are chlorine dioxide (used to preserve, bleach and age flour for use in bread), room temperature, exposure to air and ferrous sulfate (found in iron compounds).

Dosages

Recommended Dietary Allowance: The FDA has not established an RDA; however, the National Research Council feels that "fat intake should include essential unsaturated fatty acids to the extent of at least one per cent of the total calories."

Adelle Davis feels two tablespoons of vegetable oil are needed daily to supply essential fatty acids. She suggests a mixture of peanut, safflower and soy oil used as salad or cooking oil rather than a capsule or supplement to fulfill the daily needs. She warns that any oil taken as a supplement for adequate doses of fatty acids may work against the body rather than for it if the other needed vitamins and minerals are not there to synthesize the fatty acids properly.

Therapeutic Dose: Not established. Excessive amounts may cause either metabolism upset or weight gain.

Megadose: Unknown.

Toxicity

There is no known level of toxicity. Symptoms

of toxicity are metabolic disruption and/or weight gain.

Deficiency Symptoms

Without sufficient fatty acids the cells change, triggering several types of disorders. The hair may lack luster, dandruff problems may occur, nails may become brittle, the skin may become dry and flaky, and acne or eczema may result. Moreover, growth may be retarded and problems with underweight may occur. Diarrhea and varicose veins can also manifest.

More serious deficiencies could affect the heart, kidneys and circulatory system. Reproduction may be limited as well, since fatty acids help produce prostaglandins, found in the prostate, kidneys, brain and in the seminal and menstrual fluids. Without the fatty acids this type of cell cannot be created and problems related to women's disorders or ailments of the prostate for men can ensue. Gallstones may also form because fatty acids are partly responsible for keeping the cholesterol soft so that it may be broken down and used by the body instead of depositing in one area and causing stones or blockage in a vein or artery.

Recent Clinical Developments

Anyone buying supplements of fatty acids should make sure that he or she has purchased only a *cold-pressed* oil. One way to test to see if the oil is cold-pressed is to place the bottle in the refrigerator. If the contents begin to lump up, forming balls of fat after 12 hours or so, the oil is cold-pressed. But if the contents remain unchanged, the oil is not cold-pressed. Since rancid oils destroy fatty acids very quickly and do nothing to help the body, everyone should make sure of a correct purchase.

Fatty acids can help relieve diarrhea. With diarrhea food is literally run through the intestines at such a fast rate that very few nutrients are absorbed through the walls. Tests have shown that oils, in contrast to solid fats, slow down the passage of food through the intestines, allowing more vitamins and minerals to be absorbed. In addition, the absorption of oils is almost complete, whereas solid fats are not as thoroughly digested.

Anyone who is a heart or atherosclerosis patient and takes oil as an additive may incur more damage than help. Oil alone does not make the ailment better if certain other nutrients, such as magnesium, lecithin and vitamin E, are not available within the body to help synthesize the oil properly. Adelle Davis suggests that a person with a gallbladder problem should take fat-soluble vitamins along with lecithin and dried bile tablets to insure fewer vitamin deficiencies and help the body to break down the nutrients while the organ heals itself. A person with gallstones is often put on a fat-free or a low-fat diet. But, of course, too little fat in the body does not allow vitamins A, D, E and K to be properly synthesized, creating a serious deficiency.

A person who has either had a heart attack or is susceptible to one should be careful in trying reducing diets. Blood fat can be lowered by proper amounts of exercise—but not through dieting. After eating fats can reach the blood and raise the level of blood fat in two hours. After fasting or a weight-reducing diet the blood fat levels often rise six times above the normal level. This rapid rise is why so many heart attacks occur around Thanksgiving and Christmas. After a huge meal the digestive system is overtaxed and the heart is pressured tremendously by a sharp rise in blood fat, causing a heart attack or stroke.

People should beware not to eat too little fat. When very little fat is ingested as part of the diet, food leaves the stomach so quickly that the walls may become exposed to hydrochloric acid for longer periods of time. Ulcers can then form. People on low-fat diets should take precautions against such occurrences.

CHAPTER EIGHT
Minerals

Minerals are just as vital to our health as vitamins. Approximately four to five per cent of our total body weight is composed of minerals. Without them our bones, teeth, tissue, cells and muscles would cease to function.

The main difference between minerals and vitamins is that minerals are not manufactured inside our bodies as some vitamins are. Minerals are also inorganic substances.

Because they come from inorganic sources, minerals are difficult for the body to break down unless conditions are right. Digestive juices in the stomach must be operating at optimum efficiency, and certain other vitamins and/or minerals must be present to break the minerals down or to aid in their transport throughout the body. For example, without proper amounts of the intrinsic factor available in the stomach gastric juices iron will not be absorbed. Nor will iron be absorbed if copper is not available in proportionate amounts. On the other hand, if there is too much copper in the body, iron will not be correctly assimilated. And any of these circumstances can result in anemia.

Anyone who takes a mineral supplement without the right conditions to help insure the mineral's safe passage into the internal mechanism of the body will simply lose the mineral through discharge or excretion. For this reason many multimineral supplements sold today are ineffective because they are not prepared with a proper balance of other minerals and vitamins that will aid in absorption.

Sulfur, chlorine, potassium, sodium, magnesium, calcium and phosphorus are found in relatively large amounts in our bodies. The other minerals, found in much smaller amounts, are known as trace minerals. But deficiencies of trace minerals, such as iron, copper or zinc, can develop just as easily as deficiencies of other minerals.

CALCIUM

Astrological Ruler

Saturn.

Synthetic Forms

Calcium carbonate, calcium pantothenate and calcium sulfate anhydrons.

Sources

Vegetables: Chard, watercress, cauliflower, broccoli, endive, kohlrabi, rutabaga, spinach, turnips, parsnips, carrots, rhubarb, green beans, lettuce, onions, soybeans, alfalfa sprouts, beet greens, celery, chick peas (garbanzos), collards, flax seed, kidney beans, lentils, okra and tomatoes.

Fruits and Nuts: Almonds, avocados, dried apricots, bananas, cranberries, coconuts, currants, dates, figs, grapefruit, lemons, limes, plums, peaches, prunes, pineapple, raisins, raspberries and black walnuts.

Meat and Fish: Oysters, shrimp, lobster, liver and broiled chicken.

Grains: Soy flour.

Dairy Products: Buttermilk, most cheeses, evaporated milk and skim milk.

Herbs: Arrow root, carrageen (Irish moss), chamomile, chives, cleavers, coltsfoot, dandelion root, flaxseed, horsetail grass, meadow sweet, mistletoe (poisonous), nettle, pimpernel, plantain, rest harrow, shepherd's purse, silverweed, sorrel and toadflax flax.

Natural Supplements: Kelp, bone meal calcium, calcium lactate, calcium gluconate, eggshell calcium, oyster shell calcium and dolomite.

Unit of Potency

Milligram.

History and Characteristics

Several varieties of natural and synthetic calcium are available:

Bone meal calcium (natural), made from the long bones of cattle, is said to be most like the calcium found in human beings. Although this product has the best balance of all the minerals, it is the least digestible. Furthermore, Adelle Davis asserts that it is unreasonably high in phosphorus and is not a satisfactory supplement. I've found that bone meal calcium should be used only when there are problems with the bones.

Calcium pantothenate (synthetic) is used in the treatment of deficiencies of pantothenic acid and is not a good source of calcium per se.

Calcium lactate (natural), a lactic acid salt derived from milk, is easily absorbed by the body and works mainly on the muscles or muscle-related ailments. It contains twice as much calcium as the gluconate variety, but people who have allergies to milk may react adversely to it.

Calcium gluconate (natural), a gluconic acid salt derived from glucose, is easily absorbed by the body and works mainly on the nerves and blood calcium levels. Since it is not as high in calcium as lactate or bone meal varieties, more supplementation is needed. Adelle Davis recommends that if children cannot tolerate cow's milk either calcium lactate or gluconate can be substituted for the milk, since those varieties of calcium are sweet, dissolve easily and can be used in foods or juices as a substitute for calcium.

Eggshell calcium (natural) is derived from crushed chicken egg shells.

Oyster shell calcium (natural), derived from crushed oyster shells, contains a minimal amount of phosphorus with natural trace minerals.

Liquid calcium (natural) can be used when a person has problems absorbing calcium. It should be taken with vitamin D.

Di-cal (di-calcium) phosphate (natural/synthetic) has 22 per cent phosphorus added.

Dolomite (natural) is a source of bone meal calcium and magnesium in proper proportions. It may or may not have vitamin A and/or vitamin D with it. Elderly people with poor hydrochloric acid in their stomachs should not use this supplement.

The fifth most abundant element in the body, calcium, occurring in an inorganic form, is responsible for the soundness of the skeletal frame, bones and teeth. It also helps the heart to beat regularly, feeds the nerves, helps bleeding wounds to clot quickly, makes muscle responses fluid and not jerky or spastic, keeps the blood healthy and activates enzyme metabolism.

Its importance to cell structure is vital as well. Once calcium is released by a substance, cells will divide. Calcium in the blood helps to regulate the acid-alkaline balance in the body. The ratio of acid to alkali must be maintained at approximately four parts alkali to one part acid: too much acid will cause acidosis and several nerve-related problems; very high amounts of acid can cause death.

Approximately 99 per cent of calcium is found in the skeletal frame, bones and teeth. The rest is in the blood levels and other bodily fluids. Only 20 to 30 per cent of the calcium we consume is absorbed in the duodenum and lower intestinal tract. The rest is excreted in the feces. When the body is in dire need of extra calcium, however, such as during times of accelerated growth, the body tends to absorb more. A diet high in protein also allows more calcium to be absorbed.

An ample supply of vitamin D is necessary to assimilate calcium. And the ingestion of a moderate amount of fat will slow food down as it moves through the small intestine to permit calcium to be absorbed. Since all bodily calcium is replaced about every six years, a daily intake is necessary. Extra calcium is stored in the bones.

Allies: Calcium works as a team with phosphorus. Calcium also acts in cooperation with vitamins A, D and C and magnesium. Other nutrients that aid its effectiveness are fatty acids, manganese and hydrochloric acid, usually given in the form of glutamic acid hydrochloride.

Antagonists: Anytime one or both of the other members of the "trinity"—vitamin D and magnesium—are missing, calcium is not absorbed.

On the other hand, if magnesium is taken in large doses alone, a deficiency of calcium can occur.

In addition, a high intake of phosphorus will cause a loss of calcium. A lack of hydrochloric acid in the digestive juices will further retard calcium's assimilation.

Refined white sugar, dextromaltose and glucose can also decrease the absorption of calcium. Unfortunately, many of today's baby formulas have high amounts of dextrose, known to wash calcium right out of the body. Thus babies may suffer severe consequences, such as faulty bone formation.

During stress the adrenal glands release cortisone, which pulls minerals, including calcium, from the bones. Consequently, a long-term disease will drastically decrease levels of calcium. Cortisone medication or shots as well as supplements of aspirin or thyroxine to aid the thyroid also lower the levels of calcium in our bodies.

Other drugs that can stop absorption of calcium are penicillin, chloromycetin, neomycin and the steroids prednisone and dexamethasone.

Phytic acid, found in wheat, is known to block absorption of calcium, too. Moreover, foods such as spinach, rhubarb and chocolate contain oxalic acid, which will bind with free calcium to form a non-nutritious compound called calcium oxalate: this oxalate can build up crystal formations in the kidneys or bladder, creating stones.

Dosages

Infants 0-1/6 yrs. 400 mg. 1/6-1/2 yrs. 500 mg.1/2-1 yrs. 600 mg.

Children 1-2 yrs. 700 mg.2-6 yrs. 800 mg.6-8 yrs. 900 mg.8-10 yrs. 1,000 mg.

Men 10-21 yrs. 1,200 mg.12-18 yrs. 1,400 mg. 18-75+ yrs. 1,800 mg.

Women 10-12 yrs. 1,200 mg.12-18 yrs. 1,300 mg. 18-75+ yrs. 1,800 mg.

Pregnant Women 400+ mg.

Lactating Women 500+ mg.

Therapeutic Dose: Since continued immoderate doses of calcium, along with vitamin D, can cause hypercalcemia (the calcification of organs or bones) anyone who feels his or her level of calcium is low should consult a physician, undergo testing and adhere to a program set up by the doctor.

Megadose: When both phosphorus and calcium are lost during sickness, Adelle Davis recommends 2,000 milligrams of calcium daily.

Toxicity

The level of toxicity for calcium has not been established, but symptoms of toxicity include calcium deposits within the kidneys or other organs as well as sluggishness of those organs.

Deficiency Symptoms

At the onset of a deficiency of calcium there may be restlessness, nervousness and even tremors of the hands. In addition, muscles may cramp, and there may be numbness and tingling in the extremities. The heart may then race or palpitate erratically. Stunted growth and bone problems, such as rickets in children, osteoporosis (the softening of the bones or the bones becoming porous and brittle) and teeth problems, as well as slow blood clotting time, may also occur.

Insomnia seems to be the most common symptom of insufficient calcium: unfortunately, people go to their doctors and are prefunctorily issued sleeping pills to cover up the deficiency.

Other symptoms of a deficiency are a lack of courage, will power or the will to live. There may be difficulty in thinking or completing thoughts, forgetfulness, brooding, depression, afternoon headaches, sighing, excess saliva in the mouth or cramping of toes at night. The inability to relax or stay put, puffiness in parts of the body or an increase in weight can also manifest.

Recent Clinical Developments

Women who have troubles with menstruation may simply have deficiencies of calcium. Premenstrual tensions, such as nervousness, irritability, crying, tremors or trembling, restlessness and lower back aches, indicate that the blood calcium levels are low as the cycle approaches each month. Then, if the calcium is still low as the cycle begins, further problems with spotting, cramping and irregularity may occur.

Women also suffer the symptoms of a deficiency of calcium during menopause. Some women during menopause feel like they are "going crazy" and seek professional help; many others suffer silently. But nutritional supplements may relieve the discomforts of menopause. Adelle Davis suggests that 5,000 units of vitamin D, 500 milligrams of magnesium and 2,000 milligrams of calcium will help women get through such periods of changing hormone levels without tranquilizers, therapists or silent tears.

Elderly people in general can suffer several effects of deficiencies of calcium. For instance, denture wearers who complain that their dentures fit improperly may really have calcium deficiencies, which produce nervousness associated with wearing dentures. Instead of repeated appointments with frustrated dentists, these people should improve their diets to include more calcium-laden foods.

Many elderly people contract osteoporosis, a dreaded bone condition. The parathyroid gland (four pealike glands located on either side of the thyroid at the base of the throat) is responsible for how much or how little calcium enters the bloodstream. It is postulated that the hormone released by the parathyroid and thyrocalcitinon, which prevents the loss of calcium, are out of kilter with one another, causing the bones to lose too much calcium and become porous, brittle and easily breakable. Doctors can successfully keep thyrocalcitonin in check so that the other hormone does not rob the bones of needed calcium. A diet rich in calcium also helps the condition. And a little-known herb called springtime horsetail (*equisetum*), rich in silica, is being used on osteoporosis patients in California with tremendous success: patients' bones are beginning to knit and mend within two weeks of their taking the tablet-form herb under a physician's guidance.

Victims of osteoporosis are usually deficient in magnesium, vitamin D and phosphorus, as well as calcium, an indication of how closely these vitamins and minerals work as a team. Magnesium is especially important: it calms the pituitary gland, the master controller for the entire endocrine system. With too little magnesium the pituitary sends out a hormonal signal for the bones to give up their calcium and send it to the blood, part of the probable cause of osteoporosis.

A lack of calcium, magnesium and potassium can also trigger spasms of the colon, inducing constipation.

The cooperation of calcium and vitamin D is essential to good bodily functioning as well, and it is important to have the right balance of the vitamin and mineral. For example, kidney stones can form when there is not enough vitamin D to keep the tubules ready to resorb calcium as it flows through them; however, too high a dose of vitamin D by itself will cause heavy loss of both calcium and phosphorus through the urine. In addition, people who have high blood pressure often have too much salt in their bodies: adequate amounts of calcium and vitamin D will increase salt loss via the urine, thereby helping to alleviate some of the potential dangers associated with this ailment.

Vitamin A is another important ally of calcium. For instance, the vitamin and mineral together can alleviate the symptoms of sinusitis (infection of the sinus tissue and membranes causing sniffles, stuffiness and blockage of air passages): vitamin A helps repair the sinus tissue, and calcium helps straighten out the faltering metabolism. (A diet restricted from white flour also helps.)

Vitamin A in conjunct with calcium may help prevent skin cancer, too. Skin cancer can, in part, be blamed on a person overexposing sensitive skin to the ultraviolet rays of the sun: in long-term tests vitamin A and calcium carbonate were found to protect the skin from sun damage, although the role of the calcium carbonate in preventing the effects of sunburn is still largely unexplained at this point. (Vitamin A is directly concerned with the elasticity and longevity of the life of skin cells: if skin is constantly exposed to the drying conditions of the sun, more vitamin A may be required to keep the cells supple.)

Two seemingly unrelated ailments partially caused by a deficiency of calcium are conjunctivitis and lead poisoning. With conjunctivitis (pink eye) the eye burns, itches and tears: it has been found that calcium, along with vitamin D, alleviates this condition without the use of antibiotics. Lead poisoning, especially prevalent in cities, where people are constantly exposed to automobile exhaust emissions, manifests as confusion, psychosis, irritability and eventually kidney damage, convulsion and paralysis: lead, rapidly absorbed by the bones instead of calcium, will build up when there is insufficient calcium to stop it from being ingested into the body.

Children who wake up screaming in the middle of the night because of spasm and cramping in their muscles are also lacking sufficient calcium to keep up with the accelerated growth processes their bodies are undergoing. A diet high in calcium and/or supplements can bring relief.

Lower back pains may be related to a deficiency of calcium as well. Furthermore, the disks that act as shock absorbers for the bone vertebrae to cushion themselves against also rely on a continued supply of calcium so that they do not harden, become brittle or deteriorate.

Bruxism (the grinding of one's teeth during sleep) was once thought to be an emotional disorder. Instead, it is caused by a deficiency of calcium and pantothenic acid and is easily corrected.

In many cases people whose bones are slow to knit have low levels of hydrochloric acid necessary to help assimilate calcium: without adequate calcium bone healing takes much longer.

Anytime sugars are eaten, whether in the form of sweets, white sugar or the type found in baby formulas, calcium is barely absorbed because sugars trigger alkaline digestive juices instead; however, in experiments using milk sugar or lactose absorption of calcium was increased tremendously so that within 30 minutes the mineral was being whisked to the bones.

CHLORINE

Astrological Ruler
Mars.

Synthetic Forms
Unknown.

Sources
Vegetables: Lettuce, spinach, cabbage, parsnips, asparagus, carrots, tomatoes, potatoes and onions.

Fruits and Nuts: Dates, coconuts, bananas, pineapple, grapes, oranges and lemons.

Fish and Meat: Oysters, salmon, fish in general and meat in general, particularly the organs.

Grains: Whole wheat.

Dairy Products: Cheese, whites of eggs, milk and egg yolks.

Herbs: All plants contain more or less chlorine in the form of sodium chloride.

Natural Supplements: Sodium chloride (table salt), kelp, dulse and whey.

Unit of Potency
Gram.

History and Characteristics
Found with both sodium and potassium forms in the body, chlorine helps to maintain the acid-alkaline balance. Essential in regulating the pressure both outside and within the cells, chlorine helps to stimulate hydrochloric acid into the stomach to digest food. It also helps the liver to filter out waste and toxic products. Moreover, tendons and joints are kept elastic and supple because of chlorine's beneficial effects. And it helps transport hormones to where they are needed in the body.

However, it may be that we are getting way too much chemical chlorine from our drinking water. With so much chlorine in our tap water (not well water, distilled water or bottled mineral water) many experts feel we have traded typhoid, once carried in the water, for atherosclerosis (cholesterol deposits in the arteries). Furthermore, some people are allergic to the chlorine in tap water and exhibit signs of asthma, allergies or hives.

Perhaps the most frightening fact about chlorine is that to date there has been no organized investigation to study the long-term effects of the mineral on the human body. It still is not completely understood if chlorine, a poisonous gas, is chemically converted into the chloride ion, which is safe. Dr. Joshua Lederberg, biochemist, asserts that chlorine may indiscriminately kill more than just bacteria: he feels that it may affect the genetic DNA in our bodies, perhaps enough to cause deformities in our infants. It is obvious that much more study needs to be done to prove or disprove these allegations. Until then people worried about getting megadoses of chlorine from their tap water might want to use bottled water or boil their water, thereby evaporating the chlorine.

Chlorine is widely distributed throughout the cells and absorbed in the intestinal tract. The highest amounts of chlorine are found in the cerebrospinal fluid as well as in the secretions of the intestinal tract. If the body has enough chlorine, the mineral will be excreted via perspiration and urine. Vomiting and diarrhea may cause a loss of chlorine.

Allies: Unknown.

Antagonists: Unknown.

Dosages

Recommended Dietary Allowance: None has been established by the FDA because America's salt intake is high enough to provide three to nine grams of chlorine daily.

Therapeutic Dose: Fourteen to twenty-eight grams of chlorine daily is considered quite high and unnecessary.

Megadose: Megadoses are not advised, since a diet with an average intake of sodium and potassium provides adequate amounts of chlorine to the body. If taken in too high amounts, chlorine will cause side effects.

Toxicity

Although a toxicity level has not been established, anything over 14 grams is considered excessive.

Because there has been no official investigation of chlorine undertaken, the symptoms discussed here are based upon the tests and conclusions of individual doctors and professors.

Allergic reactions, such as asthma or hives, may erupt from drinking tap water that is heavily chlorinated. An individual who is extremely sensitive to chemicals may also develop such reactions. In addition, chlorine is reported to cause functional colitis in some cases.

Atherosclerosis was found among American soldiers during the Korean War because they were issued highly chlorinated water to keep from drinking unsanitized, bacteria-laden water. In autopsy reports Dr. Price observed that at an average age of 22.1 years 75 per cent of the soldiers killed in battle had atherosclerosis.

Other symptoms of toxicity, paralleling chlorine gas poisoning, are choking, dizziness and turning blue from lack of oxygen in the body.

Deficiency Symptoms

These can include loss of hair or teeth, poor muscle contraction and impaired digestion.

Recent Clinical Developments

Chlorine ingested in large amounts is responsible for the destruction of vitamin E within the body. Moreover, chlorine will destroy intestinal flora essential for absorbing nutrients to maintain health.

House plants watered with chlorinated water will not grow as well as plants fed well or bottled water. Guppies have also been known to die in heavily chlorinated water. In fact, chlorine can be such a strong killing agent that it is used as a bleach.

CHROMIUM

Astrological Ruler

Jupiter.

Synthetic Forms

Chromic sulfate.

Sources

Vegetables: Mushrooms.

Fruits and Nuts: Unknown.

Meat and Fish: Beef liver and clams.

Grains: Whole-grain breads.

Dairy Products: Unknown.

Herbs: Unknown.

Natural Supplements: Raw sugar, cane juice, yeast and unsaturated corn oil.

Unit of Potency

Microgram.

History and Characteristics

Chromium is vital to the enzymes involved with the metabolism of glucose for energy. It is a cofactor with insulin and helps remove the glucose from the circulatory system into individual cells that need the energy. Chromium may also be involved in some way with the synthesis of protein in a binding action with RNA. It is necessary for the synthesis of fats, and scientists are finding that it may also have importance in the cholesterol metabolism.

Because of farming methods the soil is depleted of this mineral. Junk foods and highly processed foods are also low in chromium. Therefore, many Americans are deficient in the mineral. Not made in individual supplements, chromium is only found in multivitamin or mineral tablets, such as vitamin B complex tablets comprised mostly of synthetics. The best sources of chromium are brewer's yeast and hard well water.

This mineral is one of the hardest to assimilate: only three per cent is retained by the body. If given in an inorganic salts compound, only about .5 per cent of the dose is absorbed by the gastrointestinal tract; therefore, naturally occurring chromium is more easily assimilated. Once in the body it is stored in the spleen, kidneys and testes. Smaller amounts are found in other organs, in some enzymes and in RNA. It is found in twenty parts to one billion parts of blood.

Allies: Unknown. Vitamin B-6 may be of service with chromium, although my theory has not been proven through research and laboratory testing.

Antagonists: Eating large amounts of white sugar can deplete the small reserve of chromium.

Dosages

Recommended Dietary Allowance: None has been established by the FDA. It is estimated that 80 to 100 micrograms daily would be beneficial. One source believes that the average adult consumes 200 micrograms or less of chromium a day: of that amount, only .5 per cent is absorbed, totaling one microgram assimilated daily.

Therapeutic Dose: In one study medical students and elderly people were given from five to one hundred milligrams on a daily basis, substantially more than the suggested amount.

Megadose: Unknown.

Toxicity

Unknown.

Deficiency Symptoms

Upset insulin production, triggering possible hyper- or hypoglycemia connected with the carbohydrate metabolism, may occur. Symptoms associated with these ailments include nervousness, irritability, faintness, dizziness, psychotic reactions for seemingly no discernible reason and bodily weakness. Other symptoms associated with hypoglycemia are fatigue or malaise three to five hours after eating. In addition, there can be possible depressed growth rate or hardening of the arteries. One of the biggest causes of a deficiency of chromium is diabetes.

Recent Clinical Developments

Diabetes is rapidly becoming one of the nation's top killers, challenging heart disease as the number one murderer. Even more frightening is the number of people who have developed hypoglycemia in the past 20 years. I predict that as Americans continue to eat highly processed foods diabetes and all other sugar-related ailments will continue to go unchecked. All people on junk food diets, high in white bread, sugar products and overcooked fruits, meats and vegetables, are prime contenders for deficiencies of chromium and erratic blood sugar metabolisms.

Kwashiorkor, a disease that attacks children from one to five years of age, is characterized by changes in the skin and hair, retarded growth, diar-

rhea, nervousness and loss of appetite: it is found to respond dramatically to chromium therapy. The ailment is a disease of malnutrition and affects the carbohydrate and protein processes.

COBALT

Astrological Ruler

Mars.

Synthetic Forms

Cobalt chloride.

Sources

Vegetables: Watercress, wax beans, beet roots, cabbage, clover and alfalfa.

Fruits and Nuts: Apricots, figs and pears.

Meat and Fish: Liver, kidney, oysters and clams.

Grains: Buckwheat grain and whole-wheat flour.

Dairy Products: Milk.

Natural Supplements: Kelp and dulse.

Unit of Potency

Microgram.

History and Characteristics

In 1948 a red crystalline compound was isolated from the liver and called vitamin B-12; however, it was soon found that cobalt was a partner to the vitamin, working in unison with the vitamin's various functions in the body. Hence vitamin B-12 was renamed cynanocobalamin to include cobalt. Found in trace amounts, cobalt is so widely distributed that scientists find it almost impossible to prepare a cobalt-free diet or culture medium from natural sources.

Humans need only 0.02 milligrams of cobalt in their bodies to stay healthy. Cobalt is primarily concerned with activating certain enzymatic functions in the body and maintaining the health of red blood cells: it helps in the formation of hemoglobin. It has been found that without sources rich in cobalt sheep develop anemia, known as "bush sickness," "pine" or "coast disease." With the soil depleted of natural cobalt the animals quickly lose weight and become anemic, and their wool is of poor quality.

Since inorganic cobalt can be lethal, only natural sources of the mineral should be used. It is not made as a single compound but rather is found as a component in multimineral tablets. A doctor's prescription is necessary to obtain cobalt by itself.

Not assimilated well, cobalt is absorbed via the intestinal tract in minute amounts with the rest either excreted in the feces or urine. Once absorbed, it is stored in the plasma and red blood cells with some amounts stored in the liver, kidneys, pancreas and spleen. The highest amounts are usually found in the liver.

Allies: Vitamin B-12, copper, iron and zinc.

Antagonists: Unknown.

Dosages

Recommended Dietary Allowance: None has been established by the FDA. A daily intake of five to eight micrograms is considered sufficient. Because folic acid can mask a deficiency of vitamin B-12 and cobalt a prescription is needed for folic acid tablets of 400 micrograms or more.

Therapeutic Dose: In a test in 1955 Davis and Fields gave five men oral doses of 150 milligrams of cobalt chloride. Approximately seven to twenty-two days afterward polycythemia (excessive red blood cells in the blood) was induced.

Megadose: Unknown.

Toxicity

According to the available results from tests, 150 or more milligrams seems to constitute a level of toxicity. Massive doses of more than 150 milligrams cause polycythemia. An enlarged thyroid gland (goiter) may also occur.

Deficiency Symptoms

Slow growth and various kinds of anemia (Cooley's anemia, anemia of sepsis, nephritis and anemia in premature infants) are attributable to deficiencies of cobalt and vitamin B-12. Pernicious anemia has also been induced when cobalt and vitamin B-12 are lacking.

Recent Clinical Developments

Cobalt's importance as a blood-builder cannot be overemphasized. Found in normal amounts in a body, cobalt helps use iron in building red blood cells and thereby curing anemia. When a person has anemia, the red blood cell count is below normal. Cobalt given in an overdose pulls available iron from the body to force accelerated production of red blood cells—polycythemia. With anemia caused by septic inflammation (blood poisoning either by microorganisms or their leavings) cobalt-induced polycythemia successfully improves absorption of iron and the use of it for synthesis of hemoglobin.

Other forms of anemia are also helped by doses of cobalt. Hypochromic anemia, characterized by a low concentration of hemoglobin, occurs when a person is on a diet heavy in milk: it is relieved by administering cobalt along with copper and iron supplements, and tests indicate that without the cobalt optimum results are not achieved. Normocytic

anemia, characterized by fewer-than-normal red blood cells in the bloodstream, and macrocytic anemia, characterized by abnormally large mature red blood cells or corpuscles, have both been successfully treated with the administration of cobalt in tandem with vitamin B-12.

To prevent triggering anemia, anyone taking supplements of folic acid should be sure to get a comparable amount of vitamin B-12 with cobalt. It is especially important for a pregnant woman to arrange with her physician to have these vitamins and minerals in correct proportions.

Copper is another ally of cobalt. Both minerals are concerned with the formation of hemoglobin in the blood. When iron does not alter an anemic patient's condition, copper in combination with vitamin B-12, containing cobalt, has been found effective.

Soil depletion over the past century has robbed our foods of basic and intrinsic minerals we need. In addition, commercial fertilizers can saturate the soil to such an extent that trace minerals, which don't dissolve well, are poorly absorbed by the growing wheat, oats, etc. Some good organic sources for gardeners to obtain necessary amounts of cobalt are horse and cattle manure, mineral rocks, yeast, legumes, vetch, peach tree refuse and Kentucky bluegrass.

COPPER

Astrological Ruler

Venus.

Synthetic Forms

Copper sulfate. (Warning: copper salts are irritants and poisons. A physician should be consulted before anyone takes supplements of copper.)

Sources

Vegetables: Kidney beans, navy beans, broccoli, corn, lima beans and mushrooms.

Fruits and Nuts: Dried prunes, dried figs, dried currants, avocados, Brazil nuts, filberts, peanut butter, peanuts, pecans, English walnuts and bitter chocolate.

Meat and Fish: Calves' liver, beef liver, lamb chops and codfish.

Grains: Wheat bran, raw oatmeal, rye flour and whole wheat.

Dairy Products: Unknown.

Herbs: Unknown. But because natural copper is found in almost all plants copper is present in just about any herb.

Natural Supplements: Molasses.

Unit of Potency
Milligram.

History and Characteristics

Copper was first identified in 1816 by Bucholtz and then in 1817 by Meissner, who was examining plants. Sarzeau then found copper in the blood of animals in 1830. It has been found in just about every plant and animal organism, demonstrating its daily importance in our diets.

One of copper's many diverse functions is to help in forming hemoglobin and red blood cells. With adequate amounts of copper iron is easily absorbed, but one mineral without the other is eventually going to produce anemia.

The myelin sheaths that enclose nerve fibers are also dependent upon copper to maintain their strength. The trace mineral is responsible for helping to break down or rebuild body tissue, synthesize phospholipids (fats) and oxidize vitamin C so that the vitamin can form elastin (a component that keeps muscles, veins and arteries elastic and flexible). It also helps form RNA. Furthermore, copper is essential for good bone formation.

Scientists became acutely aware of the roles copper plays when sheep and cattle grazing on grass deficient in copper developed anemia and osteoporosis. Further examination showed degeneration of the motor tracts of the spinal cord, a disease resembling multiple sclerosis in humans. Ewes deficient in copper to begin with gave birth to lambs that developed uncoordinated gaits, a condition known as enzootic ataxia (swayback). Abnormalities in the pigmentation of their hair and wool fibers also occurred. On the other hand, ewes given supplements of copper before birthing produced strong, healthy offspring. Scientists have also found that severe deprivation of copper in cattle produces fibrosis of the myocardium (middle layers of the wall of the heart) and what is known as "falling disease," where a cow suddenly drops dead.

Ingested copper, loosely bound to serum albumin, is stored in the liver, bone marrow and organs, later to be incorporated into copper proteins. The liver contains the highest concentrations of the trace mineral, with the kidneys, heart, brain, bones and muscles containing less.

Since copper is absorbed in the presence of acid, it is believed to begin its work in the stomach and the upper intestinal tract. Within 15 minutes it is in the bloodstream. Bile from the gallbladder is found to be the major pathway for the excretion of copper. Most of it is excreted in the feces, whereas a small percentage is passed through the urine.

Allies: Copper is most effective when taken with iron, cobalt and zinc.

Antagonists: Molybdenum is considered an antagonist of copper. When molybdenum plus sulfate is ingested, the availability of copper halts, tissue utilization is blocked, and copper is excreted. Some sources feel that molybdenum or copper sulfate alone will not create the antagonism, but taken together they will interfere with the natural sources of copper within the body. These same sources feel that a higher intake of manganese may reduce a loss of copper if both molybdenum and sulfate are taken.

There may also be an antagonistic relationship between zinc and copper. Tests in animals have shown that an increase of dietary zinc will suppress the liver copper concentrations if the intake of copper is marginal. More research needs to be undertaken to prove or disprove this hypothesis.

Dosages

Recommended Dietary Allowance: The National Research Council has stated that one to two milligrams of copper per day is safe for adults. It's also felt that most adults ingest approximately 2.5 to 5 milligrams daily in our diets.

Therapeutic Dose: Two to five or more milligrams are recommended. But scientists and doctors generally agree that supplements of copper should be used very sparingly, since immoderate doses of sulfate can be poisonous.

Megadose: Five milligrams or more are recommended.

Toxicity

The toxicity level of copper has not been established. Toxicity is rare, since only 30 per cent of copper is ingested and the rest is excreted in the feces.

If toxicity should occur, though, through natural intake of copper from plant and animal food, Wilson's disease will occur. This rare and genetic disorder comes about because the copper metabolism is out of balance, and excessive amounts of the trace mineral will be retained in the liver, brain, kidneys and corneas of the eyes. There is no explanation for the tremendous increase of copper absorption accompanying the disease: there may be a genetic abnormality in the protein metabolism, leading to the formation of proteins with high avidity for copper. The disease, which usually strikes adolescents, results in symptoms such as muscle trembling and twitching. And the individual may become highly emotional.

Copper sulfate poisoning can also occur if from 50 to 500 milligrams of copper sulfate are ingested. There can be pain in the mouth, esophagus and stomach, as well as diarrhea with abdominal pain. A metallic taste in the mouth may occur with accompanying convulsions, shock, paralysis, coma and eventually death. If a person survives, there will be widespread capillary, kidney and liver damage. For these reasons a person should consult a physician before taking any synthetic copper derivative.

Deficiency Symptoms

Although a deficiency of copper is rare, infants who are anemic will sometimes display low blood copper levels. Dysproteinemia, an ailment affecting babies, is characterized by edema, low protein, iron and copper levels plus anemia. It can be corrected through administration of iron and copper.

Low serum copper levels are also observed in kwashiorkor, sprue, celiac disease and hypoproteinemia (decrease of protein in the blood).

With insufficient copper bodily weakness may be evident in general, skin sores may erupt, or breathing may become labored or impaired.

Recent Clinical Developments

Tests conducted on humans have shown that serum copper levels are low in patients who have atherosclerosis or aneurysms. Aneurysms, usually deadly, occur suddenly and with little warning. When the walls of arteries or veins become inflexible, creating pockets and thereby becoming thinner, they begin to balloon in and out with the flow of blood. If the blood pressure is heightened, the thin walls may explode, spewing blood into the chest or abdominal cavity—the process known as an aneurysm. The aorta valve leading to the heart is an especially sensitive area for aneurysms if there is a copper enzyme deficiency. Copper administered in conjunction with vitamin C helps insure the continued elasticity of the walls of the veins and arteries so that such aneurysms will not occur.

Too little copper can also lead to osteoporosis. It has been discovered that if organ meats naturally high in copper are substituted for muscle meats in the diet such bone problems can be corrected.

Tests conducted on animals indicate that increasing the natural copper intake retards the development of cancer and lessens the chances of liver damage, too.

Although natural copper is needed; copper tubing, bowls and utensils can possibly induce copper poisoning or destroy vitamin C on contact. Thus, when a salad is tossed in a copper bowl, its vitamin C content is destroyed upon contact. Paring knives whose coatings have been worn away, exposing the copper, can also rob fruits and vegetables of this valuable vitamin. In addition, milk that is being pasteurized may be contaminated when run through copper tubing or transported in copper containers.

And beer distilled in copper containers may prove a source of chronic copper poisoning.

FLUORINE

Astrological Ruler

Saturn.

Synthetic Forms

Sodium fluoride.

Sources

Vegetables: Cauliflower, sauerkraut, Chinese cabbage, red cabbage, green cabbage, onions, beets, endive, parsley sprouts and watercress.

Fruits and Nuts: Avocados, elderberries, juniper berries and horse chestnuts.

Meat and Fish: Kidneys.

Grains: Whole wheat and oats.

Dairy Products: Goat's cheese, egg yolks, milk and roquefort cheese.

Herbs: Garlic, chamomile, caraway, parsley, wormwood, periwinkle and licorice.

Natural Supplements: Naturally hard water and calcium fluoride.

Unit of Potency

Milligram. But when added to drinking water, fluorine is discussed in terms of so many parts per million (ppm).

History and Characteristics

Up until recently fluorine was not considered an essential trace mineral but rather an inorganic element within the bone structure found in mineral portion. Found in the body in several forms, it is often referred to as *fluorides*. There are two types — calcium fluoride, a natural substance, and sodium fluoride, a synthetic variety added to the drinking supply of cities in America.

Fluorine is associated with the protection of teeth against cavities. It reduces the acid in the mouth that takes place when carbohydrate foods are eaten, and it may stop the decay of the tooth enamel in the process. It also appears that fluorine, working with calcium, strengthens the bones of the body. But for years there has been a dispute about fluorine's true effectiveness versus the potential toxic damage that can take place when sodium fluoride is consumed in too large amounts: if ingested in quantity, sodium fluoride is almost as deadly as cyanide of mercury poisoning.

Fluoride comes from three major sources — water, organic foods and dust found in industrial exposures. Once in the gastrointestinal tract, it enters the bloodstream and is rapidly distributed through the extracellular fluids of all the organs and tissue. The kidneys and hard tissue (bones, teeth, etc) have a higher incidence of fluoride than the blood levels. Excessive fluoride is excreted via the urinary tract, with minimal amounts found in the feces. The heart, liver, lungs, kidneys and spleen contain a few tenths of one ppm of the mineral.

Allies: Unknown.
Antagonists: Unknown.

Dosages

Recommended Dietary Allowance: None has been established. An average intake is considered 0.25 to 0.35 milligrams.

Therapeutic Dose: None has been established.

Megadose: An average adult may ingest 1 to 1.5 milligrams of fluorine from the water.

Toxicity

From two to eight milligrams of fluorine will cause fluorosis (tooth enamel discoloration): this disorder occurs in areas where the amount of fluoride placed in the drinking water is not controlled. With from eight to twenty ppm of fluoride, osteosclerosis (hardening of the bones with increased heaviness) will become a hazard. Crippling fluorosis is characterized by calcification of the muscle ligaments and uncontrolled new bone growth, usually to the long, flat bones of the body. Poisoning can occur at 500 ppm, or 2,500 times the recommended level.

Deficiency Symptoms

Generally speaking, adult Americans are not deficient in fluorine. If anything, we may be ingesting too much fluorine because of the amounts placed in city water supplies. However, a person who is deficient will have poor tooth development and subsequent decay.

Recent Clinical Developments

The controversy surrounding fluorine continues, with proponents from both sides issuing confusing test results; however, what seems clear is that children who are in the process of developing their permanent teeth do need fluoride—not adults. Unfortunately, though, fluoridated water is drunk by all. A simple measure that could insure that a child receives the necessary fluoride without endangering adults would be to take the fluoride out of the water and instead give the child one cup of tea daily: tea contains a sufficient supply of natural, inorganic fluoride to give teeth the best possible protection.

Too much fluoride may harm unborn children as well as adults. Fluorine crosses the placenta via the bloodstream of the unborn child, and some scientists theorize that excess fluoridation in the water may damage the fetus. Dr. Ionel Rapaport of the University of Wisconsin has studied the question of fluoridation and higher incidence of mongolism: he found a relationship between concentrations of fluorine in the water in four states and higher frequency of mongolism than average.

One of the questions in the fluoride controversy is, "Can fluoride excretion cause injury or disease in the kidneys?" In one test on rats kidney tubules were damaged and renal injury was incurred; however, in a later test another scientist cited that the rats at that particular age normally contracted ailments. The accepted theory now is that fluoride does not induce kidney damage when consumed in large amounts. More study is obviously necessary to clear up this matter.

Flurocitrate (a type of citrate acid formed in the body) inhibits the enzyme aconitase. Once the blockage of the citrate takes place, the metabolic cycle concerned with protein synthesis and lipid metabolsim is halted. Death will follow if the situation is allowed to continue.

A person who has too much fluorine in the bloodstream may take vitamin C and calcium to negate the poisonous effects and wash the fluorine out of the body.

IODINE

Astrological Ruler
The Sun.

Synthetic Forms
Potassium oxide.

Sources
Vegetables: Chard, watercress, artichokes, asparagus, broccoli, brussel sprouts, green peppers, kale, lettuce, leeks, mushrooms, onions, potato skins, red cabbage, spinach, savoy cabbage and tomatoes.

Fruits and Nuts: Avocados, apples, Bartlett pears, blueberries, oranges, strawberries and sunflower seeds.

Meat and Fish: Lobster, clams, oysters, shrimp, bluefish, mackerel, haddock, cod, halibut, scallops, salmon and to a lesser extent most other sea foods.

Grains: Unknown.

Herbs: Bladderwrack, Iceland moss and carrageen (Irish moss).

Natural Supplements: Kelp, seaweed, dulse, sea salt and agar.

Unit of Potency
Milligram or microgram.

History and Characteristics

Iodine was discovered during the Napoleonic Wars by Bernard Courtois. Francois Coidet, a Swiss doctor, later researched iodine's marvelous properties and recommended it as a remedy for goiter (a condition wherein the thyroid enlarges from lack of iodine). Once a problem for the northern and midwestern sections of America, where the people did not eat enough fish to get a natural source of iodine, goiter is now an ailment of the past because iodine was placed in salt.

Although a trace mineral, iodine is of vast and long-range importance to the basic metabolism of human beings. Its most important role is to insure proper functioning of the thyroid gland, located at the base of the throat. Once in the thyroid with the aid of the amino acid tyrosine, iodine helps produce thyroxine.

Through its work in the thyroid iodine helps determine how a person's energy is burned: if it's burned too slowly, a person can feel lethargic, dull and lifeless; if burned too quickly, a person can feel brittle, nervous and edgy. Because the soils of America's farmlands are now leached and demineralized after 200 years of intensive use, iodine is deficient, and many Americans, eating too many processed foods, suffer from hypothyroidism.

Iodine also keeps hair, skin, nails and teeth in proper health. Furthermore, mental quickness, agility and speech are aided by this trace mineral. And iodine keeps the arteries elastic, controlling the amount of cholesterol in the body and keeping newborn infants from the possible retardation ailment known as cretenism. Finally, with atomic fallout being a constant threat today natural iodine protects us from radioactive iodine 131, which may be related to lumps forming on the thyroid.

Iodine is mostly absorbed in the gastrointestinal tract, although a small amount is absorbed in the stomach. Absorbed as iodide, it moves into the bloodstream as free iodine and iodate. About 30 per cent is trapped by the thyroid, while the rest diffuses into the extracellular fluid and red blood cells. The major sites of iodine concentration are the thyroid and kidneys. Other areas are the salivary glands, stomach, small intestine, skin and hair.

Loss of iodine takes place through the kidneys and urine. Even when there is a serious deficiency of iodine, the kidneys will continue to excrete it. The trace mineral can also be lost through sweating, especially in the summertime, when temperatures will induce sweating with very little physical activity.

Allies: Vitamins E and C. Vitamin E seems especially important because, if scarred, the thyroid will become hypofunctioning or brittle. The thyroid appears to have a better chance of reactivating itself if the diet is high in natural iodine and vitamin E.

Antagonists: Unknown.

Dosages

Recommended Dietary Allowance: None has been established by the FDA. Moreover, the FDA has ruled that no daily supplement may contain more than 0.15 milligrams of the trace mineral. The National Research Council feels the following daily intake is sufficient:

Men 130 mcg.
Women 100 mcg.
Pregnant Women 125 mcg.
Lactating Women 150 mcg.

Therapeutic Dose: Adelle Davis reports that thyroid abnormalities in Japan are nonexistent because of their generous daily intakes of iodine from seaweeds and fish: they consume approximately three milligrams of iodine daily. To try to get that much from iodized salt is a big mistake, since salt in immoderate proportions causes high blood pressure and kidney damage, among other disorders. We can get that much from kelp tablets, but Davis feels that kelp tablets can be of benefit only if the label is disregarded and a person consumes 15 to 25 tablets each day.

Megadose: Certain patients, including children, have been given 2,400 milligrams of natural, organic iodine (not a synthetic variety) daily for up to five years without symptoms of toxicity; however, even natural iodine may be toxic at some point, and a physician's help is recommended in monitoring any administration of megadoses.

Toxicity

Although the toxicity level is unknown at this time, iodine prepared as a drug or medicine must be prescribed and monitored closely by a doctor to avoid poisoning. Sudden overdose may halt synthesis of thyroxine in the thyroid. Symptoms of iodine poisoning are a burning pain in the mouth, throat and stomach, thirst, vomiting, bloody diarrhea, painful and interrupted urination and eventually death from circulatory collapse.

Deficiency Symptoms

Most deficiencies of iodine are related to the thyroid gland. A sluggish thyroid is called hypothyroidism. With this condition the extremities are cold, and a person feels dragged out, dull, listless and fatigued for no reason. Other symptoms are dull pains beneath both shoulder blades, enlarged glands around the lower neck area and sides of the neck, dull headaches, little interest in living, slow thinking, slow movements, a puffy face or other parts of the body, a pulse alternating from very slow to racing, swelling of fingers and toes, a dislike for moisture in general, an inability to lose weight and overweight.

In its more severe form hypothyroidism is called cretinism. A baby will become mentally and physically retarded within its first year of life if cretinism is not discovered and promptly corrected. The disease takes two forms: either the mother was originally deficient in iodine, a deficiency transported to the placenta, or the infant's own thyroid is sluggish. Hospitals in Canada now routinely take blood samples from newborn infants to see if their thyroids are hypofunctioning: if they are, measures are taken to insure that they will begin to function normally. Unfortunately, very few hospitals in the United States take this blood test, and cretinism is a far greater risk here. With the American diet it's advisable for a pregnant woman to take kelp supplements to insure her child's healthy start in life. In addition, the child should undergo the blood test within the first ten days of life.

Hyperthyroidism (a condition caused by excessive hormonal secretion of the thyroid), on the other hand, increases the basal metabolism. As the disease occurs, a person may feel more and more irritable, nervous and jumpy. He or she will constantly eat more but seem unable to gain weight, will be unable to relax, will tremble or shake and have increased perspiration. Other symptoms are a racing heart and palpitations that feel like a heart attack coming on. Heat or extra clothing may cause a feeling of intolerable warmth. A higher supply of iodine is needed to calm down the endocrine gland and bring the basal metabolism back to a normal state.

A deficiency of iodine has also been linked with polio. Since iodine is lost through perspiration, the mineral is at its lowest in the summer, and polio has been known to strike most frequently in hot weather.

Finally, insufficient iodine may cause atherosclerosis, since iodine helps control the amount of cholesterol in the body and, if the mineral is lacking, lipids and plaque collect in the arteries.

Recent Clinical Developments

It is very important for a pregnant woman to get sufficient iodine in her diet. As I've indicated, sufficient iodine will help the unborn infant start with a healthy thyroid. In addition, the iodine will help the mother's own thyroid to control her weight both during and after the pregnancy. If deficient in iodine after the birth, the mother may not be able to lose weight and may suffer severe depression (postpartum blues) because her thyroid is hypofunctioning. Any woman who suffers these symptoms after birth

should get a T-3, T-4, T-7 test and talk to her doctor about supplementing her diet with kelp or other sources of iodine (*not* iodized salt).

With a deficiency of iodine the thyroid may hemorrhage quickly and literally float in a sea of blood. Scar tissue then forms and the gland begins to behave erratically, throwing the body's metabolism out of balance.

Foods such as peanuts, untoasted soy flour and members of the cabbage family can stop absorption of iodine. Anyone who eats many of the above foods needs an adequate increase of iodine in order not to rob the thyroid of its share of iodine.

In addition, when vitamin E is deficient in the body, the absorption of iodine into the thyroid decreases by five per cent of normal. To compensate for this lack, the gland will become overactive. Adelle Davis recommends 500 milligrams of vitamin E daily to help the thyroid absorb twice as much iodine. She also notes that people with toxic thyroid conditions are helped by taking four to six milligrams of iodine on a daily basis.

IRON

Astrological Ruler
Mars.

Synthetic Forms
Ferrous fumerate, ferrous gluconate and ferrous sulfate.

Sources
Vegetables: Greens, spinach, beets, alfalfa, dried beans, lentils, broccoli, collards, green peas, leeks, mushrooms, onions, olives, soybeans and watercress.

Fruits and Nuts: Apples, avocados, blackberries, currants, cherries, loganberries, prunes, pears, plums, peaches, strawberries, watermelon, dates, almonds, sunflower seeds, walnuts, sesame seeds and carob.

Meat and Fish: Liver, beef, kidney, chicken and lamb.

Grains: Whole grains and brown rice.

Dairy Products: Egg yolks.

Herbs: Curled or yellow dock (*Rumex crispus*, containing 40 per cent natural iron, the highest amount of all herbs), devil's bit, *Hydrocotyle asiatica*, meadow sweet, mullein leaves, parsley, rest harrow, jalap, silverweed, stinging nettle, strawberry leaves and toad flax.

Natural Supplements: Kelp, dulse, molasses, yeast and desiccated liver.

Unit of Potency
Milligram.

History and Characteristics

Iron is one of the most important minerals in the body. Found in the red blood cells, its primary function is to unite copper with protein to make hemoglobin (the red coloring of the cells). It also helps make mygolobin (a globulin found in the muscle tissue), which transports oxygen to the muscles so that they have the capacity to contract. And, extremely important to the protein process, iron works with enzymes and other nutrients to improve oxygenation throughout all the bodily processes.

Iron is also one of the least assimilable minerals: difficult to absorb, difficult to keep and easy to lose. To be assimilated to any degree at all (usually ten per cent or less), iron must form up in complex compounds with copper, folic acid, vitamin B-6 and vitamin C: a person deficient in any one of these vitamins or minerals stands a chance of poor absorption of iron. In addition, there needs to be sufficient vitamin E and a proper balance between iron and calcium and phosphorus to insure assimilation. Absorption of iron is also minimal when a person has little hydrochloric acid available in the stomach during the digestive processes. Poor intestinal peristalsis contributes to poor absorption of iron, too. And a person who drinks coffee or tea, high in alkali, will short circuit absorption of iron. Then, if conditions aren't just right, the iron will be excreted through the feces. It is also lost through perspiration, excretion of bile, sloughed-off skin cells, mucous membranes and white blood cells.

The most easily assimilable forms of iron are natural sources such as brewer's yeast, desiccated liver tablets and molasses. In fact, it is not advisable to take any of the synthetic varieties of iron, at least not without the guidance of a physician: all synthetic varieties are toxic if taken in excess. As few as 900 milligrams of ferrous sulfate can kill a child, and deaths of children who eat these little red pills that resemble candy are recorded annually. Ferrous sulfate is also an antagonist of vitamin E.

If a person must take a synthetic iron supplement, ferrous iron is much more efficiently absorbed than the ferric variety, even though scientists have proven that ascorbic acid (synthetic vitamin C) given along with ferric iron improves absorption tremendously, an effect not achieved with the ferrous variety. Adelle Davis feels that ferrous gluconate (an iron and glucose compound) is the least toxic of the ferrous synthetics presently sold over-the-counter or through prescription.

Because of the various difficulties with the absorption of iron, deficiencies of iron are quite common, and deficiencies over long periods can lead to anemia, which leaves a person worn, fatigued and without energy. Since women tend toward deficiencies of iron on a monthly basis during their menstrual cycles, they are the most prone to anemia: it is estimated that six to ten million women between the ages of 18 and 59 may have anemia or a tendency toward anemia.

Iron is absorbed in the duodenum of the upper intestinal tract, or it is absorbed directly into the bloodstream rather than by way of the lymphatic system. It is then stored intracellularly in the liver, spleen and bone marrow as ferritin and hemosiderin, with most of the iron found in hemoglobin. Iron is so precious that once it is assimilated by the body it is never destroyed: it simply leaves dead cells and moves on to help make new ones.

Allies: Iron's primary allies are vitamin B-6, folic acid and copper. It is also more effective when taken with vitamin B-12, vitamin C, calcium, cobalt, phosphorus and hydrochloric acid. Vitamin E is also an ally of chelated iron.

Antagonists: If vitamin E is taken either with ferrous sulfate or ferrous gluconate, it becomes an antagonist, more or less cancelling out iron's chemical actions and vice versa. Anyone who takes a synthetic variety of iron should wait 10 to 12 hours before taking vitamin E.

A diet high in phytates (grain-type products) or phosphates will interfere with iron absorption, too. Those radicals form highly insoluble salts with iron that are impossible to absorb via the intestinal tract. On the other hand, a diet low in phosphates will increase assimilation of iron.

In addition, arthritic victims who are on regular steroid, chloroquine or aspirin medication run the risk of lost absorption of iron. They should periodically test their hemoglobin counts. Bolstering their diets with natural sources of iron will also insure that their bodies do not become depleted of the mineral, causing anemia.

Dosages

Recommended Dietary Allowance: The National Research Council feels that 18 milligrams of iron for women and 10 milligrams for men are necessary on a daily basis; however, because of the demands on iron brought about by menstrual cycles, pregnancy and lactation, most women between the ages of 18 and 59 should consider higher dosages. Women have less iron in their bodies to begin with. Moreover, they lose up to two milligrams daily during their monthly cycles—a loss two to four times greater than the needed daily intake of average men, who get by quite well with 0.5 to 1 milligram of iron daily. Then during the third trimester of pregnancy women need up to 7.5 milligrams of iron daily. And women who breast-feed lose between 0.5 and 1 milligram of iron daily.

Babies' needs are even more dramatic than women's. In the first 25 months of life infants will grow faster than at any other time. Physicians recommend weaning babies before age one to get them on iron-plentiful food so that their voracious needs for iron can be fulfilled.

Therapeutic Dose: Twenty to one hundred milligrams daily are recommended. Because of the numerous inherent dangers of synthetic iron, any administration of synthetic iron, especially ferrous sulfate, the most common type of synthetic iron prescribed by doctors, should be carefully monitored, especially with children.

Megadose: Any dosage of 100 or more milligrams of synthetic iron a day is considered large. Over a prolonged period of time such a dosage can be toxic to some individuals, and physician should periodically check for toxic reactions.

Toxicity

The toxicity level for children is approximately 900 milligrams. The level varies for adults. Anyone having symptoms of toxicity should see a doctor at once. The normal signals are heartburn, nausea, constipation, diarrhea and other digestive upsets. If the condition is left untreated, damage can occur in the liver and pancreas.

Hemosiderosis (a kind of iron poisoning) usually occurs when too little vitamin B-6 is ingested or too many synthetic iron pills are taken without proper safeguards. With hemosiderosis excess iron is usually stored in the liver or spleen, causing scar formation, and the organs readily become calcified. The condition usually takes place when there is a marked red blood cell destruction through hemolytic or pernicious anemia or in cases of chronic infection.

Deficiency Symptoms

Exhaustion, depression, general fatigue or lassitude, shortness of breath, pallor of the skin, loss of interest in sex and dizziness are the usual symptoms of an oncoming deficiency of iron. There may also be a stinging sensation in the head, the heels, the bottom of the feet, the fingertips or the shoulder joints. Flattened fingernails, a fissured (rutted) tongue, insomnia at night and sleepiness during the day are some of the symptoms of a moderate deficiency. Other little recognized symptoms of a possible deficiency are crying for no reason, painful breathing and poor hearing.

With a lack of iron anemia will eventually result, detectable through a hemoglobin count. By that time a great amount of damage, sometimes irreversible, will have been done, depending upon the type of anemia that has manifested. Hypochromic anemia is the normal kind induced by a deficiency of iron. But hemorrhagic anemia, which points to internal bleeding, may also occur, going undetected for some time except that bruises may appear for no reason or there may be tenderness or swelling that cannot be accounted for: people who give blood too often can sometimes contract this type of anemia.

Recent Clinical Developments

People who are deficient in iron tend to absorb iron more efficiently from natural sources than do other people. And children assimilate natural iron somewhat better than do adults. While discovering these patterns, scientists found that ferric iron in eggs is strongly complex, making it hard for the body to break down for utilization. But children younger than three years old are able to absorb the iron from eggs better than do older people.

There has been a running battle among health experts about whether or not excess mucus coating the walls of the intestinal tract hinders absorption of iron. Although some test results indicate that there is a connection and other test results do not, there seems to be a general feeling that iron cannot be assimilated when there is excess mucus in the gastrointestinal tract.

Adelle Davis cites a simple test to determine if a person is anemic—eating beets. The red color will appear in the urine if the individual has anemia associated with a deficiency of iron.

Contracting anemia in its chronic stage can put an excessive strain on the heart. In one study changes were recorded in electrocardiograms in 20 per cent of the cases, and in general the doctors conducting the tests felt that the heart was affected to some degree in all cases, with the worst results being the enlargement of the muscles of the heart or abnormalities associated with the heart's rhythm.

Many sources feel that babies should be weaned off milk much sooner than is normally accepted because a quart of milk contains only 1.5 milligrams of iron. These doctors feel that at the age of six months babies should begin eating solid food higher in iron. It's also been proven that mothers who have good levels of iron give their infants healthier beginnings.

Vitamin E and iron have a sensitive relationship with each other. Natural iron and vitamin E work together as a magnificent team. But if the iron is of a synthetic variety the two nutrients are antagonists.

Pregnant women who experience muscular weakness can often blame the weakness on a vitamin E deficiency that can be induced by taking synthetic supplements of iron. Such a condition can make delivery difficult because of weak contractions.

Pancreatitis (inflammation of the organ that secretes insulin and digestive enzymes) is an ailment that will frequently result in the storage of large amounts of iron within the pancreas, a condition said to be caused by a deficiency of vitamin B-6. When a person receives enough vitamin B-6, the iron is released so that it can go about its normal duties within the body.

Constipation may also be indirectly associated with an iron problem. If the gallbladder is not putting out enough bile to break down the undigested fat, the fat can combine with calcium or iron to form insoluble soaps. This compound then forms with fecal matter to create stools that bring about constipation.

Anyone who has weak or very sensitive kidneys should be cautious about taking any kind of synthetic or inorganic iron supplements, which are said to irritate these organs.

MAGNESIUM

Astrological Ruler
The Sun.

Synthetic Forms
Magnesium citrate (a laxative), magnesium sulfate (a laxative), magnesium hydroxide (milk of magnesia), magnesium palmitate, magnesium oxide, magnesium gluconate and magnesium phosphate.

Sources
Vegetables: Asparagus, beet greens, beets, corn, cabbage, cauliflower, cucumbers, dandelion greens, kale, kohlrabi, lettuce, radishes, spinach, savoy cabbage, soybeans, okra, watercress and most leafy, green vegetables.

Fruits and Nuts: Apples, cherries, figs, gooseberries, grapes, lemons, limes, persimmons, plums, pomegranates, peaches, pears, most nuts and seeds and carob.

Meat and Fish: Kidneys.

Grains: Oats, buckwheat and raw wheat germ.

Dairy Products: Unknown.

Herbs: Bladderwrack, black willow bark, broom tops, carrot leaves, devil's bit, dandelion herb, *Hydrocotyle asiatica*, meadow sweet, mistletoe (poisonous), mullein leaves, parsley, peppermint, primrose, rest harrow, silverweed, skunk cabbage (poisonous), toad flax, walnut leaves and wintergreen.

Natural Supplements: Kelp, dulse and yeast.

Unit of Potency
Milligram.

History and Characteristics
In the sixteenth century Henry Wicker, a cow farmer, discovered a magnesium salts spring during a drought. He brought the cows down to drink from the spring well, but the animals refused to drink the water, much to his consternation. This bitter tasting water was believed to have therapeutic aspects, and in 1645 Lord Dudley North wrote a paper concerning the healthful features of the water. Soon Farmer Wicker's spring became a center for the rich and affluent to become healthy. Today that same bitter water is known as epsom salt, used externally to treat sprains and strains or to reduce swelling.

Magnesium was isolated in 1859 by Holmes. Further research showed that the mineral was an absolute necessity to plants. It is found in just about every type of food plant, with green vegetables especially high in concentrations of magnesium. About 40 years ago the mineral was found to have equal importance in animals, being essential to all animal growth, including that of humans.

One of the essential minerals, accounting for almost one ounce of the body's total weight, magnesium is of vital importance to the balance of calcium and phosphorus. The relationship between the three minerals is very delicate. If a person low in phosphorus takes supplements of magnesium, the magnesium will interfere with the body's use of calcium, inducing a deficiency of calcium. Adelle Davis states that any intake of magnesium should be ½ the intake of calcium, thereby avoiding any possible metabolic imbalances.

Magnesium works as a team with calcium in the regulation of the heartbeat. As calcium is absorbed by actin (one of the proteins in the muscle fiber) around the heart, the muscle contracts. Magnesium then provides a positive charge, pulling the calcium out of the actin, thereby creating another contraction. And so the heart continues to pulse with life. Too little magnesium may mean that the heart palpitates or skips beats. Magnesium is also partly responsible for strong teeth and bones, providing it and calcium are in sufficient levels in the body.

Magnesium is essential to the proper functioning of the central nervous system as well. It helps to carry nerve messages to and from the brain to the muscles. Thus magnesium is responsible for making our legs and arms do what we ask of them instead of twitching, cramping or behaving in a sluggish fashion.

Magnesium also helps regulate the flow of

Of crucial importance, nutritionists are discovering, is the *balanced* proportions of one mineral to another. For instance, according to one leading laboratory (see below), the human body tends to thrive best with 2,000 times as much zinc as cadmium, whereas the recommended calcium-to-phosphorus ratio is only 3-to-1.

In taking any mineral as a supplement, attention should be given to the intake of other minerals to insure that all are kept in proper balance. The "mineral wheel" at right shows by arrows which minerals, when excessively present, are antagonistic to others. For instance, calcium, copper, manganese, magnesium and zinc in large doses are antagonistic to iron (even though copper, for example, enhances iron absorption when present in proper proportion).

Minerals Need to be Balanced

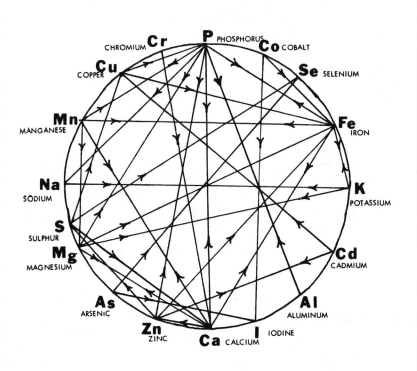

Recommended Mineral Proportions

Calcium : Lead	200 : 1
Calcium : Magnesium	8 : 1
Calcium : Phosphorus	3 : 1
Iron : Copper	1½ : 1
Phosphorus : Aluminum	230 : 1
Selenium : Mercury	45 : 1
Sodium : Potassium	2 : 1
Zinc : Cadmium	2000 : 1
Zinc : Copper	8½ : 1
Zinc : Lead	100 : 1
Zinc : Manganese	36 : 1
Zinc : Selenium	44 : 1

energy within the body. When magnesium is missing from cells an organelle called mitochondria, important for cells to receive energy, cannot function properly: no mitochondria means no energy.

The mineral is a natural analgesic, too. Doctors have found that injections of magnesium act as depressants, calming the nerves and even inducing sleep when given in sufficient quantity, although a person deficient in the mineral will probably feel a boost in energy when he or she takes supplements because the body is getting sufficient amounts to do its job. Without sufficient magnesium trembling hands and muscles and highly sensitized nerves will develop, symptoms too often treated with tranquilizers to "calm the jitters."

In addition, the endocrine system cannot work efficiently without magnesium. The mineral is a watch dog to the endocrine system, insuring that the glands and hormones do not get carried away. It countermands, quiets and picks up the reins of bodily energy, keeping a firm hold on all controls to insure maximum use of energy without wasted action. It is especially important to the pituitary gland, the master control that orders all other hormones to do their jobs properly. Moreover, without enough of the mineral the adrenal glands jump into action and over-produce adrenaline increasing heart rate and glucose production from the liver and producing hyperactivity.

Magnesium also helps maintain a healthy balance between alkaline and acid in the body. Many people suffer from acidosis, which directly affects the metabolism and can make people very nervous: people who wear jewelry that frequently turns black or green where it comes in contact with the skin are suspect of having too much acid in their bodies; heavy meat eaters can also incur acidosis, since meat is a product high in acid.

Furthermore, magnesium is a catalyst in the utilization of carbohydrates, lipids and protein. It also acts as a kind of bodily thermostat, controlling temperatures: without enough of the mineral a person may become chilled.

Because farmers may lime their soils and use chemical fertilizers that contain potassium, plants are unable to absorb the magnesium, and we are getting less and less of the mineral. High-protein diets can also create severe deficiencies of magnesium. Since the mineral acts as a coenzyme in building protein, when we deluge our bodies with excessive protein, magnesium cannot do its job. Therefore, anyone on a high-protein diet should eat foods rich in magnesium or take supplements of magnesium.

Several synthetic varieties of magnesium are available:

Magnesium gluconate is felt to work best on

nerve-related problems, including fear, nerve and muscle twitching, restlessness, bed-wetting and apprehension.

Magnesium phosphate is considered best for dealing with cramping of muscles.

Magnesium oxide is best for muscle aches and pains or stiffness in the muscles.

Because of its sedative qualities *magnesium sulfate* is used to treat delirium tremens in association with alcoholism.

For magnesium to be absorbed well, calcium, phosphate and lactose must be available in sufficient quantities. Furthermore, aldosterone (a hormone secreted by the adrenal glands) will help regulate how much magnesium is excreted or kept within the body.

Absorbed via the small intestine, magnesium is shuttled to various parts of the body. The bones contain about half the total body magnesium, whereas somewhat less is kept in the intracellular space of soft tissue. The kidneys, brain and spinal cord also store large amounts of the mineral. It is felt that magnesium in the bones is a reservoir intended to meet the needs of the soft tissue during deficiency. A person lacking in the mineral will have a much higher rate of absorption than one who is not.

Allies: Magnesium's primary ally is calcium. It is also more effective when taken with vitamin B-6, vitamin C, vitamin D, phosphorus and protein.

Antagonists: People, especially adults, who are heavy milk drinkers probably have severe deficiencies of magnesium. Other foods that inhibit absorption of magnesium are those high in phytic acid, such as brown and whole-wheat bread and oatmeal.

Several drugs are antagonists of magnesium. Diuretics as a whole are dangerous enemies of magnesium: most doctors will advise a patient on diuretics to eat sufficient amounts of food containing potassium and neglect to say that the person should also increase the amount of magnesium. Patients who suffer from congestive heart failure and are treated with ammonium chloride and mercurial diuretics will also have deficiencies of magnesium. Similarly, diabetics who go into comatose stages and receive fluids and large doses of insulin will have deficiencies of magnesium. Moreover, an antibiotic known as tetracycline interferes with magnesium in that it disrupts the energy release via the mitochondria, thereby short circuiting a very important part of magnesium's daily duties. And thyroxine, a common thyroid drug handed out by many doctors in this country, as well as testosterone and digitoxin suppresses magnesium activity.

In addition, calciferol (a synthetic variety of vitamin D) and fluorine will bind with magnesium and carry it out of the body before it can be absorbed and used. Anyone who ingests large amounts of calcium carbonate (an antacid preparation) will also suffer a severe magnesium deficiency, which, if continued, can create kidney stones.

The worst enemy of magnesium is X-rays. Tests conducted on male rabbits showed that exposure to the deadly rays decreased the amounts of magnesium in the bodies.

Dosages

Recommended Dietary Allowance:
Infants 0-1/6 yrs. 40 mg. 1/6-1/2 yrs. 60 mg. 1/2-1 yrs. 70 mg.
Children 1-2 yrs. 100 mg. 2-3 yrs. 150 mg. 3-6 yrs. 200 mg. 6-10 yrs. 250 mg.
Men 10-12 yr. 300 mg. 12-14 yrs. 350 mg. 14-22 yrs. 400 mg. 22-75 + yrs. 350 mg.
Women 10-12 yrs. 300 mg. 12-22 yrs. 350 mg. 22-75 + yrs. 300 mg.
Pregnant Women 450 mg.
Lactating Women 450 mg.

Therapuetic Dose: Dr. Paavo Airola recommends up to 700 milligrams of magnesium chloride a day. Another doctor recommends 600 milligrams daily. Another researcher feels that 420 milligrams of magnesium oxide daily is best. Adelle Davis reports that between 600 and 900 milligrams seem to be required to maintain our health in our present-day environment.

Megadose: Seven hundred milligrams are recommended. Since 30,000 milligrams daily may be toxic to some people who have kidney-related ailments, a physician should be consulted before anyone takes magnesium in megadose proportions.

Toxicity

Large amounts of magnesium (30,000 milligrams or more daily) can be harmful, especially if a person is evidencing low calcium and high phosphorus intake. Because excess magnesium is excreted via the kidneys, anyone with weak or diseased kidneys will not be able to get rid of the mineral as quickly as the body might wish, and toxicity can build up. If large amounts of magnesium outbalance the calcium ratio, what seem to be symptoms of a deficiency of calcium will develop: nervousness, muscle spasms, tics, trembling, tremors, etc.

Deficiency Symptoms

One of the most common symptoms is sensitivity to noise. A continual state of grief or depression, coupled with apprehension, may also manifest. Muscles may spasm and jerk, while eyes will have a tendency to wander. There may be a yellowish cast to the white area of the eyeballs, and people may sleep with their eyes half open. Teeth may prove to be extraordinarily sensitive to moderately cool water, or they may ache for no reason. There can be twitches or tremors in any part of the body. And the heart may suddenly race and then settle back into its normal rhythm.

Other less obvious signs of a deficiency of magnesium may be an aching neck and shoulder muscles, an allergy to woolen products, bloating of the intestines, gas, bed-wetting and a burning sensation in the mouth.

Recent Clinical Developments

Various glandular problems can deplete the body of magnesium. For example, hypothyroidism is usually treated with thyroxine (a hormone made from the defatted, desiccated thyroid glands of edible animals, such as sheep). Laboratory tests show that thyroxine interferes with the magnesium metabolism; however, if increased amounts of magnesium are given while a person is on thyroid medication, the problem can be overcome and controlled. With hyperparathyroidism (a condition wherein excess calcium is released from the parathyroid gland) magnesium is excreted through the urinary tract at a much faster rate than normal, hinting that more of the mineral should be ingested to counterbalance the situation. And if the adrenal glands are either hyper- or hypofunctioning, the magnesium balance will be affected. A doctor should be consulted to determine through lab tests the severity of the mineral imbalance from any endocrine disorder.

Too much magnesium available to the body will interfere with two very important agents—acetylcholine and potassium. Since magnesium is the calmant to the body's nerve centers, if too plentiful it can interfere with acetylcholine's job, which is to provide the spark that transmits from one nerve ending to another: the nerve message will be delayed, possibly causing muscular jerkiness, trembling and impaired muscular activity in general. (Acetylcholine may also be interfered with if the amount of calcium is too low rather than the levels of magnesium being too high: lab tests will determine which mineral is responsible.) Potassium and its relationship to the sympathetic nerve ganglion will also be slowed with too much magnesium.

Supplements of magnesium can alleviate some of the problems of pregnancy. Since magnesium stimulates the pituitary gland, especially the posterior site where hormones are released in relation to the uterus, ample magnesium can mean good, strong labor contractions, less of a waiting period for the birth of the infant and a generally easier delivery.

Another problem related to pregnancy, eclampsia (a major toxemia accompanied by high blood pressure, urine retention, convulsions and coma), has been blamed on low levels of magnesium serum. Ample magnesium will act as a sedative, halting convulsions. Furthermore, if the kidneys are weak, the mineral will help the organs process and eliminate urine instead of some urine being absorbed back into the bloodstream to cause general toxemia.

In fact, dosages of magnesium can help with several disorders related to the kidneys. For instance, nephritis (inflammation of the glomeruli, tubules or tissue of the kidneys that halts the flow and excretion of urine) has been successfully treated with administration of magnesium sulfate: a side benefit of the magnesium is that while treating the kidneys it also lowers the blood pressure. Another kidney-related problem, bed-wetting, once thought to be strictly an emotional ailment, may also be caused by a deficiency of magnesium: subjects denied sufficient magnesium under laboratory conditions have incurred bed-wetting. (Urinary problems of a prostate gland origin also respond to treatment with magnesium.)

One of the most important functions of magnesium is that it can discourage stones from gathering in the kidneys. There are different kinds of kidney stones: if they are formed from calcium phosphate, the body has a good supply of vitamin B-6 but insufficient magnesium; if formed from oxalate, magnesium is sufficient but vitamin B-6 is lacking. Both varieties, however, develop from alkalinity within the body: once chemically changed by the body, citric acid can effectively keep the stones in a more soluble state, but if magnesium serum levels are deficient, citric acid cannot be produced and stones form. In experiments patients who had passed stones over a ten-year period were administered 250 milligrams of magnesium oxide daily: while on the supplements none of them passed further stones; when the magnesium was withdrawn from their diets, some began passing stones as soon as six months afterwards.[1]

Sudden infant death is also related to deficiencies of magnesium. Known by most people as "crib death," the fatal disease strikes about 10,000 children, usually boys, in their sleep every year. Doctors have recently taken serum samples of children who died of crib death and found very low levels of magnesium in their bodies: it is felt that deprivation

[1]In cases of severe kidney disease, administration of magnesium should be carefully monitored at all times by a physician. The unavailability of magnesium measurements in the usual clinical setting make regulation of dosage and its effects difficult to determine.

or deficiencies of magnesium at birth may cause the coma-sleep death. Lab tests have also shown that animals have died of deficiencies of magnesium, although the signs of deficiency were much more clearly discernible.

Moreover, tests on alcoholics have shown that the magnesium serum levels in their blood are greatly below normal. The mineral, either injected or taken orally, can help control the delirium tremens (DTs) to a marked degree, giving alcoholics almost complete freedom from them in many cases. Delirium tremens are convulsionlike seizures in which muscles jerk uncontrollably and in spasmodic infrequency. They are accompanied by hallucenogenic nightmares and general mental confusion. A patient will be extremely sensitive to any noise. And he or she may yell incoherently.

Administration of magnesium may also help curb suicidal tendencies. Doctors in Europe have been conducting tests on suicide victims for years and have found that all had low magnesium serum levels in their bodies, pointing to too much adrenaline. When magnesium is lacking, the adrenal glands are not well-controlled and begin overproducing hormones that induce excitement, hypertension, an increase in heart rate and release of glucose. Such rushes of adrenaline induce action—in these cases, suicide.

Since magnesium helps maintain stable mental conditions, it can alleviate hypertension, a common ailment in our country. Because most of us are heavy meat eaters, the high protein can induce severe magnesium deficiencies, producing nervousness and irritability. I am not suggesting everyone become vegetarian. (Many people could not survive without an ample amount of meat each week.) But a change to the white flesh of chicken and sea food plus supplements of magnesium might help.

Babies who feed on powdered formulas of milk may become deficient in magnesium, perhaps even developing epilepsy as a result. Unless the mothers are deficient, babies who are breast-fed do not tend to have such problems. But many mothers today buy their babies' milk: the synthetic vitamin D in the formulas binds up the magnesium. Sooner or later there will be deficiencies of magnesium. Infants may get diarrhea, become restless, cry, have muscle twitching and even have convulsions: one test concluded that nine out of ten childhood epileptics drink milk.

Epilepsy (a recurring attack of disturbed brain function, characterized by motor, sensory or psychic malfunction and perhaps accompanied by convulsions) is generally thought to stem from a hereditary need for either vitamin B-6 or magnesium. In one test 30 epileptic children were given 450 milligrams of

magnesium orally: with the exception of one child all showed marked improvement, and that child responded to a supplementation of vitamin B-6 instead, with the magnesium needed to utilize the vitamin B-6. Another form of epilepsy is brought on by nephritis, which allows magnesium to be lost via the urine.

A certain type of insomnia also responds to magnesium. The insomnia associated with nervousness that leads to tossing and turning all night can be aided with magnesium.

High cholesterol can sometimes be attributed to a lack of magnesium as well. Even though vitamin B-6 may be adequate, too little magnesium available will prevent lecithin from being formed so that it can use the fats and cholesterols that have collected within the body. In one test patients with heart ailments given 500 milligrams of magnesium daily had their blood cholesterol levels fall dramatically within 30 days of beginning the supplementation.

In fact, people who have had heart attacks and severe coronary thrombosis have received second leases on life from magnesium, since with the aid of calcium it helps the pulse remain steady and constant. And high blood pressure is known to drop dramatically when ample amounts of magnesium are given to heart patients.

Diabetes is another disease that can be alleviated with dosages of magnesium in tandem with supplementations of vitamin B-6. Xanthurenic acid can inflict swift and permanent damage on the pancreas if vitamin B-6 is not available in sufficient quantity: magnesium decreases the need for vitamin B-6 and exerts a controlling rein on xanthurenic acid. If enough magnesium is supplied, the vitamin B-6 can be used by the pancreas, and the blood sugar levels won't fluctuate so wildly, causing diabetic-related symptoms. Adelle Davis recommends that diabetics take at least 10 milligrams of vitamin B-6 and 500 milligrams of magnesium daily to short circuit diabetic tendencies.

The temperature of the human body is regulated in part by the amount of magnesium available. Many tests have shown that hibernating animals have extremely high levels of magnesium in their bodies to protect them from the harsh winter temperatures and to allow them to survive comfortably. People who have depleted magnesium stores often get chilled easily.

Fields fertilized by inorganic nitrogen, such as ammonium sulfate, halt the ability of plants to absorb magnesium. Cows that feed on grass fertilized with such compounds contract hypomagnesemia (low magnesium) and eventually have seizures and convulsions and die. Heavy fertilization of the pasturelands with magnesium oxide will prevent this ailment.

MANGANESE

Astrological Ruler
Jupiter.

Synthetic Forms
Manganese gluconate and manganese sulfate.

Sources
Vegetables: Lettuce, beets, cabbage, carrots, onions, potatoes and spinach.
Fruits and Nuts: Bananas, blueberries, grapefruit and sunflower seeds.
Meat and Fish: Liver and kidney.
Grains: Wheat germ, linseed meal and cotton seed meal.
Dairy Products: Eggs and cottage cheese.
Herbs: Peppermint leaves, nasturtium leaves and parsley.
Natural Supplements: Wheat germ.

Unit of Potency
Milligram.

History and Characteristics
In Roman times manganese was recognized as possessing "female" and magnetic properties and was considered important in the creation of glass. One of the peculiarities of this mineral is that when it is missing in the female of any species, including humans, the female will reject her baby. Its magnetic properties are still being explored. Although many laboratory tests with manganese have been performed on animals, few have been conducted on humans. Therefore, information about the mineral is sparse.

Manganese was isolated in the mid-1700's by Schelle. It works with enzymes, helping to synthesize fatty acids and cholesterol. It also takes part in the production of protein, carbohydrates and fat. It works hand-in-hand with thiamine and is instrumental in aiding cholin in insuring proper functioning of the nerves. In addition, manganese is instrumental in keeping hormone levels stable, particularly those dealing with the sex hormones and the pituitary gland. And it is necessary for the proper formation of bones: with insufficient manganese spurs, twisted bones and other deformities will occur.

Although it's very difficult to get a deficiency of manganese, our fertilizers contain none of the trace mineral, and our farmlands are leached of many valuable nutrients, including manganese; therefore, there is the potential for a deficiency, especially for a person who eats a lot of highly refined foods, such as

flour and sugar, where manganese has been removed.

Scientists are still not quite clear about exactly where manganese is absorbed. What is known is that it's poorly absorbed. It is also believed that the mineral makes its way back into the bloodstream from the intestinal tract. The mineral is present in the tissue of the body, especially the reproductive organs. And the bones, liver, pancreas and pituitary gland are felt to have the highest amounts of the mineral. Excess or unabsorbed manganese is excreted with cholin in bile through the feces.

Allies: Manganese's primary allies are thiamine and cholin. It is also more effective when taken with vitamin E, calcium and phosphorus.

Antagonists: Manganese has curious relationships with calcium and phosphorus. If a diet is high in calcium and phosphorus, then there is a need for extra manganese: thus taking calcium supplements without proper intake of manganese is courting a potential deficiency. An overdose of thiamine can also result in a deficiency of manganese.

Dosages
Recommended Dietary Allowance: None has been established. The FDA does not recognize manganese as being an important requirement to the human body. The average diet has about four milligrams of the mineral, and it is estimated that between three and nine milligrams are needed daily by an adult. Some sources suggest five to ten milligrams daily.

Therapeutic Dose: None has been established. But most scientists feel that ten or more milligrams of manganese constitutes the upper limit.

Megadose: Unknown because no tests have been conducted on humans.

Toxicity
Except in the cases of laboratory animals the toxicity level for manganese is unknown. But anyone considering taking ten or more milligrams of the mineral daily should consult a physician to monitor the manganese serum levels in the blood. Manganese is *toxic in overdose.*

Workers who have inhaled manganese dust have manifested a varied assortment of symptoms, such as ataxia (muscular incoordination), loss of strength, loss of appetite, frequent headaches, mental confusion and sometimes criminal acts. They have been known to first sleep constantly and then instead suffer from insomnia. Leukopenia (low white blood cell count) and hypochromic anemia (reduced hemoglobin in the latter stages of manganese poisoning.

In lab tests massive feedings of manganese to

rats have caused negative phosphorus balances and loss of calcium in the feces: as a result, severe rickets developed. In lambs iron absorption was diminished with a high intake of manganese, and in cows tetany (low calcium in the blood and body) developed.

Deficiency Symptoms

One of the strangest and saddest symptoms of a deficiency of manganese is a woman's loss of love for her child after birth. Although she may feel very guilty about her feelings, she may not want to nurse or hold the infant or have anything to do with it. Along with this phenomenon her nipples may become very tender, and she may experience swelling of the lymph glands. She may want to be left completely alone and may suffer crying spells. Moreover, she may be testy, arguing easily.

Some other less noticeable symptoms of a deficiency of manganese are crackling or popping bones as a person gets up to walk or a burning or gripping sensation of the arms or legs. And the eyes may become red and swollen, although the individual has not cried recently.

With a severe deficiency in a child bone growth may be stunted. An outcome of a severe deficiency in an adult may be sterility or impotence.

In addition, one kind of diabetes is being blamed in part on a deficiency of manganese because the mineral plays a very important part in the glucose cycle by helping to remove excess sugar from the blood through either oxidation or storage.

Myasthenia Gravis (a disease that attacks muscle coordination and causes loss of strength) is felt to be related to a deficiency of manganese, too, as is multiple sclerosis (a nerve degeneration disease).

Recent Clinical Developments

As I've indicated, the only tests with manganese have been conducted on animals. One experiment that caused some flurry among the scientific community showed that manganese inhibits iron uptake. The experimenters thought that perhaps iron and manganese share a pathway, but the general consensus since then is that there exist separate pathways for manganese and iron.

The amount of manganese in the body appears to affect cholesterol levels. The mineral has been used to bring levels of cholesterol down in cases of atherosclerosis In another test regarding fat and lipid metabolism manganese was found to increase cholesterol synthesis.

Scientists have found that administrations of estradiol (a steroid produced by the ovary and having estrogenic properties) increase the level of manganese in the blood, whereupon the thyroid gland tends to accumulate the mineral. Scientists have also found that estradiol given in sufficient amounts will depress the basal metabolic rate in a guinea pig. Women taking estrogen-hormone drugs should inquire if estradiol is in the drugs and then note if they have been experiencing hypothyroid symptoms. If hypothyroidism is suspected, the doctor should be informed so that tests can prove out the assumption.

Studies have indicated that two experimental cancers are cured or markedly inhibited by manganese malate. Furthermore, in test tube experiments manganese malate changed the respiration of these cancers from anaerobic (when a cell can exist without free oxygen taken from the body) to aerobic (when a cell needs free oxygen taken from the body to live and grow). By producing this change the mineral killed both types of cancer.

It is also thought that manganese promotes production and development of blood cells in the bone marrow.

And myasthenia gravis may be related to a deficiency of manganese. With the disease nerve endings that rely on cholin and acetic acid (acetylcholine) to transmit messages are defective. If too little manganese is available to help cholin, it is possible that the nerve impulse messages will falter or not reach their intended destinations, causing muscular weakness or incoordination.

MOLYBDENUM

Astrological Ruler
Mars.

Synthetic Forms
Sodium molybdate.

Sources
Vegetables: Legumes.
Fruits and Nuts: Unknown.
Meat and Fish: Ox liver, pig liver, beef liver and kidney.
Grains: Brown rice and cereal grains, such as oats, wheat, millet and buckwheat.
Dairy Products: Cow's milk.
Herbs: Unknown.
Natural Supplements: Yeast and naturally occurring hard water.

Unit of Potency
Parts per million (ppm).

History and Characteristics
Molybdenum, commonly referred to as "Mo," was discovered accidentally when cattle contracted an ailment known as teart from certain pasturelands rich in the trace mineral. Nearly all the research done

thus far on molybdenum has been on animals, mostly cattle, since teart is a continuing problem in some countries.

Although very little is known about molybdenum at this time, it is found in many plants and in some animals. In 1932 Ter Meulen determined molybdenum's concentration in legumes, cereal grains, fruits and vegetables. In industry it is used to harden steel.

Molybdenum is involved with the way two enzymes in our bodies function—xanthine oxidase, concerned with the mobilization of iron from the liver, and aldehyde oxidase, concerned with the oxidation of fats.

Molybdenum is absorbed quite easily in the gastrointestinal tract. It is also readily released through the urine and some from the bile. It is rapidly taken into all tissue, especially the liver, kidneys and bones. And molybdenum increases the absorption and excretion of phosphorus and decreases the accumulation of copper in the liver.

Allies: Unknown.

Antagonists: Molybdenum has an antagonistic relationship with copper. If too much molybdenum is consumed, copper is released and a person could potentially become deficient in the copper. Cattle grazing on grass high in molybdenum have been cured by copper sulfate: with sufficient copper excess molybdenum is excreted in high quantities through the urine.

Molybdenum also has a delicate relationship with zinc. An oversupply of zinc can cause a shortage of copper. But some farmers have believed the copper deficiency resulted from too much molybdenum in the grass.

Dosages

Recommended Dietary Allowance: None has been established.

Therapeutic Dose: Unknown.

Megadose: Unknown.

Toxicity

Some sources feel that five to ten parts per million is a toxic level. Since overdoses of molybdenum have only occurred in animals, we do not know exactly what toxic effects molybdenum has on humans. But cattle have developed scours (diarrhea), their coats have become lackluster, and milk production has dropped considerably. In addition, steers have lost sexual interest, and damage has been noted in the sperm count. Brittleness of bones has been noted in both cattle and sheep when they have been given supplements of molybdenum.

I also feel that too much molybdenum may

cause a deficiency of copper in humans: anyone who suspects such a molybdenum-copper imbalance should consult a physician for tests. Under no circumstances should a person take supplements of molybdenum without specific directions from a doctor, since the trace mineral is known to be toxic.

Deficiency Symptoms

Since no information is available about the effects of molybdenum or the lack of molybdenum on humans at this time, we do not know what deficiency symptoms, if any, occur.

Recent Clinical Developments

One test by the Navy Dental Research Institute indicated that hard water, containing many trace minerals, may be instrumental in preventing cavities. Two of the minerals—molybdenum and strontium—were felt to provide protection against cavities: at least water rich in the minerals produced fewer cavities than are found among the population as a whole.

PHOSPHORUS

Astrological Ruler

Mars.

Synthetic Forms

Calcium phosphate.

Sources

Vegetables: Lima beans, brussel sprouts, chick peas (garbanzos), corn, dandelion greens, lentils, okra, parsnips, peas, soybeans, spinach and watercress.

Fruits and Nuts: Grapes, apples, avocados, cherries, grapefruit, lemons, limes, pumpkin, passion fruit, plums, raisins, almonds, pecans and walnuts.

Meat and Fish: Veal chops, beef liver, lean beef, salmon, halibut and oysters.

Grains: Oatmeal.

Dairy Products: Cheese, egg yolks and milk.

Herbs: Calamus, caraway seeds, chickweed, garlic, licorice root, marigold flowers, meadow sweet flowers, sesame and sorrel.

Natural Supplements: Bone meal.

Unit of Potency

Milligram.

History and Characteristics

Phosphorus is very important to the body. It is found in every cell and in nearly every chemical reaction and is the second most abundant mineral in the body. Since phosphorus is concerned with the skeleton, genetic traits, proper tooth development, functions of the kidneys and the nerves, the body will not grow properly unless enough of the mineral is present. Furthermore, without the help of phosphorus carbohydrates, fats and protein falter in their work of growth, maintenance and general repair of cells for energy. And two vitamins of the B complex—niacin and riboflavin—cannot be digested without the proper amount of phosphorus in the digestive system.

Phosphorus is also the unsung hero of the calcium-phosphorus duo: for every 2.5 parts of calcium there must be 1 part of phosphorus. Any change in the ratio will do damage to the body in some way, usually of a chronic variety. As well as serving in various other functions of the body, these minerals help with nerve transmission: calcium maintains normalized signals in the nervous system, and phosphorus creates a component of an energy enzyme known as ATP.

In addition, phosphorus is necessary for the production of lecithin, a nutrient that keeps us mentally sharp, prevents brain fatigue and benefits all the nerves, some of which are responsible for the normal functions of the heart as it contracts. A nutrient made in the liver, lecithin is a phospholipid concerned with the breaking down of fats and fatty acids. Widely distributed in the tissue and liquids of the body, it has much to do with respiration and the nutrition of the nervous system. The gray matter of the brain, for instance, has 17 per cent lecithin within its tissue.

Phosphorus also plays a part in the acid-alkaline balance in the blood and tissue. Because Americans are generally heavy meat-eaters, and meat is high in acid, many people suffer from acidosis. The right amount of calcium and phosphorus will equalize this imbalance.

Although Adelle Davis believes that Americans generally have too much phosphorus, new evidence is indicating that we do not. Phosphorus is only found in soil and water and is not manufactured in any human or animal body. Water is necessary to break down the nearly insoluble mineral in the soil so that plants may take it up into their root systems. But soils have been depleted over the years, and, if farmers don't continue their efforts to replace the phosphorus (usually through bone meal fertilizer), we can become deficient in this most abundant mineral.

Although there has been some disagreement, most scientists agree that phosphorus is rapidly and easily assimilated in the duodenum and small intestine. More than ½ of the mineral that is digested is absorbed, but only if vitamin D and calcium are available in the right quantities. There must also be enough hydrochloric acid in the stomach during the digestion phase because phosphorus needs an acidic medium to be absorbed.

Excess phosphorus is excreted through the kidneys and urine. Most of the mineral is stored in the bones and teeth along with calcium.

Allies: Phosphorus's primary allies are calcium and vitamin D. Vitamin C is also indispensable to phosphorus: without enough vitamin C, the mineral is depleted from the body. And phosphorus is more effective when taken with vitamins A and F, iron, manganese and protein.

Antagonists: Excess white sugar is probably the biggest threat to the phosphorus balance in the body. One doctor believes that ailments such as arthritis, pyorrhea and tooth decay are brought about by a calcium-phosphorus imbalance from high sugar intake.

Other substances that deplete phosphorus are excessive amounts of iron, aluminum and magnesium. Anti-acid tablets containing aluminum and/or magnesium hydroxide will interfere greatly with the phosphorus balance: anyone buying such over-the-counter products for digestive upset or ulcer conditions should check the labels carefully.

Aspirin, thyroid or cortisone medication and many other drugs will also leave the body deficient in both calcium and phosphorus.

Dosages

Recommended Dietary Allowance:
Infants 0-1/6 yrs. 200 mg., 1/6-½ yrs. 400 mg., ½-1 yrs. 500 mg., 1-2 yrs. 700 mg., 2-6 yrs. 800 mg., 6-8 yrs. 900 mg., 8-10 yrs. 1000 mg.
Men 10-12 yrs 1200 mg., 12-18 yrs. 1400 mg., 18+ 1800 mg.
Women 10-12 yrs. 1,200 mg. 12-18 yrs. 1,300 mg. 18+ yrs. 1,800 mg.
Pregnant Women 2,200+ mg.
Lactating Women 2,300+ mg.

Therapeutic Dose: For adults 1,800 or more milligrams are recommended.

Megadose: Anyone wishing to take megadoses of phosphorus should exercise caution. Any megadoses should be administered under a physician's care, and a proportionate amount of calcium should be ingested to insure that the metabolism will not become imbalanced.

Toxicity

There is no known toxicity with this mineral, but a person taking an excessive amount of phosphorus without a proportionate amount of calcium may begin to exhibit a deficiency of calcium.

Deficiency Symptoms

Without adequate phosphorus, vitamin D and calcium, stunted growth, poor tooth development and bone deformation will develop. And if the calcium-phosphorus metabolism is unbalanced, ailments such as arthritis, rickets, cavities of the teeth and pyorrhea of the gums may manifest.

Some of the less obvious symptoms of a moderate deficiency of phosphorus are loss of appetite, irregular weight gain or loss for no reason, irregular breath and mental or physical fatigue. Vague nervous disorders may also occur, such as being frightened of the next day, dislike of the opposite sex or of a job and fear of the unknown. Moreover, there may be a loss of muscle tone or a numbness of the arms and legs. And a deficiency of phosphorus may also induce repeated attacks of bronchitis or jaundice.

Recent Clinical Developments

As I've indicated, the correct calcium-phosphorus balance in the body is crucial. An upset in the calcium-phosphorus balance either way can produce rickets: vitamin D can help avert or lessen this disease. (Beryllium, a trace mineral toxic to the human body, can also cause a strain of rickets that vitamin D cannot cure or affect.) Phosphorus is also beneficial in preventing osteomalacia (an adult kind of rickets) and osteoporosis. In addition, because phosphorus helps calcium in the ossification to create strong bones, phosphorus speeds up healing of fractures and reduces losses of calcium. And laboratory experiments on rats indicate that a high intake of phosphorus and a low amount of calcium may cause arthritis: the condition was corrected when twice as much calcium was given.

It has also been found that phosphorus is more easily lost when a cell becomes cancerous, hinting perhaps that phosphorus and calcium added to the diet may provide a preventive measure.

Furthermore, breast-feeding places a strain on the phosphorus mobilization, and many mothers may suffer from a mineral imbalance. As milk production decreases, a woman's levels of phosphorus return to normal.

A possible answer for those who need antacid tablets is to use dolomite, which has highly digestible magnesium carbonate, calcium and phosphorus.

Emotional situations, illness or surgery may cause the adrenal glands to release large amounts of cortisone to protect the body. The cortisone then draws minerals from the bones, precipitating the urinary loss of both calcium and phosphorus—a vicious cycle that continues until the stress is relieved or until proper supplementation takes place.

POTASSIUM

Astrological Ruler
The Moon.

Synthetic Forms
Potassium gluconate and potassium chloride.

Sources
Vegetables: Lima beans, endive, soybeans, artichokes, kidney beans, chick peas (garbanzos), dandelion greens, mushrooms, parsnips, potatoes, tomatoes and watercress.

Fruits and Nuts: Dried apricots, avocados, bananas, dried dates, elderberries, grapefruit, oranges, prunes, raisins and raw, unpasteurized apple cider vinegar aged in wood.

Meat and Fish: Calf liver, goose, Canadian bacon, ham chops, beef liver, roast turkey, veal, haddock, halibut, ocean perch, pike, salmon, sardines, shad and tuna.

Grains: Unknown.

Dairy Products: Skim milk, yogurt and evaporated milk.

Herbs: American century, birch bark, borage, calamus, carrageen (Irish moss), carrot leaves, German chamomile flowers, coltsfoot, comfrey, dandelion, eyebright, fennel, mistletoe (poisonous), mullein, nettle leaves, oak bark, parsley, peppermint, plantain leaves, primrose flowers, sanicle, summer savory, walnut leaves, waywort and yarrow.

Natural Supplements: Kelp.

Unit of Potency
Milligram.

History and Characteristics
There is a precarious balance between potassium and sodium within the body: there should always be approximately two parts potassium to one part sodium. Together the two minerals act as a team to regulate water within the body. While potassium does its work from inside the cell structure, sodium works outside the cells. Between the two minerals the osmotic pressure is maintained, approximately equal to the pressure of the circulating blood. Aldosterone seems to decide how much potassium or sodium inhabits the cells. If a person eats too much table salt, the body will excrete nine times more potassium than is desirable. And if potassium is shorted, sodium enters the cells, gorging them with excess water: the result is swelling of tissue in general, usually known as edema.

Furthermore, the electrical charge between potassium and sodium is such that one mineral brings nutrition to the cells and the other takes way the waste products. If this waste is not picked up and converted into urea, toxic poisons can go through the body, creating numerous symptoms seemingly unrelated to any particular organ, endocrine dysfunction or disease. Thus potassium is a natural diuretic. The kidneys rely heavily upon potassium to get the waste products to them for excretion, and the mineral literally invigorates the organs to work at optimum to keep the body cleared of any type of toxicity.

Potassium is a jack-of-all-trades, mingling with phosphorus to insure that oxygen reaches the brain and uniting with calcium to regulate the neuromuscular movements concerned with pliancy of muscles. Without potassium muscle contractions would not be initiated smoothly and glucose would not be converted into glycogen so that it could be stored in the liver or feed the nerves to prevent tension and nervousness.

Because of its function with muscle contractions, potassium can help alleviate constipation. When muscles in the intestinal tract are not fed enough of the mineral, they go into a stage of stasis or sluggish peristalsis, thereby bringing on constipation. If the deficiency is severe, there can even be paralysis of the intestines, creating a dangerous toxic situation.

Potassium is also needed to insure a proper balance of iron. It helps maintain a proper acid-alkaline balance. And it promotes secretion of endocrine hormones that are involved with female functions.

Some sources advocate care in taking pharmaceutical or synthetic brands of potassium because they may have an irritating effect upon the intestinal tract.

Absorbed in the small intestines, potassium has trouble staying in the body after it has been absorbed. Magnesium is essential for potassium to be retained within the cells. And emotional or physical stress can suddenly deplete the stores of potassium within hours. When, rarely, there are excessive amounts of potassium in the body, aldosterone is responsible for stimulating its excretion through the kidneys and urine.

Allies: Potassium's primary ally is vitamin B-6. It is also more effective taken with sodium and magnesium.

Antagonists: Many substances can cause a deficiency of potassium. Coffee and alcohol are the worst offenders; moreover, alcohol is also an antagonist to magnesium, and without magnesium potassium is leached out of the body. Other offenders are common table salt and white sugar: heavy salt users are guaranteeing a deficiency of potassium as well as risking high blood pressure.

Some other sodium byproducts that will induce leaching are sodium benzoate, sodium ascorbate, used commercially in many products, and sodium nitrate, used to preserve meats: it pays to read labels at the grocery store.

Some drugs responsible for blocking or excreting potassium are sodium, lithium, tetraethyl ammonium, aspirin, diuretics, cortisone, DCA, aldosterone treatment and thiazide or digitalis (both used for cardiovascular diseases).

Dosages

Recommended Dietary Allowance: Although no RDA has been established, many doctors feel that 2,000 to 2,500 milligrams of potassium on a daily basis should be gotten from the diet.

Therapeutic Dose: Under a physician's guidance up to 6,000 milligrams are recommended.

Megadose: Under a physician's guidance 6,000 milligrams or more are recommended.

Toxicity

There is no known toxicity level; however, doctors report that if potassium is injected into the body in dosages that are too large it can be toxic to the point of lethality. The sudden rise of extracellular potassium, injected as potassium chloride, may result in kidney failure. The only other way that too much potassium may remain in the body is if a person is not taking fluids, necessary to provide the causeway for extra potassium to be excreted through the kidneys.

Deficiency Symptoms

Early warning signals that potassium is below level are a bitter taste in the mouth, dry throat, eczema on the feet and legs, headaches at the back of the skull, itchy, dry skin and an empty feeling in the pit of the stomach.

More discernible signals of a moderate deficiency are muscle weakness, pyorrhea, swollen ankles, swollen ovaries, swollen testicles, a general weakness in the female organs, low grade infections and constriction of the urethra without any medical cause.

Indications of a more serious deficiency are water retention, weakened or flabby muscles, distention of the stomach, inability to digest sugar and an impaired kidney function. The heart may race suddenly and then slow down, seeming like tachycardia, and the person may be extremely sensitive and irritable, displaying some mental disorientation. In addition, regular, daily chores may seem to be almost too much to cope with, and there may be a continual drain on a person's energy reserves, causing muscle weakness.

Prolonged intravenous administration of saline solution will often disrupt the potassium-sodium balance in the body, producing prolonged vomiting or bouts with diarrhea. There may also be loss of muscle tone, constipation, loss of peristalsis and excessive formation of gas.

Recent Clinical Developments

One of the inevitable results of a deficiency of potassium appears to be high blood pressure. When too much sodium is ingested, potassium is lost and sodium invades the cells, filling them with excess fluids. Then the osmotic pressure, which is supposed to be about the same as the circulating blood, shoots up. The vessels constrict themselves in an effort to slow the blood volume down. The heart then beats faster, and the result is circulatory tension, known as high blood pressure.

People taking treatments for arthritis may also suffer from deficiencies of potassium. Whenever ACTH, cortisone or aspirin are given, sodium is retained, water is held in the tissue, and a deficiency of potassium ensues. Lab experiments on rats indicate that when several one gram tablets of potassium chloride (15 grains each) are administered after the adrenals have become severely damaged, sodium and water are excreted, and the blood pressure decreases. Another report shows that a person who was taking cortisone for severe arthritis took nine grams of potassium chloride daily, reduced to three grams daily later. In the beginning he lost six pounds of water weight, and the blood pressure dropped appreciably.

Patients taking certain medications for heart problems may also be lacking in potassium. For instance, diuretics given to ease the heart's burden of having to pump excess fluids out of the body leach out potassium in the meantime, placing an even greater strain on the heart. In addition, the drug digitalis or vasodilators for heart ailments will not prove effective unless enough potassium is present: without the mineral the heart cannot pump blood with adequate force, and there may be a weakened pulse and weak heart sounds. Tachycardia (the heart racing rapidly for no apparent reason) can be controlled by supplements of potassium as well.

Insufficient levels of potassium appear to be linked with sugar-related problems, such as diabetes and hypoglycemia, too, since the mineral has to do with glucose and the carbohydrate processes. Diabetics are known to have low levels of potassium. And diabetic patients have found relief from the blood pressure problems that accompany the disease with supplements of potassium. Furthermore, potassium, which boosts the entire carbohydrate system, restores energy to the hypoglycemic in-dividual by helping to alleviate much of the continued stress on the adrenals that accompanies hypoglycemia.

Constriction or closing of the urethra seems to be related to a deficiency of potassium as well. Paralysis of the bladder and urethra may even occur with a severe deficiency. It has been reported that problems with voiding have been eliminated with adequate amounts of the mineral.

In addition, kidney stones are brought about from a diet of refined food products, too much salt and not enough fruits or vegetables containing potassium. Without potassium the urine becomes alkaline, and the minerals cannot be contained in the solution. At that point they become deposited as stones.

After surgery a condition known as secondary hypokalemia may result because of an extreme depletion of potassium. The condition commonly manifests through episodes of muscular weakness, paralysis and lack of calcium. Saline solutions given intravenously will also deplete the stores of potassium.

Colic, experienced by hundreds of thousands of babies each year, has been found to disappear with injections of potassium chloride.

Potassium can also alleviate some of the ills of older people. Elderly people frequently experience extreme fatigue, apathy, listlessness and depression. They can also become grossly underweight. Several doctors have found that for people over 65 a diet high in potassium or supplements of potassium seem to correct these problems.

In addition, people who have leukemia (over-production of white blood cells) seem always to have low levels of potassium. So far the medical establishment has not been able to explain why this phenomenon occurs.

Muscular dystrophy (a wasting away and atrophying of muscle tissue) is also thought perhaps to be related to a deficiency of potassium. Doctors postulate that a cell defect in the forming process may allow the mineral to slip away, thereby encouraging weak and flabby muscle coordination, the main symptoms of the disease.

There is a commonly believed myth that a person who works long and hard out in the Sun should take salt tablets. But taking salt tablets will induce a severe deficiency of potassium and instead of helping may hurt the body. Anyone perspiring out in the Sun should take potassium and salt substances together.

Anyone who is fasting to lose weight should probably also take supplements of potassium to help the body over the shock of going from food to no food. Although a preferable way to lose weight than taking pharmaceutical diuretics, fasting puts severe hardship on the adrenal glands. Moreover, a diet low in protein combined with a low intake of potassium will halt the growing process.

A good, natural source of potassium is raw, unpasteurized apple cider vinegar. Taken from fermented apples, the vinegar contains a substance called "mothering," a product that contains malic acid, which upon entering the stomach turns alkaline. This malic acid is of tremendous help in rebalancing the acid-alkaline metabolism, as well as feeding the body potassium. A simple solution of two tablespoons of vinegar in one eight-ounce glass of water rebalances the potassium-sodium metabolism.

SELENIUM

Astrological Ruler
Mars.

Synthetic Forms
Selenium dioxide.

Sources
Vegetables: Mushrooms, broccoli, onions and tomatoes.
Fruits and Nuts: Unknown.
Meat and Fish: Tuna and most seafoods.
Grains: Cereals, bran and wheat germ.
Dairy Products: Milk and eggs.
Herbs: The distribution of the nutrient in the soil often dictates what plants will have extra selenium; however, there are four herbs found in the western states that draw up selenium in enough parts per million to be deadly to humans and animals: astragalus (vetch), oonopsis (golden weed), stanleya (prince's plume) and xylorrhiza (woody aster). A variety of vetch known as *Astragalus mollissimus* (purple or wooly locoweed) is sometimes used as a homeopathic remedy; it is not recommended that an herbalist use this preparation as an herb or tincture involving the leaves and stems. Garlic is also a source of selenium.
Natural Supplements: Kelp and yeast.

Unit of Potency
Parts per million (ppm).

History and Characteristics
Marco Polo first noticed selenium around the year 1295. He noted that the mountains of western China contained plant vegetation that once eaten caused the hooves of beasts of burden to fall off.

The name *selenium* comes from the Greek word *selene*, meaning "the Moon." Isolated in 1957 by Schwartz and Foltz, the mineral is felt to be an essen-

tial nutrient that has a great deal to do with the intricacy of the metabolic and enzymatic functions. It helps insure proper body growth and aids in fertility.

As is vitamin E, this mineral is a natural antioxident of polyunsaturated fatty acids that will solidify tissue protein. It is also said to go after the free radicals that bring on the aging process of lines, wrinkles, sagging skin and general skin degeneration. In addition, it helps prevent red blood cells from being unduly damaged or destroyed too quickly by the oxidation process. And it protects the body from mercury poisoning.

Selenium works in concert with vitamin E. With proper amounts of selenium in the body vitamin E is spared to a degree. And selenium helps ease some of vitamin E's load: at times it can completely heal an ailment without vitamin E's assistance; at other times vitamin E is needed to complete the healing process.

Selenium is also a highly versatile mineral in industry. A bluish-gray crystal type of selenium is used in the manufacture of photographic exposure meters and other equipment that has to do with the conversion of light to electrical energy. With physical and chemical properties resembling those of sulfur, red crystal types of selenium are used to make yellow, red and orange glass. Another type is used to produce a durable, very elastic rubber compound.

Despite its various uses, selenium is very toxic. Areas such as the Gunnison River, a tributary of the Colorado River, have extremely rich selenium deposits that can cause toxicity to livestock drinking the water or ingesting certain types of grass that absorb the mineral in huge quantities. (On the other hand, the soils in parts of the United States, the provinces of Alberta, Manitoba and Saskatchewan, parts of Mexico and New Zealand appear to be selenium-poor.) Tests on animals have indicated that whereas too little selenium may lead to liver dysfunction, too much will poison the liver, ceasing it to function and causing death. Furthermore, a derivative of selenium—selenides—will poke holes in teeth.

Ingested selenium accumulates in the protein of the body tissue, particularly the liver and kidneys. It is excreted through the urine. Selenium that shows up in the feces may not have been properly absorbed.
Allies: Vitamin E.
Antagonists: Since selenium vies with sulfur for transport along the same causeways in the cells, either mineral out of balance with the other will create an unhealthy situation.

Dosages
Recommended Dietary Allowance: None has been established at this time, and it is recommended

that no selenium supplement be ingested. The mineral should be obtained naturally from brewer's yeast, where the amount is infinitesimal.

Therapeutic Dose: None has been established because of selenium's toxicity.

Megadose: None has been established because of selenium's toxicity.

Toxicity

The toxicity level for selenium is five to ten parts per million. Micronutrients, such as molybdenum, cobalt and chromium, can accent the toxic effects of selenium, which interferes with sulfur compounds in the body and interferes with the action of certain enzymes.

The liver would be the first organ to be affected by an overdose of selenium: it would either begin dysfunctioning or stop functioning completely. In animals toxicity is known as "alkali disease" or "blind staggers": the muscles lose their ability to work properly. Moreover, there is dullness and sleepiness, the gait or walk is staggering, and the animal falls down if turning quickly. The respiration is also slow and irregular, and the appetite is not good. There is a tendency toward constipation as well.

Chick embryos given toxic amounts of selenium during fetal development were deformed upon hatching. With less toxic amounts malformations occurred, but no duplication of body parts resulted.

If selenium is ingested in too large amounts, certain types of arsenic are antidotes for cleansing the deadly mineral from the system.

Deficiency Symptoms

Premature aging seems to be the only signal that there may be a deficiency of selenium. Anyone thinking about supplementation should check with a doctor.

Recent Clinical Developments

Selenium teamed up with protein helps to erradicate kwashiorkor (a protein-deficiency disease).

In lab experiments liver necrosis (death of tissue surrounded by healthy parts) was induced in rats and then cleared up by administrations sodium selenite.

When lambs and calves with muscular dystrophy were given vitamin E by itself the condition did not clear up; however, when they were administerd sodium selenite the disease disappeared.

When doctors attempted to treat people with leukemia with oral doses of selenocystine, the immature leukocytes disappeared from the blood and spleen.

SODIUM

Astrological Ruler
Mars.

Synthetic Forms
Sodium acetate, sodium amytal, sodium bicarbonate, sodium bisulfite, sodium borate, sodium chloride (table salt), sodium citrate, sodium fluoride, sodium hydroxide, sodium morrhuate, sodium nitrite, sodium salicylate, sodium sulfate and sodium thiosulfate.

Sources
Vegetables: Carrots, beets, asparagus, romaine lettuce, okra and watercress.

Fruits and Nuts: Watermelon.

Fish and Meat: Bacon, ham, salted pork, salted fish and seafood in general.

Grains: Unknown.

Dairy Products: Milk, American cheese, cottage cheese and cream cheese.

Herbs: Black willow, chives, cleavers, devil's bit, fennel seed, meadow sweet, mistletoe (poisonous), nettle, rest harrow, shepherd's purse, sorrel and stinging nettle.

Natural Supplements: Sea salt (75 per cent sodium) and kelp (18 per cent).

Unit of Potency
Gram.

History and Characteristics
Sodium is literally everywhere—in the oceans, the Sun's atmosphere, space, meteorites, mammals and plants. It ranks sixth in abundance of the elements found in the earth's crust. The mineral, alkaline in nature, is found in all living organisms. It is mandatory for life, occurring in the fluids of the body: the serum, blood, lymph and tissue.

In 1831 when cholera was a dreaded disease, O'Shaughnessy found that sodium helped to reduce the blood of cholera patients with excellent results: today several chemical derivatives are used as saline solutions in IV's. In 1901 Ringer and then in 1902 Overton showed that sodium is an essential constituent to help support the metabolism of fluids within the body.

The most common form of sodium, of course, is *sodium chloride*, ordinary table salt, a substance so valuable that it has brought about slave trading. The ancients found salt to be a useful tool for barter and trade, especially among vegetarian nations. (Since meat has a high sodium content, meat-eating nations did not crave salt.) In the Middle Ages a salt levy came into existence. Members of families were sometimes sold to attain some of this precious white mineral.

Today most Americans suffer a sodium overload because of all the salt we eat. In addition, canned foods have a high sodium content, as does meat. Cities place sodium fluoride in the water, and drug-hormone therapies usually involve a form of sodium. Below are some other sources of sodium:

Sodium acetate is used as a diuretic and laxative.

Sodium amytal is used as a sedative to control insomnia and as a preliminary prep for anesthesia and labor.

Sodium bicarbonate, otherwise known as baking soda, is used as an antacid and in cooking.

Sodium bisulfite is used as an antioxidant in industry.

Sodium borate, or borax, is used as a detergent and water softener and as an ingredient in certain pharmaceutical preparations authorized for external use.

Sodium citrate is used as an anticoagulant for blood in transfusion.

Sodium fluoride is placed in our drinking water to protect our teeth from cavities. It is used commercially in etching glassware and for killing rats, insects, ants and other pests.

Sodium hydroxide, otherwise known as lye soda or caustic soda, is used as an antacid and caustic in laundry and commercial compounds.

Sodium morrhuate is used as a sclerosing agent for the obliteration of varicose veins.

Sodium nitrite is used as an antidote for cyanide poisoning.

Sodium salicylate is used in IV's as an analgesic and antipyretic.

Sodium sulfate, otherwise known as Glauber's salt, is used as a saline cathartic and diuretic. It also has veterinary uses.

Sodium thiosulfate is used to remove stains of iodine and in IV's as an antidote for cyanide poisoning.

The list doesn't stop with these substances. There are many hidden sources of sodium. For example, seasonings such as celery salt and bouillon cubes contain large quantities of sodium. And many of our junk foods, such as potato chips, various crackers and pretzels, are high in the mineral.

Sodium and potassium have a direct bearing on one another—a fact discovered by Von Liebig in 1847. There should ideally be .58 grams of sodium to 1.28 grams of potassium ingested daily—this is a 2 to 1 ratio that should exist in everyone. Sodium, concerned with the pH of the body, the acid-alkaline metabolism, is found chiefly in the extracellular fluids, whereas potassium remains within the cells. If sodium does invade the cells, a person will take on fluid retention, commonly known as edema.

The maintenance of the precarious balance between sodium and potassium is very important. Animals who eat potassium-rich grass, for instance, will seek out salt blocks to rebalance their bodily systems. If the balance falters, many health-threatening symptoms will appear almost immediately. Since Americans tend to eat too much salt and not enough potassium in proportion, many people suffer from edema, swelling of the hands and feet and high blood pressure. Arthritis, heart disease, kidney ailments and strokes may also appear.

The adrenal glands are vitally important to the sodium and potassium balance in the body. If the glands become exhausted, aldosterone (a hormone that holds sodium in the body to prevent dehydration) is not produced in sufficient amounts; consequently, salt and water will be lost in huge quantities, and the blood pressure will fall below normal: sodium intake is necessary to rebalance the bodily functions. On the other hand, if aldosterone overproduces, the opposite effects take place: sodium will increase the blood volume, inducing edema and accelerating the heartbeat. Then, as the blood vessels automatically constrict to try to slow the blood flow down to give the heart a rest, high blood pressure will result.

Together potassium and sodium are responsible for the contraction and expansion of muscles. They also figure in the nerve stimulation. And along with calcium they regulate the osmotic pressure in cells and fluids, act as an ion balance in tissue and guard against excessive loss of water from the body.

Chlorine also works in tandem with sodium, with the two minerals responsible for the pH factor and control of the fluid volume. When acidosis occurs, generally among heavy meat-eaters, chlorine is excreted and sodium is retained by the body. When, in rare cases, alkaline conditions exist, sodium is excreted and chlorine is retained instead.

Absorption of sodium takes place in the small intestines and the stomach. Entering the system as soon as three minutes after being ingested, the mineral is absorbed faster from the intestinal area than from the stomach. To a great degree the kidneys regulate just how much sodium is needed by the body: the rest is excreted in the urine, with smaller amounts lost in the stool and through perspiration.

Sodium is located on the surface of bone crystals. Thirty to forty-five per cent of sodium is in the skeleton. The amount of this mineral is low at birth; when a person is about five months old, sodium goes to its highest levels; the mineral content then tends to decline as an individual goes into adulthood.

Allies: Sodium's primary ally is potassium. It is also more effective taken with vitamin D, calcium and pantothenic acid.

Antagonists: Without proper amounts of chlorine and potassium in the body sodium will not be able to function up to par. Several hormones, such as testosterone, estradiol and progesterone, as well as adrenocortical drugs, such as cortisone and desoxy-cortisone (DOC), will retain sodium.

Dosages

Recommended Dietary Allowance: None has been established. The National Research Council feels that daily salt intake should be one gram per kilogram of water consumed. Other sources believe daily sodium chloride intake should amount to no more than one-half to one gram; other sources say two to three grams. Some experts say that five grams of salt may be ingested if there is no family history of high blood pressure; if there is a history of the disease, a maximum of 1,000 milligrams of salt a day should be taken, with the amount of natural potassium automatically increased to two times that amount.

From these figures, varied as they are, it is clear that the less sodium chloride we ingest the better. The average person ingests three to seven grams of sodium daily plus six to eighteen grams of table salt—far above the recommended levels.

Therapeutic Dose: Anything over 14 to 28 grams of salt a day is considered excessive. A physician should determine whether or not a person has a deficiency of sodium, prescribe the dosage and monitor the situation.

Megadose: Twenty-eight or more grams of salt a day.

Toxicity

There is no known level of toxicity. Any consumption of 28 grams can be dangerous. And a loss of potassium may induce sodium to higher levels, resulting in many of the symptoms of high blood pressure, as well as swelling of the hands, feet and eyes, dizziness and a pounding pulse.

Deficiency Symptoms

General weakness, nervous disorders, weight loss, a hunger for salt, cramps and digestive upset may be experienced. Other symptoms can include vomiting and elevated blood urea, especially during times of hot, sultry weather. If exhausted adrenal glands are the root cause of the deficiency and sodium leaves through the urine, potassium will be left in the cells, resulting in greater weakness of the muscles, slowed contraction time and partial or com-plete paralysis of certain muscles. Psychological symptoms may include hysterical behavior and mental depression. In addition, hair may begin falling out, there may be loss of smell, and glasses may have to be changed often.

Recent Clinical Developments

Although most of the ailments related to sodium stem from an overabundance of the mineral rather than a deficiency, some diseases produced by deficiencies do occur. For example, when a deficiency exists in the secretion of the adrenocortical hormones, Addison's disease may result, with the accompanying phenomenon of a craving for salt: in such a case sodium is critical for the entire life-support system. Lowered sodium levels have also been observed in patients who have certain types of nervous system diseases, such as tuberculous meningitis.

Sodium may be lost through diarrhea, vomiting, spinal injuries and intestinal obstruction. People suffering from renal insufficiency may lose sodium and chlorine in the urine. Certain organic compounds, such as salyrgan and merdurin, produce sizable loss of the mineral, as well as oxygen and potassium, by acting directly on the renal tubules. And children who have cystic fibrosis of the pancreas are prone to heat prostration associated with a loss of sodium: the loss of the mineral occurs through heavy sweating associated with the disease.

Another way that a great deal of sodium is lost is through burns. With third-degree burns the body forces potassium out of the damaged cells, and sodium leaves the blood to move into them. Too much potassium slows down the action of the heart. Meanwhile, in trying to restore the balance of sodium the body must tap into its own reserves of salt water. Consequently, blood pressure falls, kidney functions become sluggish, and fainting may occur. All burn victims also exhibit an unquenchable thirst for water. Burn units supply gallons of saline solution to the victim so that the body can resupply the sodium. In some cases adults have been known to drink ten quarts within a 24-hour period because the need for the sodium to restabilize the body is so great. Once the sodium is resupplied, blood pressure goes up and the kidneys respond to excrete the excess potassium out of the body.

Alcoholics may also need additional sodium. Doctors have noted that hospitalized alcoholics always have low levels of sodium: they may be craving salt instead of liquor and may be able to curb their craving for spirits by placing a teaspoon of salt in a glass of water and drinking it.

In addition, bathing in salt water can help some

conditions. People who have sciatica trouble with the hip or thigh have found relief in salt water. Chronic rheumatism can be helped by the same method.

Perhaps the most widespread result of too much sodium is hypertension (high blood pressure), caused by constriction of the veins to slow down the volume of blood that passes through the miles of circulatory tubing. The heart must pump faster to stay up with the volume. The eventual outcome of this condition is usually a stroke. In Japan, where heart disease is rare, brain hemorrhaging brought on by hypertension is the number one killer: salted fish is Japan's principal food, and the sodium intake approximates 27 grams daily. In the West Indies, where poor people live on salted fish and pork, strokes are common occurrences.

Some of the symptoms of hypertension are headaches, dizziness, faulty vision, poor memory, pain in the region of the heart, gastrointestinal disturbances (such as gas and diarrhea), nosebleeds and shortness of breath. Blood pressure should ideally be 120 systolic (heart contractions) over 80 (between contractions): if a person's blood pressure hovers around 150/90 continually, hypertension has begun.

To halt hypertension a person must adhere to a low-sodium diet. Cholin and potassium will also help control the amount of sodium that is allowed to stay in the body. If the blood vessels are brittle and hemorrhaging occurs, supplements of vitamins E and C can help.

Low-sodium diets are also commonly instituted for cardiac failure, kidney nephritis and cirrhosis. Too much sodium is linked with the alarming increase in heart conditions among children. High levels of sodium assure elevated blood pressure levels that put stress on a child's cardiovascular system. Today there is an extremely high amount of sodium in baby foods. Cow's milk also has a sodium content nearly four times that of breast milk. Thus natural foods and breast milk will insure a child a healthier start in life.

In addition, sinus drainage and other sinus ailments have reportedly benefited from a relatively salt-free diet.

Women on high-salt diets are more prone to miscarriages, too. Figures show that during World War II in Holland, England and Switzerland, when little food therefore little salt was available, fewer children were born dead than before or after.

Some health experts feel that it is better to have sea salt on the table rather than iodized salt. They argue that sea salt contains minerals beneficial to the body, whereas the iodized variety only helps in thyroid conditions. Potassium iodide placed in salt is

also lost rather quickly from cardboard containers used for the salt: up to ⅓ of the iodine will be lost within six weeks, depending upon atmospheric conditions.

SULFUR

Astrological Ruler
Saturn.

Synthetic Forms
Available by prescription only, not in over-the-counter forms.

Sources
Vegetables: Brussel sprouts, cabbage, cauliflower, celery, okra, string beans, turnips, radishes, onions, dried peas, kale, chard, watercress and soybeans.
Fruits and Nuts: Nuts in general.
Fish and Meat: Oysters, clams and most meat products.
Grains: Bran and cereals.
Dairy Products: Eggs, cheese and cereals.
Herbs: asafetida, broom tops, calamus, carrageen (Irish moss), coltsfoot, eyebright, fennel seed, garlic, horseradish, meadow sweet, mullein, pimpernel, stinging nettle and waywort.
Natural Supplements: Cocoa and possibly complete mineral or vitamin supplements.

Unit of Potency
Milligram.

History and Characteristics
An invaluable mineral in industry, sulfur also can be very beneficial to health. Mineral waters and hot springs reputed to help many types of ailments contain much sulfur. And during World War I in England soldiers in the hospitals had their wounds treated with garlic juice, which because of its high sulfur content acts like an antibiotic and speeds up the healing process.

All vegetables and fruits contain sulfur; thus the mineral is very important to our life processes. The body consists of approximately ¼ sulfur. The mineral is found in every cell, with the highest amount stored in the hair, which contains four to six per cent of the total sulfur in the body. Without ample sulfur, hair becomes brittle and fingernails break easily.

The amino acid containing sulfur—cystine, cysteine, ergothioneine and methionine—are essential to life. These amino acids play a vital role in the protein metabolism. Without sulfur body tissue would not be created. Sulfur also makes up a good percentage of cartilage within the body and is vital for the synthesis of collagen (a fibrous protein found in connective tissue, such as the skin, bones, ligaments and cartilage). By itself collagen represents about 30 per cent of the total body protein.

Sulfur is also found in insulin, which has to do with the carbohydrate metabolism. And it exists in two of the B complex vitamins—biotin and thiamine. Working with several of the B complex vitamins, sulfur helps to maintain strong nerves. In the liver it aids in the production of bile for secretion and helps detoxify poisons produced by the body.

Sulfur also plays a part in the oxygenation process involving the tissue. Acidic in nature, it is concerned with the acid-alkaline balance of the body.

A balance exists between sulfur and nitrogen. For each gram of sulfur excreted 14 grams of nitrogen are excreted.

When sulfur is broken down within the body, it is used in many ways. The heparins aid in the blood's fluidity: heparin products, such as sodium heparin, are frequently used to prevent the blood from thickening or clotting or used in cases of phlebitis concurrently with the administration of dicumarol, an anticoagulant drug. The chondroitin sulfates are involved with the formation of cartilage and combining bodily substances with water. And the mucotin sulfates literally lubricate and protect the gastrointestinal tract from acidic conditions.

Allies: Sulfur's primary allies are biotin and thiamine. It is also more effective when taken with the rest of the vitamin B complex and vitamin C.

Antagonists: Chondroitin sulfates (chemical derivatives of sulfur) rely on vitamins A and D, growth hormone and thyroxine, released by the thyroid gland, for synthesis. Tests with animals have shown that a lack in any of those nutrients will inhibit chondroitin sulfates. Cortisone injected into rats also markedly inhibited chondroitin.

Dosages

Recommended Dietary Allowance: None has been established. Sulfur is so abundant in most types of food that a deficiency is hard to get. It can be purchased in ointment, cream and lotion forms for use with skin problems.

Therapeutic Dose: Unknown.

Megadose: Unknown.

Toxicity

There is no known toxicity level for organic sulfur; however, sources of inorganic sulfur are deadly and should not be consumed without a physician's authorization. Sulfur dioxide (a gas used in industry to manufacture acids) is highly toxic. Suffoca-tion will result if gas is inhaled. Anyone who comes in contact with the gas should see a physician at once.

Deficiency Symptoms

Although it is quite difficult to get a deficiency of sulfur because it is available in most foodstuffs, there can be problems involving the cartilage formations, such as stiffening and aching joints. The biggest indicator of a deficiency can be hair that becomes dry and dull. Fingernails may split and break off easily, never growing to any length. There may be back or disk problems, such as a hardening or loss of elasticity of the cushion that sits between each vertebra. In addition, a wound may take a long time to heal properly, health ailments in general will require a recuperation period much longer than expected, and skin problems, such as dermatitis, may appear.

Recent Clinical Developments

Many arthritics have low levels of sulfur. Cystine (an amino acid) contains a large amount of the mineral and is felt to be partly responsible for this condition.

Several skin disorders, such as dermatitis, eczema and psoriasis, can be treated with a sulfur-bearing ointment. Ringworm has also been helped with the external application of the mineral.

Organic sodium may be partly responsible for a skin's immunity against poison ivy and poison oak. According to one report, a teaspoon of sulfur a day helped keep a woman free of these irritants while she pulled the plants up around her farm.

ZINC

Astrological Ruler
Jupiter.

Synthetic Forms
Zinc gluconate and zinc sulfate.

Sources
Vegetables: Onions, mushrooms and soybeans.

Fruits and Nuts: Pumpkins, sunflower seeds and nuts in general.

Fish and Meat: All organtype meats, oysters, herring and most other sea foods.

Grains: Wheat bran and wheat germ.

Dairy Products: Milk and eggs.

Herbs: Unknown.

Natural Supplements: Yeast.

Unit of Potency
Milligram

History and Characteristics

Zinc was first discovered in plants by Raulin in 1869. Then in 1877 Raoult and Breton found the mineral in the liver of a human. Because of the difficulty in analyzing this mineral, zinc was somewhat ignored until in 1940 a human enzyme was found to contain it. It was later established that at least 25 different enzymes contain this valuable mineral, attesting to its obvious importance to bodily functions.

Approximately two grams of zinc are found in a human being. It is extremely important in the formation of RNA and DNA for synthesization of body proteins. It can also help overcome infertility problems. Found in insulin, zinc is intrinsic to the carbohydrate processes. Moreover, it is important to the phosphorus metabolism. Somewhat like sulfur, zinc has the ability to speed up healing of wounds and burns.

Zinc is believed to have a great deal to do with the red and white blood cell maturation process. Loss of zinc in the serum levels has been proven in untreated pernicious anemia; when a person is treated with zinc, the levels come back to normal. The same phenomenon occurs in myocardial infarctions, cases of malignancies and cirrhosis of the liver. Furthermore, those afflicted with anemias, polycythemia leukemia or congestive heart failure tend to have high levels of zinc to help combat these conditions. In states of remission the concentrations of zinc return to normal. Zinc in red blood cells also increases for those who have contracted sickle cell anemia. And a decrease of 50 per cent of the zinc in whole blood has been noted in people suffering from a protein deficiency, beriberi and pellagra.

White blood cells contain 25 times as much zinc as do the red blood cells. In acute and chronic lymphatic and myelogenous leukemia the amount of zinc is ten per cent below normal levels. But the administration of zinc gluconate has failed to raise the leukocyte level or influence the course of the ailment.

Breast milk contains a goodly amount of zinc; this amount falls as lactation continues. The level may be as high as 20 milligrams per liter of milk in the beginning and two or three weeks later, 3.5 milligrams per liter. The level of zinc then continues to fall off for about six months. This presence of zinc in breast milk is another good reason for breast-feeding infants.

Zinc is absorbed in the duodenum of the small intestine. What is not used is excreted in the fecal matter. Little is lost through urination. The highest amounts of zinc are found in the male prostate gland. It is also stored in the eyes, liver, pancreas, kidneys, hair and fingernails and toenails.

Allies: Zinc's primary ally is vitamin A. It is also more effective taken with calcium, copper and phosphorus.

Antagonists: Zinc and cadmium, present in exhaust pollution and phosphate fertilizers, appear to be natural enemies. Inhalation of cadmium has been proven to halt absorption of zinc. The body also seems to have a difficult time differentiating zinc from cadmium, and, if the body has a choice, it seems to store cadmium instead of zinc.

Tests on animals have also shown that zinc and copper can be antagonists, provided that neither of these minerals is taken in large doses without the other; and since copper is lethal in high doses, it is best to have a nutritional physician work up any program involving these two minerals.

People who take a great many dolomite tablets daily may deny the body enough zinc. Pigs given bone meal supplements to accelerate bone growth developed symptoms of deficiencies of zinc.

A person who consumes large amounts of the various whole grains may run the risk of the phytic acid binding with a high intake of calcium to prevent the uptake of zinc.

Insufficient phosphorus can also inhibit zinc; however, because the American diet is usually high in phosphorus this deficiency is unlikely to happen.

Dosages

Recommended Dietary Allowance: The National Research Council recommends 15 milligrams of zinc daily for an adult. The Council suggests another 15 milligrams during pregnancy and another 25 milligrams if a woman is breast-feeding.

Therapeutic Dose: Three hundred milligrams of zinc gluconate were administered intravenously to a myelogenous leukemia patient without any adverse side effects.

Megadose: Dr. Paavo Airola feels 600 milligrams is therapeutic under a doctor's supervision. Another doctor administered a total of 1,000 milligrams of zinc gluconate over many days to try to depress the white blood cell count of a myelogenous leukemia patient without success: there were no reported ill effects.

Toxicity

There is no known level of toxicity for zinc, but since large doses of zinc lower the white blood cell count, a person with a normal white blood cell count who takes too much zinc may cause an imbalance in relationship to the red blood cells. Too much zinc will also interfere with the fragile balance between copper and iron: too much zinc will halt copper, and an iron shortage will appear. Phosphorus and sulfur contents will also decrease from high dosages of zinc.

And anyone taking large doses of zinc should take an ample amount of vitamin A.

Deficiency Symptoms

Common symptoms are skin problems, white spots on the fingernails and toenails, loss of a sense of taste or smell, brittle hair, dandruff and fatigue.

Other, more severe symptoms can be dwarfism, delayed sexual growth and lowered resistance to infections. without zinc infertility may occur and sexual interest may lag. There may be underdeveloped gonads or an enlarged prostate.

Low levels of zinc have also been found in the following diseases: cystic fibrosis, liver ailments, ulcers, atherosclerosis, epilepsy, heart attacks, mongolism and osteoporosis.

Furthermore, repeated bouts with alcoholism or a moderate to heavy drinking habit will run zinc out of the body. Alcoholics with cirrhosis of the liver frequently have very low levels of zinc.

Recent Clinical Developments

Sufficient amounts of zinc are especially important to men. The highest levels of the mineral are found in the prostate gland and in the seminal fluid. It has been found that about 50 per cent of the cases of infertility may be from weakened sperm count in men: sufficient levels of zinc give the sperm endurance to make the swim up the uterus and have enough energy left to penetrate the egg.

Cadmium is known to inhibit zinc, and a person who drinks approximately five cups of coffee or tea a day will double the average intake of cadmium, thereby enhancing the risks of diseases such as high blood pressure, strokes, atherosclerosis and heart diseases.

CHAPTER 9
Bach Flower Remedies

In the early 1930's, Dr. Edward Bach, homeopathic physician in Britain, experimented for years with a number of organic substances (trees, flowers, herbs, water, rocks) to find ones that were safe and had no adverse reactions to the person. He saw that many physical manifestations of disease were directly attributed to a person's mental attitudes. In other words, emotions, acting through the brain, adversely affect the nervous/immune system creating negative stress. Stress creates illness. His philosophy was: if the person is mentally and emotionally restored to harmony, then the person can deal positively with stress in their life, not negatively, i.e., create a physical illness.

Bach found that certain plants, when picked at a particular cycle in their life, released optimum healing energies, than at other times. He tested many plants and organic substances for years. He got rid of those which were toxic, caused side affects or masked the true problem in the patient. Bach ended up with 38 essences or remedies that are known today as the "Bach Flower Remedies"—although, not all of them are flowers. For instance:

Rock Water is water found in a well or spring known to have curative or healing powers. Aspen, Beech, Cherry Plum, Chestnut Bud, Crab Apple, Elm, to name a few, are trees. Gorse, Heather and Holly, as examples, are bushes, and Wild Oat is a member of the grain family. So, to say they are all flower remedies is misleading and inaccurate. Many homeopaths will use Bach Flower Remedies as an adjunct or support for the patient while they are going through constitutional treatment.

How to prepare your remedy:
Items needed:

1. 1 ounce amber glass eyedropper bottle. (Can be purchased from Ellon Bach, USA. See Appendix.)

2. A label to put down what remedies are utilized.

3. Brandy (any brand); suggest a fruit brandy (i.e., apricot, blackberry, etc.). Alcoholic, alcohol sensitive or allergic - use apple cider vinegar as a suspension vehicle in place of brandy.

4. Water (spring or well water, never city water or distilled water).
Preparation:

5. Add 1 teaspoon of brandy or apple cider vinegar to bottle.

6. Add 2 drops of the Bach Flower Remedy(ies) concentrate(s) into the bottle.

7. Fill the bottle up with water, leaving enough room for the eyedropper.

8. Shake vigorously.

9. Keep bottle in purse, refrigerator or some place out of direct sunlight.

10. Place 4 drops under your tongue four times daily (upon rising and 1/2 hour before each of your 3 meals). NOTE: Do not touch eyedropper to tongue or body.

Did you know:

11. Keep bottle out of extreme temperatures.

12. Do not run through airport x-ray machines.

13. Alcoholics may not be able to use Bach Flower Remedies because the concentrate is in brandy and so is the diluted type. Use apple cider vinegar instead. Bach people feel you can use the dilute (without brandy base in eye dropper bottle) by putting 2 drops of concentrate in 1 ounce of water with 1 teaspoon of apple cider vinegar. If you do this, you must keep bottle refrigerated because after 7-10 days, algae will begin to form in the bottle. It must be thrown out and a new diluted mixture prepared. Also, you can place the dilution or concentrate on wrists or behind the ears. Or, put dilution in an atomizer and spray around person (it gets into her/his aura) or spray the room where s/he will be sleeping.

14. You can combine up to 6 remedies at a time. They do not cancel out one another.

15. Do not take the opposite remedy for your condition (i.e., Vine and Centaury).

16. There are no adverse side affects, and no addiction to taking these remedies. There is no chemical reaction when taking medical drugs at the same time you are taking these remedies.

17. Take a remedy(ies) for at least 7 days. If nothing has changed during that time, re-prescribe! Think about taking the shock neutralizer, Star of Bethlehem, for old, repressed shock. Then, go back and try your same remedy(ies) again. If that does not work, try Wild Oat or Holly. Then go back to your original remedy(ies).

18. For most people it takes 7-14 days to notice a subtle difference in how they are approaching or dealing with attitudinal situations. But, once you feel free of those symptoms, stop taking the remedy(ies). If they return, go back on the remedy(ies) until the symptoms have disappeared. (It can take from 1 to 12 weeks to "cure" a condition.

19. If you feel you are experiencing a reaction to the remedy(ies), you are being "cleaned out". It is NOT a side affect! So, continue with your remedy(ies).

20. Treatment bottles can be used over and again. Simply boil bottle and eyedropper in water

for 20 minutes to sterilize.

21. Pregnant mothers respond well to Rescue Remedy and Walnut during pregnancy, labor and shortly after the birth. The baby can be given the above shortly after birth, too.

22. Babies can take remedies, too (4 drops, 4 times daily). Put in teaspoon or in their bottle of milk/juice.

23. Normal dosage on pets is 4 drops in drinking water or milk once daily, or sprinkle over food. For large dogs/animals you can put 10 drops of concentrate per bucket of water, or 4 drops on sugar cube.

24. For plants, use 10 drops of Rescue Remedy concentrate in 1 gallon of water. If plants are sickly or toxic, put 10 drops of Crab Apple in 1 gallon of water.

The "down and dirty" method:

25. Take 2 drops of concentrate directly on tongue from whatever remedies you need (up to 6).

26. This will speed up the process of altering your attitudes immensely. Usually, within 3-4 days, you will note a change in your mental outlook.

If person is unconscious:

27. Place remedy concentrate or dilute on wrist or behind ear where skin is exceptionally thin and can absorb it into the body. You can also utilize Rescue Remedy the same way.

Homeopathy is the law of similars—like cures like symptoms. This means a substance given in a large, crude dose will produce specific symptoms. But, when reduced in size (potentized homeopathically) and administered in minute does, it will stimulate the body's reactive processes (and immune system, if it's involved) to remove the same symptoms (i.e., bee sting, Apis Mellifica; vomiting, Ipecac). Bach Flower Remedies are potentized homeopathically. They are made at 3X, a very low, benign potency.

BACH FLOWER REMEDIES

The following is a list of the Bach Flower Remedies in alphabetical order by nickname for a quick, handy reference:

1. *Agrimony* - "tough-it-out" remedy
2. *Aspen* - "unknown" fear" remedy
3. *Beech* - "nit-picker" remedy
4. *Centaury* - "co-dependant" remedy
5. *Cerato* - "puppet" remedy
6. *Cherry Plum* - "suicide" remedy
7. *Chestnut Bud* - "rut" remedy
8. *Chicory* - "gimme" remedy
9. *Clematis* - "daydreamer" remedy
10. *Crab Apple* - "Mr. Clean" remedy

11. *Elm* - "Oh my God" remedy
12. *Gentian* - "black cloud" remedy
13. *Gorse* - "I surrender" remedy
14. *Heather* - "hypochondriac" remedy
15. *Holly* - "apocalypse" remedy
16. *Honeysuckle* - ". . .memories. . ." remedy
17. *Hornbeam* - "Monday morning blahs" remedy
18. *Impatiens* - "nervous Nelly" remedy
19. *Larch* - "wimp" remedy
20. *Mimulus* - "known fear" remedy
21. *Mustard* - "Dr. Doom and Gloom" remedy
22. *Oak* - "atlas, holding world on shoulders" remedy
23. *Olive* - "exhaustion" remedy
24. *Pine* - "guilt" remedy
25. *Red Chestnut* - "smothering" remedy
26. *Rock Rose* - "rescue" remedy
27. *Rock Water* - "zealot" remedy
28. *Scleranthus* - "Libra" remedy
29. *Star of Bethlehem* - "shock" remedy
30. *Sweet Chestnut* - "bottom of the barrel" remedy
31. *Vervain* - "Type A" remedy
32. *Vine* - "field marshal" remedy
33. *Walnut* - "butterfly" remedy
34. *Water Violet* - "loner" remedy
35. *White Chestnut* - "squirrel's cage" remedy
36. *Wild Oat* - "chasing rainbows" remedy
37. *Wild Rose* - "milquetoast" remedy
38. *Willow* - "wet blanket" remedy
39. *Rescue Remedy* - "shock cocktail" remedy [see (a) and (b) below]

(a) *Rescue Remedy* contains Impatiens, Star of Bethlehem, Cherry Plum, Rock Rose and Clematis. It can be used for any kind of shock, bad news, family upset, sorrow, funeral, exam fears, insomnia, dental visit, hospital surgery, hospital tests, driving test, job interview, fear of flying, panic, asthma attacks, heart attacks, gallbladder attacks, anxiety attacks, public speaking, "up tight" feeling, watching disturbing movie/TV show, etc., or anything that is a stress upon you. Animals and plants respond well to it, also. If a person is unconscious, smear Rescue Remedy on wrists or behind ears. If an animal is unconscious, smear on animal's nose/muzzle area or inside of ears.

(b) *Rescue Remedy Cream* is applied externally, on skin only. Put on bruises, arthritic areas, bursitis, pain, burns, around a laceration or cut (not into the cut, please!), temples of head (if you have a headache), on brow (if headache is there), frostbitten areas, or swollen areas (edema, water retention, as in ankle or feet area).

The following is a descriptive listing of the Bach Flower Remedies according to what they can be used for:

THE ASTROLOGY OF BACH FLOWER REMEDIES

Primarily, I use either transits or progressed planets in use of Bach Flower Remedies (bfr) to a person's natal chart and planets. Simply choose a specific transit or progression and note the natal planet that it is aspecting. Hard aspects such as a conjunction, square, inconjunct (quincunx) or opposition may herald a need for a specific remedy.

For example: Transiting Saturn conjunct natal Sun would ask the reader to look at all the Bach Flower Remedies that have Saturn as a ruler. After noting those remedies, read each one and see which remedy most closely approximates your symptoms.

Another example would be transiting Neptune square natal Moon. Look up the Bach Flower Remedies that have Neptune as a part of their rulership.

For Those Who Have Fear:

Rock Rose (Helianthemum Nummularinum) (Uranus, Neptune, 12th house): Also known as Frostwort, Frostweed, Frostplant. Found in eastern U.S. Yellow flower. The "rescue" remedy. For anyone who has survived any kind of situation that was trauma and they experienced panic and/or great fright. Trauma is defined by the person, not by the prescriber. Example: a child losing a kitten might not seem to affect the parent as much as it will the child; to the child, it is a terrible loss and a shock/trauma. People who live in a constant state of fright, panic attacks, anxiety attacks, for example. If a child has a nightmare, wakes up traumatized by it, this is the right remedy to utilize. Excellent for use after viewing or being in any kind of accident; a fall from a horse, a fall from a tricycle, an auto accident, etc.

Positively: The ability to feel courage to work through the situation. A new kind of strength to walk with their fear or trauma.

Herb: Used for cancer, ulcerations, tumors (inner or outer, on skin).

Homeopathically: Canadensis, Rock Rose, is known as European Rock Rose. Some other symptoms that might help you decide Rock Rose is the correct remedy are: extremely sensitive to cold; sensation of coldness in various parts of the body; malignant disease of the glands of the neck (lymphatic ailments, including cancer); pyorrhea of mouth; hurts to extend or stick out tongue; throat is very dry; cold air passing over it causes pain; sore throat from inhaling cold air; cold feeling in stomach; cold feeling in abdomen; diarrhea from coffee or fruit; coldness in chest; bleeding in lung(s); coldness of hands or feet; cannot sleep because of coldness in throat; swelling or inflammation of breast(s); asthmatic after laying down; itching all over; painful pimples; lupus; skin on hands hard, thick, dry, fissured or deep cracks; itching of swollen hands and arms.

Mimulus (Mimulus Guttanus) (Neptune, Pisces, 12th house): "Known fear" remedy; fear of known things that may be part of everyday life. For instance, fear of leaving the house, agorophobia. Fear of being raped, robbed, of getting Cancer or AIDS, losing one's family or dearest, closest friend(s). It can extend to loss of a house or pet. The fears may involve being afraid to give a speech, or even talk to a small group of people. Mimulus blushes very easily and often. Sometimes, they may have a stammering problem, plus overwhelming shyness. This is an introvert remedy, for people who are afraid to assert themselves. There can be great fears regarding loss of a job, one's money, having an accident of some kind that might incapacitate them. Secret fears are especially a part of this remedy's sphere of action, and can include any kind of obsessive or compulsive behaviors limited only by the individual's mind and emotions.

Positively: The alleviation of whatever KNOWN fears plague the person.

Cherry Plum (Prunus Cerasifera) (Mercury, Neptune, Virgo, Pisces): "Suicide" remedy; This is for anyone who is prone to suicidal thoughts or feelings. There is also a fear of committing suicide, and because this is a deep, dark secret, the person will never speak about it to anyone because they are ashamed of the urge. There may be aggravating, persistent thoughts of a negative kind such as fear of losing one's mind, or that some invisible impulsiveness or obsessiveness will take over and make them do something they know is wrong or could hurt another. Fear of losing control over one's self in any way, and this includes a fear of uncontrolled temper, uncontrolled violence toward another, impulses such as gambling, shopoholics, and negative mental fixations toward another person or situation. Tension in this person is generated from a basis of fear and they can have tortured, terrible thoughts they wrestle with inwardly—great mental anguish and pain. For people who are hysterical, who fear doing harm to others—even to their own family and children. Children who have violent tendencies of any kind, even bang their heads against a wall.

Positively: Will restore calmness and courage;

able to retain sanity, despite mental or emotional torture.

Aspen (Populus Tremula) (Neptune, Pisces, 12th house): "Unknown fear" remedy; Used for any kind of vague, disturbing, uncomfortable, nagging feeling that cannot be identified as WHAT or WHERE it is coming from. Frequently, children and women who have been sexually molested, abused or raped, will have these kinds of vague, unknown fears. Further, they may have completely repressed memories of these terrible atrocities. The only red flag is terrible, tortured emotions bubbling up in the form of reactions such as: fear of going to sleep, or of waking up, apprehension in general, sudden perspiring for no reason, a terrible sense of apprehension that something will happen to their loved ones. Aspen people NEVER speak about these vague fears out of shame, and even those who love them may never know about their own personal hell and torment they live with daily.

Positively: Fearlessness, faith.

Homeopathically: Aconitum Napellus is an excellent remedy for Aspen people.

Red Chestnut (Aesculus Carnea) (Leo, Moon, Cancer, Virgo): "Smothering" remedy; An over-emphasis for fear for others in their lives; usually their immediate family or close friends. Hypochondriac tendency in that even a small, acute illness may turn into something chronic and devastating.

Positively: Allows other people to live their lives fully without fearful influence of the Red Chestnut individual.

For Those Who Suffer Uncertainty:

Cerato (Ceratostigma Willmottiana) (Moon, Gemini, Virgo, Pisces, Saturn): Astro blue flower. "Puppet" remedy; This person has such low self-esteem and loss of confidence in themselves that they constantly reach out for help, advice and direction from those around them. Unable to listen to their own "gut" intuition, they will not trust their own rational or logical judgment of a situation. Instead, they will defer to another person. They may be loquacious and constantly asking questions in order to validate or double check their own knowing, which they don't trust. If they get a consensus of opinion from others, then they will act on it. Won't trust self or their own experiences in any way.

Positively: They will begin to defer to their own internal "knowing" and trust their own life experiences in order to make decisions for themselves and stop asking others for direction.

Scleranthus (Scleranthus Annthus) (Libra, Mercury, Gemini, Pisces): The "Libra" remedy; can be talked into and out of just about anything by an individual—and lose their own knowing and judgment. Too easily swayed by others. Constantly moving from one pole to another of extremes. For example: having high energy and then, later on, collapsing into a state of complete exhaustion. These people don't know the meaning of moderation—they are extremists in many ways. Indecision slows them down through life.

Positively: Bestows calmness and determination; able to make quick decisions and take prompt action; keeps poise and balance on all occasions.

Gentian (Gentiana Amarella) (Saturn, Capricorn, 10th house): "Black cloud" remedy; When the least little thing goes wrong, Gentian is the first to say: "I told you so." And then, they disengage because of some small setback—whether it is personal or in their career. Easily discouraged and then they become depressed or lack assertiveness because of the failure. They don't understand their own gloomy outlook "taints" life around them completely—hence, nothing does go right for them, there's always a fly in the ointment to whatever they try to undertake. Their own lack of faith in themselves puts forth huge stumbling blocks to any success they might accomplish—and this goes for their personal, and emotional life as well as their career.

Positively: They get rid of the negative outlook about life in general and get on with it, able to make considerable accomplishments and they aren't stopped by setbacks or failures.

Gorse (Ulex Europaeus) (Moon, Saturn): "I surrender" remedy; for those who have been told to give up, that nothing more can be done in some sphere of their life—not necessarily in the process of losing someone. They give up, if ill, and don't want to fight back any longer or look at any other treatments that might help them. May be unduly influenced in decisions by others because they've given up. Depression brought on by loss of hope and lack of ability to marshal their own emotional desire to live, to survive or push one, regardless.

Positively: This remedy of great value when given early in any chronic illness; gives patient hope of recovery—that is the first step towards a cure. Insures a new jolt of hope combined with faith, giving Gorse the strength to fight back and carry on.

Hornbeam (Carpinus Betulus) (Mercury, Moon): "Monday morning blahs" remedy; For people who are unhappy with their job and/or career, who hate going back to work on Monday mornings and face the same grind. Also helps those who have a long-term illness who doubt their chances of recovering.

Positively: Imbues Hornbeam with a brighter, more optimistic outlook, and gets rid of the Monday Morning Blues.

Wild Oat (Bromus Ramosus) (Libra, Pisces, Uranus, Aquarius): "Chasing rainbows" remedy; This is for people who just can't figure what they want to do with their lives, what career to pursue, getting married now or later, having children now or later, etc. Nothing is crystal clear to them and consequently, they try many different things in life—both personally and careerwise, and they still aren't happy! The old Irish saying: "An Irishman never knows what he wants, and won't be happy until he gets it," applies to Wild Oat people. When they are uncertain, they wobble, unsure which way to go next. Scleranthus is another remedy with this kind of uncertainty.

Positively: Remedy can be of assistance in selecting a career; will help you to find your special place in life (something that gives you satisfaction); desire to experience life to the fullest; definite character, talents and ambitions; lives life filled with usefulness and happiness.

Not Sufficient Interest In Present Circumstances: (Those who "check out".)

Clematis (Clematis Vitalba) (Neptune, Taurus, Pisces, Mercury): "Daydreamer" remedy; the "couch potato" of the remedies; Physically, they may have a very "spacy" look or expression to their face. They may seem completely out of their body, ungrounded and "not here," in any sense of the word. Others will accuse them of not paying attention to what they say or show them. Often, children in school will be seen looking out dreamily at the sky or anything else—but certainly not involved in the teacher or what is being taught! Clematis does not possess a lot of 'horse sense,' and fails to understand or want to use practicality in their daily lives. They are deep sleepers who may also spend too much time sleeping, too. They enjoy their own company, often seen as loners, and don't need the company of others. When forced to deal with a situation, Clematis will try to withdraw, like an introvert, and go away. They avoid confrontations with others in every way possible. They have exhaustion, complain of being drowsy and have no fears whatsoever on any level—mental or emotional. They bury themselves into books, movies or any other resource that helps them 'check out of the real world,' for awhile. They are seen as absent-minded. This is THE remedy for anyone in a coma, who is unconscious or who has fainted. Lacks desires, assertiveness and has no goals in life.

Positively: They become grounded back into their body, become focused in their daily life and engage once again.

Honeysuckle (Lonicera Caprifolium) (Pisces, Virgo, Neptune, 8th house, 12th house): "Memories" remedy; of great help to those who lose a loved one, lose a pet, or who have moved from a wonderful place and are now transplanted at another city, state or country. Honeysuckle lives in the past, not wanting to connect with or join the present in any way—perhaps because it's too painful for them. Fear of the future, so they drag their heels and stay in the past. May sap others of vitality (psychic vampire). Honeysuckle is chained to the past by both their good and bad experiences, but they don't realize this. A gradual decline of a person's energy over a long period of time; as if they are slowly grinding to a halt. Or, perhaps 'thinning out' of the present because the bulk of their spirit, heart and mind are still caught and trapped in the past.

Positively: Living in the present and taking full part in it.

Olive (Olea Europaea) (Saturn, Capricorn, Pluto): "Exhaustion" remedy; for a person who has suffered a LONG TIME under some very negative condition. It could be a long-term illness that has sapped their energy, and they have become mentally and emotionally exhausted by the trial. Loss of endurance of some long-running situation in life, not necessarily an illness. It's difficult for them to make it through a day. Loss of interest in anything that gave them pleasure. Hornbeam people get better as day progresses, but Olive people get WORSE. They will tell you they just 'ran out of gas.' Usually, Olive has some very heavy burden they must shoulder the entire responsibility on, and over time, it has eroded them not only emotionally, but mentally as well as physically. Consequently, they will tire very easily, or the least exertion, however simple, seems to completely sap them of their energy.

Positively: Helps those who are trying to overcome a major illness. It gives the person hope and gives them a sense of peace they didn't have before. A harmony or balance that was lacking before in their lives.

White Chestnut (Aesculus Hippocastanum) (Mercury): "Squirrel's cage" remedy; for people who just can't shut their minds off—especially at night when they're trying to get to sleep. The insomniac remedy. Lacks the ability to stay concentrated on a task, or to finish it. Constantly arguing with self mentally until it affects job performance or quality of life with spouse and family. May condemn self for, "I should have said this instead..." A Type A remedy for the hurried business person who is doing too much and lays awake at night creating lists for tomorrow's activities. May be so much in their head, that they don't pay attention to driving, which could lead to an accident. Preoccupied.

Positively: Stops the persistent, "squirrel's cage" thoughts and allows the person to sleep well at night. Stops the preoccupation so they can focus completely on the task in front of them.

Mustard (Sinapis Arvensis) (Saturn, Pluto, 4th, 8th, and 12th houses): "Dr. Gloom" remedy; for people who feel this irrepressible weight surrounding them like a dark, gray blanket that colors how they see the world, and how they seem themselves. For severe depression, melancholia and despair. This remedy differs from Gentian which has discouragement, and Gorse, who's keynote is hopelessness. Mustard does not know where their depression, their darkness, comes from—cannot point to a specific, traumatic incident in their lives that might have caused it. The gloom is so deep that they have no outside interest in the world around them; they are fixated helplessly to this emotion.

Positively: The gloom is lifted, they see daylight, along with hope and renewed vitality for life.

Chestnut Bud (Aesculus Hippocastanum) (See Note below) (Moon, Saturn, Pluto): "Rut" remedy; for people who don't learn from their experiences from the past, both positive or negative. For example, a woman who keeps marrying the same kind of man over and over again. Or worse, a woman who marries an abusive man, divorces him, but then, remarries a man with the same abusiveness in him. Not learning from one's mistakes, but repeating them miserably time after time. They try to forget the past, the unhappiness of it all, and yet, they fail to learn from what they did wrong then, so they can 'right' it in the future. They may catch a cold every month—month after month. Any acute illness that reoccurs on a cyclic basis can be helped with Chestnut Bud. For example, repeated sinus infections, ulcers, allergies that occur at a certain season each year. Chestnut Bud learns slowly in school, too, having to repetitively do something over and over again to get it. For example, a child having problems learning multiplication tables has to go over it again and again—almost tortuously, to retain it and the method used. They are not very organized

NOTE: This is from the White Chestnut tree, only in bud form. The mature form is utilized differently. There is something to say about the time that something is collected as to what chemistry is present and how it will affect an individual. A bud would have the highest energy—the baby forming, a

"quickening"—providing the stimulus to get out of the repetitive "rut".

Positively: Learns from their past, repetitive mistakes and changes their lives as a result. No more cyclic appearance of acute ailments. Can learn not only from their experiences, but others, as well.

Water Violet (Hottonia Palustris) (Saturn, Pluto): "Loner" remedy; for people who have a specialized talent or skill in place, they appear to others, as perhaps egotistical. In reality, many people confuse ego with self-confidence, and Water Violet has self-confidence in their gifts. However, there can be a stubborn or rigid outlook to their existence, and they carry this tension in their body/muscles. They are self-reliant people who go their own way. Their quietness may hide a multitude of griefs or unhappiness, but they never speak about them to anyone. Bearing loads alone. Very understanding of other people, and has great objectivity with them and does not interfere in their lives as a result.

Positively: They continue to walk alone, but with more inner peace and harmony than before.

Impatiens (Impatiens Glandulifera) (Mercury, Aries, Gemini, Mars): "Nervous Nelly" remedy; for people who lack the patience to allow others to go at their own pace—certainly nowhere near the pace Impatiens sets for himself. Becomes highly irritated by slower co-workers or with family members. May be accident prone just because they're in too much of a hurry. Wants to work alone because others are too slow for them. Good for cramps, spasms or sudden pain. They can become exhausted through abuse of their nervous system and placing too much constant strain on it.

Positively: Tolerance for those who are less fast than themselves. The ability to slow down a little and be patient with co-workers or family who still won't be as fast as they are!

Heather (Calluna Vulgaris) (Neptune, Pisces, Leo, Sun): "Hypochondriac" remedy; for people who focus entirely on their problem—whether mental, physical or emotional. Heather uses their illness or problem as a way of manipulating others to pay attention to them. Centaury types are the victims of Heather. And Mimulus types can also be drained by Heather. Saps energy and is a psychic vampire to those around them. Concerned with too much trivia, and stirs up a 'hornets nest' over nothing.

Positively: Stops sapping the energy of others and allows people to go their own way without constantly manipulating them with illness or trifles.

Oversensitivity To Influences And Ideas:

Agrimony (Agrimonia Eupatoria) (Pluto, Leo, Saturn, Capricorn, 12th house): "Tough it out" remedy; alcoholic's remedy; for people who put on a cheerful facade, but inwardly, they are tortured, unhappy individuals. They love company and hate being alone. Will try exciting and dangerous things that could injure them. A turbulent state of mind and can be restless, especially at night (see White Chestnut). The addict's remedy—any drug or alcohol.

Positively: Can bring renewed faith and hope into their lives, a more positive attitude and become a good friend to others.

Centaury (Centarium Umbellatum) (Moon, Neptune, Virgo, Pisces, 6th house): "Co-dependent" remedy; for people who lack a strong, courageous backbone, who are seen as the wimps of the world. They are "doormats" for people who see this type and abuse the privilege of them. Centaury cannot say NO to anyone. They are easily drained by psychic vampires, and by the demands of others upon them and their time. They are languid and pale appearing, but they have a good mind and are alert. They may be like Cinderella: chained to their family as more of a servant than as a member with the same equality. Knows how to gives, but doesn't know how to receive. Agrimony is for the alcoholic or drug user and Centaury is for the family of the drug user or alcoholic. Codependent personality. Possibility of childhood abuse has helped create this state.

Positively: The ability to choose to serve whoever they want, and in what capacity—but not allowing themselves to be taken advantage of or drained psychically again. Holds own opinions and is able to enforce them for themselves. They learn how to give AND receive.

Chicory (Chicorium Intybus) (Pluto, Virgo, Pisces) "Gimme" remedy; can be very possessive toward others in any fashion. Often can interfere in the lives of those close to her/him. In order to keep loved ones or friends close, will hint that this is owed to Chicory. They can become overwhelmed with their own emotions and discolor the situation with others, as a result. They hate being alone and always want company around them—partly out of loneliness and partly out of desire to be the center of attention. Highly manipulative in an emotional way. A good dysfunctional family remedy for those who had to manipulate to survive. Loquacious, likes to argue with others, may cry as a way to manipulate others to their will—crocodile tears. Wants close family members to march to Chicory's version of the tune. Reacts powerfully to the slightest hurt. Shows offense at small things. The "stalker" remedy in that Chicory has possessive love and doesn't want to let go of that person for any reason.

Positively: Being unselfish toward others and allowing them to live their lives the way they want, not the way Chicory wants. Giving generously without thought of some kind of return; not keeping a list of who owes Chicory what.

Walnut (Juglans Regia) (Pluto, Uranus): "Butterfly" remedy; from cocoon to butterfly; transition in stages of life; such as marriage, divorce, death of a loved one, menopause, beginning of menstruation, teething remedy, puberty, breaking ties with a person or thing from the past, birth of a baby, change of career, change of location/move, moving out of house of parents for first time, going to college, going into the military service—any major change in a person's life should be accompanied by Walnut because it makes the transition smoother and less emotionally devastating or traumatizing to them. This is the remedy for those who have great ideas or want to change their life dramatically, but may be afraid to do so. Walnut gives the person the courage to overcome their fear and take that giant step forward and into the future. Walnut may be dominated by a very powerful person or situation in their lives that makes them scared to try or take that step. Emotionally, it means wanting to break away from old, family conditioning, the past or anything that is seen as restricting the person's freedom to make choices without fear.

Positively: The ability to step forward into the future to make that life-change without fear, but with hope and strength.

Holly (Ilex Aquiforlium) (Saturn, Pluto, Leo, Aries, Mars): "Apocalypse" remedy; for people who are envious, have a hatred of another individual or thing (such as religious hatred toward others who aren't the same religion as they are), jealous of others, overly aggressive toward other, and in general, hates Mankind—although this can be gender-specific i.e., a hatred of women, as an example. For people who have bad/violent tempers, highly irritable, has no understanding of others, and in general, there is a lack of ability to love self, so they can't love others. Holly and Wild Oak are indicated if none of the other remedies work for them. These are considered the 'catalyst' remedies and will break an inner wall to 'reach' the person.

Positively: The loss of envy, greed, jealousy, aggressive behavior and they become more tolerant of others.

Despondency And Despair:

Larch (Larix Decidua) (Saturn; Moon): "Wimp" remedy; for people who lack even a crumb of self-confidence. They never see themselves as successful, therefore do not attempt to become any-thing else but a 'loser' in mentality and action. There is an intense inferiority complex within them. They are not jealous or envious, however. They won't attempt to try anything for fear of failure, which is shaming to them. They feel they can't do as well as the next person. A good remedy to use before taking school or college tests.

Positively: Becoming success oriented in their daily life, with determination and hard work. They will take risks now and give it their best try—regard-less whether they are successful or fail at it.

Pine (Pinus Sylvestris) (Virgo, 6th house): "Guilt" remedy; for people who are inordinately bur-dened by guilt. They blame themselves for other people's mistakes and for anything else that might go wrong in another person's life—they take on the guilt about it. Frequently, they will set almost im-possibly high standards for themselves and others—and of course, Pine and the people around her fail to meet these standards. They become depressed or give up, as a result. Pine is over-conscientious toward others and are overachievers who are never happy with what they did in the past, and only strive to better it in the future. If someone isn't happy, Pine thinks its their fault and takes on the guilt or feeling bad about it.

Positively: They take responsibility for them-selves only and understand that it isn't their problem or fault if someone isn't happy.

Elm (Ulmus Procera) (Mars, Pluto, Saturn): "Oh my God" remedy; this is for people who are simply overwhelmed by Life in general, by too much responsibility and feeling wholly unable to deal with the cards life has dealt to them. This remedy is par-ticularly needed by the following occupations: super mothers, doctors, healers, corporate leaders, business owners, teachers, clergy who all shoulder a great deal of responsibility—and that one wrong decision can influence others either positively or negatively. There is exhaustion that comes along with the thought that they aren't up to the rigors of the position after awhile. Depression may occur when they realize just how much responsibility they are shouldering.

Positively: Able to continue shouldering their massive responsibilities without becoming depressed about it. Confidence to handle their chosen field or area of expertise with vigor and resourcefulness.

Sweet Chestnut (Castanea Sativa) (Saturn, 4th house, Mercury): "Bottom-of-the-barrel" remedy; this is for people who experience tortured mental anguish. It can be in response to loss of a loved one, or some other situation that has completely traumatized the person. They feel completely

destroyed, with loss of hope and serenity. They have reached the end of line figuratively and literally. They are not suicidal like Cherry Plum, and in worse shape than Agrimony types. Even worse than Gorse. They feel there is no hope for a future, and are ex-hausted and lonely.

Positively: Given the strength to see it through. Endurance and in full control of their emotions.

Star of Bethlehem (Ornithogalum Umbellatum) (Uranus): "Shock" remedy; for any person, animal or plant that has suffered from any kind of trauma, accident or injury. Plants that are repotted. Animals that undergo surgery or are hit by a car. Suffering from terrible news or bad news. Delayed shock or repressed shock (even from birth onwards, no matter how old you are). If person does not respond to ANY other remedy, including Wild Oat or Holly, use Star of Bethlehem to remove the block of repressed shock.

Positively: Able to go about one's life without the stress of trauma in their lives. It enables a per-son to regain their balance and harmony.

Wild Rose (Rosa Canina) (Neptune, Moon, Pis-ces, 12th house) "Milquetoast" remedy. The in-ability to see that however Wild Rose is living their lives, the conditions of it, are of their own making, their own decision-making process—conscious or unconscious. They surrender to whatever the cir-cumstance and live with it. Fails to realize they have other choices because they have given up. Drifts from one life event to another without joy, much less hope. Expecting to have to suffer without hope of ever changing the situation. Exhausted and lacks energy. Their voice may be monotonous sounding and their features nearly without expression. If ill, may believe she is incurable and has no strength to "fight back," and try. Lack of backbone or will change whatever their sorry living state.

Positively: They take great interest in Life, in living and become focused and hard working toward whatever goals they choose. They "plug back in," to Life and get involved instead of being a shadow skulking silently through it.

Willow (Salix Vitellina) (Saturn, Leo, Aquarius): "Wet blanket" remedy; for people who have 'sour grapes' about their life—that they didn't deserve what they got. This builds up resentment, and bitterness. There can be a sorriness for the self, and gripe a great deal about what life has handed them. They accept others generosity because they feel they deserve it. Takers, not givers. When ill, very grumpy and ungrateful. Is jealous of other people's successes, money, fame or glory. They will gossip to others with never anything good to say about another person. There is a perverse joy in spreading gloom and gossip. May use their illness as a tool to get attention. Will never sacrifice for the good of another person or situation. Is dearth to admit they might be getting better if they've been sick for awhile because they enjoy the extra pampering and attention—which they richly feel they deserved anyway.

Positively: Is a giver AND taker, with more balance in their lives. They don't begrudge others their successes and take on a more positive frame of mind.

Oak (Quercus Robur) (Saturn, Capricorn, Aquarius): "Atlas holding the world on shoulders" remedy; for people, who, like this mighty tree, shoulders a lot of responsibility for too long and they will break, not bend. People who are Type A's in personality, the true workaholic's of the world, who never stop to rest, never stop to smell the flowers or take a vacation. These are driven people, and can result in a nervous breakdown. People who are working constantly in order to avoid stopping to feel pain or get in touch with themselves. Courageous fighters who keep on plugging despite the travails of life—they never give up, but at some point, they are going to hit their own personal 'wall' where they must stop or destroy themselves. They are the mainstays of the family, company or project and don't know when to say "no." Physical exhaustion or abnormal tiredness of the Oak person is a sign that they need this remedy.

Positively: Able to bear up under loads.

Crab Apple (Malus Pumilia) (Virgo, Moon, Mercury, 6th house): "Mr. Clean" remedy; this is for anyone who has shame issues, loss of self-esteem and confidence. Crab Apple is for any child or adult who was sexually, mentally, spiritually or emotionally abused—either in the past or presently. These people feel dirty, ashamed and disgusted with themselves. Great for obese people. Wonderful remedy for pollution—whether it be the air we breathe, the water we drink, or contamination on the food we eat. Their physical appearance may be disheveled looking, skin unclean looking, hair unkempt—good for street people and those who have lost their homes and jobs. Crab Apple helps to antidote the effects of any poison, especially allopathic drugs of any kind (too much penicillin or antibiotics, as an example). Any type of unclean skin condition such as eczema, psoriasis or dermatitis. Put drops of Crab Apple in a bath and soak in it to feel clean. For people who are perfectionistic and obsessive about every detail.

Positively: Feeling of cleanliness about self, with shame issues dissolving, and getting back into balance with self on all levels.

Overcare For Another's Welfare:

Vervain (Verbena Officialis) (Mars, Aries, Scorpio, Capricorn, Leo, Mercury): "Type A" remedy; for people who are always tense, hyper and push too hard mentally to get a project completed. Mental burnout. Generally, they are like thoroughbreds, high strung, nervous and restless. Fanaticism, being a perfectionist and the inclination to tackle too many jobs at once are red flags. They may have high blood pressure, and can't relax. Injustices infuriate them, and they are sensitive on issues of fairness. Will often work to the point of physical exhaustion.

Positively: The ability to be a good role model, without always doing it for others. They can still be opinionated, yet be able to change. More tolerant with others and will defend a cause.

Vine (Vitis Vinefera) (Saturn, Pluto, Capricorn, Leo, Aquarius): "Field marshal" remedy; for people who must have control over other people—more than likely because their control was taken away from them as young children. Dominating and doesn't use their power or skills wisely. They tend to rub people the wrong way, demand unquestioning obedience from their family/friends. Often, they are ruthless in their objectives, uncaring of who it might harm or hurt. Dictators in a family or business. They can be cruel, without compassion and rule with an iron hand.

Positively: They become leaders who are role models and have learned to delegate to their people. Does not dominate others and doesn't demand unerring worship from others. A leader with a heart, with his people first on his/her agenda.

Beech (Fagus Sylvatica) (Virgo, Mercury, Saturn, Pluto, Scorpio): "Nit picker" remedy; for people who are unforgiving of others religion, ethnicity, beliefs or way of living. The "red neck" remedy. Prejudice. They lack compassion or understanding of others, finding fault and being critical at every turn with people. They gossip and complain about other people and cannot tolerate individual idiosyncrasies, unique qualities or special abilities. They usually are loners and disdain crowds or groups of people.

Positively: "Live and let live" attitude prevails, to allow other people thier individual uniqueness. Opinionated without intolerance.

Rock Water (water from well or spring known to have healing powers) (Pluto, Sagittarius, Jupiter, Saturn): "Zealot" remedy; and uptight person by nature whose main concern and focus is always on them self, never others. A martyr complex is possible, with a rigid outlook, philosophy and this can translate to a rigid body—arthritis. Very strongly opinionated about religion, philosophy and politics.

Self-motivated and driven by internal demons, they rule themselves with an iron fist. Their mental outlook is so rigid and inflexible. They apply this to themselves, not to others, fortunately.

Positively: Loosening up the restraints on themselves and becoming more flexible mentally, emotionally and physically. Striving for the finer ideals of Mankind, without the zealot temperament.

CHAPTER 10
Homeopathy And Astrology

Homeopathy is a therapeutic system of medicine developed by Dr. Samuel Hahnemann over 170 years ago in Germany. Since that time it has spread to every country of the world. It is based upon the Law of Similars: "Similia Similibus Curenter"—like cures like. This means that a substance given in large crude dosages in a person will produce specific symptoms. But, when this same material has been reduced in size and administered in minute doses, it will stimulate the body's reactive processes to remove these symptoms.

For example, Ipecac, if taken in a large quantity, will produce vomiting. Yet, when it's taken in minute doses, it cures vomiting.

There are over 2200 homeopathic remedies—all from nature in some form. The homeopathic physician is a graduate of a recognized medical school. Any substance might be used homeopathically but most are from the vegetable, animal and mineral sources which are broken down into minute quantities to stimulate the patient's own defense and immune mechanisms. This is the only type of medicine in the world that activates the immune system into lightning response and without the use of crude drugs which have proven damaging side affects. Homeopathic remedies do not cause allopathic drug reactions and will be passed off as minute amounts of a natural substance by the body, instead. For this reason, homeopathic remedies are perfectly safe to take. There is no drug-like reaction, no covering up of symptoms or allergic reactions as can be experienced by modern drug pharmaceuticals dispensed to the allopathic doctors in the U.S.

With few exceptions, substances prepared according to the specifications or the Homeopathic Pharmacopeia of the U.S. properly maintained and protected from contamination, retain their therapeutic effectiveness INDEFINITELY. The amount of the original substance in homeopathic medicine is reduced by the decimal scale and is indicated by a number and the letter "X", "C" or "M". A 3X potency means there is one part of the remedy with nine parts milk lactose or sucrose. A "C" would mean there is one part of the remedy substance mixed with ninety-nine parts of lactose or sucrose. An "M" means one part remedy to nine hundred ninety-nine parts of sucrose or lactose. In a process that is known as "trituration", the ingredients are mixed and prepared in FDA approved homeopathic pharmacies in the U.S. It is then sold to anyone, including lay homeopaths and homeopathic doctors, without a prescription. The "C" range and the "M" range are considered high dosages and should be used only by a homeopathic doctor or lay practitioner.

A homeopathic medicate is always referred to as a "remedy" to distinguish it from the crude drugs sold at drug stores as either prescriptions or over-the-counter drugs. A remedy may be taken without interference or chemical inter-reaction with any crude drug that is being taken simultaneously; although the ideal situation is to be in the hands of a homeopathic doctor.

Homeopathy, with its single purpose of attention to the WHOLE human being and the prescribing of the remedy to trigger the person's immune system to begin its own curative process, is a medical philosophy which is recognized and extensively used by physicians throughout the world.

One of the many Aquarium Age concepts regarding homeopathic medicine is that homeopathic doctors strive to teach the lay people how to recognize and use homeopathic remedies on themselves, their family and friends who ask for help. Quite often a lay homeopath will teach interested people in his or her area. And then, the lay people will gather weekly to discuss different case histories they are currently treating (on themselves or their family and/or friends) and they enlarge upon their wealth of knowledge, becoming even better lay practitioners. This is certainly one of the finest Aquarian concepts of groups getting together to help one another.

The National Center for Homeopathy ("NCH") offers courses to interested lay individuals (you need no previous medical experience or education—just a desire to learn homeopathy) once a year. This one week intensive course is highly recommended to anyone who stumbles onto the miraculous healing abilities of this 21st century medicine. Books on the topic can be ordered through NCH or Hahnemann Pharmacy (addresses in Appendix). Household kits are also sold by both of these organizations and are available for purchase by anyone.

The astrology of homeopathy is very complex and not easily applied. The entire philosophy of homeopathy embraces and honors the individual and his/her symptoms—spiritual, mental, emotional and physical. Astrology does the same thing. Both methodologies are holistic. To try and combine them is something that will take a lot of study and time. Probably the ONLY way a sure-fire method will be found will be based upon the vibrational frequency of each individual remedy and compare it to the frequency of the individual planets, signs and aspects. Radionics offers us this possibility, but has yet to come about.

Until someone is able to do this, I have, over the

years, seen certain signatures of either signs, planets or houses that typify certain homeopathic remedies. There is no formula in applying what I've found, so please don't try to make a certain remedy conform to your natal chart. The information I present below on the astrological basis is theory only. When I "take a case" homeopathically speaking, I do look at a person's natal chart. I don't prescribe a remedy based upon the chart, however. To do so is a slap in the face to the homeopathic way of honoring the individual. I offer the astrological information in hopes that some like-minded researcher will take the observations and work with them further. I'm sure that someday, someone will write a book that compares the 2200 known homeopathic remedies to astrological nomenclature.

FIRST AID AND ACUTE HOMEOPATHIC REMEDIES FOR EVERYONE:

There is no reliable astrological formula to figure out which remedy goes to which zodiacal sign-so far. It is not reliable, except in general terms. The best way to approach this is to find the planet in the chart with the most hard aspects (usually, three or more hard aspects). Go through the remedies below and look at the ones that have that planet and/or sign and read it. If most of your symptoms fit the remedy "picture", then there is a possibility that you may need it. However, consult with your homeopath FIRST. Do not take any homeopathic remedy without a practitioner's direction.

ACONITUM NAPELLUS (Uranus, Mars, 12th House)

The "personality" of Aconite is one of suddenness, surprise, shock and trauma. This remedy, made from the herb bearing the same name, is of immense help for people who have suffered a heart attack or stroke. It is also used as a "shock" remedy—if someone has an accident and is in shock. Or, it can be used for those who experience any kind of shock, including bad news, a divorce, separation, firing from a job, move to another city or state, etc. Mentally, the person is restless and nervous. There may be an overriding fear of death or of dying present. It is one of the great remedies for panic attacks or anxiety attacks. Aconite works especially well on any illness that comes on suddenly, without warning, or from a change in the weather.

Eye inflammation or pain

Sudden onset of first stage of cold or fever

Croup (if it does not work within 2 hours, try Hepar Sulph. or Spongia—all 3 are Croup remedies)

Earache (if pain persists after an hour, give Hypericum)

Burning sensation in throat

Sneezing

For fear of surgery or of going to the dentist (give 1 hour before)

In shock from fear of any sort (or any kind of trauma that produces fear)

Convulsions or epileptic seizures (if brought on by fright)

Fainting from fear

Panic caused by bleeding

After a stroke (to calm patient)

Diarrhea due to hot weather or change in weather

Slipped disc in back (if sudden with onset of severe pains)

Headache (comes on suddenly and is violent, throbbing in temples with a burning or bursting pain)

Insomnia (caused by fear or panic or after a shock/trauma; restless)

Anxiety attacks

Panic attacks

Anxiety, in general

Vomiting (from shock/trauma/fear of some sort)

ANTIMONIUM TARTARCUM (Neptune)

This remedy is made from double tartrate of antimony and potassium. It is for anyone who experiences great exhaustion, drowsiness or debility when ill. Like Neptune, which can be translated into "weak," Ant. Tart. is a premier lung and respiratory disease remedy—especially if there is a lot of rattling sounds in the chest, but with little expectoration (mucus) being coughed up. The greater the prostration of the person, especially from viral or bacterial complaints—Neptune's realm—the more this remedy should be thought about in those situations—providing the symptom picture fits.

Bronchitis

Pneumonia

Emphysema

Asthma, "dry" type

Person is usually pale and tired looking

Lung congestion (rattling of mucus but won't dislodge)

Shortness of breath

APIS MELLIFICA (Moon, Mars)

One of the great allergy reaction remedies, Apis is made from the venom of the honeybee. Where there is sudden, violent swelling of body tissue, Apis should be considered. Anti-phalactic reaction to any kind of allergy, Apis can be used to save a life, if necessary.

Bee sting allergic reaction

Insect bite allergic reaction

Drug or food allergy reaction
Sunburn
Stinging or burning pain
Swelling around head or neck
Difficult to breathe
Swelling around incision after surgery
Herpes zoster (with large blebs and stinging/burning; cool cloth helps)
Throat (raw and swollen)

ARNICA MONTANA (Mars, Saturn)

Made from a plant bearing the same name, there is probably no broader based remedy than this one. Arnica's sphere is usually muscle injuries, but also works well on injured tendons, ligaments and inflammation around joints/bones in particular. It is a premier remedy to halt hemorrhages, from acute nose bleeds to people who are known as "bleeders" or hemophiliacs.

Eases pain, swelling or soreness associated with sprains, bruises, muscles, falls, fractures (Symphytum to mend the break itself) or any kind of blow resulting from an accident
Concussion
Black eye (use Hypericum if there is pain)
Stroke (Belladonna may prove useful in tandem with Arnica)
Improves and speeds healing to any injury
Tennis elbow type of injury
Fractures (Ledum followed by Symphytum will also aid in quick recovery and knitting of bone)
Wasp stings (if this does not work, try Apis)
Dental operation (after root canals, or any sort of surgery or extraction of a tooth; use Hypericum if pain persists afterward)
Spinal injuries (use Hypericum if pain persists)
Shock (when there has been blood loss)
Abscess (bluish color to it, deep inflammation and pain)
Bloodshot eyes
NOTE: Arnica ointment can be spread on the skin. If an open wound, place around the outer edges and it will instantly reduce swelling/bruising. Never put Arnica tincture or any Arnica product into an open wound or laceration!! Wonderful for fingers crushed in car door, finger smashed by hammer or any other similar type of blow to any part of the body (I would also use some Hypericum to stop the pain.) For black eye, smear ointment around affected area, but never in the eye itself.

ARSENICUM (Mercury, Pluto, Virgo, 12th House)

Arsenicum is made from arsenic poison. In the small doses utilized in homeopathy, it poses no threat to the individual taking it. People who need this remedy are often very restless in nature, a Type A personality, hurried workaholics who get very short tempered and impatient with others who don't move at the speed of light like they do.

Asthma, wet or dry (worsens after midnight)
Skin rash which is sudden and improves with heat application
Acute diarrhea from food poisoning
Colds (later stages of)
Exhaustion
Herpes zoster (eruptions and cannot sleep after midnight, restless and with anxiety)
Hiccough (brought on by swallowing cold drinks or rise in temperature. If this doesn't work, go to Mag. Phos.)
Flu (watering eyes/nose, chilled and extremely weak)
Insomnia (after midnight)
Skin eruptions (scaly eruptions that burn and/or itch)
Hay fever (violent sneezing; not relieved by sneezing—if it doesn't arrest within an hour, try Allium Cepa or Sabadilla)

BELLADONNA (Mercury, Mars, Uranus)

Belladonna is made from the herb by the same name. It is for people who have a highly sensitized nervous system, who start if jarred, who are like barometers reacting instantly to any kind of change. Anyone who experiences a sudden onset of symptoms, no matter what they are, should think of Belladonna and/or Aconite. These people are like highly strung thoroughbreds and just as mettlesome at times.

Earaches (usually right ear) but can help stop possible shunt surgery
Sore throat (head congested with high temperature and sweating)
Sensitive to noise and light
Teething in infants (see Chamomilla, too)
Sunstroke
Fever (high and sudden—especially in a child; use Ferrum Phos. if it does not cure))
Insomnia (sleepy, yet unable to sleep)
Lactation (milk flows too freely, breast red, swollen, hot and may be stone-like in hardness)
Pre-Menstrual Tension (spasm and pain of a sudden, violent nature in uterus, flushed face or burning/heat sensation). Acuteness of ALL senses and an emotional roller coaster at this time of month.

BELLIS PERENNIS (Mars)

Follows Arnica well, especially if Arnica does not take care of swelling or bruising a week after the surgery or injury.

BRYONIA ALBA (Saturn, Cancer)

Known as the "grump" remedy, this fits Cancer very well by nature. When ill, these people want to be left alone—untouched, in a dark, quiet room. They will lay beneath a pile of covers, unmoving. Bryonia is one of the great migraine remedies of all time, along with Gelsemium.

Flu (fever, thirst, exhaustion and aches all over, made worse by movement).

Migraines, with dizziness, nausea and/or vomiting

Asthma

Colic (from ingesting rich or fatty foods, possible vomiting)

Indigestion (with headache which intensifies if one tries to sit up)

Colds (if onset is slow to develop)

Constipation (stool is dry, hard and black)

Cough (hard and dry, shakes whole body)

Headache (crushing, splitting, may feel faint or sick if attempting to rise)

CANTHARIS (Mars, Moon, Scorpio)

Made from Spanish Fly, this remedy is utilized for bladder problems. It also works in the reproductive and sexual area. If there is violent inflammation in any of these regions, then Cantharis should be remembered.

Bladder infections (cystitis, frequent urge to urinate with burning sensation)

Burns (minor or first degree that are relieved by cool cloth being applied)

Feet (burning in soles)

Nerves frayed or becoming tense (caused by drinking coffee)

Diarrhea (bloody stools with straining and burning sensation)

CARBO VEGETABILIS (Gemini, Neptune, Jupiter)

This remedy is made from animal charcoal.

Indigestion (burping, swollen abdomen, gas; especially after eating fatty foods or drinking wine)

Heartburn (sour belching or vomiting of food)

Hoarseness (worse in evening)

Cough (rattle and itching sensation in throat; possible gagging or choking up of mucous)

Asphyxia (face blue mottle and cold sweat, puffy) (use this after airway has been unobstructed)

Gasping for air/breath

Bleeding (steady seep of dark colored blood)

Desire for sweets

Desire for salty foods

CHAMOMILLA (Moon, Mars, Cancer)

Made from German Chamomile, a daisy, this remedy is a boon to all mothers who have children going through the "teething" stage. Colic is another area of expertise and has helped many a parent with a cranky, inconsolable child through this stage.

Pain sensitive

Teething (painful, irritability and/or feverish; convulsive fit in anger due to)

Colic (draws legs up and in great pain, stomach badly swollen)

Earache (severe pain made worse with application of heat)

Infant diarrhea (associated with teething, with slimy, green stools)

Insomnia (sleepless or restless first part of night)

Nerves (in turmoil; nothing is tolerable)

CHINA OFFICIALIS (Saturn)

Also known as CHINCHONA. This remedy is made from the bark of the Peruvian tree in South America and used extensively in the 1800's for malaria in Europe.

Nosebleed (if it doesn't stop within ten minutes, switch to Ferrum Phos.)

Diarrhea (acute, frequent, painless bowel movements which tire individual; can result from eating too much fruit)

Ears (ringing noise in them)

Menses (dark clots with abdominal swelling, profuse and with pain)

Fainting (from loss of blood)

Post-partum hemorrhage

Fever (a three-phase type with chills, severe shaking, fever, then followed by sweating, thirst and exhaustion)

COCCULUS INDICUS (Mercury, Uranus)

Made from the Indian Cockle shell found in the Caribbean, this remedy is well known for helping anyone who suffers from car, air or boat sickness.

Travel sickness in any kind of vehicle or airplane, nausea or dizziness

Insomnia (due to stress)

Sea sickness

Indigestion (brought on by anger, grief, stress; intensified by sight or smell of food)

COFFEA (Mercury, Uranus)

Made from the coffee bean, this remedy is well known for helping people who have a very low tolerance to ANY kind of pain. This remedy works primarily on the nervous system.

Insomnia (due to exhaustion or too much excitement)

Fainting (from excitement)

Toothache (aggravated by heat/hot fluids—could be an abscessed tooth—go to the dentist and find out)

COLOCYNTHIS (Mars, Uranus, 12th House)

This remedy is made from the Bitter Cucumber and has a marked sphere of action involving spasms anywhere in the body. The person becomes extremely irritable and crabby due to the pain, and is a good symptom to indicate use of this remedy.

Menses (cramp-like pains that can double one over in order to relieve)

Diarrhea (colicky pains associated with)

Colic (writhes or twists in pain; can't lie still)

CUPRUM METALLICUM (Mercury, Venus, Uranus, Neptune)

Made from Copper, this remedy sees action in spasmodic kinds of symptoms. It is one of our great epilepsy remedies.

Stomach cramps

Leg cramps

Epilepsy

Convulsions

EUPATORIUM PERFOLIATUM (Saturn, Cancer, Virgo)

Made from the herb, Thoroughwort, Eup. Perf. is a wonderful flu remedy—particularly a full blown case of the flu with all the accompanying aches and pains.

Flu (bone/joint pain, stiffness, restless with thirst; pain when pressure applied to the eyeballs)

Cough (chronic and loose; associated with flu)

Fever (associated with the flu, with chills, thirst, sweating and is highest at 7-9 a.m.)

FERRUM PHOSPHORICUM (Mercury, Mars, Pisces)

Made from iron, Ferrum Phos. should be thought of immediately when getting a cold or flu. If none of the symptoms have set in yet, this remedy can stop a cold or flu from developing! But it is important to take it before symptoms manifest. Also, it is an excellent remedy to take after a cold or flu has gone on, and seems to hang on too long. Anemia responds to this remedy. Great cure for fever.

Earache (early stages of)

Fever (with slow onset, pale but with red cheeks)

Head cold (early stages of)

Flu (early stages of)

Nosebleed (especially in children but can be used for adults also)

Cough (hard, dry with a tickle; chest aches from it)

Headache (throbbing and feels better with cool cloth)

Bleeding (menses) (bright red and clots readily, flow is heavy, great for razor or knife cuts)

Abscesses (early inflammation of)

GELSEMIUM (Jupiter, Neptune)

Made from the Yellow Jasmine shrub, Gelsemium is known as the "RELAPSE REMEDY"—any kind of relapse, whether it be acute or chronic. For instance, reappearance of a cold, flu, bronchitis or pneumonia can be stopped with this remedy. Chronic Fatigue Syndrome is often helped by this remedy and is known to stop a relapse from occurring.

Flu (shivering, stiffness, heaviness of limbs and headaches; not thirsty)

Summer cold (from change in weather, may be chills up and down spine)

Headache (as if band around the head, hammering at back of head, heaviness of eyelids)

Migraines

Chronic Fatigue Syndrome

Sore throat (swollen, difficulty in swallowing with pain shooting from throat to ear when swallowing, no thirst)

Fear (paralyzed with fear)

Eye strain (eyeballs sore, lids droop and feel heavy; vision dims)

Fever (no thirst, head is very hot with headache, wants it dark and quiet)

Hay fever (eyes hot and heavy, sneezing, throat tickle and dry; pain in ear (s) if swallows)

Measles (with very high fever or delirium)

Depression (after the flu, listless or anxiety over forthcoming ordeal/stress)

Menopause (when periods are late and scanty, heaviness in womb as if being crushed or squeezed)

HEPAR SULPHUR CALCAREUM (Neptune, Gemini, Pisces)

Made from Calcareum Sulphide, this remedy should be thought of for people who, like the plaster of paris the remedy is made from, build protective walls to hide within to protect themselves from the pain of the world around them. Any kind of thick yellow mucus discharge, this remedy should be used.

Skin ailments (any kind of lingering skin condition which may have eruptions or boils, festers easily)

Cold sores

Earache (stitching-type pains, sore throat, desire for heat, nothing pleases)

Nose (ulcerated or sore)

Cough (suffocating-type of cough, croupy and discharge is thick, ropy, yellow or yellow-green in color)

Croup (if it doesn't work within an hour, try Aconite or Spongia)

Toothache (teeth sensitive to touch)

Gums (bleed easily)

HYPERICUM (Mercury, Uranus)

Made from the herb, St. John's Wort, this remedy's sphere is centered in the nerves of the body. Dental pain is especially helped.

Pain (any nerve-like pain associated with any type of trauma from tooth extraction, crushed toe or finger, skin abrasion to post-operative pain)

Tooth extraction (kills pain afterward)

Fractures (takes away pain. Use Arnica to reduce swelling and finish up with Bellis Perennis)

Post-surgery pain

Concussions of brain or spine

Eye injury

Burns (relieves pain—can use ointment form or take tablets)

Wounds (puncture, incised, lacerated)

Insect bites/stings (if there is pain shooting upward from bite/sting; if not, use Apis)

Earache

Hemorrhoids (for pain associated with)

Bell's Palsy (7th facial nerve in face)

Dental surgery (of any kind—use before and after surgery)

IGNATIA AMARA (Moon, Mercury, Uranus)

Made from the St. Ignatius Bean, this is the premier "grief remedy." Grief of any kind, so long as it is still "on the surface" and not buried, can be alleviated and shortened with use of this remedy. Anyone who hates cigarette smoke is a candidate for this remedy.

Hysteria brought on by any kind of situation

Hypersensitive to emotions, pains or odors (car fumes, tobacco, and they may sigh more than normal)

Hiccoughs (caused by emotional upset, eating or smoking)

Insomnia

Headache (head feels elongated, throbbing in center of)

Fainting (after an upset)

Nerves (from sudden shock or trauma, and "goes to pieces")

IPECACUHANA (Moon, Cancer)

Made from Ipecac Root, the remedy's sphere of action is on nausea and vomiting.

Nausea (which isn't relieved by vomiting)

Vomiting

Hyperventilation

Nosebleed

Bleeding (bright red and hemorrhaging)

Asthma attack

Pregnancy (for nausea and/or vomiting)

Fever (irregular and with heat and nausea)

LEDUM PALUSTRE (Saturn, Uranus)

Made from the herb, Marsh Tea, Ledum works in the realm of puncture and nail wounds.

Puncture wounds

Nail wounds

Insect bites

Animal scratches or bites

Black eye

Fractures (can interchange with Arnica and Ledum to reduce swelling and absorbed blood. Symphytum should also be given the first few weeks to help bones knit more quickly)

NUX VOMICA (Moon, Mercury, Mars, Gemini, Pisces)

Made from the Poison Nut, this is the "addiction remedy" that can help someone say "no" to an addictive substance—whether it be cigarettes, social drugs or any kind of medical drug. Nux Vom. is also a great indigestion remedy.

Indigestion (by excessive eating or drinking with heartburn 1-2 hours after eating)

After eating indigestion

Constipation

Insomnia (occurring after mental strain or cannot sleep after 3 a.m.)

Mental strain

Headache (with vertigo or feeling as if head were split with a nail)

Vertigo

Eyes (light sensitive)

Hemorrhoids (itching)

Fainting (from sight of blood or from strong odors)

Colds (from exposure to cold weather/wind)

Colic (from overeating)

Cough (gagging, retching cough, feverish and chilled)

Diarrhea (from indiscriminate eating; alternate with constipation)

Hay fever (long bouts of unrelieved sneezing, nose stuffed all night, irritation of eyes, nose and face—if it doesn't work within an hour, try Sabadilla or Arsenicum)

Nerves (constantly frustrated, critical, fussy and hypersensitive)

Pre-menstrual tension (if with flashes of anger/temper, irregular cycle plus pain first couple of days during)

Travel sickness (nausea along with splitting headache)

PHOSPHORUS (Mercury, Mars, Pluto, Gemini)

Made from Phosphorus, this is a remedy that should be handled with great care and by an experienced homeopath. To take this remedy too often can invite disaster, as it can destroy red blood cells. A little of this remedy goes a long way. It is one of our great respiratory/lung remedies, as well as arresting hemorrhaging.

Gums (bleeding easily)

Nosebleeds

Surgery (to cut down risk of abnormal bleeding)

After surgery nausea (from anesthesia)

Menstrual (heavy flow)

Colds (both nostrils blocked or one alternately blocked)

Cough (racking type cough that shakes body; causes headache. Weight on chest)

Eyes ("floaters" or black dots before eyes)

Fever (alternates with chills)

PULSATILLA (Moon, Cancer, Virgo, Pisces)

Made from the herb, Wind Flower, this remedy is decidedly female or for people who are highly volatile, temperamental and change like the weather. It is also for any kind of runny, thin, clear discharges from any orifice of the body—including eyes and ears. It is also the Mumps remedy.

Indigestion (bloated or gas from eating fatty foods

Varicose veins

Emotional (up and down, sensitive, cries easily or is easily moved)

Pre-menstrual tension (if moods, emotional. Period may be unpredictable, late or shortened)

Cold (that is "ripe" or fully in evidence)

Asthma

Headache (periodic type; from eating fatty food or ice-cream)

Hiccough (from drinking something cold)

Lactation (breast milk is scanty)

Nerves (from bad news or emotional upset)

Eyes (sties)

RHUS TOXICODENDRON (Moon, Mars, Neptune, 12th House)

Made from the herb, Poison Ivy, this remedy works well in the area of sprains and strains that are BETTER with movement.

Poison Oak/Poison Ivy

Flu (fever, diarrhea, pains, stiffness and thirst for cold water)

Fever (with great restlessness of body/mind; thirst)

Skin (which burns or itches or with pustules, swelling or blisters)

Air sickness

Joints (stiffness or having to "warm up" before they feel loose and free)

RUTA GRAVEOLENS (Mars)

Made from Rue - Bitterwort, this remedy works chiefly on the ligaments, tendons and joints of the body. If the pain increases with movement and doesn't get better after moving around a bit, then consider this remedy.

Ligaments (trauma with stiffness)

Joints (stiff)

Muscles (bruises or soreness to)

Eyes (bruised feeling)

Sciatica (worse lying down)

Teeth (dry socket after extraction)

Sprains (use Arnica first and then Ruta Gravolens)

Bruised feelings in general—no matter what part of the body is affected)

SPONGIA TOSTA (Neptune, Gemini)

Made from the ocean-going Sponge which is roasted, this remedy is a wonderful respiratory/lung helpmate.

Hoarseness

Cold (burning in nose and sore throat)

Croup

Cough (dryness of all passageways, dry, barking)

Lymph Glands (swollen, pain when turning head)

SULPHUR (Saturn, Pluto)

This remedy is made from sulphur

Skin (dry, scaly; may be itchy or burning)

Loss of memory

Constipation

Diarrhea (in the morning)

Hands/feet (burning sensation in them)

Eyes (sties)

SYMPHYTUM OFFICINALE (Saturn)

Made from the Comfrey plant, this remedy has no equal in mending any broken bone, torn cartilage or tendons in our body. It also helps with bleeding stomach ulcers.

Broken bones (helps knit and heal faster; eases pain) (also see Hypericum)

Eyes (any trauma or blow to)

VERATRUM ALBUM (Uranus)

Made from the herb, White Hellebore, this is a premier diarrhea remedy.

Diarrhea (with abdominal pains, cramps, sweating and exhaustion)

Cramps (abdomen, legs or calves)

Surgery (good for post-operative shock)

Nausea (with severe vomiting)

OTHER HOMEOPATHIC APPLICATIONS

ARNICA OINTMENT: For use in application to minor cuts, abrasions and bruises. Takes away swelling. If an open wound, clean properly with antiseptic and then place AROUND outer edges of it but not in the wound itself. Excellent for bruises, around skin scrapes.

CALENDULA OINTMENT: (Sun ruled) Excellent healing remedy for any open wound (bed sores, ulcers, wounds, etc.); put around outer edges of it.

HYPERICUM TINCTURE: (Mercury, Uranus) Place around or over affected area where there is nerve-like pain. Will speed healing, particularly of a nerve origin.

PRESCRIBING BY ACUTE OR CHRONIC ILLNESS SYMPTOMS

Dr. Mathur, one of great homeopaths, had put a book together called "Principles of Prescribing," in which he put down specific indications for a specific remedy. This method, which names both acute and chronic conditions is presented below along with my twenty-three years of homeopathic observations. Do NOT try any of these remedy without first consulting and receiving approval from a homeopathic physician.

ACONITUM NAPELLUS (Uranus, Mars, 12th house)—Panic Attacks. Anxiety attacks.

ANACARDIUM ORIENTALIS (Pluto, Mars, 4th, 8th, 12th houses)—"Gang banger" remedy. For persons who show tendency toward violence, lack of morals, sociopathic behavior. Mental burnout. Impaired memory. Lack of self-confidence. Easily offended. Malicious behavior. Weak memory — cannot remember what had just been read. (Gelsemium is good for those whose FEAR of tests make them forget what they've retained).

ANTIMONIUM TART. (Neptune)—Asphyxia, especially from drowning. Suffocation from being overcome by smoke. Suffocation from foreign object in throat (make sure object is removed before giving this remedy). Pneumonia, emphysema, bronchitis or asthma where the person feels as if they are going to suffocate. Great rattling in chest with little mucus coughed up.

ARGENTUM NITRICUM (Mercury, Gemini)—Apprehension in general. Craving for sweets and sugar of all kinds. Uncomfortable using elevators. Hoarseness. Total loss of voice in singers or speakers.

ARSENICUM ALBUM (Pluto, Mercury, Virgo, 12th house)—Food poisoning, herbicide, insecticide or heavy metals poisoning. Good for any kind of inhaled noxious or chemical fumes. Flu remedy. Phlebitis. Great fears of death, being left alone or of being robbed. Great mental anguish. Moves from room to room, cannot sit still when under pressure. Asthma remedy—worse around midnight. Hayfever (Sabadilla and Natrum Mur. are good for this condition).

BARYTA CARB (Saturn) — Mental retardation. Autism. Senile dementia. Slow in speech. Slow in thinking. Confusion. Loss of memory. Loss of strength, particularly in respiratory ailments—even a cough, they lack strength to cough up phlegm.

BELLADONA (Uranus, Mars, Mercury)—Scarlet fever, air sickness (Cocculus or Tabacum). Sudden onset of any acute illness with high fever, redness to face/cheeks. Painless sore throat. Ear infections/aches — can save a child from a shunt operation.

BELLIS PERENNIS (Mars)—Soreness after any kind of traumatic blow. Tumors or semi-hard tissue that forms after a blow that is not dissolved with Arnica. Bellis is especially helpful in severe ligament or tendon ailments and broken bones (Symphytum to heal bones quickly, but Bellis to remove the tissue trauma around the break.)

BRYONIA (Saturn, Cancer) Migraine headaches. Hoarseness. Pneumonia, bronchitis. "The grump" remedy because these people when they get ill, want to be left alone, crawl into bed, pull down the shades, have absolutely no noise around them. If a person comes to talk to them or help them, they get exceedingly irritable and grumpy with them. Like an old wounded bear being prodded—you'll get bit.

CACTUS GRANDIFLORUS (Saturn, Mars, Leo)—pre-eminent heart attack remedy (Aconite, also). For mitral valve. Weight on chest. Unable to breathe. Violent palpitations. Endocarditis. Angina Pectoris.

CALCAREA CARBONICA (Saturn, Jupiter, Moon, Taurus, Cancer) — Teeth problems of all kinds. Chalk teeth. Slow to speak as a toddler. Sudden spurts of growth that leave child "crippled" due to bones growing too fast for muscle's growth to keep up. Forgetful. Confused. Fear of insanity or loss of reason. Painless hoarseness.

CALCAREA FLOURICA (Saturn, Jupiter, Cancer, Pisces)—hard, bony growths of any kind.

Nerve ganglia. Croup. Goiter. Hard knots in woman's breast.

CANTHARIS (Mars, Moon, Scorpio)—Bladder infections. First or second degree burns with burning sensation.

CAPSICUM (Mars, Moon)—Homesickness. Delirium tremens.

CARBO. VEGETABILIS (Neptune, Jupiter, Gemini)—Shock remedy (also, Rescue Remedy). For people who have NEVER completely recovered from an illness (Gelsemium is also a relapse remedy). Asthma, with blue skin.

CAUSTICUM (Saturn, Moon)—Fear of dogs. Post-operative urinary retention. Rheumatic pains in limbs. Arthritis. Restless legs at night (Nitric Acid, also).

CEANOTHUS (Neptune)—Agent Orange remedy. Spleen enlargement.

CHAMOMILLA (Mars, Moon, Cancer)—Teething. Colic. Earaches (Belladonna is also very useful—especially in infections). Very irritable when sick.

CHELIDONIUM MAJUS (Jupiter)—Liver disorders. Gallstone colic. Gallbladder attack.

CINA (Neptune)—Worms. Grinding teeth may be indications of parasites/worms in body). Child craves sweets because worms thrive on sugar of any kind. Will stick finger up nose and bore into nasal cavity because of the "itching" in the nose—a signal of worms/parasites. Child or adult is VERY cross, ugly and is often always hungry. Always rubbing nose because it itches. Eggs hatch at new moon and full moon—so watch for these reactions especially around these time frames. Get tested by doctor to confirm parasite/worm infestation—many people have them in the U.S.!

DROSERA (Mercury, Gemini)—Whooping Cough. With the return of so many old diseases, Whooping Cough among them, plus others, if you have children, this is a good remedy to have on hand—just in case.

ECHINACEA (Neptune)—Cancer pallative—will ease the last stages of a person dying from this disease. Blood poisoning or septic states—be SURE and get to emergency room or see doctor if you see a red streak on skin originating from wound area! Gangrene.

EUPATORIUM PERFOLIATUM (Saturn, Cancer, Virgo)—aching bones or muscles with flu. Dengue fever. Soreness of flesh with flu.

EUPHRASIA (Mars, Moon, Cancer)—Hayfever (Sabadilla, Arsenicum also good).

FERRUM MET. (Mars)—Anemia due to iron deficiency.

FERRUM PHOS. (Mars, Mercury, Pisces)—

Fever of an unknown origin. Fever that responds to nothing else. Relapse remedy (Gelsemium, Carbo. Veg.).

FOLLICULINUM (Moon)—Loss of sex drive. Menopause, estrogen-replacement—take this instead of allopathic estrogen. Mastitis. Hair falling out in women. Pre-menstrual migraines. PMS symptoms with extreme emotional and mental instability. Hayfever. Recurring cystitis in women. Weight gain without excessive eating, worse before menses or during ovulation.

GELSEMIUM (Neptune, Uranus, Jupiter)—Never well since any acute or chronic illness. Relapse remedy (see Ferr. Phos., Carbo. Veg.). Illness brought on by nervous stress. Nervousness. Fear of tests. Flu. Diarrhea from emotional/nervous excitement. Diarrhea from from fright, bad news or good news.

GLONOINE (Sun, Mars)—Sunstroke. Heat stroke. Bursting headache from over-exposure to sun.

GRAPHITES (Jupiter)—Keloid scar tissue. Nails brittle and crumble. Nails deformed, painful, sore, thick or crippled.

HEDEOMA (Saturn, Mars)—Poison oak remedy (Rhus Venenata will also cure it).

HEPAR SULPH. (Neptune, Pisces, Gemini)—Imbedded splinters. Sinus infections—acute and chronic. Sinusitis. Abscessed teeth (low dose to dissolve it). Conjunctivitis. Pains in bones of face, particularly above and below eyes. Used to bring up stubborn mucus from lungs. Thick, stringy, yellow/green mucus. Do NOT give to a Tuberculosis patient!

HYDRANGEA (Moon, Aries, Cancer, Scorpio)—Kidney nephritis, kidney aches of any kind. Use in tincture form only and do NOT give to a person who either genetically has kidney stones in family tree or who has a known history of kidney stones. Kidney flush to clean them out of all kinds of debris, including mucus.

HYPERICUM (Uranus, Mercury)—Injuries to nerves. Root canal. Crowns being placed on teeth. (If remedy doesn't work, try Carbo. An. or Coffea.)

IGNATIA (Uranus, Mercury, Moon)—For grief of any kind. Loss of person or animal in your life. Grief caused by a move to another country or location. Loss of friends, loved one, etc. Coffee craving diminishes. Depression caused by grief. Hysterical. Hates smell of tobacco in any form. If grief is not cured with this remedy, consider Natrum Mur.

IODUM (Sun, Mars, Taurus)—Hyperthyroid. Goiter. The Plague.

IPECACUANHA (Moon, Cancer)—Vomiting. Nausea with pregnancy.

KALI BICH. (Jupiter)—Sciatica. Sinus. Sinusitis. Thick green/yellow mucus or discharge. Eye discharge, thick. Aching across forehead from headache or sinus inflammation.

KALI BROM. (Uranus, Saturn)—Psoriasis. Chronic gout. Epilepsy (with salt-free diet).

KALI MUR. (Gemini, Pisces)—Menstruation with clots and possible hemorrhage.

KALI PHOS. (Uranus, Mercury, Aries)—Mental strain. Mental burnout. Humming and buzzing in ears. Nervous dread.

LAC CANIUM (Uranus, Moon, Taurus)—Pains which are erratic and shift from side to side. Diphtheria. Rheumatism. Arthritic pains that shift or alternate constantly.

LACHESIS (Neptune, Moon, Jupiter, Mercury, Gemini, Scorpio)—Snake bite. Venom poisoning. Diphtheria. PMS symptoms BEFORE onset of menses. Craving for alcohol. Alcoholism. Cellulitis. Menopause "hot flashes." (Sepia will help some cases also).

LATHYRUS (Neptune)—Polio. Paralysis of limbs. Infantile paralysis.

LATRODECTUS MACTANS (Neptune, Uranus, Leo)—Angina Pectoris with pain radiating down left arm and fingers with numbness.

LEDUM (Uranus, Saturn)—Puncture wounds. Bites of insects. Black eye from blow. Poison oak. Anal fissures.

LILIUM TIGRINUM (Mars, Moon, Scorpio)—PMS symptoms, especially emotionally volatile, swinging from depression to anxiety. Rheumatoid arthritis.

LYCOPODIUM (Saturn, Moon, Capricorn)—Pre-senility remedy. Good for elderly who have weak memory, thin, withered, always chilly with poor circulation. Gas and flatulence. Afraid to be alone. Depression. Malnutrition. Weakness of muscles. Constipation. Hemorrhoids.

MAGNESIA PHOS. (Uranus, Mercury, Leo)—Hiccoughs. Sciatica. Injuries to nerves (Hypericum). Goiter. Toothaches better with heat or hot liquids. Angina pectoris. Asthma. Cramps in calves. Darting pains. Twitching of muscles. Great muscular weakness.

MEDORRHINUM (Neptune, Uranus)—Gonorrhea. Chronic rheumatism. Child dwarfed or stunted. Chronic pelvic inflammation disorders—PID. NOTE: This is a miasm remedy and must not be taken without specific direction from a homeopathic physician.

MERCURIUS VIV. (Pluto, Neptune)—Syphilis, second stage. Rheumatoid pains. Tremors throughout body. Foul smelling breath. Diarrhea. Trembling of hands. Thinks they are losing their minds. Slow in answering questions.

MERCURIUS IODATUS RUBER (Mars, Pisces) Diphtheria, especially if left side of throat is ulcerated.

MILLEFOLIUM (Mars)—Hemorrhage. Small pox with pain in stomach. Nosebleed. Bleeding hemorrhoids. Painful varicose veins in pregnant women. Continued high temperatures (Ferrum Phos.). Bloody urine.

NATRUM BROM. (Saturn)—Acne simplex.

NATRUM CARB. (Neptune, Aquarius)—Great debility or weakness caused by summer heat. Sunstroke. Exhaustion. Weak ankles. Slow mental comprehension. Headaches from slightest mental exertion. Easy dislocation or spraining of ankles.

NATRUM MUR. (Saturn, Moon, Aquarius, 12th house)—Salt craving. Hyperthyroid. Coffee craving. Deep, suppressed emotions of any kind, particularly grief and anger. Good for people who have experienced shock treatment in hospital. Electric shock of any kind. Hayfever. Migraine headache. Hangnails. Sweats while eating. Loss of hair. Hives. Greasy skin. Eczema. Warts on palms of hands. Headache (migraine variety) that begins with blindness.

NAT. PHOS. (Mars, Libra)—Heartburn. Indigestion. Conditions arising from eating TOO MUCH sugar. Acidity of stomach. Joints crack and pop. Colic. Yellow Jaundice.

NATRUM SULPH. (Jupiter, Taurus)—Head injuries of any kind. Asthma in children. Chronic headaches in general. Spinal meningitis. Warts on fingers and toes. Gonorrhea in males. Chronic gout.

NITRICUM ACIDUM (Pluto, Mars, Scorpio)—Bleeding, painful hemorrhoids. White spots on nails. Warts, jagging and bleeding. Black pores on face. Hoarseness. Restless legs.

NUX MOSCHATA (Neptune)—Narcolepsy. Faints at the sight of blood.

NUX VOMICA (Mars, Moon, Mercury, Gemini, Pisces)— Alcoholism. Antidotes bad effects of allopathic drugs—short or long term use. Hang over. Addiction remedy—trying to get off any kind of addictive substance such as cocaine, marijuana, heroine, etc. Liver ailments. Good liver cleanser.

ONOSMODIUM (Saturn, Moon)—Migraine headaches. Sexual desire completely destroyed. Loss of sexual desire. See Folliculinum for loss of sexual desire.

OOPHORINUM (Venus, Moon)—Ovarian cysts. Menopause where estrogen is given, this remedy can replace it—naturally and without side effects—see homeopathic physician. Menopausal problems in general. See: Folliculinum, another menses and menopause remedy.

PALLADIUM (Mars, Venus, Moon)—Ovarian cysts. Premier ovarian remedy for many ovary conditions. See: Folliculinum and Oophorinum.

PETROLEUM (Neptune, Saturn)—Car or ship sickness (Cocculus, Tabacum). Antidotes lead poisoning. Hair falling out. Herpes. Eczema. Psoriasis. Of special use where skin conditions have improved and gone away, but the person does not improve.

PETROSELINUM (Neptune)—Gonorrhea remedy that has accompanying urinary symptoms. Bladder infections (Cantharis).

PHOSPHORICUM ACIDUM (Neptune, Uranus)—Relieves Cancer pain. Mental exhaustion. Nervous exhaustion. Blue rings around eyes. Of great use to children who grow up rapidly, and who are overtaxed mentally or physically. Used when the person has been exposed to a debilitating acute or chronic disease, excesses of any kind (mental, emotional), grief or loss of vital fluids (blood, urine, excessive sweating, etc.), this remedy is excellent.

PHOSPHORUS (Pluto, Neptune, Mars, Mercury, Gemini)—Writer's block. Hemorrhage. Bad effects of anesthesia after surgery. Mental burn out (Kali. Phos.). Cataracts. Post-operative vomiting. Yellow Jaundice. Hepatitis. Uterine polyps. Hoarseness with pain. Pneumonia. Bronchitis. Joints suddenly give way. Scurvy. Skin fungus. NOTE: This remedy should never be used without the direct intervention of a homeopathic physician. NEVER give this remedy to someone who has a known case of Tuberculosis, or has had it in the past. It is dangerous!

PHYSOTIGMA (Uranus, Mars, Mercury)—Spinal injuries. Paralysis caused by spinal injury. Tetanus. Post-Diptheria paralysis. Spinal cord inflammation; polymyelitis. Cerebro-spinal meningitis. Night blindness.

PHYTOLACCA (Saturn, Mars, Pisces)—Mastitis. Retarded dentition—teeth slow in coming into mouth. Swollen lymph glands. Rheumatism. Diphtheria. Mumps. Swollen tonsils.

PILOCARPUS MICROPHYLLUS (Mars)—Limits duration of Mumps. Eye strain. White spots before eyes. Excessive perspiration from all parts of the body.

PLATINA (Neptune, Mars, Moon)—Sterility caused by ovary problems. Nymphomania. Pain in vaginal area. Ovaries sensitive and burning.

PLUMBUM METALLICUM (Saturn)—Progressive muscular atrophy. Gout. Loss of sexual power in males. Tinnitus. Distinct blue lines along margins of gums. Glaucoma.

PULSATILLA (Moon, Cancer, Virgo, Pisces)—

Measles. Mumps (if this remedy doesn't work, go to Rhus. Tox). Panic Attacks. Anxiety attacks. Styes. Runny, thin discharges of any kind—coming from eyes, ears, nose, mouth, urinary or anal.

RAPHANUS (Jupiter, Mars)—Post-operative gas pains or flatulence.

RHODODENDRON (Uranus, Mars)—Rheumatism. Swollen joints. Arthritis worse before a storm. Gout of toe joints. Tearing pain in all limbs. Neuralgia type pain of eye, orbit and head. Carpal tunnel of wrist (Ruta Grav. and Rhus Tox. may also help).

RHUS TOXICODENDRON (Neptune, Mars, Moon, 12th house)—Arthritis. Joints hot or swollen—better with motion. Rheumatic pains anywhere in body, bones, muscles or joints that are always better with motion and movement. Limb stiffness. Numbness of extremities. Typhoid. Cellulitis. Poison Oak (Rhus Venenata). Knee-joint tenderness. Bursitis. "Tennis Elbow." Chicken-poxHerpes zoster. Fever blisters around mouth.

RHUS VENENATA (Saturn, Mars)—Poison oak. (When Rhus Tox. does not cure it).

RUTA GRAVOLENS (Mars)—Tendon injuries. Sprains or strains (Arnica/Bellis Perennis). Cartilage injuries. Ganglia. Sciatica. Stiffness of hands and wrists. Arthritis. Pain in bones of feet and ankles. NOTE: All the above conditions are WORSE with movement.

SABADILLA (Neptune, Pisces)—Hayfever. Worm infections in children (Cina, Silica). Constant sneezing.

SCROPHULARIA NODOSA (Jupiter, Moon)—Breast cancer remedy. (Conium is another breast cancer remedy.) Hodgkin's disease. Painful hemorrhoids.

SCUTELLARIA LATERIFLORA (Uranus)—Chronic Fatigue Syndrome (Gelsemium, Nat. Carb. may also work). Flu—after over it, great weakness.

SEPIA (Saturn, Moon, Gemini, Virgo, Pisces)—Chocolate craving before menses. Menopause. Morning sickness. Hot flashes (See: Lachesis, Folliculinum, Oophrinum, Platina).

SILICEA (Neptune, Saturn, Sagittarius, Pisces)—Wounds that refuse to heal (Sulphur). Abscesses. Boils. Ganglia. Eliminates scar tissue (Graphites.) Fissures. Nails crack. Bursa. Tumors. Nodes. Keloid scars. Sciatica. White spots on nails. Sore feet. NOTE: Do not give this remedy to anyone who has a transplanted organ or pace-maker in their body—it will expel them! Do NOT give this remedy to anyone with a known history of Tuberculosis or who has it presently.

STAPHYSAGRIA (Pluto, Mars, Moon, Scorpio, 12th house)—Rape. Anger. Suppressed anger.

(Also, Nat. Mur.) Colic after anger in children. Sexually molested babies/children. Helps the anger to get out and not allow it to be suppressed for decades.

STRAMONIUM (Neptune, Mercury, 12th house)—Stammering. Talkative. Delusions, hears voices, sees ghosts, hears voices and talks with spirits. Violent and lewd. Delirium tremens.

SULPHUR (Pluto, Saturn)—Allergic to milk which causes diarrhea. Forgetful. Difficult to think. Relapse remedy (Gelsemium). Hang nails. Eczema. Psoriasis.

SYMPHYTUM (Saturn)—Healing of bone fractures. Bones that won't heal. Blows to the eye (Aconite). Tendon, ligament injuries. Pain in knees. Knee injuries.

TABACUM (Neptune)—Motion sickness of any kind. (Cocculus, Petroleum.) Allergy to tobacco of any kind. Vomiting during pregnancy.

TARENTULA HISPANIA (Uranus, Mercury)—Multiple Sclerosis. Epilepsy of a hysterical origin. Hysteria. Extreme restlessness.

TARAXACUM (Jupiter, Virgo)—Bladder cancer.

TELLURIUM (Neptune)—Ringworm. (Nat. Mur. and Sepia will also help this condition.) Sciatica. Eczema behind ear. Herpes circinatus.

Tendon contraction in knees. Eczema.

TEREBINTHINA (Neptune, Mars)—Worms or parasites accompanied with foul odor on breath. Bright's disease (kidney). Dropsy (excessive liquid in some part of the body).

THUJA OCCIDENTALIS (Moon)—Warts; large, seedy or pedunculated. After-effects of any vaccination reaction. If child has never been well after any vaccination, this remedy should be considered. Gonorrhea.

URTICA URENS (Mars)—First degree burns. Rheumatism associated with rash-like skin eruption. Antidotes ill-effects of eating shell fish. Gout. Uric acid. Herpes labialis. Chicken pox. Burns or scalds of a first degree nature.

VERATRUM ALBUM (Uranus)—Post-operative shock (Aconite). Cholera. Violent vomiting and/or diarrhea.

VIBURNUM OPULUS (Uranus, Moon)—Prevents miscarriage. Colic. Menstrual cramps.

VIBURNUM PRUNIFOLIUM (Uranus, Neptune)—Tongue cancer. Hiccoughs.

VIPERA (Neptune, Saturn)—Phlebitis, with legs hanging down. Liver enlargement. Polyneuritis. Polio-myelitis.

CHAPTER ELEVEN
The Endocrine System

The endocrine system, one of the many systems of the body, consists of the following glands: the thyroid, the parathyroid, the pituitary, the adrenals, the thymus, portions of the glands with ducts (the islands of Langerhans in the pancreas) and parts of the ovaries and testes.

The main function of these glands is to contribute hormones to the body that affect the activity of other cellular mechanisms and organs. Each of these glands manufactures hormones, chemical messengers that regulate many of the metabolic functions of the body. Thus when just one of these glands begins to dysfunction, the metabolism falters.

Although for many decades doctors have ignored the endocrine system or tested the glands only when nothing else could explain why a patient was ill, the medical world today is gradually paying more attention to the system, which is often the root of a problem and needs to be tested first rather than last.

Because of its vital importance to health, medical astrologers should have a working knowledge of the endocrine system. With the natal chart as a guide any endocrine problem can usually be quickly detected. Then the necessary test or tests can be initiated. Because tests involving the endocrine system can be very expensive, time-consuming and even dangerous, an endocrinologist should always be consulted in a case that involves a potential glandular dysfunction.

PITUITARY GLAND

Astrological Rulers
Capricorn (anterior pituitary) and Cancer (posterior pituitary).

Characteristics
The bean-sized pituitary gland is located within a depression in the middle of the skull and is attached to the brain by a narrow stalk. There are two portions—the anterior and posterior lobes. Each secretes its own hormones, and each has its own functions, although the hormones secreted by the posterior lobe are still somewhat of a mystery.

The anterior pituitary gland produces hormones that stimulate the other ductless glands to manufacture their own hormones. It also produces a hormone called somatatrophic that controls the rate of growth and has a relationship with the breast glands that produce a mother's milk. This growth hormone is related to every cell in the body: its thyrotrophic hormone activates the thyroid gland, which in turn regulates the intermediary metabolic processes of all cells. The thyroid and growth hormone between them control the size of the body as a whole.

Diseases and Tests
Diseases of the pituitary are often very difficult to diagnose. The target glands of the pituitary—the thyroid, gonads and adrenals—are capable of producing their own hormones without the pituitary, but not very effectively. Because of this complex interrelationship between the pituitary and its target glands it is often difficult to determine whether a disease originates with the pituitary or with a secondary target gland.

Tests for the pituitary are also very difficult to perform. They require highly trained personnel and specialized laboratories. There is also a high degree of patient risk with these tests, since the laboratory measurement of the growth hormone is still being researched. Therefore, most present-day testing is conducted upon the hormone function of the target glands. Pituitary testing done on blood serum, plasma, urine or hair samples is considered safe. Hyperpituitarism: Because of the mystery surrounding the posterior lobe, when the terms *hypo* and *hyper* are used in connection with the pituitary gland, they usually refer to the anterior lobe. Hyperpituitarism of the anterior lobe is excess production of the growth hormone. If the hyperpituitarism occurs before the epiphyseal closure, giantism results; if it occurs after the epiphyseal closure, the result in adults is acromegaly, wherein the jaw, bones, hands and feet show overdevelopment and features become large.

The standard glucose tolerance test with blood samples can measure growth hormone production to determine if hyperpituitarism exists. *Hypopituitarism*: With hypopituitarism growth of the body and sexual development are normally arrested. When hormone secretion from the anterior lobe is slow or completely halted, dwarfism results. Other related ailments are Simmond's disease, Sheehan's syndrome, acromicria, eunuchoidism and hypogonadism. Emaciation, muscular debility, loss of sexual function and general smallness of extremities may also occur.

An endocrine specialist should conduct any test to determine hypopituitarism. One procedure is to X-ray the skull to see if the sella turcica is depressed in the sphenoid bone of the skull where the pituitary gland rests. The x-ray also checks for possible erosion or enlargement. And a doctor should not overlook the possibility that a blow to the skull may have injured either the hypothalamus or pituitary.

Diet
The best diet for the pituitary gland is one consisting of many raw foods high in mineral content, especially magnesium, manganese, zinc and trace minerals. Alfalfa and wheat sprouts are good for the

general maintenance of the gland because they are rich in vitamins and minerals important for the gland's proper functioning: alfalfa tablets, which trigger the release of excess water through the urine, have been found to be beneficial in ailments involving the pituitary ADH factor. Other plants high in minerals good for the pituitary are yellow dock, parsley, watercress and kelp.

Carlson Wade, a medical researcher-reporter, suggests taking a morning "mineral tonic" for best performance of the pituitary gland—tomato juice, ½ lemon, 2 tablespoons celery juice and 1 tablespoon desiccated liver stirred together and drunk to influence quick activation of the pituitary for maximum morning efficiency.

Another suggested food is two tablespoons of brewer's yeast combined with natural cottage cheese: the vitamin B complex of the yeast feeds the nerve cells and the cottage cheese is a source of vitamins and essential minerals.

THYROID

Astrological Rulers

Mercury and Taurus.

Characteristics

Located at the base of the neck and around the trachea, the thyroid consists of two lobes on either side of the windpipe, which give the gland an H-shaped appearance. Iodine ingested from food and taken from the intestinal tract eventually reaches the thyroid, where it is oxidized and combined with the amino acid tyrosine to produce the hormones thyroxine and triiodothyronine. Under the influence of the pituitary's TSH release these hormones are slowly secreted into the circulation as needed.

The thyroid is very important. It stimulates the oxidative reactions of most cells in the body and aids in the regulation of lipid and carbohydrate metabolisms.

Diseases and Tests

Hyperthyroidism: Excessive secretion of thyroxine can bring on many of the following symptoms: weight loss, extreme nervousness, tremors of the hands or body, protruding eyeballs, an elevated basal metabolism rate (BMR) and in the extreme diffused toxic goiter (Grave's disease). In borderline cases of hyperthyroidism there may be sudden sweating, rapid heart beating for no apparent reason (tachycardia) and fever. In some cases insomnia also occurs.

Women are more susceptible to hyperthyroidism than men. During pregnancy the endocrine system adjusts for the fetus. Afterward the shock of the birth throws the system out of kilter, what is known as postpartum blues. The glands try to restabilize and normalize their functions for a woman without a baby, but that metabolic balance is frequently never attained. After pregnancy many women suddenly gain weight and can't lose it. Moreover, their hair loses its natural gloss and becomes dry and brittle, symptoms of glandular disorders.

The birth control pill can also adversely influence the endocrine system, bringing on damage to the pancreas, sudden hypoglycemia and hyperthyroidism. Weight gain is normal for a woman taking birth control pills, which appear to upset the balance of the thyroid gland.

There are various tests to determine hyperthyroidism, but the most common one is the T-3, T-4, T-7 test, a simple blood test that can determine the levels of the two hormones in the thyroid.

Hypothyroidism: This condition is usually characterized by a gain in weight and fatigue. Constipation and subnormal temperatures are other signals. Hair may become dry and brittle; skin, excessively dry and flaky. Since the basal metabolism rate is lowered, the pulse may slow and low blood pressure may occur. Sluggishness of all functions will eventually ensue, and muscular activity will become depressed. Other symptoms include sensitivity to cold, inducing a person to wear more clothes, sluggish nerve reflexes and a general thickening of the skin. The outer third of each eyebrow may become hairless. And there can be a decrease of bone marrow and the beginning of anemia.

Hypothyroidism in an adult, if not caught and controlled in time, is called myxedema. In some cases, because of an inborn metabolic error, the body will produce antibodies to destroy the thyroid secretions, accounting for many heretofore unexplained cases of spontaneous myxedema.

Hypothyroidism in infants manifests as cretinism, usually caused because a mother suffers a deficiency of iodine during pregnancy. (Other genetic factors may be involved.) If undetected, cretinism will permanently render an infant mentally disabled and physically handicapped within six months to a year. For that reason it is imperative that a pregnant woman known to have a hypothyroid condition consult her doctor so that the fetus's thyroid will not suffer because of the mother's insufficiency. As I've indicated, in Canada every infant receives a blood test a few days after birth to determine if cretinism exists.

There are different tests for determining whether or not the thyroid is slow-functioning. The serum TSH test is one of the best. It is also helpful in differentiating between primary and secondary hypothyroidism: a normal serum level of TSH excludes primary hypothyroidism. But if the hypothalamus is suspect of triggering the problem in the thyroid, advance tests are indicated.

Diet

During the eighteenth century many people who lived in the midwestern states suffered from goiter, which was corrected by adding more foods containing iodine to their diets. Saltwater fish were also eaten to help the thyroid maintain its normal level of activity. And it is still a good idea to include saltwater fish in the diet, especially for those people who do not live near the ocean.

Supplements such as algae, kelp tablets and Irish moss (an herb seaweed) are good for an ailing thyroid. Algae are good sources of zinc, a mineral found in high amounts in the thyroid, as well as vitamins A and D. Thus ½ teaspoon of algae powder a day will help the gland.

Brewer's yeast is also beneficial for the thyroid gland. Yeast contains riboflavin, niacin and thiamine, all integral in the transport of oxygen within the cells. Iodine then works to help the hormone thyroxine step up the oxidation process.

PARATHYROID

Astrological Ruler

Saturn.

Characteristics

The four small glands of the parathyroid are connected with and embedded in the thyroid. They secrete the hormone parathormone, which regulates the calcium-phosphorus metabolism. The bones of the body as well as the cardiac muscles depend upon this gland to release the proper amount of calcium to maintain a level of strength in the skeletal system and consistency of heartbeat. Parathormone is also necessary for neuromuscular activity, blood clotting, cell membrane permeability and proper functioning of several enzymes.

Diseases and Tests

Hyperparathyroidism: Whenever the gland increases the secretion of calcium, several problems result. Muscular weakness occurs because of excessive calcium levels in the bloodstream. Kidney disease may eventuate as deposits of calcium or calcium stones occur within the organs. And calcium is stolen from the bones to flow into the blood, causing demineralization and resorption of the bones to occur: such excess calcium in the blood is called hypercalcemia.

To determine hypercalcemia a serum calcium

blood test may be run. If the test proves that hypercalcemia exists, then a phosphate clearance test and phosphate resorption test may be given to see if the parathyroid gland is causing the rise in blood calcium levels.

Hypoparathyroidism: The first symptoms of hypoparathyroidism are bodily stiffness, cramps and spasms of the muscles at different times for no apparent reasons (not Charlie horses, caused by sudden physical exercise), twitchings of the muscles, increased excitability, tension, worry, fear, sleeplessness, confusion and depression. An infant of two years old or so who is labeled hyperactive because he or she is cranky, irritable and emotionally excitable may actually be suffering from a lowered calcium level.

The severe form of hypoparathyroidism is known as tetany, a nervous affection in which the muscles of the legs and arms jerk involuntarily. It occurs most frequently among younger children or women who are pregnant or breast-feeding. With tetany there is a numbness and tingling of the extremities, especially the hands. It can be fatal if allowed to go untreated.

The first step in determining hypoparathyroidism is to get a blood serum calcium test. A test to find out if the parathyroid hormone is the root of the problem has still not been perfected.

Diet

A diet high in calcium, vitamin D and magnesium is best for the parathyroid. Without adequate vitamin D calcium is not absorbed properly, and magnesium plays an important part in the release of parathormone. It is not wise, however, to use milk as a source of calcium: adults do not need milk, which only creates pockets of mucus in the body that eventually slow down the internal absorption processes. In fact, any dairy product should be taken in moderation, since they all are mucous-producing. Supplements of calcium gluconate or dolomite tablets with vitamin D (fish liver oil only) will do the job instead.

The diet should perhaps also be low in phosphorus. With hypoparathyroidism phosphorus levels increase. Furthermore, Americans generally consume large amounts of foods very high in phosphorus. But of course, anyone contemplating a phosphorus-free diet should first consult a physician.

Several herbs are good for the parathyroid. Springtime horsetail is 50 per cent silica and excellent for rebuilding brittle or calcium-robbed bones. Other herbs with high calcium contents are lamb's-quarters, mallow, mint and field mustard. Dandelions, soybeans, watercress and filberts (hazelnuts) are also rich in calcium.

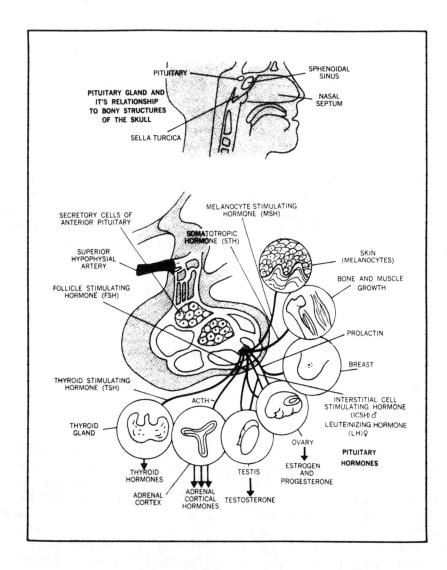

The Pituitary
Master Gland of the Endocrine System

Reprinted with permission of: F.A. Davis Company, Taber's
Cyclopedic Medical Dictionary, Edition 13, revised, 1977.

ADRENALS

Astrological Ruler
Mars.

Characteristics
Perched atop each of the kidneys, the adrenals actually consist of two separate glands: the cortex tissue and the medulla. The cortex secretes hormones, such as cortisone, that deal with fluid and electrolyte balance, influence the carbohydrate metabolism and help determine the levels of sex hormones. The medulla helps with the release of adrenaline (epinephrine), a hormone that is responsible for the breakdown and mobilization of glycogen and fatty acids so that energy is available upon call.

The adrenal glands are very important in the body. When the pituitary gland releases ACTH, activity is triggered in the adrenal cortex: the resulting hormones, cortisol and corticosterone, affect protein, carbohydrate and lipid metabolisms. In addition, aldosterone affects the excretion of sodium and potassium in the body. And androgens and estrogens are released, which affect secondary sex characteristics, such as an individual's degree ·of maleness or femaleness.

Diseases and Tests
Stress situations play a big part in the function of the adrenal glands. Some people, who are extremely sensitive to their environments or to other people in general, can stress the glands so badly that exhaustion sets in, initiating various other ramifications.

Because of the complexity of the adrenal glands there is no clear-cut case of hyper- or hypoadrenalism. Instead there are disorders involving each of the hormones released by the adrenals. Following are some of the more common adrenal malfunctions that may occur.

Cortical Hypofunction: Known medically as Addison's disease, cortical hypofunction is characterized by muscular weakness, apathy, gastrointestinal complaints, pigment changes in the skin, loss of weight and depressed sexual drive. Primary Addison's is caused by the failure of the adrenal glands; secondary Addison's is caused by the failure of the pituitary gland to secrete ACTH.

For any test involving the adrenal glands, an endocrine specialist should be consulted. The 17-ketosteroid test is one of the most common tests run to see if the adrenal cortex is functioning properly. Another test, plasma ACTH, may also be run.

Elevated Aldosterone Levels: High output of aldosterone produces high blood pressure, a condition that then creates hypertension and prepares the body for other vascular diseases.

Cushing's Syndrome: When there is excess secretion of the cortical hormones, many diverse symptoms appear. There is a loss of protein, fatigue, weakness, sexual impotence, capillary fragility, edema, excessive hair growth, diabetes mellitus and skin discoloration.

Hypoglycemia and Diabetes: Stress is often a factor in these two related ailments. For people who have suffered severe stress at some time the adrenal glands usually falter. The stress is then transferred to the pancreas and eventually either hypoglycemia or diabetes will occur.

Diet
The adrenals contain a good supply of phosphorus, pantothenic acid and zinc. Since most Americans receive enough phsophorus through their daily diets, this mineral is not usually lacking; but if a person is undergoing a continued stress situation, foods high in zinc should be considered.

Brewer's yeast, high in minerals, is also very good for anyone under stress and is beneficial in any program to rebuild the adrenal glands. (Of course, it is also important to remove the stress situation if possible.)

Several herbs are useful in rebuilding the adrenal glands. Chamomile and catnip are mild nervines. Licorice root, another herb good for the adrenal glands, should be used in conjunction with hawthorn, but heart patients should consult their doctors before using hawthorn. In fact, anyone using powerful herbs such as skullcap and valerian root, recommended for the adrenal glands, should receive a physician's permission. A person who is taking drugs should especially check with the doctor to see if there are incompatabilities between the above mentioned herbs and the drugs.

THYMUS

Astrological Ruler
Neptune.

Characteristics
Located in the chest directly behind the sternum, the thymus gland weighs 13 grams at birth, growing rapidly the first two years of life. At puberty it weighs approximately 30 grams. Then after puberty the thymus diminishes until by adulthood it has become small and fibrosed.

The thymus gland is of major importance in fighting infections that invade the body. It releases small lymphocytes (distinguished from large lymphocytes that come from a different source within the body) called thymocytes, which, when released, move to other lymphoid organs and into the lymph glands. Even after the thymus shrinks and atrophies, the gland continues to function, with the thymocytes acting as watchdogs that recognize antigen and alert the body to any intruders so that the immunity system may function. Thymocytes are also converted into fibroblasts when a wound is beginning to heal.

Considered part of the lymph system, the thymus functions during stress situations caused by illness. It filters toxins through the lymph containing the tissue of the tonsils and the lymph nodes in the immediate area of bacterial or viral invasion.

Diseases and Tests

Since the thymus helps fortify the immunization system of the body, if it is not functioning properly, bacterial and viral infections can occur, causing continual sniffles, colds and flu. In children ailments can include more serious viral infections, such as rheumatic fever and scarlet fever.

At present there is no specific test to determine activity of the thymus. Instead several kinds of blood chemistry tests may be run to ascertain the gland's activity or lack of activity.

Diet

Some sources suggest that the mineral chloride is very beneficial to the thymus. Foods high in chloride are cabbage, beets, onions, turnips and cucumber.

The vitamin B complex is necessary for the continuing function of the thymus. Lecithin and riboflavin are of particular importance.

PANCREAS

Astrological Ruler
Virgo.

Characteristics

The pancreas is a comet-shaped gland situated behind the stomach. Its head is attached to the duodenum, and its tail reaches back to the spleen.

The first function of the pancreas is to release enzymes from the gland when food enters the duodenum. These enzymes are important to the further chemical breakdown of the food so that once it begins its journey through the intestines the nutrients can be assimilated through the walls for use by the body.

The second function of the pancreas involves the alpha and beta cells found within the glands.

The beta cells of the islands of Langerhans secrete a protein substance called insulin. When the

level of blood sugar (glucose) increases, the vagus nerve is stimulated or the presence of the food in the duodenum activates insulin. How much or how little insulin goes into the bloodstream is determined by the level of glucose in the blood.

The alpha cells of the islands secrete glucagon, which acts on the liver to break down stored sugar (glycogen) to increase the sugar in the blood. Whenever we become ill, exercise, experience fear or other kinds of stress, the glucagon is released from the pancreas. Glucagon has other jobs involved with the lipid and protein metabolisms, and it is felt to affect the kidney's excretion of inorganic substances, such as sodium, potassium, calcium and phosphorus.

Diseases and Tests

Hyperglycemia: Hyperglycemia is commonly known as diabetes, but not always. Simply put, diabetes is any condition in which the blood sugar is elevated and not assimilated. For sugar to be taken up into tissue insulin is necessary. If there is a deficiency of insulin, the sugar is not absorbed, and a great metabolic imbalance occurs, involving mineral, protein, fat, carbohydrate and water metabolisms. A metabolic imbalance of such proportions is called *diabetes mellitus.*

There are several possible reasons for diabetes to occur. A person suffering from Cushing's disease may experience elevated cortisone levels that will trigger elevated sugar levels. Cushing's disease itself may be caused by a pituitary tumor involving the growth hormone and causing elevated blood sugar. Tumors or abnormal growth of tissue within the pancreas will also antagonize insulin production. And any destruction of the cells of the islands of Langerhans will result in either acute or chronic pancreatic insufficiency and create hyperglycemia.

People taking various drugs for medical reasons may develop the disease, too. Individuals treated with steroid drugs are susceptible to diabetes. Birth control pills can alter the pancreatic output of hormones. And thiazide and loop diuretics, commonly known as water pills, taken in too high a dosage or for too long a time, are likely to cause low potassium levels (hypokalemia), which in turn will suppress the release of insulin from the pancreas.

Stress caused by an acute infection or myocardial infarction can bring on hereditary diabetes. Other types of stress, such as severe emotional hardship or suffering, may also cause the disease. In addition, an overactive thyroid induces hyperglycemia because of the increase of certain active amino acids derived from tyrosine.

There are also many symptoms of diabetes. The first and most common is excessive thirst: a person will drink glass after glass of water to try to curb his or her thirst, but to no avail. There is also increased hunger, with a person eating more food to try to curb his or her appetite. Boils and carbuncles may appear on the skin. There can be a loss of weight, emaciation, weakness and debility. Headaches are common, and tiredness ensues. There may be a sweetish odor to the breath. If the disease is allowed to go uncontrolled, nausea, vomiting and air hunger, resulting in labored or difficult breathing because insufficient oxygen gets to the lungs, take place, accompanied by a sense of intoxication and delirium. A deep coma may eventually result, causing death.

To determine the root cause of diabetes, a person should undergo a five-hour glucose tolerance test, followed up by other special tests.

Hypoglycemia: Hypoglycemia, rapidly becoming the most common ailment in the United States because of the amount of the sugar we consume, results when too much insulin is secreted, regardless of whether or not the glucose level rises in the body. The overstimulation of insulin beta cells will create lowered levels of glucose, and for an unknown reason glucagon is not released to elevate the necessary sugar to bring the metabolism level back up to a safe operating level.

The reasons for hypoglycemia are many and varied. A tumor in a cell in the island of Langerhans may secrete insulin without the monitoring of the normal metabolism orders. A tumor within the abdominal cavity or liver may interfere with the pancreatic duties. A diminished pituitary function may result in diminished hormone secretion. Similarly, a hypofunction of the adrenocortical hormones (Addison's disease) may result in hypoglycemia. Liver ailments, such as hepatitis, can badly damage the liver, creating a sugar (glucagon) problem without pancreatic influence. And a diabetic woman giving birth may pass on hypoglycemia to her child via genetic and nutritional deficiencies.

The major symptom of hypoglycemia is that three to five hours after eating a meal a person will suddenly feel extremely tired for no seeming reason because the blood sugar levels are falling rapidly. Eating protein brings the levels back up, but if the individual does not eat, he or she will feel weak and trembly: hands may shake, or the whole body may quiver. The person will become extremely nervous, restless and tense. Confusion and loss of coherent speech patterns may also manifest. Finally, the individual may faint, go into a coma or possibly die, if he or she does not eat.

These symptoms may be accompanied by signs of mental disorder.[1] A person may feel as though he or she is going insane. There will be loss of con-

fidence, fear without reason and delirium. Mood changes are immediate, accompanied by inappropriate emotional responses, lack of empathy or introverted activity. In some cases, a hypoglycemic may hear voices or see things that do not exist. In moderate and severe cases he or she may even contemplate suicide.

The standard, authorized test for determining hypoglycemia is the five-hour glucose tolerance test. As I've indicated, anyone wishing a test for hypoglycemia should make sure that it is a five-hour test, not a two- or three-hour test. Since some hypoglycemics don't begin to manifest lowered blood sugar levels for several hours, the five-hour test is the only sure way to diagnose this ailment.

Furthermore, people diagnosed as "borderline" hypoglycemics should consider themselves to have hypoglycemia and follow a regimin to stabilize the condition. Because their bodies are much more acutely sensitive to changes than those of other people, some borderline cases exhibit all the signs of hypoglycemia while still registering in the "normal" range. For example, people with planets in Virgo or Pisces or with strongly placed Neptunes—e.g., Neptune conjunct the First or Tenth House cusps or conjunct another planet—are usually sensitive to metabolic changes. So are people with planets in the Sixth and Twelfth Houses.

Diet

Sulfur is necessary for the pancreas because the hormone insulin contains the mineral as one of its important constituents. Diabetics respond well to pineapple juice because it is rich in the mineral. Other juices containing sulfur are the juices of watercress, cabbage, radishes and turnip tops, all of which also contain riboflavin.

Brewer's yeast is of great importance as well. It contains chromium, vital to the proper functioning of the pancreas. The vitamin B complex in the yeast also benefits the adrenal glands, which can be partly responsible for a hypoglycemic condition.

OVARIES

Astrological Rulers

Scorpio and Pluto, but for pregnant women, Cancer and the Moon.

---

[1] In fact, doctors formerly believed hypoglycemia to be a mental illness, perhaps schizophrenia, and treated it by prescribing tranquilizers or having patients committed to mental wards, sanitariums and insane asylums. Fortunately, today's doctors are beginning to recognize hypoglycemia as a genuine physical ailment, but some hypoglycemics even today, if not tested, are committed to mental institutions.

Characteristics

A woman's ovaries produce the hormones estrogen and progesterone, responsible for sexual characteristics, uterus preparation for pregnancy and development of the mammary glands in the breast. The follicle stimulating hormone (FSH) encourages the growth of the ovarian follicles. As they grow, another hormone, progesterone, thickens the lining of the uterus to receive the egg. The hormone stimulates the pituitary gland to release the luteinizing hormone (LH).

It takes a balance between these two hormones to bring about the release of the egg for fertilization down in the uterus. The corpus luteum of the ovary produces progesterone, which will halt ovulation production and secretion of estrogen. This action will cease menstruation in a woman during pregnancy. If there is no fertilization, the progesterone decreases and the familiar 28-day cycle starts all over again.

Diseases and Tests

Many women complain of premenstrual cramping or excessive bleeding, verging on hemorrhaging. Some women also have trouble conceiving, a problem that may be attributed to an endocrine malfunction. And during menopause many women experience hot flashes and mental instability while the endocrine system is shutting down some of its hormonal secretions.

Estrogen levels are usually determined through tissue sampling, easily undertaken with a Pap test. There are as yet no laboratory procedures available to check the endocrine functions.

Diet

Among the vitamins and minerals beneficial for the ovaries are vitamin E, vitamin A, fatty acids, calcium, magnesium and selenium. Vitamin E and selenium are highly recommended to help increase chances of fertilization. Vitamin A helps keep the mucous membranes of the ovaries healthy. Fatty acids are good for alleviating some generative problems. As dolomite, a combination of magnesium and calcium, has been known to make hot flashes disappear during menopause.

Among the herbs that are good for the ovaries, black cohosh contains some natural estrogen supplement, and cramp bark and raspberry leaves are well-known for prevention of cramps.

Women who experience severe hemorrhaging may get relief from the cell salt kali muriaticum (chloride of potassium). This cell salt, given at 6X potency, can halt most heavy menstrual bleeding within ½ hour to 45 minutes if four milk-lactose tablets are taken every five minutes until the bleeding

ceases and normal flow begins. Once the flow is controlled, four tablets taken three times a day between meals will usually insure menstruation without heavy flow or clotting.

TESTES

Astrological Rulers

Scorpio and Pluto.

Characteristics

The male endocrine glands, the testes, are located in the scrotum. Secondary male sexual characteristics are produced from several other glands. The pituitary gland sends FSH, a special hormone, to the testes, where testosterone is produced and circulated throughout the bloodstream for the masculinization of the body. This FSH is responsible for production of sperm.

Diseases and Tests

Very little seems to go wrong with the testes; however, if the hormone androgen is missing, sexual interest can abate and erection may fail, creating impotence. There also may be troubles with the prostate gland, located around the neck of the bladder and urethra in men, which produces a glandular secretion that helps form semen. A common ailment in men after middle age (45) is that the prostate becomes enlarged, causing partial or complete blockage of urine from the bladder. After men reach the age of 60, tumors and calculi stones related to ailments of the prostate gland are also quite common.

The prostate can be checked through a rectal examination. A sperm count can also be taken to check fertility. And androgen levels can be ascertained through various tests that a physician may choose.

Diet

Several supplements and foods can aid an ailing prostate. Pumpkin seeds, an excellent source of zinc, help the gland. Vitamin E, sunflower seeds and the herb yarrow also contain zinc as well as certain amino acids very beneficial to the prostate. And magnesium has been quite successful in treating prostate enlargement.

Unsaturated fatty acids, such as sunflower, cottonseed and wheat germ oil, will stimulate the testes to manufacture testosterone. And the herb sarsaparilla contains three hormones beneficial to the testes—progesterone, cortin and testosterone. A cup of sarsaparilla tea a day is recommended.

PINEAL

Astrological Ruler
Neptune.

Characteristics
Pineal is the French word for "pine cone." This oval, red gland sits in the brain and is often called the third eye because it looks like an eye. Descartes, the seventeenth-century philosopher, felt that the pineal gland was the seat of the soul. The gland could possibly be involved in extrasensory perception, such as telepathy and intuition.

Scientists know very little about the mysterious pineal. They have been unable to trace a hormone to the gland. However, they do know that, somewhat like the thymus, the pineal gland is more enlarged through puberty then shrinks as adulthood approaches. Some biochemists feel that the pineal gland might be the computer that activates the body.

Diseases and Tests
Some medical sources suggest that the pineal may stimulate the adrenal cortex: if the gland is overactive, it may be partly responsible for certain types of mental illness; if underactive, backward development of children may occur. Calcium salts, known as "brain sand," can silt the gland: the deposits tend to harden the arteries and cause atrophy or deterioration of the pineal.

There is no laboratory test available to determine whether or not the pineal is malfunctioning.

Diet
Organic sodium and potassium found in green salad vegetables seem to be excellent nutritional sources for keeping the pineal gland in good working order. Fatty acids and kelp tablets are important supplementary foods. Alfalfa sprouts, pineapple juice and parsley are also good sources of food for the pineal.

CHAPTER 12
Transits And Medical Astrology

Below are POTENTIAL health indication via the transits, or daily motion of the planets. The best way to use HEALTH TRANSIT is in conjunction with the Med-Scan Technique ("MST") (see Appendix, Cosmic Patterns), which outlines the potential vitamin/mineral deficiency symptoms for the individual. With the slower moving transits, such as Saturn, Uranus, Neptune and Pluto, potential nutritional deficiencies may be created within the individual during that time. However, to make sure, check your MST and see if you are potentially deficient in that specific nutrient. If you are not, do not worry about it.

However, if it is indicated by your MST that you have a natal potential for this particular nutrient deficiency, then a licensed health practitioner should be consulted to confirm the symptoms and dosage.

If homeopathic remedies are mentioned in the transit, write to the National Center of Homeopathy (see Appendix). They can provide a list of homeopathic doctors in your area, and you can consult one to confirm the use of that particular remedy. Any time a remedy is suggested, an (hr) will appear after it, meaning homeopathic remedy. You may order from Hahnemann Pharmacy (see Appendix). If it specifies Calm's Forte, see Appendix for Standard Homeopathic Company information. If a Bach Flower Remedy (see Appendix for information) is mentioned, it will be designated with a (bfr) behind it.

WARNING: As with any homeopathic remedy, you take it 1 to 3 times for one day only and stop after that. Homeopathic remedies work on the principle that when the symptoms stop, you stop taking the remedy!

TRANSITING MERCURY:
CONJUNCT VENUS: Because you may be nervous and more on edge than normal, you could develop a mild sweet tooth and crave sugar and desserts. Mentally, you're in a good state of mind and happy.

SQUARE VENUS: Your nerves are on edge due to possible lack of affection or love during this period. You may unconsciously eat sweets to make up for lack of affection. Try Sepia 6X (hr) if you have a chocolate craving attack.

TRINE VENUS: You're in a pleasant and happy state of mind. Rewards pop to mind and you're liable to reach for more desserts or sweets than usual. Careful! You don't want to gain weight. Moderation, please.

INCONJUNCT VENUS: You're in a situation that demands flexibility. Can you bend? If not, your nerves may be set on edge and you'll reach for sugar products and desserts to pacify them. Possible mild weight gain during this transit. Try Sepia 6X (hr) if you have a chocolate craving attack.

OPPOSITION VENUS: Feelings center around emotional issues and affection needs, creating a temporary state of nervousness. If not fulfilled, your need for sugar or desserts is likely to skyrocket for a day or two. Sweets are not a viable trade off for lack of affection. Think before you reach for extra sweets or desserts. If you have a chocolate craving, try Sepia 6X (hr) to curb it.

CONJUNCT MARS: You're a case of nervous and seemingly inexhaustible energy. Careful where you focus it. Possible injuries to fingers or hands, by burns or around mechanical contraptions. Muscle sprains or strains are also possible. If feeling "wired," try Calm's Forte (hr) which is designed to feed the nerves and quiet them.

SQUARE MARS: Nervous and skittish, you're wired for action. You may leap before you look, causing possible bruises, muscles strains and sprains. If working around mechanical things, be careful; your fingers or hands could suffer in a mild mishap. At home, especially in the kitchen, look out for burned fingers, or burns around a fire. Try Calm's Forte (hr) to feed and, therefore, calm your screaming nerves. Take some deep breaths and "chill out."

INCONJUNCT MARS: Accidents are in the air. Your nervous energy combines to make you less attentive than usual. Watch out around any firearms, fires (stoves, fireplaces, etc.) or for straining a muscle by doing too much too quickly. Restless and flighty, you cannot sit down because you are restless. Pay attention to your driving, where you're walking, or any other daily activities! Try Calm's Forte (hr) to help feed and calm your raw nerves.

OPPOSITION MARS: Accidents are still in the air—and more likely to occur. You will be bumping into things, dropping things and, in general, feeling nervous and out of kilter. Be attentive around fire (stoves, fireplaces, etc.), firearms, mechanical things and driving. Remain focused and concentrated—channel this nervous energy—do not let it run you or minor accidents could happen. Possible sprained muscle from over-exertion. Try Calm's Forte (hr) to help feed and calm nerves.

CONJUNCT JUPITER: Nerves are on edge and sweet things, especially sugar and desserts, will appeal greatly to you. Weight gain due to nervousness and overeating. If craving chocolate, try Sepia 6X (hr) to neutralize it. Indigestion possible from nervousness. Try Lycopodium 6X (hr). Possible Vitamin B-1 deficiency which can also cause sugar craving.

SQUARE JUPITER: You are jumpy and nervous; try to relax and do not blow things out of proportion. There is a tendency to overeat because of your nerves. Curb your tendency to binge by working it off in exercise of some kind.

INCONJUNCT JUPITER: You could be a bundle or raw nerves right now. Try Calm's Forte (hr) to feed and support your nerves during this period. A situation could present itself and you will be asked to bend (not break). Be a willow and your health, specifically your nerves, will be fine through this period.

OPPOSITION JUPITER: Nervousness on a big time scale is going to make you feel restless, even frantic occasionally. Insomnia may occur. Try Calm's Forte (hr) to soothe and feed your nerves during this time. Binge eating also a possibility. Bleed off excess nerves with some mild form of exercise.

CONJUNCT SATURN: Possible mild depression, with a gloomy outlook for a couple of days. Exercise in some form will help "lift" outlook. Nervous exhaustion that may be helped with Vitamin B-1 or Calm's Forte (hr). If beaten down via nerve-induced stress, a possible cold may occur. Try taking Vitamin C during this transit to alleviate this possibility.

SQUARE SATURN: Mentally you may find yourself pessimistic or in a mild state of gloom. If nerves are frayed, rest. This is a time to sit back and ease off the throttles or a cold may catch up with you as a result. Try Calm's Forte (hr) to supplement the nerves during this time period.

INCONJUNCT SATURN: Nervous exhaustion may create a mild form of depression or gloom. Some Calm's Forte (hr) may be in order to feed nerves and soothe them. Get some form of mild exercise to create a more positive state of mind. Eat plenty of fresh fruit high, in Vitamin C, to stave off possible cold or flu.

CONJUNCT URANUS: Nerves are taut, you are restless and super-energized. Be careful around electrical appliances and plugs. Possible electric shocks. Accident prone—pay attention to what you are doing; do not lose focus or concentration. You may bump into things and drop objects. Try Calm's Forte (hr) to soothe and feed your nerves.

SQUARE URANUS: Accidents can occur! Your nervous energy makes you frazzled and unfocused, which puts you in that mode. Pay attention to your driving! Concentrate! Nerves are taut, and insomnia is a possibility. Help with Calm's Forte (hr).

INCONJUNCT URANUS: Your nerves are at a breaking point, or so it seems. Accidents are possible, so be alert. Problems around electricity or electrical shock. Injuries to fingers or hands. Try Calm's Forte

(hr) to soothe and feed nerves. Trauma or shock situations may occur. Try Rescue Remedy (bfr).

OPPOSITION URANUS: Nerves are raw, and you are jumpy, restless and taut. Possible electric shock or sudden, unexpected trauma situation presents itself. Use Rescue Remedy (bfr). Injuries to fingers and hands occur in odd, quirky ways. Insomnia. Try Calm's Forte (hr).

CONJUNCT NEPTUNE: Mentally feeling confused, disoriented, poor sense of time and in general, sluggish or lethargic. Mind will not focus well. You may want to sleep or lay around and rest more than usual—do so. Kali Phos. 6X (hr) will help keep mind sharp and concentration will return. Potential misdiagnosis by health practitioner—get a second opinion! Poor time to do surgery; possible infection, malpractice or reaction to drug(s) and/or anesthesia. Apathy.

SQUARE NEPTUNE: Mentally feeling diffused and you may lack concentration. Try Kali Phos. 6X (hr) to stay alert and focused. Medical misdiagnosis possible-seek second opinion. Not a good time for surgery. Infection, malpractice or drug reaction may occur. Low tolerance to drugs in general—especially tranquilizers. Try Calm's Forte (hr) instead. The need to sleep more and rest up. Do so.

INCONJUNCT NEPTUNE: Watch out for medical misdiagnosis! Seek a second or even third opinion. Allergic reactions possible to drugs (of any kind). Try not to schedule surgery at this time—may get infection, malpractice or nasty drug reaction. Medical test results may be lost, switched, or invalid. Tests may have to be repeated to ensure accuracy. The need to sleep more than usual—do so. Try Kali Phos. 6X (hr) to keep mentally alert and focused. There will be a tendency to become spacey, dreamy and ungrounded during this time.

OPPOSITION NEPTUNE: If ill during this period and you must go to a doctor, beware of misdiagnosis! If serious, seek a second or even a third opinion. Test results may be inaccurate, switched or lost! Mentally fuzzy and unfocused. Try Kali Phos. 6X (hr) to feed brain cells to keep going at intense pace successfully.

SQUARE PLUTO: Nerves will be tested and they may feel raw. Restless and nervous, Calm's Forte (hr) will help support them during this period. Intense mental effort may be required. Try Kali Phos. 6X (hr) to keep from getting burn out.

INCONJUNCT PLUTO: Your nerves may feel at the breaking point, plus you may suffer from mental burn out. If nervous, try Calm's Forte (hr). If intense mental effort is required, Kali Phos. 6X (hr) may help.

OPPOSITION PLUTO: Intense mental effort

may be required. Kali Phos. 6X (hr) will support inundated brain cells. Nerves will be stretched thin and Calm's Forte (hr) may help.

TRANSITING MOON:
CONJUNCT/SQUARE/OPPOSITION MERCURY: Nerves may play havoc with emotions during this period. Restless and may have insomnia. Try Calm's Forte (hr).

TRINE VENUS: There will be the temptation to indulge in extra sweets or desserts during this period. If craving chocolate, try Sepia 6X (hr).

CONJUNCT/SQUARE/OPPOSITION MARS: Possibility for emotional flare ups that could manifest as anger. For women, uterine complaints connected with menstrual cycle.

CONJUNCT/SQUARE/OPPOSITION SATURN: Mild depression may lurk around, but it's only temporary. Wanting to be alone or quiet. Seek solitude and quiet as a positive health outlet. Meditate, go for a quiet walk with nature, or do something that appeals to your inner needs.

CONJUNCT/SQUARE/INCONJUNCT/ OPPOSITION NEPTUNE: If ill and going to doctor, be very careful of misdiagnosis. Seek a second opinion. Medical tests run during this time are suspect of being inaccurate, switched or lost. Problems with taking any medical drugs during this time—adverse side effects or perhaps allergic reaction—be careful! Otherwise, a period of confusion, lethargy and even exhaustion. A time to catch up on sleep. Rest is indicated, otherwise you are susceptible to colds or flu. This should be a day of quiet to feed your spirit and inner being. Meditation, yoga or other more spiritually oriented work-outs are best.

CONJUNCT/SQUARE/INCONJUNCT/ OPPOSITION URANUS: Accidents may happen. If you have not cleared out emotions such as anger, frustration or disgust, they may manifest as a small accident. Remain focused and pay attention to what you are doing—do not be drawn off by some emotional situation that is still hanging around you.

CONJUNCT/OPPOSITION PLUTO: A highly intense emotional period. Be prepared for a marathon where you are possibly "running on your feelings" or your emotions are catapulting you into a situation. If the stress being applied is positive, no problem. However, if you perceive it as negative stress, then the immune system will depress, possibly leaving you open for a cold or flu to follow shortly after the emotional "blow out".

TRANSITING VENUS:
CONJUNCT MOON: A desire for more sweets or desserts at this time. There may be a need for extra Vitamin B-2 during this time period to help curb excess sugar hunger. Check for deficiency symptoms.

SQUARE MOON: Because your emotions are being battered, you may reach for sugar products or sweets to buoy you during this period. Check Vitamin B-2 deficiency symptoms that may contribute to sweet craving. Or, consider a Vitamin B-complex during this period to support potentially depressed immune system. If you have hypoglycemia or diabetes, this period may bring about a crisis—watch food intake and insulin needs.

INCONJUNCT MOON: A decided sugar hunger may rear its ugly head. Check Vitamin B-2 for deficiency symptoms. Emotions are ragged, and sweets are often used in lieu of real affection or love that may be denied during this period.

OPPOSITION MOON: You will desire sweets more than usual during this period. Possibly, a Vitamin B-2 supplement is in order to curb this desire. Check for deficiency symptoms. Overeating or binge eating is possible due to emotional developments that are stressful.

CONJUNCT MARS: The desire for sweets or sugar may become intense. Check for Vitamin B-2 deficiency symptoms. If craving chocolate, try Sepia 6X (hr). Possible weight gain during this period. Binge eating or overeating due to love/affection emotions not being properly supported.

SQUARE MARS: If not getting proper support from your loved ones there is a tendency to replace it with sugar products or binge eating. Skin may get dry during this period. Check Vitamin E deficiency symptoms. For women, possible problems with menstrual cycle. Vitamin E may help. Generally, if emotionally upset, indigestion may be helped with Nat. Phos. 6X (hr). Possible weight gain.

INCONJUNCT MARS: Binge eating is possible, or over consumption of sweets and sugar because the love and affection you need may not be getting proper support from those around you. Check Vitamin B-2 deficiency symptoms. If craving chocolate, try Sepia 6X (hr). Skin may become excessively dry. Check Vitamin E deficiency symptoms. Possible weight gain. If feeling exhausted or lethargic, test for anemia; iron may be needed.

OPPOSITION MARS: Indigestion due to emotional upset with a loved one. Nat. Phos. 6X (hr) may help. Craving for sweets because love and affection may not be returned. Check for Vitamin B-2 deficiency symptoms. If craving chocolate, try Sepia 6X (hr). If feeling tired or exhausted, test for anemia; iron may be needed.

CONJUNCT/SQUARE/INCONJUNCT/

OPPOSITION JUPITER: There is a tendency to overeat with great ease here. Binging is possible! If craving sweets, check for a Vitamin B-2 deficiency. If craving chocolate, try Sepia 6X (hr). Moderate weight gain is possible if you do not curb your inclination to overeat. Do not use food as a placebo for emotional needs.

TRINE JUPITER: Overeating will be easy at this time; so, if you do not want a weight gain, monitor your intake of how much and what food you eat! There will be a definite desire for more sweets and sugar than usual. Check for Vitamin B-2 deficiency symptoms. If craving chocolate, try Sepia 6X (hr).

CONJUNCT/SQUARE/INCONJUNCT/ OPPOSITION SATURN: Appetite may be suppressed due to emotions. An excellent time to start a diet. Skin may be dry, so check for Vitamin E deficiency symptoms. Also, if skin problems appear, try Sulphur 6X (hr). If wrestling with loved one(s) on emotional issues during this time, the immune system could become depressed. Extra Vitamin C may be needed to stave off possible colds or flu that could result. Protect skin against sunburn. If sunburned, try Calendula lotion (hr).

SQUARE/INCONJUNCT/OPPOSITION URANUS: Sudden binge eating episodes or craving for sugar. Check for Vitamin B-2 deficiency symptoms. If craving chocolate, try Sepia 6X (hr). Blood pressure may change if you are under sudden, traumatic stress; have it checked. Sudden and unexpected skin changes. Check for Vitamin E deficiency symptoms. Or, if sudden skin ailments erupt, try Sulphur 6X (hr).

CONJUNCT/SQUARE/INCONJUNCT/ OPPOSITION NEPTUNE: If hypoglycemic or diabetic, pay attention to diet and insulin needs during this period. Unconsciously eating a lot of sugar or sweets as a placebo for the love you are not receiving from those around you. Check for Vitamin B-2 deficiency symptoms. If craving chocolate, try Sepia 6X (hr). Infections involving the skin may arise. Try Sulphur 6X (hr). If skin does not seem as healthy as it could be, check for Vitamin E deficiency symptoms. If going to a doctor, possible misdiagnosis. Get a second opinion! Problems with any kind of drug (including alcohol), and possible allergic reaction to it. Medical tests may be lost, switched or wrong. Blood sugar problems (hypoglycemia/diabetes) may be root cause of many other symptoms. Get proper tests to confirm or deny. Weight gain possible.

CONJUNCT/SQUARE/INCONJUNCT/ OPPOSITION PLUTO: Binge eating indicated here because you are not getting the love from those around you, and you may replace that need with food. Watch it! Intense sugar and sweet craving. Possible Vitamin B-2 deficiency symptom here. Check for deficiency. If craving chocolate, try Sepia 6X (hr). Skin problems. Check for Vitamin E deficiency. If skin ailments arise, think of Sulphur 6X (hr) to help them. If hypoglycemic or diabetic, problems could arise—so do not skip meals and monitor blood glucose levels for insulin needs. Indigestion that may be a Niacin lack—check deficiency symptoms first.

TRANSITING MARS:
CONJUNCT/SQUARE/OPPOSITION MOON: For women, possible menstrual/menopausal problems. Abnormal menstrual bleeding, try Kali Mur. 6X (hr). If getting "hot flashes" try Sepia 6X (hr). A focus on breasts and uterus during this period. Possible water retention or swelling. Check for Potassium deficiency. Limit intake of salt, which helps cause this condition. Try Nat. Mur. 6X (hr) to curb salt craving. For **both sexes:** if tired and exhausted, check for anemia. Emotions will be emphasized, and if negative, depress the immune system if under duress. Or use in conjunction with Vitamin C. Over consumption of dairy products (milk, cheese, ice cream); limit your intake.

INCONJUNCT MOON: If tired and exhausted, go and get tested for anemia. Check Vitamin B-12 and Iron deficiency symptoms. A craving for dairy products in general—try to limit intake. Salt craving, try Nat. Mur. 6X (hr). Emotions are frayed during this time; you may be explosive and anger will surface. Let it come out; do not suppress it. Just do it in the most positive way possible. Situations require you to be flexible, not dig in your heels. If you refuse to compromise, your immune system will be depressed and colds or flu could follow. A Vitamin B-complex and Vitamin C could be helpful in supporting the system during such a time. **FOR WOMEN:** menstrual/menopausal difficulties. If heavy bleeding during menstrual cycle, try Kali Mur. 6X (hr). If having "hot flashes", try Sepia 6X (hr). Water retention and edema possible. Curb salt intake. Check for potassium deficiency symptoms. Or try Nat. Mur. 6X (hr). PMS symptoms will be highly aggravated at this time. Try Sepia 6X or Lachesis 6X (hr).

CONJUNCT/SQUARE/INCONJUNCT/ OPPOSITION MERCURY: Your nerves are the focus. If stretched too thin, or feel raw, try Calm's Forte (hr) to soothe and feed them during this period. A lot of stress is applied to you and results may be restlessness, insomnia or a tautness (unable to unwind and relax). Watch out for injuries involving your fingers and hands. Be alert around any kind of machinery, knives or appliances at this time. Loss of focus and concentration may set you up for an accident. If alert, you will be fine. Possible nerve inflammation (Bell's Palsy). Check for Vitamin B-1 deficiency symptoms. If nerves are inured, consider Hypericum 6X (hr).

CONJUNCT/SQUARE/INCONJUNCT/ OPPOSITION VENUS: If feeling exhausted or excessively tired from the normal, possible anemia. May be deficient in either Vitamin B-12 or Iron. Eating binges on sweets possible if you are trading affection for food. Communication with loved ones may be needed. If craving chocolate, try Sepia 6X (hr). Skin may be drier than normal. Try Vitamin E. If skin problems erupt, Sulphur 6X (hr) may help. Weight gain because of ingesting too many sweets or starches.

SQUARE/INCONJUNCT/OPPOSITION JUPITER: Check cholesterol and triglyceride levels. If excessively tired or fatigued, it may be anemia, and a greater need for Vitamin B-6 to assimilate iron. Check for deficiency. Without enough Vitamins B-6 and B-12, Iron cannot be assimilated. Possible liver dysfunction may show up as indigestion. Try Chelidonium 6X (hr). Lecithin helps lower cholesterol and triglyceride levels, and also aids in digestive disturbances that involve the liver. A good time to initiate a diet or some form of exercise. Metabolism burns at a faster rate, therefore easier to take off unwanted pounds. Muscle strains possible, try Arnica 6X (hr). Possible ligament/tendon injury, try Ruta Grav. or Rhus Tox. 6X (hr). **FOR MEN:** possible prostate enlargement—may be due to lack of zinc. Check for deficiency.

TRINE JUPITER: Over expansion can happen now! And that means adding to the waist line—so watch how much and what you are eating! An excellent time to start a diet and burn off unwanted pounds. Just do not go to extremes, make it sensible.

CONJUNCT/SQUARE/INCONJUNCT/ OPPOSITION SATURN: Bone-related ailments may crop up at this time. This is a "grit your teeth" time, so problems with teeth, fillings or root canals may manifest. If root canal is eminent, try Hepar Sulph. 6X (hr) to get rid of infection and settle the tooth back to normal. If you have bone breaks, try Symphytum 6X (hr). Possible phlebitis; try Vitamins C and E. Anemia is possible. Check Vitamin B-12 deficiency symptoms. Arthritic conditions may pop up. Check Calcium and Magnesium (dolomite) and Vitamin D for deficiency symptoms to halt. Ruta Grav. or Rhus Tox. 6X (hr) may also give relief. Gallbladder problem can be healed with Lecithin. In general, a period that breeds frustration,

which manifests in a pressure cooker of feelings being blocked up inside of you. If the energy is not "drained" or released, it may make you prone to accidents in general, but especially involving cars, knives, firearms, fires (burns) and appliances. Other kinds of accidents could involve muscle strains or sprain, try Arnica 6X (hr). If a tendon or ligament is involved, try Ruta Grav. or Rhus Tox. 6X (hr). Try to deal positively with the frustration you are having to endure with mild exercise, meditation or music to help "bleed off" excess energy.

CONJUNCTION/SQUARE/INCONJUNCT/ OPPOSITION URANUS: Accident prone! Possible surgery or sudden, unexpected stress can traumatize you. Carry Rescue Remedy (bfr) with you during this period and take on an "as needed basis" when you are caught in a crisis. Muscle pulls and strains are possible, try Arnica 6X (hr). If ligaments or tendons involved, try Rhus Tox. or Ruta Grav. 6X (hr). This is an explosive period for your emotions. You will probably be volatile, restless, energetic and lack focus or concentration. Try Calm's Forte 6X (hr) to soothe and feed nerves, plus get rid of unwanted insomnia (White Chestnut, bfr). If going in for surgery during this period, consider the following homeopathic remedies: Arnica 6X for bruising and trauma to tissue, and Calendula non-alcoholic liquid to speed up healing with less scarring taking place. Injury could take place on any vehicle (including airplanes). Be careful around fires, firearms, appliances, knives or engines of any kind. Stay focused and remain alert, and you will skate through this period unscathed. Do not become fanatic or unfocused. Accidents may then occur.

CONJUNCT/SQUARE/INCONJUNCT/ OPPOSITION NEPTUNE: Misdiagnosis of some vague health condition is very possible. Please seek a second or third opinion. Be very careful taking any kind of drugs (including alcohol). There may be an allergic reaction or adverse side affect from taking them. Allergies may crop up, try Sabadilla 6X (hr). Entire immune system is under heavy stress, and can easily fold. Colds or flu are especially rampant during this transit. Try Vitamin C to stabilize immune system, along with Vitamin A. Check out deficiency symptoms. A general feeling of lethargy, no energy and no reserves. Possible adrenal exhaustion—Pantothenic Acid may help. See deficiency symptoms. Rest and sleep are a must—get plenty of both! This is NOT the time to push hard or be a workaholic. If you do or are, then you will be catching a lot of viruses to slow you down. You are extremely susceptible to any bacterial or viral infections right now. If food poisoning or botulism, try Arsenicum 6X (hr) to relieve immediately. If under constant stress, try Aconite 6X (hr) to relieve it, or Rescue Remedy (bfr). Low grade fevers, vague complaints and no clear-cut symptoms of illness, and yet, you may not be feeling in tip top condition. A good time to get a general physical examination! Anemia is possible. Check for deficiency of Vitamin B-12 or Iron. Use condoms during intercourse; you are particularly susceptible to ANY and ALL kinds of reproductive bacterial or viral infections!!!

CONJUNCT/SQUARE/INCONJUNCT/ OPPOSITION PLUTO: Possible endocrine dysfunction, the thyroid, adrenals or ovaries may be most suspect, but do not eliminate the others. Get testing if you are feeling under the weather. You are in a hard charging mode right now, the perfect workaholic syndrome. You have more energy, more drive right now, but it is a question as to whether your physical body can stand your fervent zeal. The body may break down if you do not get sufficient rest and stop going to extremes. If you exercise, do so moderately, otherwise, muscle injuries may develop; try Arnica 6X (hr). If there is injury to tendon/ligament, try Rhus Tox. or Ruta Grav. 6X (hr). Adrenal exhaustion because of your extreme drive may occur. Check out Pantothenic Acid deficiency symptoms. Possible blood problems, such as anemia. Check Vitamin B-12 and Iron deficiency symptoms. Also, severe allergy problems. See Vitamin B-12 or try Sabadilla 6X (hr). Possible severe edema or water weight problems. Try Rhus Tox. or Nat. Mur. 6X (hr). If hives occur, try Cantharis 6X (hr). If skin breaks out, think about Sulphur 6X (hr).

JUPITER TRANSITS:

CONJUNCT/SQUARE/INCONJUNCT/ OPPOSITION MOON: Because emotions may be under stress, there is a tendency to binge out on food, or possibly even bulimia. Weight gain possible. Moods may become over exaggerated or dramatic swings. There is a tendency to blow things out of proportion. Possible indigestion (liver oriented) that may be helped with lecithin. Check deficiency symptoms of Vitamin B-6. Check cholesterol and triglyceride levels. Vitamins E and F, as well as Lecithin may help in lowering it, if it is high. **FOR WOMEN:** Water weight problem might be helped with Vitamin B-6 or Nat. Mur. 6X (hr). PMS may be worse than usual—try Sepia 6X (hr). Mood swings may increase, particularly if your menstrual cycle begins five days before a full moon. Sepia 6X (hr) will help. Reproductive problems, involving either breasts or uterus; try Sepia 6X (hr).

CONJUNCT/SQUARE/INCONJUNCT/

OPPOSITION MERCURY: You will be more restless and prone to nervousness during this period. Try Calm's Forte (hr) to soothe and feed nerves. Emphasis on mental efforts. If feeling "burned out" mentally, try Kali Phos. 6X (hr) to feed brain cells to keep on going. Potential thyroid difficulties. Go to doctor and get blood test to confirm or deny if you are feeling more sluggish, mentally forgetful and are sleeping more than usual. Or, just the opposite—tightly wound up, heart palpitations and breaking into a sweat.

CONJUNCT/SQUARE/INCONJUNCT/ OPPOSITION VENUS: A tendency to over eat during this period. If affection and love are denied you, sweets, desserts and weight gaining food may replace it. Stick to fresh fruit and vegetables instead, so your weight remains steady. More Vitamin E may be needed during this time, so check deficiency symptoms before taking. Skin ailments may crop up that could be helped with Vitamin E or Sulphur 6X (hr). If under severe and unrelenting stress, hypoglycemia (low blood sugar) caused by a liver dysfunction is a possibility.

CONJUNCT/SQUARE/INCONJUNCT/ OPPOSITION MARS: Possible blood disorders, such as anemia. If tired, fatigued and exhausted, check Iron, B-6 and Cobalt deficiency symptoms. More muscle strains than usual. Try Arnica 6X (hr). Or, if more serious with ligament/tendon involvement, try Ruta Grav. 6X or Rhus Tox. 6X (hr). Cholesterol levels are suspect—go in and get it checked out. If high, try Vitamins E and F and Lecithin to lower, plus a common sense change in diet habits. A period of great exertion on some level of self. A tendency toward extremism, such as turning into a workaholic. Good time to diet, as metabolism is burning at a higher, faster rate. **FOR MEN:** prostate enlargement possible and can be helped with Zinc. Check for deficiency symptoms.

CONJUNCT/SQUARE/INCONJUNCT/ OPPOSITION SATURN: Assimilation of nutrients may be worse than usual. Try an enzyme tablet before each meal to increase absorption of vitamins and minerals. An excellent time to begin a diet, because resolve is firmer at this time. Hypoglycemia (liver) or diabetes (pancreas) may appear. Check with blood test from doctor. Liver complaints in general may be involved. If suffering from indigestion, try lecithin or Lycopodium 6X (hr). Possible gallbladder involvement, try lecithin. Skin problems may erupt, try Sulphur 6X (hr). Your feelings of insecurity or inadequacy may increase, and if they do, you may substitute food for the feeling—watch what you are eating and how much of it. Circumstances may be making you feel as if responsibilities are simply too heavy to carry by yourself any longer. If feeling decidedly pessimistic and depressed, try Aurum Met. 6X (hr) or Oak (bfr).

CONJUNCT/SQUARE/INCONJUNCT/ OPPOSITION URANUS: Possibility of spasms, tics or tremors during this period. If you get Bell's Palsy, try Vitamin B-1. Check deficiency symptoms. Nerves can take a battering all due to sudden, unexpected pressures thrust upon you. Check deficiency symptoms of Vitamin B-6 and Dolomite (a combination of Calcium and Magnesium). Nerve related ailments cropping up. Zinc is needed to feed nerves. Try Calm's Forte (hr), Wild Oat or Impatiens (bfr). Hypoglycemia (low blood sugar) may occur. A good time to carry Rescue Remedy (bfr) on you at all times to alleviate shock/trauma that you must deal with. You may be more accident prone at this time, but this can be alleviated by remaining focused and concentrated on what you are doing—especially driving.

CONJUNCT/SQUARE/INCONJUNCT/ OPPOSITION NEPTUNE: A time when you can be misdiagnosed! Get a second, or even a third, opinion! The immune system is depressed, allowing greater frequency of colds or flu. Try Vitamin C, to alleviate. Potential blood ailments having to do with bacterial or viral infection. Check for anemia, possible staph or strep infection in bloodstream. You may have many seemingly unconnected, vague symptoms. Get to a homeopathic physician and have your case taken to get proper remedy. You will want to sleep more, rest more, and in general, be out of focus with the world around you. Let yourself relax. Meditation, being alone in a tranquil environment, is the best thing for you right now. Music is therapeutic. Problems with drugs of any kind (including alcohol). Allergic reactions to them, or worse, adverse side effects. If you must take, consider one half the normal adult dose. Blood sugar level may fluctuate, check for hypoglycemia and diabetes. Potential adrenal gland exhaustion. Check Pantothenic Acid deficiency symptoms. Also, cholesterol levels may "sneak" up on you. Go in for a check to monitor it. Lecithin, Vitamins E and F may help lower it. If having to go in for surgery, possibility of infection arising from it, malpractice or problems with anesthesia during the operation. Be VERY careful about this. Elective surgery should NOT be performed during this period!

CONJUNCT/SQUARE/INCONJUNCT/ OPPOSITION PLUTO: A period of intensity on some level of your life. There is a tendency toward extremism of emotions, behavior or stressful physical demands. Try not to go over board with working too hard. Get ample rest and unplug from what is

"driving" you during this period. You may feel as if you can do anything; but remember, you are living in a body that cannot always take it. Endocrine dysfunction is possible, particularly the pancreas (diabetes) or thyroid. Indigestion problems involving liver and enzyme processes. An enzyme tablet before each meal may help, or possibly, Lecithin. If indigestion occurs anyway, try Lycopodium 6X (hr) or Nux Vomica 6X (hr). **FOR WOMEN:** there may be ovary involvement, upsetting your menstrual cycle. For older women, possible to begin menopause. Try Sepia 6X (hr) in both of the above. **FOR MEN:** possible prostate enlargement. Check for Zinc deficiency symptoms.

TRANSITS OF SATURN:
CONJUNCT/SQUARE/INCONJUNCT/ OPPOSITION MOON: In general, a time of the "blahs". Emotionally feeling depressed, more pessimistic than usual and probably, more responsibilities with women in your family (i.e., a mother/grandmother). Emotions may become threadbare during this demanding period. If depressed, try Aurum Met. 6X (hr). Feelings of inadequacy, insecurity and irrational fears may come and go—but will be particularly powerful five days before each full moon. Ignatia or Nat. Mur. 6X (hr) may help lift the gloom, as will Aurum Met. 6X (hr), Gorse (bfr) or Cherry Plum (bfr). Skin problems may arise, try Sulphur 6X (hr). There can be a lot of mental symptoms as you wrestle with emotional "ghosts" from your past, i.e., problems with your mother/home environment when you were growing up, etc. This is a time of shedding old, past conditioning tapes and responses molded by your childhood, seeing them, recognizing what they are, and breaking them. Suggest finding a homeopathic physician and have your case taken to find your constitutional remedy. This will assist you in working through them and put you into a happy, "normal" frame of mind. Bone-related problems (such as osteoporosis), possibly caused by lack of Calcium. Check deficiency symptoms. **FOR WOMEN:** reproductive/breast problems. Menstrual cycle may become scanty or non-existent due to stress. Menopause may begin for older women. PMS may be worse than usual; ovarian, uterine or vaginal involvement. Try Vitamin E or Sepia 6X (hr).

CONJUNCT/SQUARE/INCONJUNCT/ OPPOSITION MERCURY: Mentally, you may be depressed, overworked and carrying a lot more responsibility than usual. If depression is setting in, seek out the services of homeopathic physician for help. Diarrhea or colitis are possible because of the stress you are experiencing. Nerve involvement. If going to the dentist, try Hypericum 6X (hr) afterwards to soothe tooth nerve. Try Aconite 6X (hr) before hand to calm YOUR fears of the dentist! Shaking or trembling of limbs may be a Calcium and/or Magnesium deficiency. Check out symptoms. Skin disorders such as hives or herpes zoster may come on because of nervous tension/stress. Try Apis 6X (hr) for hives, and Cantharis 6X (hr) for herpes zoster. If doing a lot of demanding mental work and brain is feeling "burned out", try Kali Phos. 6X (hr). Possible to have aches and pains in general, in hands and wrists, elbows or shoulders at this time. If diagnosed with Bell's Palsy, try Vitamin B-1. Check deficiency symptoms.

CONJUNCT/SQUARE/INCONJUNCT/ OPPOSITION VENUS: Because you may not be receiving the affection and/or love you deserve during this period, you may be trading off food as a replacement for it. You may get a severe sweet/sugar/dessert craving. If chocolate craving, try Sepia 6X (hr). Weight gain is possible if this happens and you do not consciously stop yourself from over eating on sweets. Or, in some people, the opposite may occur—anorexia. Seek out a homeopathic physician. Phlebitis may occur. Try Vitamins C and E. Check deficiency symptoms. If feeling tired and dragged out, it may be anemia. Moderate skin problems (ranging from dry skin to possible dermatitis). Try Sulphur 6X (hr). You may acquire a sense of low self esteem or self worth during this period because feelings of love have been withdrawn and unavailable to you. Do not replace it with food. A homeopathic doctor can help by getting you the correct constitutional remedy to see you through this period in your life.

CONJUNCT/SQUARE/INCONJUNCT/ OPPOSITION MARS: A period of frustration that may boil and seethe just beneath the surface. This combination can breed a lot of anger that has been suppressed. Be careful! If you cannot get rid of these emotions in a positive way, accidents are waiting to happen. Be careful around any kind of machinery, appliances, knives, fires and firearms. Pay attention to what you are doing, and do not lose your focus. Serious muscle injuries. Try Arnica 6X (hr). If tendon/ligament involvement, try Rhus Tox. 6X (hr) or Ruta Grav. 6X (hr). Possible flare up of arthritis in joints. Teeth problems, such as needing a root canal. Try Hepar Sulph. 6X (hr). Potential blood problems such as anemia. Very susceptible to a Calcium deficiency during this time. Check your symptoms.

CONJUNCT/SQUARE/INCONJUNCT/ OPPOSITION JUPITER: Liver-related ailments such as hypoglycemia (low blood sugar) or indigestion (try Lecithin) could crop up. Have your cholesterol and triglycerides checked by a doctor. If high, try Vitamins E and F and Lecithin to lower. An excellent time to start a diet! Your resolve will be stronger than usual. Weight loss. Suppressed appetite; watch for anorexia. May be a Vitamin B-6 deficiency. See a homeopath. Check symptoms. Potential gallbladder problems. Try Lecithin.

CONJUNCT/SQUARE/INCONJUNCT/ OPPOSITION NEPTUNE: Although this is only a transit, it is one of the major health indicators that something may be going wrong—perhaps so slowly, that you may not realize it. Little things, such as being more tired than usual, needing more sleep, or having less pep and energy, may slowly be encroaching upon you. Vitamin C is excellent at this time to help boost the immune system to stave off potential colds or flu. Most worrisome is the fact that you can be misdiagnosed during this period of time. Please get a second, even third opinion before you agree to a plan of action on any medical problem, particularly if surgery is involved. Your x-rays may get lost, your test results disappear, or worse, the wrong test results are given to you and you would never know it—until it was too late! Ask questions of your doctor, and do not be afraid to get retested, if necessary.

Stress is placing a load on your immune system right now, in subtle ways; but they are there, nevertheless. Get more sleep, and do not push as hard. If you are a workaholic, your body will break down on you—ease off the throttles during this time in order to stay healthy. Colds and flu may cycle again and again—a warning that your immune system is not working well. It is important to identify what is stressing you, and remove the source as much as humanly possible. Otherwise, you are just not going to "bounce back" with any great degree of success. See a homeopath.

This is a good time to go off and meditate, center yourself, and find your own island of harmony from within. Silence, peace and quiet are accented and needed by your body and soul; seek that solace which will keep you healthy.

If your immune system is suppressed, then bacterial (strep and staph infections), viral or parasite invasion is possible. Do not overlook parasites and worms! More people carry them around than you think—even in the United States! They can often be the foundation of a problem, yet the least likely place a doctor would look or suspect. So, the possibility of getting endlessly misdiagnosed is real.

Other vitamins that might be needed could be Pantothenic Acid or Calcium. Check the deficiency symptoms and see if you have some of them.

CONJUNCT/SQUARE/INCONJUNCT/ OPPOSITION URANUS: Accidents are in the air!

Be careful, stay alert when driving, and do not "drift off". Try Clematis (bfr). Lack of attention to where you are driving, or placing your feet or hands in the wrong place, can spell injury for you. If you are bumping into things, dropping articles, pay attention! You are trying to "bleed off" accident energy into a more harmless direction. This is a signal that you are in the accident mode, and to tread with caution and remain alert. If you do, no accident will occur.

Spasms, "charlie horses", nerve-related pains, jerking or twitching of muscles may occur. Check deficiency symptoms to see if you might need Calcium during this period. You will be under sudden and unexpected stress—and that will impact your immune system. The potential for nervousness, tautness and inability to unwind may occur. The homeopathic remedy, Calm's Forte, "feeds" the nerves, and may be something to consider.

Breaking a bone is possible. Consider Calcium or the homeopathic remedy known as Symphytum 6X (hr), to help speed healing and recovery of the broken bone.

CONJUNCT/SQUARE/INCONJUNCT/ OPPOSITION PLUTO:

The endocrine, or glandular system in a person's body may suffer during this transit. If you feel tired or worn out all the time, a possible area to be tested, is the thyroid. Or, if you suddenly become hyper and tense, with erratic heartbeats, that can also mean a dysfunctional thyroid. If you have been working hard, without much rest or relaxation, then the adrenal glands may be exhausted. Then, you can look to Vitamin C and Pantothenic Acid to "feed" them so they will stabilize. It also means you must rest and recoup during this period. Another potential area for trouble is the parathyroid gland, and either too much or not enough calcium is being released into the bloodstream. If concerned about this, check out Calcium deficiency symptoms. If you have several of these symptoms, go to the doctor and have your parathyroid gland tested.

Bone and teeth problems can surface under this transit. Lack of Calcium could be a root cause. If a root canal is eminent, get to a homeopathic doctor, for there are excellent remedies to halt the infection and inflammation, thereby saving you from an expensive dental bill! Bones may become more brittle during this period—again, from lack of necessary Calcium. You may want to increase foods that are high in Vitamins C, D, and Calcium during this period.

For women over 45, get a general physical to make sure you are not suffering from osteoporosis—something many women are susceptible to after this age. Arthritic symptoms may occur, although they

will probably disappear or be less troublesome after the transit has left. Anything dealing with tendons, ligaments or joints can break down. There are several homeopathic remedies that can be considered: Arnica 6X, Ruta Grav. 6X and Rhus Tox. 6X (hr).

Skin ailments may arise, going from simple dry skin to possible dermatitis or psoriasis. Sulphur 6X (hr) often helps any and all of these conditions. If dry skin, Vitamins A, D, E or F (fatty acids) may want to be considered. Check your deficiency symptoms against them.

Unfortunately, this transit can create poisoning of many kinds—even heavy metal poisoning. If you are ill, and are getting misdiagnosed, or nothing seems to help your condition, get tested for poisoning. At the other end of the spectrum, food poisoning is possible, so carry Arsenicum 6X (hr), the food poison remedy, with you!

CONJUNCT ASCENDANT: Frequently, ailments involving the teeth, appear at this time. It is a good time for a dental check up. Arthritis can temporarily raise its ugly head. It is a warning, so before it gets worse, check your diet! Are you eating high fiber foods, plenty of lightly steamed green, leafy vegetables, and fresh fruit on a daily basis? Or, are you a "meat and potatoes" person? If you are, this contributes to arthritis. The choice is yours: change your diet now, or suffer later on down the road.

Dry skin may be an irritant, try Sulphur 6X (hr). Skin ailments in general may occur. You may be more susceptible to sunburn at this time. Use Calendula (hr—non-alcoholic tincture) to treat and protect your skin.

TRANSITS OF URANUS:
URANUS CONJUNCT/SQUARE/ INCONJUNCT/OPPOSITION NEPTUNE:

Your nerves may be "shot". It is possible that you have taken a huge shock and it has affected your entire nervous system as a result. Calm's Forte (hr) or Aconite 6X (hr) may be needed. Any time you are working around electricity, be alert and be careful! Electrical shocks are not out of the question. Right now, you tend to be day dreamy, and not as sharp or in focus as you usually are. Try Clematis (bfr). As a consequence, injury can result either from being around electricity or the water. Be careful swimming; know your physical limits and endurance. Do not stupidly make dives into an area where you are not sure of the depth of the water. If living by the ocean, watch out for unexpected rip tides or sharks on the prowl.

Trauma may shock your entire system, and your

immunity may slip for a while. If so, you can expect hard hitting colds or flu to catch you off guard. Recovery will be slow. If it is, try Gelsemium 6X (hr), so you do not relapse. You will be on your feet sooner rather than later. There are also homeopathic flu remedies on the market—try one at the first sign of flu onset.

Adrenal exhaustion is possible, so look to Vitamin C and Pantothenic Acid to "feed" these glands and recover more quickly. Rest is in order—plenty of it, although insomnia may dog your heels. There are homeopathic remedies to cure this problem.

CONJUNCT/SQUARE/INCONJUNCT/ OPPOSITION PLUTO: Sudden stress is unexpected and hard hitting. Nerves may suffer during this particularly stressful, traumatic time in your life. Calm's Forte (hr) can "feed" your nervous system during this period, or Aconite 6X (hr) or Rescue Remedy (bfr). Another area where ailments may occur is the endocrine system, primarily the thyroid gland, although ALL endocrine glands may be suspect until you see an Endocrinologist.

Accidents, if they happen, will not be minor in nature. Do not go off day dreaming or into an altered state when driving! Serious accidents are in the wind. Stay alert! Try Clematis (bfr).

Instead, use this day dreamy energy in positive way—go meditate, get back to nature or set some time aside for yourself to be quiet. This is also a period of intense introspection, and therapy may be warranted—consider it. Help from an outside, objective source, can put you in touch with a great deal of repressed or suppressed feelings and emotions— particularly anger and fear. If these feelings are not dealt with, attended to or coped with, then serious accidents can occur to make you sit immobile for a couple of weeks or months so that you have little else to do but sit and think—something you needed to do anyway. Let's take the positive route, and not choose an accident to put you in touch with yourself.

CONJUNCT ASCENDANT: Look out for accidents! Whether they be by car, airplane or around electricity is a moot point. This is a time to "dump" a lot of repressed or suppressed feelings such as anger and fear into a positive instead of a negative experience. Accidents that occur may force you to be immobile so that you have the time you refused to take earlier, to get in touch with the deeper levels of yourself—your true wants and needs. Are they being met? If they are not, accidents are mis-channeled energy manifesting and expressing itself on a physical level. Take time now to look at ways to get in touch with yourself—perhaps through traditional therapy, or, with Uranus activated, through some unusual, although positive, means.

Uranus is the planet of "individuation", a psychological term meaning the uniqueness of being you—not what others want you to be, but who you really are. This planet may provide plenty of shocks, sudden upsets and unexpected events to get you to come full circle with your own being. Utilize this time in a psychological manner to align yourself! An excellent time to consult a homeopath.

The nervous system takes a beating at this time, and Calm's Forte (hr) may help stabilize and feed the nerves during the transit. You may feel extremely restless, unable to sit still for more than two minutes, and yet, may not know why. If this particular set of symptoms occur, get to a therapist and find out why.

Sleeplessness may also occur, and Calm's Forte (hr), or White Chestnut (bfr) may help. Spasms, "charlie horses", twitches and cramps can be helped with Calcium. If you are injured, try Arnica 6X (hr) for swelling, bruising to the muscles and Hypericum 6X (hr) for any nerve-related injury.

TRANSITS OF NEPTUNE:
CONJUNCT/SQUARE/INCONJUNCT/ OPPOSITION PLUTO: Severe, long-term stress can have possibly suppressed your immune system, making you highly susceptible to cyclic bouts with colds, flu or allergy ailments. Pantothenic Acid and Vitamin C may help boost your beleaguered immune system and support it. It is advisable to get "constitutionalized" by a homeopathic doctor during this period, to help stabilize the fluctuation occurring within your body.

Most susceptible is your endocrine system, particularly the thyroid gland and the adrenal glands. Mood swings, depression and roller coaster feelings may indicate a glandular imbalance, and tests should be run to validate this.

Neptune always promises you that you can be misdiagnosed. Please seek a second, perhaps a third opinion if you are feeling uneasy about the primary diagnosis. Follow your intuition during this time frame! Other ailments having to do with bacterial (staph and strep) and viral infections, as well as parasitic invasion, are possible. A sore throat could turn out to be a strep infection. So, get to the doctor and get a throat culture to make sure—one way or another! Do not be blase' about your health at this time.

You may suffer from long bouts of being tired, exhausted or unable to muster much enthusiasm for life like you usually do. This combination of planets is asking you to quiet your busy outer world and go inward—into yourself. This can be a good time for therapy; but also, a bad time for getting caught up in cults of any kind, religious or metaphysical. The best person to help you is yourself. Meditation is recommended. Quiet walks, being alone, or by the water, is healing and beneficial. Getting back to nature will be positive, and lower the stress on your immune system.

Heavy metal poisoning, and for that matter, any kind of poising (insecticides, botulism, salmonella, etc.) is possible. Do not put yourself in a highly polluted environment, because your body will rebel and break down on you—particularly via the lungs. So, chest colds and even pneumonia, are possible. Be careful of the air you breathe, and the water or liquids you drink. An excellent homeopathic remedy to carry with you during this time for any kind of poisoning (particularly food) is Arsenicum.

Blood problems can arise, especially anemia. If you are tired and draggy feeling, go in and get a blood test to find out. Usually, it can be a white blood cell problem, or the doctor may discover a low level of infection in your bloodstream, indicating a higher white blood count than normal.

If you do get ill during this time, recuperation is not going to be quick. The best way to help is to take Gelsemium 6X (hr) to stop any possible relapse and speed recovery. This transit asks you to shift from the outside world, slow down, and masticate some issues that you may have been avoiding for quite some time. If you do not address these issues· (usually through some kind of therapy modality), then physical illness may manifest as an expression of your inner turmoil. Seek proper homeopathic help, and you can avoid becoming sick.

CONJUNCT ASCENDANT: You will be susceptible to many types of infections, ranging from bacterial (staph and strep), viral or parasite intrusion. Any one of these can be the root cause of your feeling draggy, tired and in general, exhausted. Stress has been a part of your life too long, and as this transit manifests, it asks you to rest and stop pushing so hard. If you do not, you will get sick. Colds and flu are apt to become common place. If this does happen, consult a homeopathic doctor who can give you a remedy to bolster your beleaguered immune system and get you back on the road to health.

The possibility of a long-term, low-grade infection which raises your white blood count could occur. Pay particular attention to your teeth because an infection in the root can go on for months without being detected, and you will gradually feel more and more tired. Watch what kind of water or liquids you consume. Poisoning is not out of the question, and may come from a highly unusual or nebulous source. Even garden insecticides or herbicides can be dangerous to you, so handle any kind of poison with great care. Food poisoning is possible, so carry Ar-

senicum 6X (hr) with you to antidote it.

If you do fall ill, doctors are going to have a difficult time trying to diagnose what you have contracted. Tests may fail to show anything is wrong. Or, your test results get lost, or worse, you get some else's test results! Do not be afraid to run the same test twice. Also, misdiagnosis will be the bane of your existence. Get a second and third opinion before deciding on any course of action. I strongly recommend seeing a homeopathic physician during this period to get your "constitutional" remedy to support your immune system and avoid all the potential health problems that can manifest.

The immune system is under fire, so you might try Vitamin C and Pantothenic Acid to help support and bolster it during this time frame. Also, eating healthy will help: lots of fresh fruit, vegetables (particularly leafy variety) and low intake of meat is advised. Get the proper amount of sleep—you will want to sleep more. Some of your "get-up-and-go" has temporarily left. Respect your body's need to simply rest, stop pushing so hard, and RELAX! Meditation, quiet periods each day, gentle music, getting back to nature and attuning yourself to your own spiritual needs, will help you stay well.

If you are ill, be very careful about taking any drug—the over-the-counter variety or prescription. Your body is highly sensitized, and usually needs half the dosage recommended for an adult. The same goes for a child—half the normal dose. The possibility of drug reaction (even allergic in nature) is real. Find out about the drug you are supposed to take before taking it! Ask your homeopathic doctor and/or pharmacist. Getting overdosed or experiencing adverse side affects is highly possible.

TRANSITS IN PLUTO:

CONJUNCT ASCENDANT: Psychologically, this is a period in your life where repressed or suppressed issues such as anger, hate, fear or dysfunctional behavior must be openly and consciously addressed. It is an excellent time for therapy—to get to the bottom of these issues, clean yourself out, so that you can make that transformation to becoming a whole person. To ignore them any longer will not work. Pluto is obsessive/compulsive by nature, and if you refuse to start cleaning out your own house (your emotions and attitudes), then this type of behavior may take root at this time. It is a warning shot, and can be handled with proper help from the proper resources.

On the physical level, it can mean that you have turned into a workaholic (perhaps not by choice) and you are pushing hard day in and day out. Just keep a sensitive ear keyed to how your body is holding up under the brutal pressure. You do need to rest AND relax. If you refuse to, your body will rebel and break down. Any injury that does occur will not be a minor in nature—it can turn into a major problem. This is why you need to slow down, rest and be sensible about your work and play schedule. The younger you are, the more you feel you can get away with abusing your physical body. It will still catch up with you during this time.

The endocrine system may falter and the two glands which are particularly vulnerable are the thyroid gland and the adrenal glands. Adrenal exhaustion is a real possibility right now. Try Pantothenic Acid and Vitamin C to support the adrenals during this period. If you are feeling hyper, getting heart palpitations, unable to unwind, insomnia or breaking out in a sweat for seemingly no reason, this may be a signal of a hyperthyroid condition. On the other hand, if you feel exhausted, experience insomnia, your skin is drying out, hair is falling out and "crash and burn" about 3 p.m. every day, these are symptoms of a hypothyroid. Get it checked by a homeopathic doctor!

This is a time for EXTREMES on all levels of yourself. You may experience mental burnout, so try Kali Phos. 6X (hr) to help feed those frazzled brain cells. If physical exhaustion occurs, get the rest you need. If it is emotional extremism, there are many kinds of therapy available, so seek out the one that feels best for you. Spiritually, if all the rest of your "vehicles" are together and cleaned out, this can be an intense period of clairvoyant activity. Out-of-body experiences are not unusual, dreams become more vivid, active and intense.

However you choose to manifest this Pluto cycle, it is guaranteed to transform you—completely, on some level of yourself. It is relentless, though usually gentle, about forcing you to make the changes that will make you a happier, healthier person. Only when you fight change will you experience illness. So, the choice is yours—change and grow, or stubbornly stick your heels in and get sick for a while!

HEALTH TRANSITS THROUGH THE 6TH AND 12TH HOUSES

TRANSITING PLANETS THOUGH THE 6TH HOUSE:

The transits are in italics. The aspect mentioned denotes the transit in that specific house to a natal or progressed planet. {Example: VENUS (conjunction, sextile, trine, opposition), means that transiting Venus is in the 6th house, and if it makes any of these aspects to one or more of your natal planets,

then read the definition below.}

VENUS (conjunction, sextile, trine, opposition): If one must go in for an operation, this is a good time because Venus is like a "guardian angel".

MARS (conjunction, sextile, trine, opposition): You will think about your diet and do something about it. If you want to lose unwanted pounds, a good time to initiate the program. You may want to take up an exercise class or some sport that will give you a physical workout.

MARS (Square or inconjunct): You may think about a change in diet or a new exercise program, but be careful not to over do it or start a "crash" diet. Moderation is the key here for best results.

SATURN (conjunction, sextile, trine, opposition): Your eating patterns, which have not changed through the years, will now take a shift in the next two and one-half year period. There will be a new found interest in anything pertaining to your health from what you put into your mouth into the latest in exercise options. An excellent time to lose weight and keep it off.

SATURN (square, inconjunct): There may be times when you must attend to someone else's needs during this period who is experiencing poor health or a stay in the hospital.

URANUS (conjunction, sextile, trine, opposition): Your interest in health borders on the fanatical or the bizarre. If you were a meat and potato eater, you may suddenly change to a vegetarian diet. Fad diets are in with you—just try to moderate for the sake of your body. You may find some unique, little known way to control your weight and gain optimum health. However, do not think fad diets are going to help you, they won't. As fast as you lose weight, you can put it back on. Better try and stick to some moderate, sensible diet for long term advantages. If you must go in for surgery, this is a good time for it. Also, this is a good time for mental health by seeking a counselor of your choice to "clean out" old emotions that have been festering in your subconscious for years.

URANUS (square, inconjunct): Someone you know may be put in the hospital or have ill health. You must be there to help them. A time when you can be accident prone.

NEPTUNE (conjunction, sextile, trine, opposition): Health is a nebulous thing at best with you during this period. For best results, listen to your body, it will tell you what it wants to eat. A diet strong in fruits and vegetables and a small amount of meat (if a meat eater) is best. However, this is a cleansing and purification time for the body and the heavier food products such as meat, fats and dairy products should be moderated in favor of fresh meatless foods. Meditation or bio-feed back can be practiced with ease.

NEPTUNE (sextile, trine): A good time for surgery because of the presence of a "guardian angel" aspect.

NEPTUNE (square, inconjunct): You may find yourself in a confusing situation with someone who is ill and needs to be cared for. Not a good time for surgery because infection or adverse reactions to drugs/anesthesia may occur.

PLUTO (conjunction, sextile, trine, opposition): Your eating habits will very gradually change over the next decade. You will slowly acquaint yourself with health and how it affects you from food to exercise and possibly even into the health healing arts. Whatever you find an interest in, it will change the way you eat or the way you exercise. Try not to go overboard at first; moderation is a powerful key here to your better health. Do not subject to the body to shocking or tortuous diet changes. Balance in what you eat is more desirable.

PLUTO (square, inconjunct): Try not to let a fad diet rob you of a balanced diet. There is a concern here for going to extremes in diet or exercise—if you do, it will work against you.

TRANSITS THROUGH YOUR 12TH HOUSE AND TO NATAL PLANETS IN YOUR 12TH HOUSE:

The twelfth house is the most important house in the chart concerning your health and potential illness. This section will have two functions: first, a transit through your natal 12th house. Secondly, if you have a natal planet(s) in the 12th house, the meaning of the transiting planet to your natal planet will be given if important in a health or medical sense. These will be the conjunction aspect only. An orb of 2-3 degrees applying and 1 degree separating will be used.

TRANSITING SUN: A time when you will want to seek some peace and quiet to get away from all the frantic activity in your life. This is an excellent time for meditation, a vacation, getting back to nature to get to know yourself. Activities involving water or the mountains is best. This is a healing time; a let down time for you—use it.

TO NATAL:

(conjunct) MARS: Potential to sprain/strain ligament or muscles.

(conjunct) JUPITER: You may consciously overeat, thereby adding a few pounds. Watch craving for sweets or fats.

(conjunct) SATURN: You may feel slightly depressed or lonely. This is a period of aloneness so that you can get back in touch with yourself.

(conjunct) URANUS: Accidents can happen in the strangest of ways.

(conjunct) NEPTUNE: A cold or flu could sneak up on you. Try Vitamin A or C to stave it off. Also, you are susceptible to viral/bacterial infections at this time. Not a good time for surgery due to infection or drug/anesthesia problems.

(conjunct) PLUTO: A need for solitude and to go deep within yourself. Tranquility and peace are a must for you at this time.

TRANSITING MOON: A period when you want to be left alone and in to yourself. Go for a walk in the woods or near the water. If music is soothing, use it to relax. A time of being alone; not being lonely. There is introspection into yourself or your actions; zero in on them. A period of analysis.

TO NATAL:

(conjunct) MERCURY: You may feel highly strung or nervous for no apparent reason at all.

(conjunct) VENUS: A period of pleasure that might include solitude, peaceful walks, listening to music or doing something for yourself that you need to make you feel fulfilled and happy. Do it!

(conjunct) MARS: Harboring a lot of pent up feelings of anger or aggression may be simmering just below your surface. Release these negative feelings in a positive way, if possible. Swallowing anger or frustration is not good, so let it out!

(conjunct) SATURN: For some, a feeling of depression. For those in touch with themselves, a time of inner contemplation and quietness. A period of wanting to be by yourself, but this does not mean necessarily feeling lonely.

(conjunct) URANUS: Sporadic nervous tension that can snowball into minor accidents if not watchful. Emotionally volatile; do not swallow feelings. Instead, let them out and express yourself in a positive way.

(conjunct) NEPTUNE: If your emotions have been withheld, they may come out in the form of a cold or flu. Usually, a period of vagueness and wanting to be left alone. Meditation during this period brings excellent and healing results, however. Not a good time for surgery because of potential infection or drug/anesthesia reactions.

(conjunct) PLUTO: A time of intense introspection into yourself. Wanting to be by yourself instead of in a crowd. Be sure you have your "quiet time" to pursue something that gives you a feeling of satisfaction and wholeness.

TRANSITING MERCURY: Mentally, you want to be left alone. This is an excellent time for therapy and delving into your subconscious. Ideas of creative nature abound. Getting in touch with yourself through a hobby, meditation or some other positive form is indicated.

TO NATAL:

(conjunct) SUN: Mental energies will be high. Sleep may escape you during this period. Creative ideas should be pursued, even if it means getting up in the middle of the night to write them down. You want to be alone and seek quiet; an excellent time to catch up on reading.

(conjunct) MERCURY: Mental energies run optimum and so do ideas. Nervous energy can also be there. Do not abuse your mental powers just now; try to get enough sleep or rest. Creative ideas abound. Insomnia may result. Use Calm's Forte (hr) to moderate this tendency.

(conjunct) VENUS: A time for the pleasure of the five senses. Apply them to you. Do something good for yourself during this period when you want to be alone.

(conjunct) MARS: Nervous energy abounds; it is a question of what you do with it that counts. Brain power is turned on and up; use the ideas that come. Restless sleep or insomnia may occur because you are thinking so much on so many things. Use Calm's Forte (hr) to sleep.

(conjunct) JUPITER: Your mental energies are at an all time high. You could stay up all night reading or working on some mental pursuit—but don't. It will be too easy for you to extend yourself so you need moderation. Get some sleep and allow your tired eyes and over-active brain to get some rest. Excellent for creative ideas.

(conjunct) SATURN: For some, this may be a period of depression. If so, turn to a hobby or something that gives you pleasure and a sense of inner satisfaction. For others, it will be a time of crystalizing ideas and manifesting them into reality.

(conjunct) URANUS: Nervous tension will run hand-in-hand with inventive ideas that pop up from you now. Insomnia or broken sleep can occur. Use Calm's Forte (hr) if your nerves get the best of you or to improve sleep. A time when minor accidents can occur. Drive defensively and use the seat belt! Accidents involving electrical equipment. Protect hands and eyes, especially.

(conjunct) NEPTUNE: A time of dreamy contemplation that can be teamed up with meditation, creative writing or relaxation. An excellent time for creative brain-storming but not good for anything that centers around hard-core reality, or confusion will reign supreme. A period of rest, take it. Not a good time for surgery; infection or drug reaction/overdose situation may arise.

(conjunct) PLUTO: A period of intense mental focus of energies; try not to burn yourself out as a result. Good time for therapy. Wanting to be alone.

Go for a walk in the woods; get back to nature.

TRANSITING VENUS: A period of harmony within yourself. However, if you are not receiving the affection you need from the outer world, it can mean that you unconsciously begin eating more sweets than normal during this period. An excellent time for an operation with the "guardian angel" around you. This is a quiet time in your life; the eye of the hurricane. Take time out to give yourself a pleasure you deserve or desire. A time of wanting to be alone without feeling lonely.

TO NATAL:

(conjunct) SUN: A good sense of well being around you. Take time out of your hectic schedule and give yourself a gift that will please you. A time of being happy by being alone or sharing it with a special person.

(conjunct) MOON: There is a sense of emotional well being around you. However, if you are emotionally being deprived of affection, you could be tempted to binge on sweets during this time—try to moderate and understand this behavior.

(conjunct) MERCURY: Any activities that have to do with the mind, mental exercise or brain power will be pursued now. Curl up with a good book because you are in the frame of mind to be alone and yet give yourself one of life's little pleasures; whether it be reading a book, going for a walk, working in the garden—whatever suits you, do it during this time.

(conjunct) VENUS: A period of intense pleasure and happiness can surround you although you share it within yourself or very few others. A time of being alone and enjoying the solitude and peace. Also, if emotionally deprived of affection, you may crave sweets. A good time for surgery.

(conjunct) MARS: Being by yourself or sharing it with someone special is good emotional and mental health. A time to take pleasure with the world and those you want to include in your small circle of loved ones or friends. A good time for surgery.

(conjunct) JUPITER: Your waistline may grow a little if you do not watch what you eat! The desire for sweets may be triggered if you are not getting enough affection out in your world. Moderation. Also, It can be a time of intense pleasures through the five senses that you will share with just a few, close people around you. A good time for surgery.

(conjunct) SATURN: A period of wanting to be alone by yourself to enjoy the pleasures and senses of your world. For some, it may mean feeling lonely and the need to eat sweets may become acute—try to moderate for the sake of a possible weight gain.

(conjunct) URANUS: For some, unconscious binging on sweets or food in general may crop up and a weight gain is in evidence. For others, unexpected surprise and pleasure shared with self or perhaps one other individual. A good time for surgery.

(conjunct) NEPTUNE: Not a good time for surgery because problems with infection or drug/anesthesia reactions may occur. Take this time to "float" in the world of your five senses any way that you choose. Places that have water nearby or the forest are ideal. Nevertheless, you want to be alone and need this period of solitude for good emotional and mental health. A time of healing and peace.

(conjunct) PLUTO: The need to experience the five senses or some part of them in an intense and focused way. Binging on sweets is a potential if you are not getting enough affection from others. Unconscious eating habits stirred up by bereft emotions can add weight to you.

TRANSITING MARS: You will want to experience privacy during this time; it can be a period of regeneration and healing, if you choose. This is a time for getting back in tune with yourself, who you are and what you want from life. An excellent period for therapy to explore yourself. Also, a time for surgery or injury if you have not released the backlog of negative, harbored emotions. If surgery has to be performed, loss of blood may be more than expected or desired and should be monitored carefully. A time for acute types of ailments to crop up; but nothing so serious to keep you down more than a few days or a week at the most.

TO NATAL:

(conjunct) SUN: A period of high energy and vitality. Strong recuperative powers. If you have been experiencing negative emotions, a time for acute ailments to pop up. Vitamins A and C will help stave them off.

(conjunct) MOON: A volatile emotional period marks this time. As a result, do not swallow negative feelings. Rather, choose a positive way of expressing and venting them. If you don't acute ailments may pop up as a result.

(conjunct) MERCURY: Heavy mental activity can cause headaches or brain fatigue; try not to over do it and moderate work behind the scenes.

(conjunct) VENUS: The five senses are involved and you want to share this quiet period with one special person. A time for pleasure in a stress-free environment. Be good to yourself and enjoy the solitude and peace around you. A good time for surgery.

(conjunct) MARS: A period of intense work activity marked with a need to be alone or around very few people. Not a good time for surgery as hemorrhaging is a possibility. A time for accidents involv-

ing muscles and ligaments. Do not over exercise as you might be inclined to do—moderation, instead.

(conjunct) JUPITER: Extravagance in whatever activities you choose to do; make sure diet is moderate on sweets and fats. An excellent time for surgery, although hemorrhaging may become a distinct possibility.

(conjunct) SATURN: A period of frustration or feeling as if you are backed into the corner. And, you may be, but vent those negative feelings or an accident can occur involving bones or muscles. A good time for surgery—less bleeding than usual as a result.

(conjunct) URANUS: If you have been sitting on accumulated negative emotions such as anger and frustration, accidents are a strong possibility; especially involving cars and mechanical devices or electricity. Drive defensively (wear a seat belt) and be alert around machinery. A good time for surgery. High, nervous energy can be moderated with the use of Calm's Forte (hr).

(conjunct) NEPTUNE: Colds and flu are a strong possibility if you have been sitting on festering negative emotions—release them and avoid physical ailments instead! Confusing symptoms; prone to misdiagnosis. If already sick, get a second opinion, if necessary. Not a good time for surgery because infection and drug/anesthesia reaction are possible. Mistakes on the part of the hospital staff/doctors. Allergy reactions are a possibility. Try Pantothenic Acid to relieve them. Potential water accidents; be safe and swim with others.

(conjunct) PLUTO: The desire to be left alone and get out of the crowd. A period of isolation, but intense, focused energies on a project of your choice. Accidents involving cars, machinery, or fire a possibility. Severe muscle or ligament trauma if in an accident. The desire to go to extremes—try not to.

TRANSITING JUPITER: Beware of added weight! You may unconsciously be eating a lot more than you realize. It may be a subconscious insecurity spurring you to placate the feeling by using food as a substitute. Otherwise, an excellent time for therapy and finding out more about yourself in the positive. Good for surgery unless otherwise indicated, as this is a "guardian angel" aspect.

TO NATAL:

(conjunct) SUN: Being alone and being happy; a good time for vacation with one special person or to find health and healing in a quiet environment of your choice. Added weight gain—so watch what you are eating. Stick to fresh fruits and vegetables, very little meat, fats or sweets—you will remain svelte. A good time for surgery, if necessary.

(conjunct) MOON: Added water weight may be

a problem and edema the result. There may be a potassium deficiency; check for symptoms. A time of binging on dairy products—most likely ice cream. Sweets or fats in general will put on weight if you are not wise in your choice of foods. If surgery is a necessity, there may be abnormal swelling/bruising/leakage of lymph fluids after the operation. Not good for cosmetic surgery because swelling will take longer than normal to disappear.

(conjunct) MERCURY: A happy frame of mind and optimistic, although you want to have some quiet time to yourself. A good time for creative ideas or using your mental facilities.

(conjunct) VENUS: A period of extreme happiness for you even if you are alone. Watch the types of goods you consume because weight gain is favored. There may be a desire for sweets—use moderation. Excellent for cosmetic surgery or surgery in general—little scarring as a result. This is a "guardian angel" aspect.

(conjunct) MARS: A driving need to work hard behind the scenes. Just make sure you get some rest between bouts of work! Excellent for surgery. Exhaustion because of intensity of your work schedule can be helped with Pantothenic Acid.

(conjunct) JUPITER: Weight gain if you are not careful about what you unconsciously eat. Make sure you are not eating because of some emotional deprivation (real or imagined). Good for surgery, although abnormal swelling/bruising or lymph fluid leakage afterward is a strong possibility. Not good for cosmetic surgery as swelling will take longer than normal to disappear. Good for surgery in general.

(conjunct) SATURN: A good time to go on a diet and lose those unwanted pounds. The need for privacy—be sure you get it. Excellent for any operation; less bleeding, bruising, swelling, lymph leakage as a result. The ability to want to be alone without feeling lonely. A good time to accomplish much if you are incapacitated.

(conjunct) URANUS: Sudden weight gain; seemingly from nowhere. Check to see what food you are unconsciously putting into your mouth. Sudden craving for sweets if you are feeling emotionally deprived of affection. Excellent for operations of all kinds. A "guardian angel" aspect. Accidents can happen; so be careful around electricity and airplanes. However, if an accident does occur, you will be lucky and walk away from it or with very little injury.

(conjunct) NEPTUNE: Not a good time for any surgery because of possible infection or drug/anaesthesia reaction. Allergies crop up. Misdiagnosis of any symptoms you manifest—make sure you get a

second opinion and another set of tests before you decide to go for an operation. Best to wait, if at all possible, until this period is past before going in for surgery.

(conjunct) PLUTO: A large weight gain; either induced by edema (water retention) or consuming too many meats, fat, or sweet-type foods. Bingeing is possible if you feel emotionally deprived in some way. A workaholic syndrome may strike you now—try not to exhaust yourself.

TRANSITING SATURN: A period in your life for the next two and one-half years where health matters can come to the foreground. If you have harbored a great store of negative emotions such as anger and frustration, then the possibility of dealing with a chronic health problem becomes a potential. However, in order to "vent" this subconscious "garbage", therapy can release it in a positive sense and no health problems need arise as a result. Trying to hold on to a backlog of stored emotions is useless and they will erupt to be dealt with, whether it is a positive or a negative expression is up to you—your free-will choice. On the positive, if you are happy and contented with yourself as a person, you may shoulder the responsibility of caring for someone who is ill or hospitalized. Or, you may become connected with the health field, or healing techniques in some way.

TO NATAL:

(conjunct) SUN: Your health and vitality may wane. If it does, Vitamins A and C may be necessary to keep you from catching colds or flu that may be around. Problems with bones or teeth may crop up to be dealt with. Loss of Calcium is possible, making bones brittle or teeth susceptible to decay. This is a time to be alone or with a limited number of people. A good time to get matters accomplished in privacy.

(conjunct) MOON: If a woman, your breast or reproductive region may become a source of health problems. If vaginitis is experienced, Vitamin B-2 will help. A loss of potassium may cause water retention and can be remedied with the addition of this mineral. For some, it may be a time of emotional depression. If it is, see a counselor or homeopath and begin to clean out all the festering negative emotions. For others, it can be a time of steady emotions and quiet solitude.

(conjunct) MERCURY: Mentally, some may be depressed during this period, but that need not happen. A time for sharp, mental clarity and focus where much work can be accomplished; just make sure you do not exhaust your brain. Insomnia may come and go. Calm's Forte (hr) will aid in soothing nerves and White Chestnut (bfr) for quieting the brain.

(conjunct) VENUS: Health problems related to the veins of the body or sugar ailments may surface. Varicose veins, capillaries breaking and causing bruising can be helped with Vitamins C, E, F and bioflavonoids. Skin may dry out more than normal. Use Vitamins A, E or F to correct. Hypoglycemia or diabetes may surface and can come from a liver or pancreatic origin. Attacks of sugar craving are strong and should be moderated or weight gain is possible.

(conjunct) MARS: A period of intense frustration can manifest in a long-term ailment involving muscles, tendon or ligaments. Try to vent emotions in a positive way instead of physically debilitating yourself. A good time for hard work and accomplishing much—just do not exhaust yourself. Anemia may crop up as a result (get tested). Or, adrenal exhaustion. Use Pantothenic Acid to help adrenals.

(conjunct) JUPITER: A time of leaning down, losing weight or being successful in starting a diet — weight will come off slow but sure. If cholesterol is high, it will gradually come down with less meat and fat in diet. A good time for surgery if needed.

(conjunct) SATURN: Positively, a time of great accomplishment of something you wanted to do and working hard behind the scenes to make it manifest. Otherwise, bone or teeth problems that may require attention. Skin may turn dry and can be helped with Vitamins A, D, E or F. A good time for surgery because of less swelling, bruising or bleeding at this time.

(conjunct) URANUS: Sudden inventive urges can strike, giving you creative ideas. Accident prone and can involve broken bones or problems with them. A good time for surgery if needed.

(conjunct) NEPTUNE: A long-term illness could begin now (viral/bacterial) and you will not know about it until later. If there are any symptoms, they will be slight or seemingly unrelated to one another, causing confusion or misdiagnosis. Not a good time for surgery because of possible infection, drug over-dose, drug sensitivity or allergic reaction. Energy drain; try to get more sleep and not work as hard. If allergies appear, try Pantothenic Acid to help. Bone or teeth problems that are misdiagnosed; get a second opinion. Positively, a wonderful time to get away, meditate or be by yourself with nature or near water. A good time to see a homeopath.

(conjunct) PLUTO: A time of hard work behind the scenes and getting a great deal accomplished— pace yourself accordingly and do not become a workaholic (exhaustion will mount up). Bone or teeth complaints which are serious in nature or trans-

forming in some way. Possible severe need for Vitamin C or Calcium during this period—check deficiency symptoms. Endocrine disorders; a gland may go hypo or slow down (test to find out), especially parathyroid or the thyroid gland.

TRANSITING URANUS: Accidents can take place, but understand that any accident can be avoided providing you release negative energy, withheld emotions or feelings. Venting your anger, frustration, etc., will "defuse" the possibility of an accident. But, if you insist upon harboring these pent-up feelings, then a physical release of that energy can occur and it's called an accident. Otherwise, surgery is possible—if you are to go in for surgery.

TO NATAL:

(conjunct) SUN: Accidents can manifest. Also a time of high nervous tension and that can be helped with Calm's Forte (hr). Great for inventive or new ideas that come to you suddenly. The need to unexpectedly get away by yourself for a while—do it. Good time for surgery if you need to go in for it.

(conjunct) MOON: Accidents may occur because of withheld emotions that are choked up inside of you. Release and vent these negative feelings and neutralize the possibility of an accident. Emotions will be up and down during this period. Explosive emotional displays; go ahead and release them in a positive fashion.

(conjunct) MERCURY: Accidents involving the hands may occur. Nerves can be strung tautly; use Calm's Forte (hr) to relax and feed the nervous system. Mentally, you are sharp, inventive and creative, just do not over do on mental tasks or "burn out" may occur during this period.

(conjunct) VENUS: Excellent time for surgery if you need to go in for it; promises less scarring and a positive outcome. A "guardian angel" aspect. Good for cosmetic surgery also.

(conjunct) MARS: Accidents involving machinery and/or cars can occur if negative emotions have not been actively released. Drive defensively and use a seat belt during this time. Surgery may occur, if needed. Otherwise, a period of frantic activity in a stop-start fashion. Possible adrenal exhaustion and Pantothenic Acid can help. Quick to anger, make sure you deal with it in a positive fashion.

(conjunct) JUPITER: An excellent time for surgery if you need it. A "guardian angel" aspect. Tendency to overeat in general—watch your waistline or it will increase.

(conjunct) SATURN: A time when surgery can take place if you need it. Can a period of intense nervousness that can be helped with Calm's Forte (hr). Accidents involving the bones of the body or the repair of teeth. Workwise, unexpected stresses and pressures brought to bear; try to get some rest by being alone or in a peaceful setting in order to relax off and on through this period.

(conjunct) URANUS: Unexpected surgery or an accident may occur. Also, a time of brilliant, inventive or creative insights. Nerves may be strung tautly and Calm's Forte (hr) will help, or try Wild Oat or Impatiens (bfr).

(conjunct) NEPTUNE: Possible viral/bacterial infection that takes a long time to be discovered. Symptoms will not be obvious. Possible misdiagnosis of situation—get a second opinion. Immune system may be weak and colds or flu might hang around. Vitamin C or Pantothenic Acid may help. Not a good time for surgery because of possible infection, drug reaction or adverse side effects.

(conjunct) PLUTO: Possible surgery of a transforming nature. Also a time for insights into self and others.

TRANSITING NEPTUNE: The chance of contracting a viral, bacterial or parasitic ailment which may not become obvious for a long time afterward. Symptoms will not be clear or be constant, causing misdiagnosis or an undiagnosable situation. Infections, allergy complaints, drug sensitivity or reaction, are all a possibility. Drug overdose to even over-the-counter medicines may occur—cut dosages in half to begin with if you must use them. This is a period where you would rather daydream and become less active than normal. In many ways, a time of rest for you; take the time because this is a period of healing for you.

TO NATAL:

(conjunct) SUN: Bacterial/viral complaints of a seeming undetermined origin that can cause misdiagnosis. Get a second or even a third opinion. Not a good time for surgery because of possible infection or drug/anesthesia problems. Colds and flu may appear and can be tamped with Vitamins A or C. Excellent time for meditation, getting off by yourself to rest and relax. Do it.

(conjunct) MOON: If a woman, complaints involving the reproductive region of your body. Vitamin B-2 may help if you contract vaginitis. Viral/bacterial complaints in this region may appear and/or be misdiagnosed. In general, emotions may feel anesthetized or vaguely confused. An excellent time for self-understanding, meditation or seeking a refuge of peace and quiet. Do it. Not a good time for surgery because of possible infection or drug/anesthesia problems.

(conjunct) MERCURY: Mentally, it can be a time of confusion. Or, you can choose to use it in a creative way. Vague nerve complaints that seem to

have no origin or cause. Not a good time for surgery because of potential infection or drug/anesthesia problems. Meditation or getting back to nature is best. A time for relaxing the mental faculties; a "down time" to rest.

(conjunct) VENUS: If going in for surgery, an excellent time for it. A "guardian angel" aspect.

(conjunct) MARS: Viral/bacterial ailments of an acute nature may flare up unexpectedly. Possible adrenal exhaustion; try Pantothenic Acid to help. Energy may drain and you will feel more tired than usual. This is a time of rest and relaxation for you in every way—so take it and do not try to push or work too hard. Otherwise, you may come down with a cold or flu. Not a good time for surgery because of infection or drug/anesthesia reaction.

(conjunct) JUPITER: If surgery is indicated, then a good time to go in for it. "Guardian angel" aspect. Otherwise, unconscious eating of calorie-laden foods will cause a weight gain. A wonderful period for being alone and meditating or getting back to a place where you can relax completely. Do it! A high time of creativity; tap into it.

(conjunct) SATURN: Problems with bones or teeth from an undetermined origin may occur. Potential misdiagnosis; make sure you get a second opinion. Not a good time for surgery because of possible infection or drug/anesthesia problems. Long-term bouts with colds and flu so try Vitamins A and C to avoid. Watch for mysterious loss of Calcium; check against deficiency symptoms. Positively, a time to develop self awareness through meditation or getting back to nature or a place where you feel completely relaxed.

(conjunct) URANUS: Not a good time for surgery if you must have it. Beware of infection or drug/anesthesia reactions. Misdiagnosis; get a second opinion first. Complaints of a nerve-related nature that may mysteriously come and go. Positively, a period of high creativity. The sudden need to escape and get a way to a place of solitude and relaxation; do it! Unusual accidents may occur, especially around water or electrical appliances.

TRANSITING PLUTO: There is no better period for self-analysis or getting therapy in which to come to know yourself better. There is much going on subconsciously, and you may not be aware of most of it. However, if during this period you get restless, feel as if you are going to explode from the inside out, then you need to get in contact with what is bothering you. Chances are, it's stored up negative emotions such as anger or grief that needs to be positively vented. Getting guidance from a counselor of your choice is strongly recommended so that this cleansing process can take place. Otherwise, a chronic ailment may begin to fester beneath the surface and years later, come to light in the form of physical health problems that you must grapple with. If surgery becomes necessary, it will be transformative in nature. Endocrine problems may appear involving the pituitary, thyroid, parathyroid, thymus (if a child), adrenals or the ovaries (in a woman). Get the proper tests to find out.

TO NATAL:

(conjunct) SUN: A time for intense self inspection. This may mean therapy of your choice to release long withheld negative emotions. A period of intense hard work; just do not exhaust yourself even though your energies run high and constant. If surgery is planned, a transformation will take place as a result.

(conjunct) MOON: A time to come to terms with yourself emotionally. Therapy or counseling can help you uncover the "layers" of yourself; do so. Strong, powerful and intense emotions can sweep through you; a time of feeling highs and lows. Just be sure to feel and work through them. Do not shut them down or swallow them or hide from them.

(conjunct) MERCURY: Intense mental powers and ability. Brain fatigue is a very real problem here; do not exhaust yourself. Try for moderation. Excellent time for therapy to understand yourself. Nerves may go through a high stress period; try Calm's Forte (hr) to feed them during this intense time. Nervous exhaustion or nerve debilitation, try White Chestnut, Impatiens or Wild Oat (bfr).

(conjunct) VENUS: A period where the five senses are heightened to a powerful degree. Problems involving the sexual organs can occur. A possible weight gain through consumption of sweets; try to eat them in moderation. Veins may require some attention; try Vitamin E. Excellent time for cosmetic surgery; little scarring will take place. Good for surgery in general. A "guardian angel" aspect.

(conjunct) MARS: A period of adrenal exhaustion which can affect the immune system. Infections, colds or flu can be the result if this occurs. Pantothenic Acid may help. Working hard behind the scenes may cause exhaustion because of long hours. Try to moderate and get rest in between bouts of activity. Blood ailments may occur such as anemia if you exhaust yourself. Muscles may be strained and injured to a severe degree. Do not over-exercise. The driving need to be alone and by yourself; do it. Not a good time for surgery because of the possibility of excessive or unexpected bleeding. If there is surgery, it will be transforming in nature and complete.

(conjunct) JUPITER: A period where weight gain is experienced. Watch what you are unconsciously eating. Stay away from sweets and fats. Liver or gallbladder ailments should be monitored. Excellent time for surgery if you must go in. A "guardian angel" aspect. A time when you want to be alone; do so. Meditation or any other form of relaxation is emphasized during this time.

(conjunct) SATURN: Bone or teeth problems of a chronic or transforming nature may come up. The need for more Calcium may appear; check against deficiency symptoms to make sure. The need to be alone without feeling lonely. A time when much can be accomplished by yourself behind the scenes; just do not exhaust yourself with over work as a result. Therapy or counseling, if needed, will produce positive, life-time results.

(conjunct) URANUS: The possibility of a severe accident, if there is withheld negative emotions which have not been shed or vented. Excellent for therapy or counseling and getting to know yourself better on all levels. Surgery, if needed, will be transformative in nature. A time when you suddenly need time alone, do it. A period of high and almost genius-like insight and creativity; inventive in some way.

(conjunct) NEPTUNE: A time when you want to be alone; do it. Meditation or other forms of knowing one's self may be accomplished with ease. Endocrine disorders of a mysterious nature may crop up. The immune system may weaken, leaving you open to infection, virus or bacterial problems. Pantothenic Acid will help. Not a good time for surgery because of possible infection or drug/anesthesia reaction.

CHAPTER THIRTEEN
Herbs

Since the 1600s when Nicholas Culpepper, an English astronomer, herbalist and doctor, correlated planets and herbs to treat his patients, astrologers have tried to classify herbs according to planetary rulership. The result has been sheer confusion. No astrologer or scientist has yet proven that Culpepper's correlations are valid. Nor do astrologers agree upon the planetary assignations of the various herbs.

At this time it is impossible for an astrologer to say with any confidence that a certain planet rules a certain herb. One reason is that not enough biochemical research has been undertaken to determine the main action or chemical ingredient of each herb, which, depending on its chemical makeup, has from two to six different areas of application.

For example, how do we astrologically catalogue the common, well-known herb chamomile? Culpepper believed it to be ruled by the Sun, presumably because the oil of the herb turns yellow with age. But when first pressed, chamomile oil is light blue: should there be a different planetary signature for the herb before it turns yellow with age? Furthermore, the Sun is not considered to govern any of the *actions* of chamomile, which is a tonic, stomachic, anodyne and antispasmodic: Saturn rules tonic and antispasmodic actions, Mars rules stomachic, and Neptune rules anodyne.

Nor can we successfully assign chamomile a planet because of the herb's chemistry. Its principal active agent is a volatile oil. It also has a little anthemic acid, tannic acid and glucoside. It has a good amount of vitamin C as well as calcium, phosphorus and potassium. Should we assign it a planet according to whatever nutrient it contains the most? Or should we assign it a planet because of the volatile oil?

Astrology and medicine have not made enough advances in this particular field to have answers to such questions. It will take years of research, laboratory testing and gathering of information from case histories before a true planet or sign significance for each herb can be obtained. And until experts can actually align the chemistry of the herbs with astrological rulership, it can be potentially dangerous to prescribe a certain herb because of a person's natal or progressed chart.

For instance, Mars is considered by some astrologers to rule the herb capsicum (cayenne or red pepper), since Mars is associated with things hot, feverish, acute and swelling. It might happen that an astrologer, seeing a well-aspected Mars in a natal or progressed chart, may advise a client to take five grains of capsicum a day. But if the person has a peptic ulcer, the capsicum, given in immoderate doses,

could inflame the ulcer so that it bled or ruptured, perhaps even eating a hole through the stomach and causing peritonitis.

Because of the confusion and inherent danger involved in applying astrological significance to various herbs, in this chapter I do not correlate herbs with planets: herbs should be taken because a person exhibits certain symptoms, not because of astrological configurations in that person's chart. Instead, the chapter covers the properties and uses of herbs, their preparations, chemistry and history. It also includes a glossary of terms used in herbal medicine.

INCOMPATIBILITY

One of the dangers in prescribing herbs is that many herbs are antagonists with each other or with other substances. In fact, combining the wrong herbs can have deadly results. For example, an alkaline herb does not mix with an acidic one. The outcome of such a chemical interreaction can be great sickness.

The mixture of an alkaline herb with an acidic one is an example of *chemical incompatibility*, a problem that plagued herbalists in the nineteenth century. (Unfortunately, most of our knowledge about herbs comes only from nineteenth-century texts.) Dr. Cuthbert Bowen, writing in 1888, lamented that students in medical schools in the east were having problems mixing the proper herbs to get best results.

Through trial and error these nineteenth-century herbalists learned to avoid making herbal formulas that produced hydrates, carbonates, phosphates, borates or tannates of alkaloids and metals. For instance, if a person mixes quinine, derived from certain cinchona barks, with phosphoric acid, used as an auxillary to provide necessary duration, the chemical result is phosphate of quinine. This insoluble salt will fall to the bottom of the bottle, forming a thick, unsightly precipitate: two salts should not be combined in a solution that will change their radicals and form a third, insoluble compound, which the body is unable to break down. Or, if limewater, used frequently as a vehicle to mask the taste of an herbal formula, is brought into contact with sulphate of calcium, which is insoluble, another insoluble is precipitated. In addition, quinine sulphate and potassium acetate in solution will produce a heavy, unmanageable precipitate of acetate of quinine. And if a vehicle such as syrup of squills, containing acetic acid, is combined with alkaline carbonates, carbonic acid gas will evolve—a very painful substance when ingested.

There can also be *therapeutical incompatibility* between herbs or herbs and other substances, when the action of two substances on the human system is mutually antagonistic. For example, if belladonna and calabar bean are ingested at the same time, the results can be very bad. Because of such therapeutical incompatibility among various herbs it is a dangerous practice for someone who does not know the chemical makeup of herbs to mix and match them. Two books that outline the chemical properties of most of the well-known herbs in use in the United States and Great Britain are *A Modern Herbal* by Mrs. M. Grieve and *American Medical Plants* by Charles F. Millspaugh.

In addition, a person should take great care in taking an herb while he or she is on any sort of drug medication ordered by a doctor. Atropine and morphine, for instance, are mutual antagonists. Anyone contemplating taking an herbal while on medication should consult his or her physician to make sure that the herb in conjunction with the drug will not produce adverse side effects.

Following is a list of various herbs and those substances with which they are incompatible. Herbs listed in boldface type are those used by modern herbalists. Herbs listed in boldface italics are those not generally in use at the present but used in old-time remedies.

acacia: alcohol, nitric acid, chloride of iron and lead.

acetic acid: alkalies and alkaline and earthy carbonates.

gallic acid: limewater, salts of copper, lead, nitrate of silver, tartar emetic, opium and alkaline carbonates.

nitrite acid: oxides, carbonates, oils and acacia.

phosphoric acid: salts of calcium, barium, lead and quinine.

salicylic acid: mineral acids, salts of metals and preparations of iron.

tannic acid (found in many modern herbs): albumin, gelatin, salts of iron, antimony, lead, silver, alkalies, carbonates, alkaline earths, tartar emetic, acetate of lead and mineral acids.

tartar acid: alkalies and their carbonates.

ammonia: acids, salts and alum.

anthemis (Roman chamomile, *Anthemis nobilis*): gallic acid, salts of iron and lead, bichloride of mercury and nitrate of silver.

arnica (leopard's bane): mineral acids, sulphates of iron and zinc and lead acetate.

belladonna (deadly nightshade, *Atropa belladonna*: vegetable astringents, tannic acid and caustic alkalies.

calamus (sweet flag, *Acorus calamus*): acetate of lead.

calumba (climbing vine of Mozambique, *Coc-*

culus palmatus): mineral acids, limewater, ammonia, nitrate of silver, chloride of iron and acetate of lead.

camphor: alkaline and earthy salts, water (when in alcohol or spirit solution).

Cannabus indica: acids and caustic alkalies.

capsicum (cayenne or red pepper): sulphates of iron, zinc and copper, acetate of lead and nitrate of silver.

cardamom (fruit of *Elettaria cardomaomum*): acids and ferri sulphas.

caryophyllus (cloves): tartar emetic and sulphates of iron and zinc.

cascarilla (bark of the *Croton eleuteria*): limewater, sulphates of iron and zinc and infusions of gallic acid and tannic acid.

Cassia fistula (pulpy portion of the fruit of the *Cassia fistula* tree grown in Egypt and India): alcohol.

catechu (extract from the wood of the East Indian tree, *Acacia catechu*): alkalies and salts of iron.

cimicifuga (black cohosh or snakeroot): salts of iron.

cinchona (Peruvian bark, *Cinchona officinalis*): strong acids, alkalies, sulphates of iron and zinc, tartar emetic, nitrate of silver, lime, magnesia, tincture of iodine and tannic acid.

coca (*Erythroxylon coca*): metallic salts and mineral acids.

colchicum (meadow saffron): acids and tannic acid.

colocynthis (bitter cucumber): sulphate of iron, nitrate of silver and lead acetate.

conium (poison hemlock): strong acids, alkalies and tannic acid.

digitalis (foxglove): tannic acid, vegetable astringents, sulphate and chloride of iron, acetate of lead and cinchona.

eucalyptus (blue gum tree, *Eucalyptus globulus*): alkalies, mineral acids and salts of iron, mercury, lead and zinc.

gelsemium (yellow jasmine): caustic alkalies and tannic acid.

gentian (yellow gentian, *Gentiana lutea*): sulphate of iron and salts of silver and lead.

grindelia (rosinwood): water, mineral salts and caustic alkalies.

guaiacum (resin of *Lignum vitae*): water, mineral acids, spirits of nitrous ether and salts of metals.

haematoxylon (logwood): mineral acids, tartar emetic, sulphate of iron and copper, alum and acetate of lead.

hydrastis (goldenseal, of the ragweed family, unsafe for people with allergies): alkalies and tannic and hydrochloric acids.

hyoscyamus (henbane): acetate of lead, tannic acid, vegetable astringents and sulphate of iron.

iodinum (iodine): starch, alkalies, alkaline earths, mineral earths, metallic salts and alkaloids.

ipecacuanhna (ipecac root): vegetable astringents, salts of lead and mercury, vegetable acids and tannic acid.

lobelia (Indian tobacco, *Lobelia inflata*): caustic alkalies.

physotigma (calabar bean): vegetable astringents, tannic acid and caustic alkalies.

pilocarpus (jaborandi, *Pilocarpus microphyllus*): caustic alkalies and salts of iron and of metals in general.

pulsatilla (wind flower): metallic salts, caustic alkalies and tannic acid.

quassia (quassia wood, *Picraena excelsa*): limewater and alkalies and their carbonates.

rheum (rhubarb): acids, tartar emetic, bichloride of mercury and sulphates of iron and zinc.

salix (black willow, *Salix nigra*): sulphate of iron, limewater and alkaline carbonates.

sanguinaria (blood root): tannic acid, alkalies and metallic salts.

sarsaparilla (smilax): acetate of lead, alkalies and iodine.

squills (sea onion, *Urginea martima*): acetate of lead, alkaline carbonates and nitrate of silver.

senna (*Cassia acutifolia*): strong acids, tartar emetic and carbonates.

taraxacum (dandelion): nitrate of silver, acetate of lead, infusion of galls, corrosive sublimate and sulphate of iron.

ulmus (slippery elm, *Ulmus fulva*): alcoholic tinctures.

Uva ursi (bearberry): Tartar emetic and salts of iron.

FORMS OF MEDICINAL PREPARATIONS

Infusions

These preparations are generally made by pouring boiling water over ground or bruised roots, barks, herbs or seeds, letting the drug stand ½ hour, stirring occasionally and then carefully straining the clear liquid off. When a ground drug—e.g., calumba or quassia—yields its properties to water without heat, cold water may be used. The usual quantity of drug to one pint of water is one ounce, but in a few cases, when a drug contains very active principles, less of the drug is sufficient. The dosages of most infusions vary from a tablespoonful to a wineglassful or a teacupful.

Decoctions

As a rule, decoctions are made by pouring cold water over cut, bruised or ground herbs. The mixture is boiled for 20 minutes to ½ hour then cooled and strained. Roots and barks are usually prepared as decoctions, since they need longer subjection to heat than leaves or seeds to extract their virtues. Decoctions are generally made in a strength of one ounce to one pint, but since the water boils away, it is perhaps best to use a pint and a half of water so that the decoction will measure one pint when the boiling is finished. The length of time to boil the decoction depends upon the readiness with which the drug gives up its active principles to the liquid. Dosages vary from two teaspoonsful to one or two wineglassesful.

Liquid Extracts

These are the most popular and convenient preparations, since if properly made, they are the most concentrated liquid forms in which vegetable drugs may be obtained. Liquid extracts are made in a variety of ways, including evaporation by heat, cold percolation and high pressure. Each drug is treated in the manner that will best extract its properties and hold the herb in concentrated solution. The strength of a liquid extract is one to one, or one ounce of fluid represents one ounce of a crude drug.

Solid Extracts

Solid extracts are prepared by evaporating the fresh juices or strong infusions of vegetable drugs to the consistency of honey. Solid extracts may also be manufactured by a spirituous process, wherein the alcohol is recovered by means of distillation from a strong tincture of the drug. Solid extracts are used chiefly in the manufacture of pills, plasters, ointments and compressed tablets.

Tinctures

Tinctures are spirituous preparations made with pure or diluted spirits of wine of drugs containing gummy, resinous or volatile principles; of drugs rendered useless by the application of heat; or of drugs that will not yield their properties to water alone, since their active principles are more readily extracted, better held in solution and better preserved from deterioration by spirits. Tinctures are generally made in a strength of one to two ounces of drug to one pint liquid. Dosages vary according to the active principles contained in the drugs.

Pills

Pills are perhaps the best known and most widely used form of medication, mainly because of their handy form and convenience, as well as their comparative tastelessness. For the most part pills are composed of concentrated extracts and alkaloids in

THE NUTRITIONAL COMPOSITION OF

Name	Calories	Protein (grams)	Fat (grams)	Calcium (mg.)	Phosphorus (mg.)	Iron (mg.)	Sodium (mg.)	Potassium (mg.)	Vitamin A (I.U.)	Thiamine (mg.)	Riboflavin (mg.)	Niacin (mg.)	Vitamin C (mg.)
Alfalfa, or Lucerne (*Medicago sativa*)	52	6.0	0.4	12	51	5.4	—	—	3,410	0.13	0.14	0.5	162
Amaranth, or Pigweed (*Amaranthus* spp.)	42	3.7	0.8	313	74	5.6	—	411	1,600	0.05	0.24	1.2	65
Arrowhead, or Duck Potatoes (*Sagittaria* spp.)	107	5.0	0.3	13	165	2.6	—	729	—	1.60	0.40	1.4	5
Asparagus (*Asparagus officinalis*)	20	2.2	0.2	21	50	0.6	1	183	900	0.16	0.18	1.4	26
Bamboo (*Bambusa* spp.)	27	2.6	0.3	13	59	0.5	—	533	20	0.15	0.07	0.6	4
Beechnut, American (*Fagus grandifolia*)	568	19.4	50.0	—	—	—	—	—	—	—	—	—	—
Beggarticks (*Bidens bipinnata*)	33	2.8	0.6	111	39	2.3	—	—	—	—	—	—	—
Blackberry (*Rubus* spp.)	58	1.2	0.9	32	19	0.9	1	170	200	0.03	0.04	0.4	21
Blueberry (*Vaccinium* spp.)	62	0.7	0.5	15	13	1.0	1	81	100	0.03	0.06	0.5	14
Burdock, Great (*Arctium lappa*)	89	2.5	0.1	50	58	1.2	30	180	—	0.25	0.08	0.03	2
Butternut (*Juglans cinerea*)	629	23.7	61.2	—	—	6.8	—	—	—	—	—	—	—
Cherry, Sour Red (*Prunus cerasus*)	58	1.2	0.3	22	19	0.4	2	191	1,000	0.05	0.06	0.4	10
Cherry, Sweet (*Prunus avium*)	48	0.9	0.2	15	13	0.3	1	130	60	0.02	0.02	0.2	3
Chestnut (*Castanea* spp.)	194	2.9	1.5	27	88	1.7	6	454	—	0.22	0.22	0.6	—
Chicory (*Cichorium intybus*)	20	1.8	0.3	86	40	0.9	—	420	4,000	0.06	0.10	0.5	22
Chives (*Allium schoenoprasum*)	27	2.7	0.6	83	41	0.8	—	—	—	0.10	0.06	0.5	32
Chufa, or Yellow Nut Grass (*Cyperus esculentus*)	311	4.4	17.2	59	155	2.4	—	—	—	0.90	—	—	—
Crabapple (*Pyrus* spp.)	68	0.4	0.3	6	13	0.3	1	110	40	0.03	0.02	0.1	8
Cranberry, Large (*Vaccinium macrocarpon*)	46	0.4	0.7	14	10	0.5	2	82	40	0.03	0.02	0.1	11
Currant, Garden Red (*Ribes sativum*)	50	1.4	0.2	32	23	1.0	2	257	120	0.04	0.05	0.1	41
Dandelion (*Taraxacum officinale*)	45	2.7	0.7	187	66	3.1	76	397	14,000	0.19	0.26	—	35
Dayflower (*Commelina* spp.)	43	2.3	0.4	210	52	—	—	—	—	—	—	—	—
Day Lily (*Hemerocallis fulva*)	42	2.0	0.4	87	176	1.2	24	170	3,000	0.16	0.21	0.8	88
Dock (*Rumex* spp.)	28	2.1	0.3	66	41	1.6	5	338	12,900	0.09	0.22	0.5	119
Dock, Curled (*Rumex crispus*)	21	1.5	0.3	74	56	5.6	—	—	1,385	0.06	0.08	0.4	30
Duckweed (*Lemna* spp.)	18	2.1	0.3	142	4	—	—	—	560	0.06	0.13	0.6	5
Elderberry, Common (*Sambucus canadensis*)	72	2.6	0.5	38	28	1.6	—	300	600	0.07	0.06	0.5	36
Fame Flower (*Talinum* spp.)	23	1.9	0.4	90	21	4.8	10	392	1,790	0.09	0.19	0.6	58
Fennel (*Foeniculum vulgare*)	31	2.9	0.5	114	54	2.9	—	338	1,566	0.12	0.15	0.7	34
Filbert, or Hazelnut (*Corylus americana*)	634	12.6	62.4	209	337	3.4	2	704	—	0.46	—	0.9	—
Galinsoga, or Quick Weed (*Galinsoga parviflora*)	42	3.2	0.5	245	45	7.1	—	—	1,120	0.11	0.27	2.1	30
Garlic (*Allium* spp.)	137	6.2	0.2	29	202	1.5	19	529	trace	0.25	0.08	0.5	15
Grape, Concord (*Vitis* spp.)	69	1.3	1.0	16	12	0.4	3	158	100	0.05	0.03	0.3	4
Ground-Cherry, or Husk-Tomato (*Physalis* spp.)	40	1.6	0.5	10	34	0.9	—	—	25	0.90	0.04	2.4	6
Hickory (nuts) (*Carya* spp.)	673	13.2	68.7	trace	360	2.4	—	—	—	—	—	—	—
Honewort, or wild Chervil (*Cryptotaenia* spp.)	18	2.0	0.1	81	45	1.8	7	490	488	0.15	0.20	0.5	60
Horsetail, Common (*Equisetum arvense*)	20	1.0	0.2	58	93	4.4	—	—	180	—	0.07	5.6	50
Jerusalem Artichoke (*Helianthus tuberosus*)	77	2.3	0.1	14	78	3.4	—	—	20	0.20	0.06	1.3	4
Knotweed (*Polygonum* spp.)	64	3.6	0.3	150	46	—	—	—	—	—	—	—	—
Kudzu (roots) (*Pueraria lobata*)	113	2.1	0.1	15	18	0.6	—	—	—	—	—	—	—
Lamb's-Quarters, or Pigweed (*Chenopodium album*)	43	4.2	0.8	309	72	1.2	—	—	11,600	0.16	0.44	1.2	80

Figure 26

WILD FOOD PLANTS (per 100 grams)

Name	Calories	Protein (grams)	Fat (grams)	Calcium (mg.)	Phosphorus (mg.)	Iron (mg.)	Sodium (mg.)	Potassium (mg.)	Vitamin A (I.U.)	Thiamine (mg.)	Riboflavin (mg.)	Niacin (mg.)	Vitamin C (mg.)
Leek, or Ramp (bulbs) (*Allium* spp.)	52	2.2	0.3	52	50	1.1	5	347	40	0.11	0.06	0.5	17
Mallow (*Malva* spp.)	37	4.4	0.6	249	69	12.7	—	—	2,190	0.13	0.20	1.0	35
Mallow, High (*Malva sylvestris*)	28	3.6	1.4	90	42	3.7	—	—	1,989	0.17	0.29	0.5	24
Maple (sugar) (*Acer saccharum*)	348	—	—	143	11	1.4	14	242	—	—	—	—	—
Mexican Tea (*Chenopodium ambrosioides*)	42	3.8	0.7	304	52	5.2	—	—	1,210	0.06	0.28	0.6	11
Milkweed (*Asclepias syriaca*)	—	0.8	0.5	—	—	—	—	—	—	—	—	—	—
Mint (*Mentha* spp.)	32	3.0	0.7	194	48	3.8	2	179	1,296	0.13	0.16	0.7	64
Mugwort, Common (*Artemisia vulgaris*)	35	5.2	0.8	82	40	1.5	—	—	1,284	0.15	0.16	3.0	72
Mulberry, White (*Morus alba*)	53	1.7	0.4	30	32	3.7	37	152	—	0.03	0.06	0.7	5
Mustard (greens) (*Brassica* spp.)	23	2.2	0.4	138	32	1.8	18	220	5,800	0.80	0.14	0.6	48
Nettle, Stinging (*Urtica dioica*)	65	5.5	0.7	—	—	—	—	—	6,500	—	—	—	76
Oak (acorns) (*Quercus* spp.)	48	0.2	0.1	12	314	0.2	—	—	6	0.02	0.40	0.5	0
Pawpaw (*Asimina triloba*)	85	5.2	0.9	—	—	—	—	—	—	—	—	—	—
Pecan (*Carya illinoensis*)	610	11.0	84.0	86	341	0.8	—	712	150	1.00	0.15	1.1	2
Peppergrass (*Lepidium* spp.)	32	2.6	0.7	81	76	1.3	14	606	9,300	0.08	0.26	1.0	69
Persimmon (*Diospyros virginiana*)	127	0.8	0.4	27	26	2.5	1	310	—	—	—	—	66
Pokeweed (spring greens) (*Phytolacca americana*)	23	2.6	0.4	53	44	1.7	—	—	8,700	0.80	0.33	1.2	136
Prickly Pear (*Opuntia humifusa*)	42	0.5	0.1	20	28	0.3	2	166	60	0.10	0.30	0.4	22
Primrose-Willow (*Jussiaea* spp.)	41	3.3	0.4	57	300	12.7	—	—	3,555	0.00	0.01	2.8	3
Purslane (*Portulaca oleracea*)	21	1.7	0.4	103	39	3.5	—	—	2,500	0.03	0.10	0.5	25
Rape, or Field Mustard (*Brassica rapa*)	32	3.6	0.6	252	62	3.0	—	—	1,355	0.12	0.29	1.1	118
Raspberry, Black (*Rubus occidentalis*)	57	1.2	0.5	22	22	0.9	1	168	130	0.03	0.09	0.9	25
Raspberry, Red (*Rubus idaeus*)	73	1.5	1.4	30	22	0.9	1	199	—	0.03	0.09	0.9	18
Rice, Wild (*Zizania aquatica*)	353	14.1	0.7	19	339	4.2	7	220	—	0.45	0.63	6.2	0
Sheep Sorrel (*Rumex acetosella*)	77	1.9	—	55	82	5.0	—	—	—	—	—	—	—
Shepherd's Purse (*Capsella bursa-pastoris*)	33	4.2	0.5	208	86	4.8	—	394	1,554	0.25	0.17	0.4	36
Silverberry (*Elaeagnus* spp.)	51	1.3	0.9	7	20	0.4	—	—	12	0.03	0.05	0.4	10
Sow Thistle, Common (*Sonchus oleraceus*)	20	2.4	0.3	93	35	3.1	—	—	2,185	0.70	0.12	0.4	5
Soybean (*Glycine max*)	400	35.1	17.7	226	546	8.6	—	1,504	6	0.66	0.22	2.2	0
Storksbill, or Alfilaria (*Erodium cicutarium*)	—	2.5	—	—	—	—	—	—	7,000	—	—	—	—
Strawberry, Wild (*Fragaria* spp.)	37	0.7	0.5	21	21	1.0	1	164	60	0.03	0.07	0.6	59
Sunflower (seed) (*Helianthus annuus*)	560	24.0	47.3	120	837	7.1	30	920	50	2.00	0.23	5.4	—
Vegetable Oyster, or Salsify (*Tragopogon porrifolius*)	89	1.4	0.2	48	50	1.4	—	—	—	0.04	0.04	0.3	10
Violet (leaves) (*Viola* spp.)	—	—	—	—	—	—	—	—	8,200	—	—	—	210
Walnut, Black (*Juglans nigra*)	628	20.5	59.3	trace	570	6.0	3	460	300	0.22	0.11	0.7	—
Watercress (*Nasturtium officinale*)	19	2.2	0.3	151	54	1.7	52	282	4,900	0.08	0.16	0.9	79
Water Hyacinth (*Eichhornia crassipes*)	30	0.5	0.1	—	—	—	—	—	—	—	—	—	—
Water Primrose (*Jussiaea repens*)	43	2.5	1.0	144	65	8.0	—	—	1,725	0.04	0.12	0.8	87
Water Shield (*Brasenia schreberi*)	10	0.7	0.2	9	23	2.0	—	—	6	0.03	0.03	0.3	0
Wood Sorrel (*Oxalis* spp.)	—	0.9	—	—	—	—	—	—	2,800	—	—	—	—
Yucca (flowers) (*Yucca aloifolia*)	33	3.1	0.2	47	73	0.8	—	—	10	0.14	0.09	0.6	—

Reprinted with permission from *The Mother Earth News*, copyright © 1979 by the Mother Earth News, Inc., P.O. Box 70, Hendersonville, N.C. 28739. One-year subscription, $15.

combination with active crude drugs. They may be obtained coated or uncoated, but the pearl-coated pill is the favorite, since it is quite tasteless, and the coating, if properly made, is readily soluble in the stomach.

Tablets

Tablets are made by compressing drugs into a very small compass. Some people claim tablets are superior to pills, since tablets are more easily administered and are quicker in action because of their rapid dissolution in the stomach.

Suppositories

Suppositories are small cones made of some convenient and easily soluble base. They are used when it is desirable to apply medicines through the rectum. Made of nutrients, suppositories are passed into the bowels when a patient is unable to take nourishment orally. They are invaluable in the treatement of such diseases as internal piles, cancer and fistula.

Pessaries

Pessaries are similar to suppositories, but they are made in shapes suitable for female complaints, when it is desirable to apply remedies to the walls of the internal passages.

Concentrations

Concentrations are a class of medicinal resins or resinoids obtained from medicinal drugs by precipitation from alcoholic preparations by water, distillation or other suitable means. Those at present in use contain one or more, but not always all, the therapeutic virtues of the drugs from which they are made. In many cases concentrations are only powdered extracts.

LIST OF DESCRIPTIVE TERMS

Following is a brief dictionary of the technical terms I use in this chapter to describe the medicinal uses of each of the herbs.

abortifacient An agent that induces or causes premature expulsion of a fetus.

acrid Having a hot, biting taste or causing heat and irritation when applied to the skin.

adjuvant An herb added to a mixture to aid the effect of the principal ingredient.

alterative An agent that produces gradual beneficial change in the body usually by improving nutrition without having any marked specific effect and without causing sensible evacuation.

analgesic A drug that relieves or diminishes pain.

anaphrodisiac An agent that reduces sexual desire or potency.

anesthetic An agent that deadens sensation.

anodyne An agent that relieves pain.

antihelmintic An agent that destroys or expels intestinal worms.

antibiotic An agent that destroys or arrests the growth of microorganisms.

anticoagulant An agent that prevents clotting in a liquid, such as blood.

antiemetic An agent that counteracts nausea and relieves vomiting.

antihydrotic An agent that reduces or supresses perspiration.

antilithic An agent that reduces or suppresses urinary stones (calculi) and acts to dissolve those already present.

antiperiodic An agent that counteracts periodic or intermittent diseases.

antiphlogistic An agent that reduces inflammation.

antipyretic An agent that prevents or reduces fever.

antiscorbutic A source of vitamin C for curing or preventing scurvy.

antiscrofulous Counteracting scrofula (*tuberculous adenitis*).

antiseptic An agent for destroying or inhibiting pathogenic or putrefactive bacteria.

antispasmodic An agent that relieves or checks spasms or cramps.

antitussive An agent that relieves coughing.

aperient A mild stimulant for the bowels, a gentle purgative.

aphrodisiac An agent for arousing or increasing sexual desire or potency.

appetizer An agent that excites the appetite.

aromatic A substance having an agreeable odor and stimulating qualities.

Astringent An agent that contracts organic tissue, reducing secretions or discharges.

balsam A soothing or healing agent or a resinous substance obtained from the exudations of various trees and used in medicinal preparations.

bitter Characterized by a bitter principle that acts on the mucous membranes of the mouth and stomach to increase appetite and promote digestion.

calmative An agent that has a mild sedative or tranquilizing effect.

cardiac An agent that stimulates or otherwise affects the heart.

carminative An agent for expelling gas from the intestines.

cathartic An agent that acts to empty the bowels, a laxative.

caustic A corrosive substance capable of burning or eating away tissue.

cholagogue An agent for increasing the flow of bile into the intestines.

coagulant An agent that induces clotting in a liquid, such as blood.

counterirritant An agent for producing irritation in one part of the body to counteract irritation or inflammation in another part.

demulcent A substance that soothes irritated tissue, particularly mucuous membranes.

decoction A liquid preparation made by boiling a substance with water.

deodorant An herb that has the effect of destroying or masking odors.

depressant An agent that lessens nervous or functional activity, the opposite of a stimulant.

depurative An agent that cleanses and purifies the system, particularly the blood.

detergent An agent that cleanses wounds and sores of diseased or dead matter.

diaphoretic An agent that promotes perspiration, a sudorific.

digestive An agent that promotes or aids digestion.

disinfectant An agent that cleanses infection by destroying or inhibiting the activity of disease-producing microorganisms.

diuretic An agent that increases the secretion and expulsion of urine.

emetic An agent that causes vomiting.

emmenagogue An agent that promotes menstrual flow.

emollient An agent used externally to soften and soothe.

errhine An agent that promotes sneezing and nasal discharges.

euphoriant, euphorigen An agent that induces an abnormal sense of vigor and buoyancy.

exanthematous Relating to skin diseases or eruptions.

expectorant An agent that promotes the discharge of mucus from the respiratory passages.

febrifuge An agent that reduces or eliminates fever.

galactagogue An agent that encourages or increases the secretion of milk.

hallucinogen An agent that induces hallucinations.

hemostatic An agent that stops bleeding.

hepatic A drug that acts on the liver.

hydragogue A purgative that produces abundant watery discharge.

hypnotic An agent that promotes or produces sleep.

infusion A liquid preparation made by steeping a substance in hot or cold water to obtain its active principle.

irritant An agent that causes inflammation or abnormal sensitivity in living tissue.

laxative An agent promoting evacuation of the bowels, a mild purgative.

mucilaginous Characterized by a gummy or gelatinous consistency.

nervine A substance that soothes nerves.

nutritive An agent that provides nutrition.

pectoral An agent for relieving chest diseases.

pungent A substance that acts as an irritant.

purgative An agent that cleanses or purges, especially the bowels.

refrigerant A substance used to produce refrigeration.

resolvent An agent that reduces inflammation or swelling.

restorative A substance that restores health or strength.

rubefacient An agent that irritates the skin, causing redness.

sedative A substance that has a soothing, calming or tranquilizing effect.

sialagogue An agent that produces a flow of saliva.

stimulant An agent that arouses or accelerates physiological or organic activity.

stomachic A substance that strengthens or stimulates the stomach.

tonic An agent that invigorates, refreshens or restores.

vulnerary A substance used to heal or treat wounds.

HOMEGROWN HERBS

Many herbs can be grown by anyone with relative ease. City dwellers can raise them in pots lined up along the ledges of their windows. Country dwellers, of course, can use their gardens. Then the leaves and seeds of the plants may be harvested for cooking or medicinal purposes according to the following instructions.

Harvest the leaves of herbs in dry weather and in the morning after the dew is off the ground: the strength of the plants decreases during the day. And leave enough growth on plants for them to bush out again.

Do not dry the leaves in direct sunlight. Place flowers or small amounts of leaves between two screens for drying. Hang annuals in labeled bunches in a warm, dry, airy room. Dry herbs that have been harvested in wet weather in the oven at a temperature of 150 degrees, turning the herbs frequently.

On the other hand, gather seeds while the dew is still on the plants: the seeds stick to the seed pods better when they are wet. After harvesting put the entire seed pods into a pillow case. To remove the seeds from the pods or stems, gently rub or shake the pillow case: place a sheet on the ground and hold the pillow case a few feet above it sometime when there is mild breeze. The heavier seeds will drop onto the sheet, and the chaff will blow away—a process known as winnowing. Then place the clean seeds on a window screen out of direct sunlight until the seeds are thoroughly dry.

The best containers for storing herbs are tinted glass jars, although you may also use regular glass jars or even plastic containers. Paper bags are not acceptable because the flavors of herbs dissipate on contact with air. Then place the herbs in a dark, cool cupboard or closet—not near the oven because that area becomes too hot. In a couple of days check the herbs to make sure they are thoroughly dry and that no moisture is present. If the herbs are not dry, place them on a window screen to complete the process and restore them.

Another way to store herbs is through freezing. Simply wrap them in freezer wrap after drying and place in the freezer. This method assures flavorful herbs that will keep for a very long time.

Following is a section outlining the properties and uses of herbs that can usually be easily grown at home. No poisonous herbs are discussed in this section.

Anise (*Pimpinella anisum*)

Plant this annual from seed in the spring under 1/4 inch soil. The rows should be 12 inches apart. There is a seven- to fourteen-day germination period. Thin the plants to eight inches apart when they are two inches tall. Seeds will be ready to harvest in 75 days. Do not transplant anise.

Anise makes good flavoring for pastry and bread. The leaves can be used sparingly in salads and are also good with fish. Seeds can flavor salads and be used in brandy and cordials. Seeds are good with stew, soups and candy, too.

Chemistry: Two and a half to three and a half per cent of the volatile oil is anethol. Other constituents of the plant are a fixed oil, mucilage, sugar and cholin.

Medicinal Uses: Anise is an antispasmodic, aromatic, carminative, digestive, expectorant, stimulant, stomachic and tonic. It improves appetite, promotes digestion, alleviates nausea and cramps and relieves flatulence and colic.

Preparations: For an infusion pour ½ to 1 cup boiling water over 1 teaspoon crushed seed. Steep 20 minutes and strain. Dosage is one cup a day, one mouthful at a time.

For decoction pour ½ pint milk over 1 tablespoon of the seeds for ten minutes and strain. Use for colic.

For a tincture pour ½ quart brandy over 2 ounces of seeds. Add a few clean lemon peels and stand the mixture in a sunny place for 20 days. Then strain. Take one teaspoon at a time.

For anise water boil ½ teaspoon of the seeds in ½ pint of water and strain.

Basil (*Ocimum basilicum*)

Plant this annual 1/4 inch deep in rows 12 inches apart. Do not plant basil next to rue. You may plant it near tomatoes and asparagus. Since the plant is sensitive to frost, it does well indoors. There is a five- to ten-day germination period. When the plants are two or three inches tall, thin them to one foot apart. Harvest in about 85 days.

Sweet basil is good in salads, gravies and tomato dishes. It is also good in pork, mutton and veal dishes.

Chemistry: Basil contains an aromatic, volatile and camphoraceous oil.

Medicinal Uses: Sweet basil is an aromatic, appetizer, antispasmodic, carminative, stomachic and galactagogue. It can be used for stomach cramps, gastric catarrh, vomiting, intestinal catarrh, constipation and enteritis. It is also a mild sedative.

Preparations: Steep 1 teaspoon of dried herbs in ½ cup water. Take 1 to 1 ½ cups a day, a mouthful at a time.

For a tea use one teaspoon of leaves per one cup of water.

Borage (*Borago offinalis*)

Plant this annual from seed in early June, 1/4 inch deep. You may plant borage near tomatoes and strawberries. Sow the seeds about 18 inches apart. There will be a seven- to fourteen-day germination period. When the plants are two inches tall, thin them to fifteen inches apart. Harvest in 80 days. Do not transplant borage.

Borage is good for cabbage dishes, spiced punch and ragout. It may also be braised with beef. The flower is candied for confection.

Chemistry: Borage contains potassium and calcium combined with mineral acids. The fresh juice affords 30 per cent of these nutrients, whereas the dried leaves afford only 3 per cent.

Medicinal Uses: Borage is a diaphoretic, aperient, febrifuge, pectoral, tonic and galactagogue. It is good for reducing fever by promoting sweating.

Under a physician's guidance it is also good for pleurisy and peritonitis. If skin is sensitive, a borage poultice may cause dermititis. Prolonged use is not advisable.

Preparations: For an infusion use one teaspoon of dried flowers or two to three teaspoons of dried leaves with one cup of water. Steep for 20 minutes and drain.

Caraway (*Carum carvi*)

Plant this biennial in the spring in soil 1/4 inch deep and in rows 12 inches apart. Plant one year for harvest the next. You may plant caraway near peas and beans, but keep it away from fennel. When the plants are two inches high, thin them by pinching them to six inches apart.

Caraway is used in breads, cakes and candies, as well as cabbage, soup, salads, sauerkraut, goulash and baked apples. The roots are eaten like carrots or parsnips.

Chemistry: The main constituent of caraway is a hydrocarbon oil called carvene. Seeds contain anywhere from four to seven per cent of the oil, depending upon the variety of caraway being used and how it is distilled.

Medicinal Uses: Caraway is a carminative, antispasmodic, appetizer, expectorant, emmenagogue and stomachic. It has a good effect on appetite and digestion. It also relieves uterine cramps and promotes secretion of milk. It is used for flatulent colic in infants and to settle the stomach of a person who has taken distasteful medicines and feels nauseous.

Preparations: For an infusion pour ½ cup water over 3 teaspoons crushed seeds.

For a decoction use ½ cup water to 1 teaspoon seeds. Boil for a short time. Then steep and strain. Take 1 to 1 ½ cups per day, a mouthful at a time. You may use milk instead of water.

The dosage for caraway oil is three to four drops three times a day.

The dosage for a powder is 1/4 to ½ teaspoon in a natural fruit juice of your choice two or three times per day.

For a tea use three teaspoons of bruised seeds per one cup of water.

Catnip (*Nepeta cataria*)

Plant this perennial in the spring or fall in soil 1/8 inch deep. Since catnip does not fare well with transplating, grow from seed. It germinates in from ten to twelve days. After the plants are firmly rooted, thin to 20 inches apart. If you cut the catnip all down before the seeds drop in the fall, the plants will come up again in the spring. You can get up to three harvests a year. It makes a good border to help repel flea beetles.

Catnip is good with fish and salads.

Chemistry: Catnip's chemistry is unknown. For some reason rats dislike the plant immensely and will not approach it; thus it makes a good border around a barn or other place where rats tend to congregate. On the other hand, cats find the plant fascinating and will destroy it when it has been transplanted outdoors from inside. (They won't bother the plant if it has been grown from its inception outside.)

Medicinal Uses: Catnip is an aromatic, carminative, anodyne, antispasmodic and diaphoretic. As part of a formula for children (1/2 teaspoon catnip to 1 cup water), it is good for convulsions. It is also good for gas, wind colic and stomach acidity.

Preparations: For an infusion use one teaspooon of the herb with one cup boiling water. Steep and strain. Take one to two cups per day.

For a tincture use the same proportions of catnip to water. Take 1/2 to 1 teaspoon at a time.

For a tea steep one teaspoon leaves to one cup water.

Chamomile (*Anthemis nobilis, Matricaria chamomilla*)

Plant this annual in the spring in soil ¼ inch deep. You may plant chamomile anywhere in the garden, since it helps keep all plants healthy. It germinates in from seven to fourteen days. When the plants are two inches tall, thin them to six inches apart.

Chemistry: A powerful alkali contained in the single flowers of chamomile may destroy the coating of the stomach and bowels; therefore, the double-flower type, which is usually cultivated and sold commercially, is recommended. Wild chamomile usually has a double row of petals. Both types contain a pale blue volatile oil that turns yellow with age as well as some anthemic acid and tannic acid. And it is a glucoside.

Medicinal Uses: Chamomile is an antispasmodic, calmative, anodyne, carminative, antiphlogistic and tonic. It is good for mild nervous complaints, insomnia, neuralgia, rheumatic condition and rashes. It reduces inflammation. As an oil it relieves tootache.[1]

Preparations: For an infusion pour ½ cup boiling water over 2 teaspoons flowers. Steep 20 minutes. Take two to three times daily as desired.

For a bath additive hang a bag containing one

[1]Since ancient times there have been arguments about which type of chamomile is best—the Roman or German variety. Actually, both have comparable medicinal value. Even Dioscorides and Pliny didn't differentiate between the plants. It also makes no difference how the herb is spelled —with a *cha* or *ca*. In Spain the plant is called *manzanilla* and is used for both headaches and bladder problems.

ounce of flowers in a tub of bathwater for skin tightening and cleansing.

For an oil preparation to apply to the skin for rheumatism, strained muscles or cramped muscles, beat up one ounce of flowers with olive oil. Let stand for 24 hours at room temperature away from direct sunlight. Strain and rub on affected parts of the body as needed.

Chives *(Allium schoenoprasum)*

Plant this perennial in the spring in ¼ inch soil. It may be grown from seed, with the seeds planted one inch apart. Do not plant next to peas or beans. You may plant chives near celery or carrots. There is a germination period of from two to three weeks. When the plants are two inches tall, thin them to six inches apart.

Chives give flavor to vegetable soups and soft cheese. You may chop bulbs to use as soft onion flavor in sausage. And you may use the herb in salads and egg dishes as well as jacket potatoes.

Chemistry: Chives contain a volatile oil, rich in sulfur and vitamin C. (Dried chives are not as potent in nutrients as fresh chives.)

Medicinal Uses: Chives promote digestive processes and stimulate appetite.

Preparations: Use fresh chives or dry them.

Comfrey *(Symphytum officinale)*

Start this perennial from root cuttings. Plant the cuttings three feet from each other in soil six inches deep. Plant in the early spring. Comfrey needs soil rich in lime. Harvest just before the plants bloom, usually the beginning of the second or third year. Cut back the plants, leaving at least two inches of stem.

Comfrey may be used in place of greens. Cook the leaves once then throw out the water and cook again. It is similar to spinach in taste and contains vitamin B-12, useful for vegetarians.

Chemistry: Comfrey contains a large amount of mucilage, 0.6 to 0.8 per cent allantoin and a small amount of tannin. Starch is also present in miniscule amounts.

Medicinal Uses: Comfrey is an astringent, demulcent, anodyne, emollient, hemostatic, expectorant, refrigerant and vulnerary. Comfrey is helpful for diarrhea. It can be used for wounds and insect bites as well.

A decoction of rootstock makes a good gargle and mouthwash for throat inflammation, hoarseness and bleeding gums. It also helps digestive and stomach problems as well as excessive menstrual flow. A rootstock may be used in baths for better skin tone. One of the best bone-knitting herbs, called *boneknit* by native Americans, comfrey may be taken

internally or applied in a poultice to a broken bone area.

Preparations: For a decoction boil two teaspoons rootstock in one cup of water or wine. Take a wineglassful two or three times daily.

For an infusion use 2 teaspoons per ½ cup water. Take one or two warm cups a day, a mouthful at a time.

The dosage for a tincture is ½ to 1 teaspoon at a time.

For tea use three teaspoons fresh or dried root per one cup of water. Let stand for ten hours and strain. Bring the soaked rootstock to a boil in ½ cup water and strain. Mix cold and warm extracts together and drink a mouthful at a time during the day.

For a poultice stir roots into a little hot water and form a thick mash. Spread the mixture on a cloth and apply. Or bruise five leaves and lay them across the skin with a hot, wet cloth covering them.

Coriander *(Coriandrum sativum)*

Plant the seeds of this annual in small clumps in ¼ inch soil. Do not transplant. Coriander may be grown near anise and caraway. It may also be planted near cabbage to discourage cabbage moths.

The seeds of coriander may be used in hot curries and sauces and sparingly in soups and stews. They provide good flavoring for sausage, cabbage, red beets, cookies, baked apples and stuffing.

Chemistry: Coriander seeds contain one per cent volatile oil, the active ingredient, which may be colorless or pale yellow. Seeds also have five per cent ash and malic acid as well as tannin and some fatty matter. If used too freely, the seeds have a narcotic effect.

Medicinal Uses: Coriander is an appetizer, antispasmodic, carminative, stomachic and aromatic. It may be applied for rheumatism and painful joints. And it is often used as an aromatic to improve the taste of other medicines.

Preparations: For an infusion steep two teaspoons of seeds in one cup water. Take one cup a day.

The dosage for a powder is ¼ to ½ teaspoon at a time in a fruit juice of your choice.

Dandelion *(Taraxacum officinale)*

Dandelion is a perennial plant that grows wild. The leaves may be cooked as greens, and the roots may be used as a substitute for coffee.

Chemistry: The main constituent is taraxacin, an acrid resin that contains insulin, gluten, gum and potash. In the spring the sugar is uncrystallizable laevulin. In the fall it becomes insulin. Dandelion is high in vitamin C.

Medicinal Uses: Dandelion is a cholagogue, diuretic, aperient, stomachic, stimulant and tonic. It promotes formation of bile and removes excess water from the body. It is good for removing poisons from the body. It relieves fever and insomnia. An infusion of fresh roots is good for gallstones, jaundice and all liver problems.

Preparation: Regardless of the preparation, use the whole plant before flowering, the leaves during flowering and the roots in the fall.

For an infusion steep two teaspoons of the root or plant in one cup boiling water. Take ½ to 1 cup of the lukewarm or cold mixture per day.

For a decoction use four ounces of fresh plant with two pints of water. Boil down slowly to one pint and strain. Take three teaspoons six times per day.

For a juice or spring tonic use one teaspoon juice pressed from leaves in milk one to three times daily.

For a cold extract mix two teaspoons of the plant with one cup water. Let stand for eight hours.

Dill *(Anethum graveolens)*

Plant this annual in midspring in ¼ inch soil. Do not plant near carrots. Plant near cabbage, lettuce, onions or cucumbers. There will be a seven- to fourteen-day germination period. Thin the plants to eight inches apart when they are two inches tall. Harvest the leaves before the plant flowers. Harvest seeds when the lower part of the seed cluster is ripe: you don't have to wait for all the seeds to ripen.

Dill is used for pickling, sauces and salads. You should not cook the plant; just soak it. Seeds can be ground and used with salt for preserving.

Chemistry: The oil in dill is a pale yellow color that darkens with age—a mixture of a paraffin hydrocarbon and 40 to 60 per cent of d-carvone with d-lionene. Phellandrine is present in the English and Spanish varieties but not the German variety.

Medicinal Uses: Dill is a carminative, diuretic, antispasmodic, calmative, stomachic and galactagogue. Dill tea is good for upset stomach. The herb also helps stimulate appetite. Chewing the seeds is good for halitosis.

Preparations: For an infusion steep two teaspoons of seeds in one cup water for 15 minutes. Take ½ cup three to four times daily.

Fennel *(Foeniculum vulgare)*

Plant this biennial in early spring in ½ inch soil. Plant fennel alone since it will affect other plants. There is a 14- to 21-day germination period. To harvest the stalk or bulb of the plant wait until the base is the size of a large egg. Pile soil heavily around the base, and it will blanch, becoming tender and white. When the base is four inches, cut it off just

above the roots. Harvest seeds just after they have changed color.

Use fennel grains or seeds with breads, soups, fish and marinades.

Chemistry: Fennel contains a volatile oil called anethol and fenchone, which has a pungent camphoraceous smell and taste. Also present in the oil are d-pinene, phellandrine, anisic acid and aldehyde. Limonene is sometimes present. The plant gives off ozone, which repels fleas.

Medicinal Uses: Fennel is an aromatic, antispasmodic, carminative, expectorant, galactagogue, diuretic, stimulant and stomachic. Both seeds and roots are good intestinal and stomachic remedies. Fennel relieves colic, abdominal cramps and flatulence. It is good for expelling mucus. It stimulates the flow of milk in nursing mothers. It may be rubbed on to relieve rheumatic pains. And as a decoction it is a good eyewash.

Preparations: For an infusion steep one tablespoon of fresh, crushed seeds in one cup water for five minutes.

For a decoction boil ½ teaspoon seeds in water. Strain and use as an eyewash three times a day.

For a milk decoction boil 1 teaspoon seeds in ½ cup milk for ten minutes. This decoction is good for colic.

The dosage for a tincture is ten to thirty drops in water as required.

Garlic *(Allium sativum)*

Plant the cloves of this perennial in the spring in two inches of soil. You may plant garlic throughout the garden, since it deters all kinds of pests. When harvesting, be careful not to injure the tops. Dig the plant up; don't pull because the bulb may rot. When the plant is dry, cut off the tops and store the bulbs.

Garlic is used in salads, meat, fish and poultry. Combined with parsley, it is much used in Italian and French cooking.

Chemistry: Garlic contains a pungent, volatile oil that is a sulphide of allyl. The oil is rich in sulfur and contains no oxygen. Garlic, when taken in excessive amounts, reportedly makes the retina of the eye more sensitive and less able to bear strong light. More tests need to be conducted to prove or disprove this theory.

Medicinal Uses: Garlic is an antispasmodic, carminative, antihelmintic, diuretic, cholagogue, expectorant and febrifuge. It stimulates the digestive organs, and as an expectorant it is useful for intestinal catarrh and chronic bronchitis. It regularizes actions of the gallbladder and liver. A garlic tincture lowers blood pressure and helps counteract arteriosclerosis. Garlic is also beneficial for blood circulation and heart action. And it stops gangrene.

Preparations: For a juice thin ½ teaspoon of juice pressed from the bulb with water and take two times daily.

For a cold extract for pinworms set 4 cloves of garlic in ½ cup water for eight hours.

For a tincture soak ½ pound of peeled cloves in 1 quart of brandy for 14 days at a temperature of approximately 85 degrees Farenheit in an airtight bottle. Shake several times per day. Strain after 14 days. The tincture will keep one year. Take five to twenty-five drops several times per day as needed.

Fix grated garlic mixed with honey for coughs.

Horehound *(Marrubium vulgare)*

Plant the seeds of this perennial, usually called *white horehound*, in the early spring in 1/4 inch soil. The plants will germinate in 10 to 20 days. When the plants are two inches tall, thin them to nine inches apart. Flowers will appear in the second year because of cold winters. By the second year the plants will be very hardy.

Chemistry: White horehound contains a bitter principle called marrubium, with a small amount of volatile oil, resin, tannin, wax, fat and sugar.

Medicinal Uses: White horehound is a diuretic, expectorant, diaphoretic, stimulant and tonic. It is excellent for coughs and bronchial problems in general. It has also been used for typhoid fever. It restores the normal balance of secretions of various glands and organs. And it is good for mild nervous conditions.

As an expectorant and for coughs and hoarseness it can be taken as a tea, syrup or a diluted alochol extract. Taken cold, it is good as a stomach tonic; warm, it is diaphoretic and diuretic. Both tea and crushed leaves can be applied externally for skin problems and insect bites.

Preparations: For an infusion steep 1 teaspoon of the herb in ½ cup water and sweeten with honey. Take 1 to 1½ cups daily, a mouthful at a time, for lung and heart problems.

For a syrup add one pound of sugar to one pint of infusion.

The dosage for a juice is one teaspoon in fresh juice twice daily.

The dosage for a tincture is five to forty drops in hot water as needed.

Horseradish *(Armoracia lapathiofolia)*

Grow this perennial from root cuttings. Plant the cuttings in early spring in five inches of soil.

Horseradish is whipped into sauces and added to cream, mayonnaise and butter. It may also be mixed with sausage, ham, liver and fish.

Chemistry: Horseradish contains sinigrin, a crystalline glucoside that will decompose in water, and the enzyme myrosin. Only the scraping of the root in its fresh state unites sinigrin and myrosin so that a volatile oil, allyl, is formed. On exposure to air the root will turn color and lose its strength. It will also lose strength if boiled in water. Horseradish contains much sulfur and some bitter resin, sugar, starch, gum, albumin and acetates.

Medicinal Uses: Horeradish is a rubefacient, diuretic and stomachic. Fresh it is good for rheumatic problems and bladder infections. As a juice it is helpful in colitis and intestinal problems. It may be used externally as an irritant to stimulate blood circulation or as a poultice for pains in joints. For bladder infections horseradish wine is used.

NOTE: Anyone who experiences diarrhea or night sweating should stop taking a horesradish preparation.

Preparations: Only undried horseradish is effective. It should be packed in wet sand or frozen. Honey or molasses makes the herb more palatable.

For a vinegar cover grated horseradish with vinegar and let stand for ten days. Take one teaspoon, diluted well with water, two to three times daily. This vinegar can also be used externally.

For a poultice spread fresh, grated root on a cloth. Lay the cloth on the affected area with the cloth against the skin until a burning sensation is felt. Then remove the poultice.

For a syrup steep 1 teaspoon root in ½ cup boiling water in a covered pan for two hours. Strain and add sugar until a syrupy texture is achieved.

Hyssop *(Hyssopus officinalis)*

Plant this perennial in late spring in 1/8 inch soil. Hyssop is easily transplanted and will reseed itself. Plant it near cabbage or grapevines and away from radishes. It will germinate in eight to fourteen days. When plants are six inches high, thin or transplant to twelve inches apart.

Hyssop may be used in stews and salads and with rich or fatty fish. It also tames the flavor of game meats.

Chemistry: The chemistry of hyssop is unknown, except that it contains a volatile oil.

Medicinal Uses: Hyssop is a carminative, astringent, emmenagogue, expectorant, stomachic, tonic and stimulant. It can be combined with sage to make a gargle for sore throat. Hyssop tea can be used for poor digestion and lung and breast problems as well as for nose and throat infections, mucous congestion, jaundice and dropsy. A decoction helps relieve inflammations, and a wash is used for bruises, skin irritations and burns. Crushed leaves can be directly applied to wounds to cure infection and promote healing.

Preparations: Peppermint is a good flavoring for this herb.

For an infusion steep 1 teaspoon dried herbs in ½ cup water and sweeten with honey. Take ½ to 1 cup daily, a mouthful at a time, for lung or breast problems.

For a decoction use one teaspoon of the herb with one cup water. Take one or two cups daily.

For a poultice soak fresh herbs in boiling water for 15 minutes and place on a cloth for application.

Oregano *(Origanum vulgare)*

Plant this perennial in the late spring in 1/8 inch soil. Plants will germinate in eight to fourteen days. When plants are three inches tall, thin them to ten inches apart.

Use oregano with meats. You may also cook leaves with peas and beans. It is good with tomato soups. And it is much used in Italian and Mexican cooking.

Medicinal Uses: Oregano is a pungent, stomachic, aromatic, tonic, stimulant, emmenagogue, carminative and diaphoretic. It strengthens the stomach and promotes appetite. It is good for consumption. It expels poisons from the body. In addition, it is used for supressed menstruation, yellow jaundice and dropsy. Oregano expels gas from the stomach and bowels.

Oregano juice is helpful against deafness and pain and noise in the ears. Oil dropped in the hollow of an aching tooth will stop pain. A poultice is good for swellings, sprains, boils and carbuncles. Oregano is also good for nerves.

Preparations: For a compress steep one tablespoon of the herb in a pint of boiling water for 30 minutes. Dip a cloth in the hot tea and apply, binding loosely with a dry cloth. Change the compress when it is cool.

For a cold extract use one teaspoon oregano to one cup of boiling water. Steep for 20 minutes. Strain and drink one or two cold cupsful daily.

For an oil mix 1 cup cold-pressed olive oil with ½ ounce oregano. Let stand for four hours. Strain. Use as needed. Oregano oil is particularly helpful for gallbladder problems.

Parsley *(Petroselinum crispum)*

Plant this biennial during spring in ¼ inch soil. Do not transplant. Plant the seeds in rich soil and make sure they are well-watered. Parsley grows well near onions, carrots, tomatoes and asparagus. Plants will germinate in three to four weeks.

Parsley may be added to soups, sauces, vegetables, stews, noodles, rice, cheese dishes, souffles and meats. It is a good breath freshener.

Chemistry: Parsley contains starch, mucilage, sugar, volatile oil and apiin. In the seeds there is fixed oil, resin, apiin, mucilage and ash. The herb is insoluble in water but soluble in alcohol. Apiol, an oily, nonnitrogenous allyl compound, is also found in parsley. And the herb is an oleoresin, which has apiol, apiolin and myristicin. In addition, parsley is high in vitamin C.

Medicinal Uses: Parsley is a carminative, antispasmodic, diuretic, emmenagogue and expectorant. Parsley tea and fresh juice are used for jaundice, asthma, dropsy, coughs and difficult menstruation. Juice may be used for inflammation of eyelids. An infusion is effective against gallstones.

NOTE: If parsley is taken in sufficient quantity, it will lower blood pressure and slow the pulse. If taken in excessive amounts over a period of time, it may produce paralysis, followed by fatty degeneration of the liver and kidneys. Further investigation is needed either to confirm or dismiss such a hypothesis. No one should use parsley if a kidney condition exists because it acts as a diuretic, forcing water from body, thereby causing the injured kidneys to work overtime and possibly damage themselves even more.

Preparations: For an infusion steep one tablespoon of bruised leaves in one cup water for 20 minutes.

For a decoction boil 1 teaspoon crushed seeds in ½ cup water. Take ½ to 1 cup daily.

Sage *(Salvia officinalis)*

Plant this perennial in late spring in 1/4 inch of calcium-rich soil. Sage makes a good house plant. Plant it near cabbage or carrots but don't plant it near cucumbers. The germination period is 10 to 21 days. As the sage grows, thin the plants to 12 to 18 inches apart.

Sage is used in stuffings, fowl, fish, liver and vegetables. It tastes a little like nutmeg. It may also be used in cheeses, souffles, sausage, veal, eel and fatty meats.

Chemistry: Sage contains a yellow or yellow-green volatile oil. Tannin and resin are also present in the leaves. Sage oil has salvene, a hydrocarbon, some pinene, cineol, borneol, a small quantity of esters and the ketone thujone. The English variety also contains cedrene.

Medicinal Uses: Sage is an antispasmodic, antihydrotic and astringent. As a tea or tincture it is good for reduction of perspiration. A tea will help stop the flow of a mother's milk after weaning. Tea is also good for depression, vertigo and trembling. As a gargle sage helps alleviate sore throats, tonsillitis and laryngitis. It is excellent for eliminating mucous congestion in the stomach and respiratory passages.

NOTE: Extensive or excessive use of sage will cause symptoms of poisoning.

Preparations: For an infusion steep 1 teaspoon leaves in 1/2 cup water for 30 minutes. Take one cup daily, a tablespoon at a time.

The dosage for a powder is ¼ to ½ teaspoon of powdered leaves at a time.

The dosage for a tincture is 15 to 40 drops, three or four times daily.

Thyme *(Thymus vulgaris)*

Since thyme is a very tender perennial, it should be started from seed indoors. Plant it ¼ inch deep in pots. Be sure it is well-watered and that the temperature is even. There is a five- to ten-day germination period. When plants reach three inches, transplant them to stand eight to ten inches apart. Thyme is a good houseplant. You may wish to keep it outdoors in summer and indoors in winter. Outside plant it near cabbage to repel cabbage worms. Harvest the plants before they flower in early summer. Cut the plants down to two inches, leaving a second growth so they can survive the winter if outdoors.

Thyme is spicy and a little bitter. It is good in clam chowder, chopped meats, gravies, stews, meatball mixtures and stuffings.

Chemistry: Oil of thyme has thymol and carvacrol. Cymene and pinene are also present with menthone.

Medicinal Uses: Thyme is an antispasmodic, antihelmintic, carminative, diaphoretic, expectorant and sedative. It is excellent for use with throat and bronchial problems. It is also used for whooping cough, chronic gastritis and lack of appetite. A warm infusion promotes perspiration and relieves flatulence and colic. Oil of thyme (thymol) is used in mouthwashes and toothpastes. Thyme baths are useful for rheumatic problems, paralysis, swellings and sprains.

NOTE: Extensive use of thyme internally will give symptoms of poisoning and will overstimulate the thyroid gland, causing nervous complaints, irritability, dizziness and heart palpitations. Anyone experiencing such symptoms should see a doctor.

Preparations: For an infusion steep ½ teaspoon fresh herb or 1 teaspoon dried herb in ½ cup water for five minutes. Take 1 to 1 ½ daily, a mouthful at a time.

The dosage for an oil is two to three drops on a

sugar cube two or three times daily.

MEDICINAL HERBS

The following section consists of herbs that are easily obtainable at most health food stores that carry herbs. Most of these medicinal herbs are not poisonous, but, when some are taken in excessive amounts, there can be negative reactions, as I shall note. It is advisable for anyone taking herbs to notify his or her physician of which herbs are being consumed so the doctor can determine if there is any incompatibility with drugs the patient is presently taking.

Angelica *(Angelica atropurpurea)*

According to legend, long ago in Europe an angel appeared to a monk in a dream, telling him that a particular herb was a cure for pestilence. From that time the herb was called *angelica* and was supposedly the most effective treatment against pestilence.

Common names for the herb are American angelica, archangel, bellyache root, high angelica, masterwort, purple angelica, wild archangel and dead nettle.

Chemistry: Angelica contains a volatile oil, valeric acid, angelic acid, sugar, a bitter principle and a resin called angelicin. The roots contain the essential oil teberbanelene and other terpenes. Seeds contain methyl-ethylacetic acid and hydroxymyristic acid.

Medicinal Uses: Angelica is a stimulant, diaphoretic, carminative, aromatic, diuretic, expectorant and emmenagogue. It is good for stomach and intestinal difficulties, including ulcers and vomiting with stomach cramps. It is also good for intermittent fever and nervous headache as well as general weakness.

Angelica tea or tincture will stimulate appetite, relieve flatulence and muscle spasms and stimulate kidney action. Angelica salve is useful as a skin lotion and will relieve rheumatic pains. Used in a bath the herb is soothing to the nerves. A decoction of the root can be applied to the skin for itching and for wounds. And it may be used as a compress for gout.

NOTE: Used in large doses, angelica has troublesome effects on heart action, blood pressure and respiration. It should not be given to people who have diabetes, since it causes an increase of sugar in urine.

Preparations: For an infusion use 1 teaspoon crushed seeds with ½ cup boiling water. Take as needed.

For a decoction use 1 teaspoon root and rootstock with ¾ cup cold water. Bring to a boil and steep five minutes. Take the ¾ cup in two equal parts during the day.

For a bath additive make a decoction from seven ounces of root and rootstock.

For a cold extract mix 1 teaspoon dried root and rootstock with ¾ cup water. Let stand eight to ten hours and strain. Take 1 to 1 ½ cups daily.

The dosage for a powder is ¼ to 1 teaspoon three times daily in your favorite natural fruit juice or water.

Black Cohosh *(Cimicifuga racemosa)*

This herb was brought to the United States from France, Germany and Great Britain. It now grows from Canada to Georgia and east of the Mississippi River.

Its common names are black snakeroot, bugbane, bugwort, cimicifuga, rattleroot, rattleweek, richweek and squawroot.

Chemistry: Black cohosh contains an amorphous resinous substance known as cimicifugin or macrotin. Its bitter principle is a crystalline called racemosin. It contains two resins with fat, wax, starch, gum, sugar and an astringent substance.

Medicinal Uses: Black cohosh is an astringent, diuretic, antispasmodic, emmenagogue, expectorant and sedative. It is a potent remedy for hysteria and spasmodic problems—e.g., whooping cough, consumption and St. Vitus dance. It has a sedative effect on the nervous system while also acting as a cardiac stimulant. Black cohosh infusions and decoctions are useful for rheumatism and chronic bronchitis. Black cohosh is also good for female complaints, since it is an excellent source of estrogen.

NOTE: Large and prolonged doses of black cohosh can cause symptoms of poisoning, such as vomiting and very painful headaches.

Preparations: For a decoction boil two teaspoons of rootstock in one pint of water. Take two to three teaspoons of cold decoction six times a day.

The dosage for a tincture is from ten to sixty drops, made from fresh root dug in October.

The dosage for a fluid extract is from five to thirty drops.

Buchu *(Barosma betulina)*

This herb is usually imported from South Africa, where it grows in the southwestern region of Cape Colony.

Its common names are bookoo, bucco, oval bucho, short buchu and bucku.

Chemistry: Buchu contains a volatile oil and mucilage. Diosphenol, which is antiseptic in property, is considered its most important ingredient.

Medicinal Uses: Buchu is a carminative, aromatic, diaphoretic, stimulant and diuretic. A strong buchu tea is helpful for painful urination and for inflammation, gravel and catarrh of the bladder. You may mix brandy with an infusion of leaves and drink the mixture as a stimulant, tonic and stomachic.

Preparations: For an infusion steep one tablespoon leaves in one cup water for 30 minutes. Take three or four tablespoons three or four times daily.

The dosage for a tincture is ten to twenty drops in water three times daily.

Cayenne *(Capsicum frutescens)*

Capsicum has been used since before the time of Columbus. Central and South American Indians used it for foods flavoring and medicine. Then Columbus introduced capsicum to Europe in 1493, and by 1650 it was grown over the greater part of Europe. Cayenne is the hottest form of the pepper, and Latin Americans use it in great abundance in their cooking. It also has a wide range of medicinal uses.

Its common names are African pepper, American pepper, bird pepper, chili pepper, cockspur pepper, goat's pepper, pod pepper, Spanish pepper, red pepper and Zanzibar pepper.

Chemistry: Cayenne contains capsaicin as well as oleic, palmitic and stearic acids.

Medicinal Uses: Cayenne is a digestive, irritant, appetizer, sialagogue, stimulant and tonic. In powder or capsule form it is useful for general stimulation and for building up resistance at the beginning of colds. An infusion is useful for stomach and bowel pains or cramps. Small quantities of fresh fruit or powder will stimulate the appetite. A cayenne plaster, linament or tincture applied externally will increase blood flow to areas afflicted with arthritis and rheumatism. Cayenne also promotes healthy blood circulation.

NOTE: Prolonged application of cayenne to skin can cause dermatitis and raise blisters. Excessive consumption can cause gastroenteritis and kidney damage.

Preparations: For an infusion pour 1 cup of boiling water over ½ to 1 teaspoon of peppper. Take warm, one teaspoon at a time.

For acute conditions take three to ten grains of cayenne powder; for chronic conditions, one to three grains.

Comfrey *(Symphytum officinale)*

Comfrey has been used extensively for centuries by the gypsies. It became so popular that old herbalists greatly exaggerated its cures; Culpepper even said it would both knit bones and join together two pieces of flesh. Unfortunately, it is not that good.

Its common names are blackwort, bruisewort, gum plant, healing herb, knitback, salsigy, slippery root and wallwort.

Chemistry: Comfrey contains much gum and mucilage, some allantoin and very little tannin. Starch in small amounts is also present.

Medicinal Uses Comfrey is an astringent, demulcent, anodyne, emollient, hemostatic, expectorant, refrigerant and vulnerary. A decoction of rootstock makes a good gargle and mouthwash for throat inflammations, hoarseness and bleeding gums. Comfrey also helps digestive and stomach problems, excessive menstrual flow and diarrhea. It can be used for wounds and insect bites. You may also add rootstock to a bath for better skin tone.

Preparations: For a decoction boil two teaspoons of rootstock in a cup of water or wine. Take a wineglassfull two or three times daily.

For an infusion use 2 teaspoons per ½ cup water. Take one or two warm cups daily, a mouthful at a time.

The dosage for a tincture is ½ to 1 teaspoon at a time.

For a cold extract tea use three teaspoons of fresh or dried root per one cup of water. Let stand for ten hours and strain. Bring the soaked rootstock to a boil in ½ cup water and strain. Mix cold and warm extracts together and drink a mouthful at a time during the day.

For a poultice stir roots into a little hot water and form a thick mash. Spread on a cloth and apply.

Echinacea *(Echinacea angustifolia, Brauneria angustifolia)*

Echinacea has been used in North America since before Columbus. The Sioux Indians used it for snake bites and hydrophobia.

Its common names are narrow-leaved purple coneflower, Kansas niggerhead and Sampson root.

Chemistry: Echinacea contains oil and resin, masses of insulin, inuloid, sucrose, vulose, betaine, two phytosterols and fatty acids—oleic, creotic, linolic and palmatic.

Medicinal Uses: Echinacea is a depurative, digestive, antiseptic and alterative. It is a blood-purifying plant used for conditions that indicate contaminants in the blood, such as acne, boils and eczema. It is excellent for swelling of lymph glands. It promotes proper digestion. Rootstock helps dispel flatulence. It is also helpful against pus formations, sores, wounds, infections and tonsillitis. It combines well with myrrh for all of the above conditions.

Preparations: For a decoction use one teaspoon rootstock with one cup water. Take one tablespoon three to six times daily.

The dosage for a tincture is 15 to 30 drops in water every one to three hours.

Fenugreek *(Trigonella foenum-graecum)*

The common names for fenugreek are fenugreek seed and Greek hay.

Chemistry: About 28 per cent of fenugreek is mucilage; the rest is 22 per cent protein, a volatile oil, two alkaloids, trigonelline and cholin. The chemical makeup resembles cod liver oil, and the herb is rich in phosphates, lecithin and nuclealbumin that has rich quantities of iron in the organic form, making it easily absorbed. Fenugreek can be substituted for cod liver oil in the treatment of scrofula, rickets, anemia and infectious diseases. For neurasthenia, gout and diabetes fenugreek can be combined with insulin.

Medicinal Uses: Fenugreek is mucilaginous. It is also an expectorant and restorative. Large amounts of a decoction will strengthen people suffering from tuberculosis or recovering from other serious illnesses. It is also useful for bronchitis and fevers. And it can be gargled for sore throats. A poultice of pulverized seeds is good for gouty pains, neuralgia, swollen glands, sciatica, tumors, sores, wounds and skin irritations.

Preparations: For a decoction use two teaspoons seed with one cup cold water. Let stand for five hours. Then heat and boil for one minute. Take two to three cups daily. You may add peppermint oil, lemon extract or honey for taste.

Fringe Tree *(Chionanthus virginicus)*

The common names for fringe tree are gray beard tree, old man's beard, poison ash, snowflower and white fringe.

Chemistry: Although the theory has not been fully proven, it is believed that fringe tree contains saponin and a glucoside.

Medicinal Uses: Fringe tree is a diuretic, aperient, febrifuge and tonic. The herb also has a beneficial effect on the kidneys. It is good against dyspepsia and cirrhosis of the liver. And it has a beneficial effect on the gallbladder. You may make the bark into a poultice for external use on wounds and skin irritations.

Preparations: For a decoction boil one teaspoon of bark in one cup water. Take one cup daily.

The dosage for a tincture is seven to ten drops in water.

Goldenseal *(Hydrastis canadensis)*

Goldenseal has been used since ancient times in Germany, France, Great Britain and all through Europe. It is a superior herb and greatly respected. Gypsies and native Americans have used it for centuries.

Its common names are eye balm, eye root, ground raspberry, Indian plant, jaundice root, orange root, tumeric root, yellow puccoon and yellowroot.

Chemistry: Goldenseal contains three alkaloids—berberine, hydrastine and canadine—as well as resin, albumin, starch, fatty matter, sugar, lignin and a small amount of volatile oil.

Medicinal Uses: Goldenseal is an antiperiodic, astringent, antiseptic, laxative, tonic, diuretic and alterative. It has both internal and external uses. It particularly acts on mucous membranes and can be used for catarrhal conditions.

An infusion can be a vaginal douche or an antiseptic mouthwash. Tea can be applied with a toothbrush for sore gums. An external wash can be used for skin diseases, sores, erysipelas or ringworm. (After washing with tea sprinkle on powdered rootstock.) Powder can be snuffed up nostrils for nasal congestion and catarrh. Small doses of goldenseal taken frequently will help allay nausea during pregnancy. Goldenseal mixed with boric acid makes a soothing eyewash. And powder may be sprinkled over wounds for quick healing.

Preparations: For an infusion add one teaspoon powdered rootstock to one pint boiling hot water. Let set until cold. Take one to two teaspoons three to six times daily.

For an eyewash add one teaspoon rootstock and one teaspoon boric acid to one pint boiling hot water. Stir, cool and pour off liquid. And 1 teaspoon of the liquid to ½ cup water to make the eyewash.

NOTE: Eating the fresh plant will produce ulcerations and inflammation of mucous tissue. Large amounts of goldenseal are poisonous. It is part of the ragweed family; therefore, people with allergies to ragweed should not take it. People with hypoglycemia may also react negatively to the herb.

Hawthorn *(Crataegus oxyacantha)*
The hawthorn tree has a long and illustrious history. It is said to still bear the smell of the Great Plague of London. It was regarded as sacred and was used as a symbol on the insignia of King Henry VIII.

Its common names are Mayblossom, quick, whitehorn, hazels and hagthorn.

Chemistry: The bark of hawthorn contains the alkaloid crataegin, which, when isolated, is greyish-white crystals, bitter in taste, soluble in water and partially insoluble in alcohol.

Medicinal Uses: Hawthorn is a cardiac, diuretic, astringent and tonic. It is used primarily as a cardiac tonic for organic and functional heart problems. It is also useful for diuretic problems involving edema and kidney complaints.

Preparations: For an infusion boil one pint of distilled water. Pour it over one ounce of hawthorn

berries. Cover and steep for 15 minutes. Cool, strain and bottle, keeping the mixture in a refrigerated area. Take a wineglassful three to four times daily.

To make a fluid extract of berries, place ten to fifteen drops in water or fruit juice.

Hydrangea *(Hydrangea aborescens)*
Hydrangea has been used by native Americans, who passed on the knowledge of the properties of the herb to the European settlers of America.

Common names for hydrangea are seven barks and wild hydrangea.

Chemistry: Hydrangea contains two resins, gum, sugar, starch, albumen, soda, lime potassium, magnesium, sulphuric and phosphoric acids, a protosalt of iron and the glucose hydrangin. It also contains a fixed and volatile oil. Two crystallines are found in the flowers—hydragenol and hydrangeaic acid.

Medicinal Uses: The root of hydrangea is a diuretic. The leaves are a tonic, diuretic, cathartic and sialagogue. The herb is valuable for relieving bladder problems.

Although hydrangea will not cure stones in the bladder, it will remove the stones as well as the pain accompanying them, a fact proved by Dr. S. W. Butler of Burlington, New Jersey: as many as 120 calculi have come from one person using the herb.

Hydrangea will also relieve backache caused by kidney problems. And it is good for chronic rheumatism, scurvy, paralysis and edema.

NOTE: Hydrangea is poisonous when taken in immoderate amounts. Anyone wishing to take the herb should receive the permission of his or her physician first. Overdoses will cause vertigo and oppression of the chest.

Preparations: A tincture of hydrangea is best ordered from Standard Homeopathic Co., Los Angeles, California. Take ten to twenty-five drops daily.

Lobelia *(Lobelia inflata)*
Lobelia can be found in warm, moderate and northern latitudes; however, if the season is cold or excessively wet or dry lobelia will not appear that year.

Lobelia has been the cause of great and often heated controversy about its poisonous qualities. The majority of experts now believe that it is a wonderful healing and relieving agent with remarkable powers.

Its common names are bladderpod, emetic weed, gagroot, emetic herb, Indian tobacco, vomitroot, vomitwort and wild tobacco.

Chemistry: Lobelia contains a liquid alkaloid called lobeline as well as lobelic acid, gum, resin, chlorophyl, fixed oil, legnin, salts of lime and potassium and ferric oxide. The seeds contain higher amounts of lobeline than the rest of the plant.

Medicinal Uses: Lobelia is a diaphoretic, antispasmodic, diuretic, emetic, nervine and expectorant. It is used for its antispasmodic qualities to treat asthma and whooping cough. It is excellent for lung congestion and is also used to induce vomiting.

A poultice is good for bruises, insect bites, sprains, felons, ringworm and poison ivy irritation. If a patient is delirious, an enema of lobelia and catnip will relieve the brain. Combined with slippery elm, lobelia makes an excellent poultice for abscesses, boils and carbuncles.

Lobelia is a relaxant and will cause drowsiness; relaxation is counteracted by an infusion of capsicum, a stimulant.

NOTE: No one should take more than three cups daily of lobelia. And no one should drink and drive with this herb, which produces relaxation, drowsiness and shallow breathing.

Preparations: For a tincture combine two ounces lobelia herb with two ounces crushed lobelia seed and one pint apple vinegar. Soak for two weeks in a well-stoppered bottle, shaking daily. Strain and use. Take one tablespoon at a time to clear the lung passages. Used externally, the tincture is good for rubbing on shoulders and chest for asthma.

For a poultice combine ⅓ part lobelia with ⅔ part slippery elm and enough warm water to make a paste.

For a lobelia compound combine 1 pound lobelia seed, ¾ pound lady's slipper and ¼ pound capsicum with 80 per cent alcohol to make ½ gallon. Use externally only.

For lobelia syrup put two teaspoons of lobelia compound into a four-ounce bottle and fill with Karo syrup, malt honey or a simple syrup of three pounds of brown sugar dissolved in one pint of boiling water.

Marsh Mallow *(Althaea officinalis)*

Marsh mallow is found in almost all tropical and subtropical parts of the world and almost all tropical parts of the United States. It was once eaten as a food. The Romans regarded it as a vegetable dish. There is very little known of its history in Great Britain and France.

Its common names are wymote, mortification root, sweat weed and althea.

Chemistry: Marsh mallow contains starch, mucilage, pectin, oil, sugar, asparagin, phosphate of lime, cellulose and glutinous matter.

Medicinal Uses: Marsh mallow is a demulcent, diuretic and emollient. It is also mucilaginous. As a poultice it's good for sore or inflamed areas: it

soothes and lubricates. An infusion is good for lung troubles, hoarseness, catarrh, dysentery and diarrhea. The tea is also good to bathe sore eyes. It's valuable in all kidney diseases and pneumonia.

Preparations: For an infusion pour one cup water over one teaspoon leaves or rootstock. Simmer for 15 minutes. Drink two cupsful daily, a mouthful at a time.

Milkweed *(Asclepias syriaca)*

Both native Americans and western pioneers used this herb. The Appalachian tribes brewed a tea from leaves; the Shoshones pressed it in the hand until it was firm, then chewed it like a gum; the Rappahannocks used it to cure ringworm and rubbed it on warts.

During World War II the Department of Agriculture experimented to see if milkweed could take the place of kapok, used in flotation devices: experiments were conducted to see if the sap could be used as a substitute for rubber.

Its common names are common milkweed, cottonweed, common silkweed, silky swallowwort, Virginia silk and swallowwort.

Chemistry: Milkweed contains a crystalline substance called asclepione, allied closely to lactucone, as well as fatty matter of a waxlike character, caoutchouc, gum, sugar, salts of acetic acid and other salts.

Medicinal Uses: Milkweed is an emetic, diuretic and purgative. It is useful for kidney problems, water retention, dropsy, gallstones, asthma and stomach ailments. Milkweed juice may be used externally on warts. An infusion of rootstock may produce temporary sterility.

NOTE: Milkweed is poisonous in large quantities.

Preparations: For an infusion for gallstones mix equal parts milkweed and althea. Steep one teaspoon of the mixture in one cup of boiling water. Take three cups daily, one of them warm, at bedtime.

For another infusion pour one cup boiling water over one teaspoon rootstock. Take two to three cups daily.

Mullein *(Verbascum thapsus)*

This herb was introduced from Europe and is now common in the United States. The Navajos combined it with ordinary tobacco to help mental disorders. Others used smoke from the herb for curing pulmonary troubles. Mullein was listed as an official medicine in the National Formulary up to 1936.

Its common names are Aaron's rod, candlewick, blanketleaf, feltwort, flannelflower, great mullein, Jacob's staff, hedgetaper, shepherd's club, velvet dock, mullein dock and velvet plant.

Chemistry: Mullein leaves contain mucilage and gum as well as two resins—one soluble in ether, the other not. The flowers contain rum, resin, fatty matter, a glucoside, acrid fatty matter, free acid, phosphoric acid, uncrystallizable sugar, mineral salts, some potassium and lime and yellow volatile oil.

Medicinal Uses: Mullein is a demulcent, emollient, astringent, expectorant and vulnerary.

Mullein tea from the leaves is a good remedy for hoarseness, bronchitis, coughs, bronchial catarrh and whooping cough. The tea is also used for gastrointestinal catarrh and cramping in the digestive tract. Tea made from flowers relieves pain and induces sleep. The tea or fomentation of leaves boiled or steeped in hot vinegar and water may be used externally for inflammations or painful skin conditions.

For respiratory problems or nasal congestion a person may breathe a vapor from hot water with a handful of leaves added. A poultice can be used for wounds and sores.

Preparations: For an infusion steep one teaspoon leaves or flowers in one cup water. Take one to two cups daily.

The dosage for a tincture is 15 to 40 drops in one cup of warm water every two to four hours.

Peppermint *(Mentha piperita)*

The name *mentha* comes from a Greek nymph, Minthe, who loved Pluto so much that Persephone became jealous and turned her into a plant.

Peppermint has been used since the early dynasties of China. Roman physicians used it. Nineteenth-century herbalists used it. We still use it. Leaves are sometimes strewn on church floors because the leaves smell so good. In India the herb is used in clumps to freshen rooms.

Common names are brandy mint and lamb mint.

Chemistry: Peppermint contains an essential oil that is yellow or green with a burning, camphorescent taste: it becomes red with age. Peppermint also contains menthol, menthyl acetate and isovalerate, as well as menthone, cineol, inactive pinene and limonene.

Medicinal Uses: Peppermint is a carminative, cholagogue, refrigerant, stomachic, anodyne, antispasmodic and tonic. The herb is said to be an aphrodisiac when taken in large quantities. Peppermint is also used frequently in combination with other herbs to make them more palatable.

Peppermint tea or oil is useful for poor digestion, nausea, abdominal pains, cramps, migraine headaches and insomnia. The leaves make a cooling external application that relieves slight pain. Made into a salve, the leaves are wonderful for itching skin conditions.

NOTE: Peppermint may cause minor heart problems if taken for a prolonged period.

Preparations: For an infusion steep three teaspoons leaves in one cup water. Take one to two cups daily. Since this herb may cause minor heart problems, do not take if for more than eight to twelve consecutive days and then wait at least two weeks before taking it again.

The dosage for peppermint oil is three to four drops in one teaspoon honey with hot tea.

The dosage for a tincture is ten to forty drops, depending on a person's age and the severity of the problem.

Poke Root *(Phytolacca decandra)*

Poke root has been used for centuries in France, Germany, Africa and the United States. It was one of the first natural inks in the New World. Voyagers found it here, tried it and promptly took some back to their native countries, where it became very popular.

Its common names are red weed, pokeweed, garget, red ink plant, pigeon berry, Virginia polk, scoke coakum, pocan bush, American nightshade, cancer jalap and red ink berries.

Chemistry: The berries contain phytolaccic acid and tannin. The root contains a nonreducing sugar, formic acid and bitter resin. The alkaloid phytolaccin may be present in minute quantities in the root. The herb also contains vitamin C.

Medicinal Uses: Poke root is an alterative, deobstruent, detergent, resolvent, antisphilitic and antiscorbutic. It is good for enlargements of the spleen and glands, especially the thyroid. It is also useful for treating a hard liver, inflammation of the kidneys, biliousness and enlarged lymphatic glands. To treat goiter it is taken internally as well as used as a liniment and poultice. It is effective against enlargements of bone from chronic injuries and for growths.

NOTE: Overdoses of poke root may produce vomiting, purging, prostration, convulsion and death.

Preparations: For an infusion steep one teaspoon rootstock in one cup water. Take two time daily.

Red Clover *(Trifolium pratense)*

Red clover has been grown in Europe, Central and Northern Asia, Canada and the United States since before written history.

Its common names are marl grass, cow grass and cleaver grass.

Chemistry: Unknown.

Medicinal Uses: Red clover is an alterative, depurative, detergent and mild stimulant. It is a wonderful blood purifier and is very high in iron. Red clover blossom tea is effective for bronchial troubles, bad nerves, whooping cough and wounds. The herb also may help cancer of the stomach or any part of the body: bathe parts of the body freely with tea and drink four cups daily on an empty stomach for internal healing.

Preparations: For cancerous growths, use leprosy and pellagra. Mix equal parts of red clover flower, yellow dock, blue violet, dandelion root, burdock, rock rose and goldenseal.

For a tea combine the above ingredients and mix three teaspoons in one cup boiling water. Use externally or internally.

Rue (Ruta graveolens)

Rue, primarily a medicinal herb, dates back to the early Greeks. The name itself comes from the Greek *reuo*, which means "to set free." The Roman herbalist Pliny thought rue to be a remedy for nearly 85 different ailments. In the Middle Ages people though rue would protect them from witches and wild beasts: it does repel insects. It is also often used in sprigs to sprinkle holy water prior to High Mass.

Its common names are common rue, garden rue, German rue and herb-of-grace.

Chemistry: Rue contains a volatile oil that contains caprinic, plagonic, caprylic and oenanthylic acids. It also contains a yellow, crystalline body called rutin.

Medicinal Uses: Rue is an emmenagogue, antihelmintic, carminative, stomachic and stimulant. It is well-known for relieving gout and rheumatic pains and for treating nervous heart problems. It is also useful for menopausal heart palpitations. Rue promotes onset of menstruation and is good for relieving gas and colic.

NOTE: Rue can cause a poison ivylike rash in sensitive people. No one should take large doses of the herb or take it for prolonged periods of time because it can cause mild poisoning. *It is not to be used by pregnant women.*

Preparations: For an infusion steep 1 teaspoon of dried herb in ½ cup water. Take ½ cup daily.

For a cold extract soak 1 teaspoon dried herb in ¾ cup cold water for 10 hours and strain. Take ¾ cup daily.

The dosage for a tincture is from five to twenty drops.

Skullcap (Scutellaria lateriflora)

Skullcap is indigenous to the North America, growing best in wet and shady ground. There are sister plants throughout the world with similar properties.

The common names are blue skullcap, blue pimpernel, helmet flower, hoodwort, mad-dog-weed and side-flowering skullcap.

Chemistry: Skullcap contains a volatile oil, scultellarin, with a glucoside that yields scultellarin on hydrolysis. It also contains tannin, fat, sugar and cellulose.

Medicinal Uses: Skullcap is a sedative, tonic, antispasmodic and nervine. As an infusion it is good for spasms, convulsions and nervous conditions, such as insomnia and general restlessness. It may also be used for rheumatism and neuralgia.

NOTE: Overdoses of skullcap cause giddiness, stupor, convulsions indicative of epilepsy and intermission of the pulse.

Preparations: For an infusion steep one teaspoon of dried plant in a teacup of water for 30 minutes. The dosage is one cup three or four times daily.

The dosage for a tincture is from three to twelve drops taken in hot water.

Slippery Elm (Ulmus fulva)

In Appalachia people use slippery elm as a protective agent and a healing agent for wounds. Native Americans have used it to ease the removal of lead from gunshot wounds. Native American midwives use it to ease the births of children.

Its common names are red elm, elm bark, moose elm, Indian elm, rock elm, sweet elm and American elm.

Chemistry: Slippery elm contains a mucilage similar to that found in linseed. The bark shows starch grains and very characteristic twin crystals of calcium oxalate.

Medicinal Uses: Slippery elm is an emollient, nutritive, demulcent, pectoral and tonic. It may be used internally or externally.

Slightly astringent, slippery elm is very gentle aned can be retained by the most delicate of stomachs. It is soothing and healing to irritated and inflamed surfaces, such as wounds, burns and chapped skin. It is also useful for consumption or tuberculosis, asthma, pneumonia, bronchitis, nephritis, gastritis, gastric ulcers, phloric inflammation or ulceration, calculi, scalding urine, abscesses, tumors, sore throat, ulcerated stomach and stomach weakness.

Preparations: For an infusion steep one teaspoon of powdered or shredded bark in water for 20 minutes. The preparation may be drunk three to four times daily.

Squaw Vine *(Mitchella repens)*

Found in most of North America to the Rocky Mountains, squaw vine is held in high esteem by native Americans.

Its common names are checkerberry, hive vine, deerberry, oneberry partridgeberry, twinberry, winter clover and squawberry.

Chemistry: Squaw vine contains resin, wax, mucilage, dextrin and possibly saponin.

Medicinal Uses: Squaw vine is a diuretic, tonic and astringent. It makes childbirth faster and easier when used in the last few weeks of pregnancy. As a diuretic it is used for gravel and urinary ailments. Squaw vine tea makes a good wash for skin problems and sore eyes. It will also help relieve insomnia.

Preparations: For an infusion steep one teaspoon leaves in one cup water for 30 minutes. Take one to three cups daily.

As a tonic take four to fifteen drops of tincture three times daily.

Strawberry Leaves *(Fragaria vesca)*

This plant was originally called *strewberry* because the berries appear to be scattered among the leaves of the plant. Both Virgil and Pliny the Elder wrote about strawberries. In art and literature they usually symbolize sensuality and desire, whereas in religion they symbolize perfection and righteousness.

Common names are pineapple strawberry, mountain strawberry, wood strawberry, common strawberry and wild strawberry.

Chemistry: Strawberrry leaves contain cissotanic, malic and citric acids, as well as sugar and mucilage.

Medicinal Uses: Strawberry leaves are a tonic, diuretic and astringent. The fruit is a diuretic and refrigerant. The herb may be used internally or externally. Strawberry tea stimulates appetite, is good for bowel troubles and cleans the stomach. As an external wash it helps exzema. It is also good for diarrhea and weakness of the intestines.

Preparations: For an infusion steep one teaspoon leaves in one cup water for 20 minutes. Take one to three cups daily.

Uva Ursi *(Arctostaphylos uva ursi)*

Uva ursi is found in northern Europe, Asia and North America.

Its common names are universe vine, bearberry, upland cranberry, mountain cranberry, wild cranberry, moutain box, bear's grape, kinnikinnick, sagackhomi and mealberry.

Chemistry: Uva ursi contains the glucoside arbutin, ursone, gallic and ellagic acids, a yellow principle somewhat like quercetin and possibly myricetin. The leaves also contain six to seven per cent tannin.

Medicinal Uses: Uva ursi is an astringent, tonic and diuretic. It is very good for kidney problems, diabetes, hemorrhoids, piles, excessive menstruation, spleen, liver troubles, pancreas problems and mucous discharges containing pus and blood from the bladder. It is helpful for gonorrhea and ulceration of the neck of the womb. It may be taken internally and externally as a douche.

Preparations: For an infusion steep one teaspoon in a pint of boiling water for 30 minutes. Take ½ cup every four hours.

Valerian *(Valeriana officinalis)*

Valerian is cultivated in Great Britain, Germany, the Netherlands and the United States. A smaller, wild variety also grows in Europe.

Common names are German valerian, English valerian, great wild valerian, vermon valerian, allheal, vandal root, set wall and American English valerian.

Chemistry: Valerian contains a brown-yellow oil that contains valerianic, formic and acetic acids. The root contains two alkaloids—chatarine and valerianine—plus a glucoside and resin.

Medicinal Uses: Valerian is a stimulant, tonic, anodyne, antispasmodic and nervine. It is a very good nerve tonic. When taken hot it will help promote menstruation. For children it is excellent for measles, scarlet fever and restlessness. It is also helpful for relieving colic, breaking up colds, lowering fevers and relieving gravel in the bladder. It is healing to an ulcerated stomach. Valerian tea can be used externally for sores and pimples as well as taken internally.

NOTE: Large doses of valerian, repeated too often, produce pain in the head, heaviness and stupor. One should not drive or fly after drinking a cup of it because it dulls the senses.

Preparations: For an infusion use one heaping teaspoon in one cup boiling water. Steep for 20 minutes. An adult should take no more than two cups daily; a child, ½ cup.

White Oak Bark *(Querous alba)*

White oak is native to Italy, Spain and other parts of Europe, as well as the United States, where a large proportion grows. Native Americans in New England drank oak tea for bleeding and internal hemorrhaging. The Ojibwas used the root bark for diarrhea. Other tribes used the herb for loosening phlegm in the lungs.

Its other common name is tanner's bark.

Chemistry: Unknown.

Medicinal Uses: White oak bark is an astringent, tonic and antiseptic. Its tea is excellent for various problems of the womb. The herb will also expel pin worms. And it is used as an enema for piles, hemorrhoids and problems in the rectum. It will stop hemorrhages in the lungs, stomach and bowels, as well as bleeding at the mouth. It increases urination and removes gallstones and kidney stones. It is use useful in lowering fevers and helpful for an ulcerated bladder or bloody urine. It may be taken internally and rubbed externally for varicose veins.

Preparations: For pinworms simmer one tablespoon in one pint of water for ten minutes. Drink three cups daily.

For enemas and douches steep one tablespoon in one quart boiling water for 30 minutes. Strain and use as hot as possible.

For varicose veins steep one tablespoon in one pint water for 20 minutes. Drink two cups daily. Bathe the veins three or four times daily. You may moisten a cloth with tea, wrap the cloth around a leg and cover with flannel.

Yellow Dock *(Rumex crispus)*

Yellow dock was native to Europe and brought to the United States as people immigrated to our shores.

Its common names are garden patience, narrow dock, curled dock, sour dock and rumex.

Chemistry: Rumicin is the active ingredient. The root contains chrysarobin. Yellow dock is also one of the best forms of natural iron available, containing approximately 40 per cent iron.

Medicinal Uses: Yellow dock is a cholagogue, tonic and astringent. It is used as a laxative and blood purifier. It is useful for eruptive diseases and skin problems. The ointment is good for itching, swelling, sores and scabby eruptions. Hot tea is used for glandular tumors and swelling. The herb also relieves congested liver conditions.

Preparations: For a decoction boil one teaspoon root in one cup of water. Take one to two cups daily.

For skin problems use a dose of 12 grains of powder.

POISONOUS HERBS

At one time the Federal Trade Commission (FTC) was going to require warning labels on dangerous plants. But the plan was scrapped because it would necessitate burdensome and inflationary regulations: it had been estimated that 500 million plants might have to be labeled each year at a cost of perhaps $16 million. In addition, there had not been

a single death recorded from touching or eating such plants in 16 years. Accounts of deaths and injuries are largely in medical literature from many years ago. To protect consumers, however, the staff of the FTC did compile a list of plants that should not be touched or eaten. Following is the list of plants or categories of plants considered dangerous by the FTC.

Angel's Trumpet *(Datura)*

This plant is an hallucinogen that can cause convulsions. Injuries have been reported.

Bird of Paradise *(Poincians gilliesif)*

Severe poisoning can occur when this plant is ingested. Several injuries have been reported.

Black Locust *(Robinia pseudoacacia)*

The seeds of this plant can cause dullness and depression, vomiting and a weak pulse. Injuries have been reported.

Castor Bean *(Ricinus communis)*

Large doses of the seeds of this plant may lead to convulsions, exhaustion and death. Many injuries have been reported.

Crownflower *(Calotropis gigantea)*

The sap from this plant can cause severe eye injury. Injuries have been reported.

Dumbcane *(Dieffenbachia)*

This plant can cause a swollen tongue and loss of speech if ingested. Numerous injuries have been reported.

Elephant Ear *(Alocasia macrorrhiza)*

If this plant is chewed, there can be intense pain around the lips, mouth and tongue. Injuries and some deaths have been reported.

Foxglove *(Digitalis)*

This plant can cause nausea, vomiting and dizziness. It also affects the rhythms of the heart. Injuries have been reported.

Golden Chain *(Laburnum anagyoides)*

Ingestion of this plant can cause excitement, lack of coordination and death through asphyxiation. One death and several injuries have been reported.

Jequirity Bean *(Abrus precatorius L)*

The seeds from this plant, also known as *rosary pea*, are violently poisonous. Fatalities have been reported.

Jerusalem Cherry *(Solanum pseudocapsicuma)*

Alkaloids in this plant can cause vomiting when it is ingested. There may also be local irritation and a slowing action on the heart. Injuries have been reported.

Lily of the Valley *(Convallaria najalis)*

The roots, leaves and fruit of this plant can stimulate the heart muscles in much the same way digitalis can. No injuries have been reported.

Meadow Saffron *(Colchicum autumnale)*

This plant, also called *autumn crocus*, can cause burning of the throat, intense thirst and vomiting, followed by possible death from respiratory failure. Fatalities have been reported.

Philodendron *(Philodendron)*

If ingested, this plant can cause a skin rash requiring long-term medical care as well as swelling of the mouth and throat. Injuries have been reported.

Red Peppers *(Capsicum)*

This plant is also called *bird peppers* and *chilies*. Although peppers make a very good seasoning and are a beneficial herb, they can be dangerous in overdoses. They can burn the skin and mouth, and large doses may cause severe poisoning. Injuries have been reported.

Rhododendron (Rhododendron)

This plant can cause intense pain, diarrhea and discomfort. Injuries have been reported.

Spurge Laurel *(Daphne)*

Ingestion of this plant can cause intense irritation of the mouth and convulsions. One death has been reported.

Tobacco Tree *(Nicotiana)*

Severe stomach upset and pain can occur when this plant is ingested.

Tropical Woodrose *(Argyrela nervosa)*

This plant, also called *baby Hawaiian woodrose*, is an hallucinogen if ingested.

Wisteria *(Wisteria)*

Ingestion of the pods of this plant can cause severe gastrointestinal symptoms. Injuries have been reported.

Yellow Oleander *(Thevetia peruviana)*

All parts of this plant, also called *be-still tree*, are dangerous, acting as a heart poison. One death has been reported.

Yew *(Taxus)*

This plant contains a violent gastrointestinal irritant. Ingestion causes a quick pulse, fainting, convulsions and death. Injuries have been reported.

Several other plants not listed by the FTC are also poisonous. Until the properties of these herbs are well-known, the best rule of thumb is to underdose, not overdose. Following is a list of other herbs that should be avoided: aconite, atropa, belladonna, Chinaberry tree, elderberry, jack-in-the-pulpit, mandrake, mistletoe, monkshood, poke root, skunk cabbage, water hemlock and yellow jasmine.

CHAPTER FOURTEEN
Natural Essences

USING NATURAL ESSENCES

Another tool in our box of natural healing options is known as natural essences. Many readers are familiar with Dr. Edward Bach's Flower Remedies. He was a British homeopathic doctor, famous between the early 1900s and the 1930s, who pioneered new concepts in homeopathy, including bowel nosodes, a discovery shared with Dr. Paterson.

Bach was always looking for something from nature that would not cause aggravations or "retracing" (Hering's Law of Cure) such as homeopathy could bring on. It should be noted that only twenty percent of all people suffered from an aggravation (an intensification of the symptoms they had at the time they took the homeopathic remedy), and it would last a few seconds to weeks, depending upon the strength of the potency given and the problems the patient had at the time.

Hering's Law of Cure states that when someone takes a homeopathic remedy, the Vital Force, in its infinite wisdom, will begin the cure on the most important organs (the brain and heart) and progress to the least important ones (the skin). It will start at the head and work downward to the feet. It will work from the inside to the outside. I call this law "retracing" because the Vital Force will make the body release whatever is still held in the cells, tissue, bone, cartilage and so on that has not run its full course. This could range from emotional trauma to shock from a car accident and include anything in between. The body does hold memory of all damage done to us — whether it's on a spiritual, mental, emotional or physical level.

Our bodies are sponges that retain all injuries experienced by us — unless we work through those events completely. If we don't, then what is left is retained and remembered by the body. That, in part, is what helps to create dis-ease, or being out of balance or harmony, because we haven't been able to release that shock or trauma from our system. Homeopathy is an energy medicine and connects first with the etheric body, which is like a glove that wraps snugly around the physical body. This etheric body is literally a blueprint or template for the physical body, and they "talk" to one another through various means. Electromagnetic "messages" come from the etheric and translate, with the help of the chakras (power stations in the etheric), into physical manifestations, which stimulate the body's central nervous system or parasympathetic nervous system.

Bach was always striving to find a gentle cure that would help a patient return to a state of harmony and wellness. He finally left the field of homeopathy and moved into the one I call "natural essences." For over a decade he worked with buds from trees and flowers, and even with water, to try to find a safe, natural healing process. Eventually he chose 38 natural essences, and the name Bach Flower Remedies was coined. Today they are known and used around the world. More importantly, they have opened a huge door and the subject had been little explored until just recently. Bach Flower Remedies are not only safe, but are even more gentle than homeopathy.

Methods of Storing Natural Essences

As a homeopathic practitioner I started using Bach Flower Remedies decades ago, right along with the remedies I dispensed to my patient. I began to use them because I wanted to spare my patients as much of the discomfort of aggravations and retracing as I could. The Bach Flower Remedies were reputed to help mental and emotional areas of discomfort. I've found they resonate not only spiritually, but physically as well. I have talked to many other users of these natural essences over the years, and they have had similar experiences with them. From a legal standpoint (at least in the United States, under FDA law), they can be sold with no claims at all about what they are used for. Thank goodness there are a number of books available on these natural essences for interested people to consult to know how to use them and in what areas.

As the years went on, I saw my patients experience discomforts on the spiritual, mental, emotional and physical levels that the Bach natural essences did not address. Having been raised by a mother who was an herbalist and a father who was an Eastern Cherokee shaman, I was no stranger to our connection with the plant people, be they flowers, trees, "weeds" or any organic substance. I was trained by an Apache medicine woman, Oh Shinnah Fast Wolf, on how to work with gems and crystals and how to "charge" water.

Once the water was charged, it retained the energy for upwards of 24 hours, before the energy dissipated. I would teach my patients how to charge water so that they would have a renewable supply of the natural essence that best suited their symptomatologies. It was a good idea, because I've always believed that healing is in the hands of the patient, not the doctor.

I took this charging method she taught me and decided to use it with something other than rocks. I used charged gem and crystal water, another form of natural essences, on my patients when indicated. Long before the crystal fad came in, I was using this Native American method for my patients to relieve their discomfort as they went through homeopathic constitutional treatment. I noted over time that not every patient needed a Bach or gem natural essence, so I began expanding my natural-essence supply to flowers, plants, trees and grasses.

I have found, as Bach did, that each and every plant, tree, rock, blade of grass, and every other natural material has a unique and specialized area of skill and expertise that can immediately translate to a particular human condition. Native Americans have known for thousands of years that wherever they live, the Great Spirit provides medicines that can heal them. They have learned of herbs, flowers, grasses and trees that can help them come back into harmony and balance and therefore get healthy once again.

A year ago I had the good fortune of meeting Rhonda Pallas Downey, who had been doing eight years of research into natural essences, utilizing Dr. Bach's method of creating them. The main difference between the water-charging method and the Bach method is that Bach's utilizes the energy of the sun to imprint the natural essence into the water, and water-charging depends upon the practitioner's intense concentration and personal energy to imprint the water.

Pallas used Bach's method, setting the flower blossoms into a bowl of water outside in direct sunlight for one to three hours. She enlarged upon this concept by setting night-blossoming flowers out in moonlight. The natural essence would then be strained out and mixed with a certain amount of brandy, and the energy imprint would be held in it forever — not for just 24 hours, as with charging. I liked the idea of "forever," as opposed to 24 hours. For one thing, it meant I could begin to stock my natural essence tinctures for future patients.

One of the greatest benefits of using natural essences is that they are safe, causing no addiction, no adverse side effects or aggravation. They "dance" in concert with homeopathic remedies and do not antidote them — a big plus, as many items can antidote a homeopathic substance. For every human ill or ailment, I'm sure that there's an equivalent out there in nature to help them.

The field of natural essences is small indeed. When you consider that Dr. Bach had 38 essences he settled upon for use with his patients, and that there are literally millions of flowers and other plants out there to be researched, you can see what a long scientific road lies ahead of us. But what an exciting prospect! In my natural-essence pharmacopoeia I have about 100 essences I've used on patients over the years.

Natural essences can help all human conditions on the spiritual, mental, emotional and physical fields of manifestation. Generally speaking, when a natural essence does affect the physical body, it is much more gentle in its movement than a homeopathic remedy. Roughly ten percent of the population can't utilize homeopathic treatment because they are too sensitive to it; they prove every remedy they take, which is a miserable experience for them. Natural essences can help this ten percent without the rigors or suffering brought on by homeopathic treatment. The more sensitive you are, the better a candidate you are to utilize natural essences as a tool in your wellness kit to stay healthy. They can be used acutely (for short duration, when the illness has a natural end, usually in seven days or less, such as a cold or flu) or for chronic conditions, such as major disease patterns.

Often, when a patient has been through the medical mill and come out the other end worse for wear and financially destitute, natural essences can be like a miracle to them. They not only gently stimulate the Vital Force to begin healing, but they are also a cheap resource compared to pharmacy drugs. Natural essences are especially useful when a patient has been drugged too long and too often; a typical case is one in which too many rounds of antibiotics have been prescribed. The elderly, who fall into a special category because they are on a fixed income and their Vital Force may not be strong enough to respond sufficiently to a homeopathic remedy, often respond to a natural essence, and it can make all the difference in the world, sometimes miraculously.

Uses of Aquamarine

Let me give you an example. One of the earliest natural essences I experimented with, first on myself and later on patients who volunteered to try them in charged-water form, was a beautiful gemstone known as aquamarine. The history of this stone, whose name is Latin for "seawater," is interesting. During the Middle Ages, people thought that if they held an aquamarine stone in the mouth, the gem would convey insight into the most perplexing questions they could ask. When this stone was consecrated by the Church, many believed it would conquer all forms of wickedness. When an elixir of aquamarine was made, the water used was either placed over the eyes for eye problems or drunk to cure respiratory ailments and hiccups.

Symbolically, it was seen as a gem of joy and youthfulness. Today the jewelry market touts aquamarine as *the* stone for the month of March, the time of equinox and the coming of spring. This transparent gem, which comes from Brazil, Madagascar and Utah, may have a color from a turquoise-green to the blue of the Caribbean. It's known as the sea-green gem. Even though it's a rock, it was associated with the ocean because of its clarity and waterlike color.

In homeopathic philosophy, there is a hypothesis we call the Doctrine of Signatures. The DOS, as I refer to it, says that the shape, color, environment, conditions, and whatever else makes it what it is (a gem in this case), says something about it symbolically and tells us how it will interact with a human being. The DOS of aquamarine would begin with the following. It is a beryl (as is emerald) and has a refractive light of 1.5. (Diamond, on the other hand, is 2.5 — considerably "brighter.") It has a hexagonal crystalline structure.

Even though it is considered a semiprecious stone, its color suggests the aqua of water. Many stones are formed out of the steam and heat of volcanic eruption, or from the pressures of the ocean floor settling layer by layer upon it; so there is a speck of scientific fact in saying that water is involved in the formation of aquamarine — as well as many other stones. It's the beauty and clarity of the sea-green/blue color that conjures up the clear, sparkling Bahamian ocean waters that surround those islands and set our imaginations on fire.

Water symbolically stands for feelings, emotions and intuition or knowing. Blue is also the color of the throat chakra, which sits out in the etheric field, a few inches away from the physical body. The throat funnels the blue color of the light spectrum through it, and it is generally accepted that this color stands for truth, communication and devout spiritual (as well as religious) leanings. Blue is one of the three primary colors and is considered the "cool" color. It is sedative, calming and soothing. So too is aquamarine.

The Chakras

The color of any natural essence has a correspondence to one of the major chakras located in the etheric field and it directly affects the physical body — the endocrine glands and the major organs and systems. In order to understand the effect of natural essences, we have to detour for a moment into the physics of metaphysics — which can be defined as that which is beyond the visible. Below are general and very brief definitions of our major chakras or energy-exchange centers and their correspondences to the physical body.

The **root** chakra is seated at the base of the spine, the tailbone region. This is the location of the kundalini, or snake energy. The testes of the male are located in this region, and it concerns the male reproductive system as well as male sexuality. It is about being grounded and fully in the body. If a person is out of his body, he will be spacy, forgetful, a "space cadet," a daydreamer, disorganized and unable to finish what he starts. He might have poor circulation in the feet and legs, even numbness. Color: red.

The **navel** chakra is located below the belly button (some also place it in the region of the spleen, above and to the left of the belly button). Women's reproductive organs are located in this area. This is where victimization and codependent behavior have their roots. It's about service to others (doctors, teachers, nurses and so on), but not at the expense of ourselves. Damage and trauma to this area tend to create a victim mentality — a give-give-give perspective without knowing how to graciously receive in return. This area concerns self-esteem and shame issues. Many women have problems with this particular chakra. Color: orange.

The **solar plexus** chakra is located in the region of the stomach. This is where we keep our anger, hatred, anxieties and fears. It is the seat of our opinions, our perspective on life and our prejudices. Many of us, when we're frightened suddenly or receive bad news, literally feel our stomachs clench — this clenching sensation is actually the chakra snapping shut for a time. People have problems with ulcers, indigestion and nausea in this region. Color: yellow.

The **heart** chakra is located over the physical heart. This is the seat of our love: being able to love (give and receive), loving and liking ourselves, and grief because of loss of a loved one (animal or human). Walling off our emotions for whatever reason can create a possible heart attack, palpitations or high blood-pressure. Immune-system depression. Many men have problems with this chakra. Color: green.

The **throat** chakra is located over the larynx, in the neck. It concerns the ability to speak out and up for ourselves, to communicate and "talk" in some way, be it through speech, singing, teaching or writing. Thyroid problems for women. Overstressed central and parasympathetic nervous systems. Color: blue.

The **brow** chakra is located in the center of the forehead. This is our "third eye" that can look into the other dimensions; it is tied strongly with the right hemisphere of the brain. It has to do with the biological cycles of life, such as the seasonal changes and the hormone functions connected with them; an example would be sunlight-deprivation problems during winter when people can become depressed. Not being able to trust what you know, even if you don't "see it" with your physical eyes. Distrust of your intuition. Color: purple.

The **crown** chakra is located on top of the head. The ability to receive the higher-consciousness energy from God/Cosmos. Our spiritual umbilical cord. If it is closed down, there is a sense of loss, hopelessness, or being disconnected from a higher source of love. Sickness of the spirit originates here and can later manifest on the mental, emotional or physical plane of expression. Color: white.

Each natural essence has a color or colors that indicate which chakra or energy points it can begin to stimulate. The simple fact that each color has a vibrational resonance wave-frequency pattern, and utilizing the homeopathic maxim "Like cures like," can indeed influence these powerful major centers of energy conversion.

Let's go back to our example, the aquamarine gemstone. Its blue color indicates that the throat region and chakra can be stimulated, nurtured and supported in all of its various functions. Normally, when a gemstone is used to make an essence, the formula is called an elixir. I generally refer to any usable substance as a natural essence. Whether the water is charged or made via Bach's method (setting the stone under sunlight) is a moot point. Both systems work, and that's the bottom line for the patient.

When the essence is taken — usually three or four drops under the tongue three times daily for several weeks — the energy signature of that substance is introduced into the Vital Force. Just like a homeopathic remedy, it stimulates the appropriate organ, endocrine gland or system into responding and reacting. The aquamarine will open up the throat chakra if it is closed down for any reason. When the throat chakra is open, a person is able to speak up for himself. When it's closed down, the person generally has problems standing up for himself or saying much of anything to anyone.

Aquamarine can also gently stimulate the central and parasympathetic nervous systems, for the blue color cools and soothes those systems. It is a gem essence specifically for curing stressed-out individuals and people with insomnia caused by an inability to turn off the mind at night, and for stimulating the thyroid into normal functioning. I call this gemstone essence Mother Nature's natural tranquilizer. It's a lot safer and effective than taking sleeping pills or antidepressants.

Gemstone Essences Can Cure Animals

Aquamarine essence is wonderful for calming hyperactive children and even animals. I once had a woman bring her poodle to me because the dog was so hyperactive it couldn't stand still and was in a constant state of high stress and tension. At my suggestion, she charged the dog's water once a day for seven days with a small, rough-cut aquamarine. On the eighth day she called to tell me that a miracle had happened: her poodle was calm, no longer stressed-out, and acting like a "normal" dog. Eventually she went to a rock shop and bought a rough, natural aquamarine for a couple of dollars and taped it onto the dog's collar, with the same result.

It would be pretty tough to say this was the "placebo effect," because animals don't understand English, nor do they reason like human beings. If you suspect the placebo effect, animals are a wonderful laboratory for your experiments with natural essences. The medical field believes that roughly thirty percent of all people given a sugar pill with no actual medication in it will get well. They call this psychosomatic reaction, but when you give the same essence or homeopathic remedy to an animal and it works — then the placebo effect must be ruled out.

We owned an Arabian horse farm in Ohio for nine years, and I routinely used not only homeopathic remedies, but natural essences too — with excellent results. It saved a lot on vet bills, let me tell you! These animals couldn't have been psychosomatically affected or influenced. Homeopathy and natural essences worked on them time and again. As a matter of fact, I used an aquamarine on a very fractious, spoiled, high-strung Arabian mare we had bought when she was six years old. Neygem was her name, so it's sort of interesting that I used a "gem" on her to unplug her high-strung state and get her full, undivided attention so that I could not only begin training her, but riding her. Like cures like! I always put the gem being worn by an animal or person on the left side of the body, which is the feminine-energy side, the place where we absorb energy into our own, personal Vital Force or aura.

USING COLOR TO UNDERSTAND NATURAL ESSENCES

Natural essences can be made from any organic or inorganic substance. They are safe and nonaddictive, with no adverse side effects, and they can be used by anyone. Further, they won't antidote a homeopathic remedy and in fact are often used in concert with them to help lower aggravations or retracings of old ailment symptoms. They can alter disease on the spiritual, mental, emotional or physical level and work toward cure.

As discussed earlier, the chakras in our etheric template — that energy field that surrounds the physical body — have a specific color. Each color in the light spectrum has a corresponding vibrational wavelike frequency. In nature, gems and flowers (to name a few) have a primary, and sometimes secondary, color, and they duplicate those wavelike frequencies precisely. For instance, roses may be a single color or several colors, depending upon the variety.

At our home, La Casa de Madre Tierra (The House of Mother Earth), we have nearly fifty rose bushes. About half of them are the "tree" variety and the others are the bush type. I've named each bush, and I don't go by their species names, which seem very distant and disconnected. Every fruit tree on the land we steward has a personal name, too.

One of the roses in our garden is known as Astarte, and she's an Angel Face species sporting lush lavender-colored rose "babies" — her children, in a sense. Astarte has an incredibly sweet fragrance to her. This particular rose is a tree rose and has a rather "tight" bloom. If you peeled back the petals on one of her blossoms, you would find the same lavender color consistently throughout it.

Another rose, Delilah, has orange as her primary color, with yellow and red as her secondary colors. She's a huge rose bush that stands over eight feet tall, and her "children" have a heady fragrance that swirls around you whenever you walk near her. The petals are an apricot color on the outer edge, becoming an intense red-orange color as you look toward the center of the large, soft petal. There is a deep gold color at the base of the petal that moves upward to mix with the deeper orange color in the center of the petal. Add to that dark red veins that run throughout the center of the petal, which vividly remind one of capillaries filled with blood.

Each rose's color defines an area of skill; their essences address particular chakras in a human body. Let's look at the chakra overlay with these two roses. Astarte has lavender-colored blooms, corresponding with the brow chakra, which transmits the purple (violet and lavender) spectrum of color and energy. Whereas Delilah has connections with her primary color, orange, and is connected to the navel chakra, her secondary colors, yellow and red, correspond to the solar plexus and root chakras, respectively.

Color helps us to define which energy system or systems a natural essence can help in a human being.

Another example of this is gemstones. Everyone is familiar with the emerald, which is a beautiful green color. Green corresponds to the heart chakra. It is the color of healing — a soothing energy as well as a growth energy (don't forget that most plants are green in color). Emerald essence could be utilized to open up a closed-down heart chakra, deal with issues of the heart (emotions and feelings), and help to heal them.

The transparency or opacity of a stone gives us a clue about the strength or the energy signal from the stone. The more transparent or clear the stone, the more power it has.

One of my hobbies is raising orchids, which is difficult, to say the least, in the dry, hot Arizona climate. Orchids are an incredible natural essence. They are exotic, lush, unusual, and temperamentally sensitive to the least change in humidity and temperature. Getting to know orchids is to have a completely unique world open up to you. Many of the natural essences I'm observing, experimenting with and proving are fruit-tree blossoms, roses, bulb plants and orchids.

There is one orchid, known as a White Kasem, which has incredibly pale green petals; it isn't white at all. This orchid, on the inner area of its lip or sixth petal, has six magenta or red vertical stripes. This is a heart-chakra flower, because it is green; its secondary influence is the root chakra, which is red. This particular orchid, with its unique color scheme, has a powerful, healing effect on anyone who has been sexually molested or raped either as a child or adult, and helps to reconnect that person's root chakra with the heart chakra in order to promote healing from this violent experience. Frequently, survivors of childhood incest won't trust or love anyone again because of the violation done to them, and White Kasem works toward healing that issue.

Essences are made in many ways. I use my knowledge and Native American training along with what Rhonda Pallas Downey shared with me of Dr. Edward Bach's method of collection and essence-making. I go to a flower, a tree or a rock that draws me. Everyone has a favorite plant, flower or gemstone that draws him, and again you might say that "Like cures like." I try to stay true to my own knowing, or where the eyes of my heart draw me. There are a number of essence companies that devote their attention exclusively to wildflowers. Because there are millions of flowers and other natural essences out there, everyone can afford to follow their own love of a particular flower or other natural item.

Natural essences are lacking scientific or left-brain influence. As a homeopath, I have brought some scientific demands into the field of natural essences. I created the Natural Essence Society, a group of individuals who meet once a month to test and prove new essences that either I or Rhonda Pallas Downey have gone into the field and collected. It could be a flower, a gemstone, a tree or whatever. A one-ounce eye-dropper bottle containing the untested essence is passed around the group, each person putting four drops under her tongue. No one knows ahead of time what the natural essence is, and no hints or suggestions are given to the provers.

Each individual chosen for this group is extraordinarily sensitive, even psychic. We write down any colors or sensations that occur and which chakra is affected. Then, one by one, we share our experiences with the group. Without fail, the group reaches a consensus as far as symptoms go, and a larger picture on the essence starts to take form. After everyone has shared their experiences, Pallas or I will tell the group what the essence was. Then we compare the Doctrine of Signature by passing around colored photos of the plant, flower or whatever it is, to be observed and talked about in depth.

In this way we begin to build an overall concept about the essence. This is known as stage 1 of understanding a particular natural essence, its skills, chakra(s) and unique talents. Stage 2 is a longer-term experiment. We take four essences a month, marked A, B, C and D; no one knows which remedy they are getting. Proving diaries are handed out with each bottle, and each member takes them home. Bottle A is taken four times daily for seven days, and the prover keeps a diary of any sensations, locality, or changes that occur, also noting anything that is brought on by taking the essence repeatedly. In the second week, bottle B is taken, and so on. By the time the provers come back for the monthly meeting, there is a tremendous amount of information compiled on four new natural essences.

This information is then gone over and carefully sorted out, compared and compiled. With help from the members of the cooperative, along with our knowledge and observation techniques, we garner tremendous amounts of information on what the natural essence can be used for and compile a repertory of symptoms. This repertory is specific and can be matched to the patient's symptom picture. This is utilizing the homeopathic "Like cures like" philosophy.

Stage 3 consists of keeping careful, thorough records of patients taking a particular natural essence and building an even stronger base of information regarding it. This allows us to understand the underpinnings of a remedy even more clearly. At that point, the information garnered is compiled for an ongoing multiple-volume set I'm writing, called *Natural Essence Materia Medica with Repertory*.

Most companies who sell natural essences don't go through such rigorous scientific demands, but they *should* in order to have these wonderful, subtle energy tools taken seriously by our traditional medical establishment and eventually embraced as a viable healing tool in our health arsenal.

A New Essence from Start to Finish

I'd like to take you on an essence trip with me, to give you a bird's-eye view of the complete gathering-and-testing cycle. When I take a field trip to make essences, I have a special knapsack to carry certain items I'll need. Among those items are flower/shrub/tree identification books, a magnifying glass, tweezers, a set of colored pencils, a special essence-log that's five pages long and must be filled out on each essence, a camera to take photos of the plant, a glass bowl, spring water, a small bag of cornmeal, labels, a pen, squares of muslin cloth for straining, and a set of long quartz crystals (one is a tabby and the other is wand-shaped).

My husband, David, and my 78-year old mother, Ruth, accompanied me on a recent trip. I was after a particular flower essence known as a Crested Prickly Poppy. We spent half a day looking for some, and located a patch on some private property. I asked the owner if I could gather some to make my essence, and she gave me permission.

Prickly Poppy is a tall, thorny plant that stands as high as four feet tall, depending upon the amount of rain it receives. It's usually found in the Sonoran Desert area, which means it loves a hot, sandy, inhospitable climate. The flowers are highly drought-resistant and are also known as a "cowboy's fried eggs" because they have paper-thin white petals with a huge, yellow, egg-yolk-like center.

Most people are familiar with what a nettle looks like, and Prickly Poppy is quite similar in structure. Prickly Poppy is a big, intimidating plant with the most beautiful, gossamer, almost otherworldly flower blossoms I've ever seen. This poppy flower has six long, oval petals which are extremely delicate, flexible, feminine-looking and nearly transparent. Quite a difference from the bristling, nasty thorns and general demeanor of its green leaves and stalk, isn't it? The two seem almost incongruous to one another.

I chose a possible "volunteer" among the Prickly Poppy people that stood waving gently in the warm April breeze and 80-degree conditions. Giving that particular plant some cornmeal, I squatted down in front of it and mentally communicated with the plant spirit. I told her my name, what I wanted to do (take three of her flowers) and said that if she gave me permission, her essence would help humanity in some positive way — thereby helping her in her own spiritual evolution (after all, when we give to others from the heart, it's automatic dharma).

Believe it or not, plants, trees and shrubs don't always give permission to have their flowers picked. As an Eastern Cherokee, I was taught to treat everything around me as if it were my relative, which means I don't go around taking off blossoms without permission! This particular plant had quite an arrogant attitude about her; she knew she was big, powerful and beautiful, the queen of the roost. I gave her homage according to her demeanor, and finally she relented and gave me three of her incredible blossoms.

I filled my clear glass bowl with spring water and set it aside. Then, taking my two quartz crystals, my "surgery tools," from a leather pouch, I gently cut off each flower head without contaminating the blossoms with my fingers or energy. Dave held the bowl for me and all three blossoms dropped into the water. I then placed the bowl next to the bristly, thorny stem of the plant and asked her to send her energy into the water. The bowl was placed in direct sunlight so that the energy of the blossoms would be imprinted into the water.

I spread out my towel next to the plant, opened my field notebook and began to observe the plant visually. (Having a degree in botany would certainly be of help!) Every part of the flower, stem and leaves has a very specific name, and I try to catalogue them according to the botanical names that science accepts and understands. I note the color of the leaves, front and back, the stem (round, square or some other shape?), how flexible or inflexible the plant is, the fragrance, if any, and many other minute details that help build an overall picture of what this plant essence is about and how it can help us.

When I got up and inhaled the odor of the flower on the stalk, it was the most mesmerizing fragrance I'd smelled in a long time. There was a sickeningly sweet odor to it that hit me strongly; I felt a repugnance to it, and at the same time I was drawn back to inhale it again and again against my will — a very interesting dichotomy, just like the fact that this was a bristly, thorny, tough plant with such ethereal, delicate and incredibly beautiful white blooms on top of it. The plant was certainly full of contradictions!

After cataloguing my observations, I pulled out my identification books and looked up the plant. One book noted that the seeds of this poppy contained a narcotic that was more potent than opium!

Shocked at first, I began to realize that the repulsive fragrance I was drawn to smell again and again really did remind me of an addiction — you hate to do it but you keep on reaching for the drink or shooting the drugs.

I began to realize that this plant related to addictions in general, and the botany information that was available on it verified my own observations. "Beautiful but deadly" went through my mind. Here was a plant that was thorny, arrogant, with an incredible will to survive even the driest of climates and flourish; and yet it had addictive qualities. My mind ranged over people I knew who were addicts of some sort, who had the same kind of bristly, thorny, I-can-do-it-alone-and-survive attitude about themselves. Even though these people might be ensnared, entrapped or imprisoned in their own thorny states of addiction, there was still something beautiful, pure and pristine about them. No one is ever all bad — every one of us has our shadow side, but we have our humanity, too.

Prickly Poppy was really beginning to clue me in on her essence and how we might use her energy signature to help others — anyone addicted to a substance, be it a drug, food, chocolate or something else.

As I sat with the plant spirit, I noticed after about an hour that the petals in the water had their white color leached out of them, and now many of the petals were quite literally floating transparent in the water! This was unusual. I'd seen petals lose some of their color before, but never go from opaque to transparent! Such was the power of this plant and what she has within her essence signature.

At this point, I asked for and received permission to journey shamanically into the plant via her root structure to "feel" what she was about. Journeying in a shamanic state is about opening up the valves of the right hemisphere of the brain while keeping a tenuous hold on the left brain in order to stay grounded and remain "here" to transmit any unusual sensations, feelings and messages that have to be recorded. It's a difficult task requiring laser-like concentration combined with expanding one's consciousness in order to "talk" to the plant spirit. And plants don't speak English, either! They are filled with sensations, colors and feelings, and these translate into my six senses so that I can try to faithfully record what I'm receiving from the spirit.

After an hour, I pulled out my funnel and muslin and strained off the contents into an eight-ounce amber bottle that was half filled with cherry brandy, the stabilizer. I normally drink any essence water left in the bowl afterward and I note the sensations in my field log book. On this day I didn't. Although the flower was not at seed stage, and therefore not narcotic, I had to drive a long way home and I didn't want to be influenced by it in any way. So I poured the extra water out and gave it back to the plant, as a gift and a thank-you for her help.

When I got home, I decided to be very careful with this essence because of its powerful qualities. It wasn't one that I would let the women of the Society test at first. I would use myself as a guinea pig and then ask one of my provers to try it after determining that it wasn't going to be harmful in any way.

I took a one-ounce eye-dropper bottle and put a teaspoon of cherry brandy in it, and placed four drops of the mother essence (the original water garnered from the Prickly Poppy essence) and filled it up with spring water. This is known as "stock" because it has been highly diluted from the original mother essence and is safer to work with. I decided to take two drops beneath my tongue at bedtime. I did this for three nights in a row.

Every night I had a shadow dream. For those who are unaware of Carl G. Jung's work in the field of psychology, Jung was a leader in understanding the unconscious and its contents. One of the theories he postulated was that everyone has a facet known as the shadow. This is a dark, primal, survival-oriented energy that rests deep in the subconscious. The shadow is the one who holds our fears, anxieties, hatreds, rage and any other negative emotion you can think of.

Jung discovered that if a person dreamed that someone — human, animal or otherwise — was chasing him and trying to harm or kill him, this could be symbolic of our shadow trying to "talk" to us in our dream state. To be able to integrate our shadow is extremely positive; but few people actually accomplish it. And, when it comes to addictions of any kind, the shadow has control over us at that point.

So after recording these interesting dreams for three days, I began to understand some more of the phenomenal power of this natural essence: addictions are about being out of control, being controlled by something other than our positive willpower. The shadow is directly implicated in any type of addictive behavior, and this includes love addiction, which isn't a food or organic drug, but rather an emotional state of being. They're all forms of addiction.

I also noticed that my addiction to sweets (I *love* chocolate!) was really curbed even though I was taking only two drops of the stock essence once a day! I found myself being more deeply contemplative than usual and having some profound insights into the "dark" areas of my life I hadn't consciously been

aware of before taking this remarkable essence.

I took it faithfully for almost two more weeks and had other shadow dreams. Normally, if I have two shadow dreams a year, that's a lot for me; so this is a highly irregular pattern showing up in my life. It is due to this essence dragging up a lot of hidden, negative issues for me to work on and work through, which is healing in itself!

Rosemarie Brown, DIHom (UK), has been taking Prickly Poppy three times daily and has reported feeling "spacy and slightly disconnected" from her otherwise very grounded, in-the-body personality. I postulate that this remedy will be excellent for people who are generally daydreamy, spacy or to some degree out of their bodies. With the help of this essence, they will come out of the stratosphere and be physically and mentally one hundred percent *present* every minute of the day instead of drifting in and out of the third-dimensional world we live in.

Stage 2 for this remedy, once we get done with these preliminary tests (a month-long investigation and experimentation), is to allow the group to take it home and use it for a week, along with a prover's bible. I'm sure that this essence has some powerful and wonderful attributes that can help many of us who battle some kind of addiction!

I know a husband and wife who took it for 30 days, and they've gotten some interesting information on it. The first week, the man noticed muscle stiffness in his shoulders. He said he felt emotionally calmer, a feeling of time initially expanding. He also experienced slight anxiety when he wondered what would happen if the ego didn't have the usual persona or face that he always wore at his job and in public.

After the third day on the remedy, the husband and wife noticed a very pleasant euphoria — an ethereal, almost surreal appreciation and light-heartedness about nature. There was more awareness of their five senses, and they were more fully engaged in everyday, small and large, appreciation of life around them.

He noticed a "groundlessness," and just when he felt as if he were going to "flip out emotionally" and become unstable (this man has a highly emotional job with a lot of tension, dealing with human misery up close), the remedy seemed to help him deal with the situation without a lot of emotional reaction or angst, as he normally would have. He feels the remedy "almost curbs anxiety through an underlying strengthening" of the person's "real" personality, not the facade or mask we all wear.

By the sixth day the man noted an "enjoyable underlying strength, the kind that just would not tolerate nonsense by myself or others." It was not a judgmental space, just a "let's get on with it and leave the B.S. behind" kind of feeling. He also found himself more loving toward his wife. Food tasted better, and there was an overall feeling of being satisfied with each day, and a greater appreciation of the nuances, small but important moments that make up each day.

Mentally, he felt clearer regarding his thinking processes. He experienced some confusion during the first two days, but he feels that this was his right hemisphere beginning to engage in earnest, and that his left hemisphere was giving up some of its dominance. We felt he was becoming more "whole-brained" as a result, and the confusion left after that. He liked getting away from his "left-brained analytical thinking."

He also has noticed a "general quietness of my mind away from compelled rat-mind thinking." He feels "a very interesting and positive experience thus far" with the remedy.

Now that you know more about natural essences, let's look at many different ones — gemstones as well as flowers to get an idea of how they can improve the quality of your life!

ORCHIDS AND BROMELIADS

I've grouped the natural essences available from our company into several different categories. We have orchids, cacti, wildflowers, gemstones, bulbs and bromeliads. Each category seems to have an underlying theme, and this can be the first indicator of what might be needed by an individual.

Orchids

Anyone who has tried to raise an orchid knows immediately what I'm talking about when I say they are sensitive plants. Over the past year I've been refining and honing my knowledge of these incredible flowers, and my respect for them has grown accordingly. Orchids can grow anywhere, and there are three types: air, bark and ground types. Regardless of where they come from — and orchids live around the globe, even here in the U.S. — they share one thing in common: conditions have to be just right for them to (a) grow and (b) bloom; they require constant light, flowing air, watering and soil-fertilizing.

When we apply the Doctrine of Signatures to a certain type of personality, we find that it would fit people who, generally speaking, need a great deal of cultivation in order to grow and/or bloom into their full potential. Orchids are supersensitive to temperature and humidity (or the lack of it), so from a

DOS standpoint we could conjecture that people who are highly sensitive to temperature and humidity changes might do well with an orchid essence.

These people might be highly sensitive to the darkening of the days toward fall and winter and tend to go into depression or some kind of internalization as darkness takes over from the light, for orchids thrive and live for light — not necessarily direct sunlight, but just the brightness of the Sun at a south window, for instance.

Fertilizing orchids is something one pays attention to with a great deal of strictness, lest a year's worth of care goes for naught and no blooms are forthcoming. How can we apply this to people? I often think of children in ghetto situations or welfare situations where they don't get the fertilization of the mind — the education — that many other children outside these conditions might. Perhaps orchids, in general, would be for someone who came from some kind of deprived background. There is more to fertilize than just the mind; there is lack of the right "fertilizer" for emotional growth and blossoming, too. A child put into a warring situation within a dysfunctional family might come out of it with Post-Traumatic Stress Disorder, for he or she certainly hasn't been fertilized with the right amount of love, care and attention that a child needs.

There is fertilization of the spirit, too — and I'm not talking dogmatic religion here. All of our spirits need tending, a certain kind of "fertilization." Did we get it growing up? Do we have it now? Anyone who feels spiritually starved, directionless or confused should seriously think about an orchid essence to help "light" the way and "feed" them in a way appropriate for themselves and their unique growth.

When one beholds an orchid, there is usually a gasp of utter awe. The colors of an orchid are vivid and they literally shout at you. Their petals are frequently waxy, thick, succulent, strong, and yet delicate-looking to the point that we wonder how something so ethereal and lovely could exist in the third dimension at all. Who do you know that fits that description?

We are continuing our research on orchids as an important and viable natural essence, but I'd like to share our research thus far. Who knows — you may find yourself in one of them. Also included will be a bromeliad, a cousin to the orchid.

Phalaenopsis 3272/3280 Orchid

This orchid is brilliant white, with six thick petals. The inner column is a bright yellow with vivid crimson spots. Opposite the column is a figure that seems to be standing up, with its arms open.

The Phalaenopsis orchid group is known as "moth orchids" and are shade-loving plants. They love fresh, moving air and can't handle stagnant air. They don't like cold draughts, either. They prefer fifty to seventy percent humidity.

Folklore. None, except that they are known as Moth Orchids due to the shape of their petals.

Indications. For anyone with Post-Traumatic Stress Disorder. It is good for sociopathic personalities, for gang members who have disassociated themselves from society, and for anyone who has endured a "wartime" situation — be it on the job or in a severe dysfunctional family situation. For anyone who is in shock or trauma and has disconnected because of it.

It is for anyone who has lost his or her ability to feel anything that is soft, humanizing, emotional or touching. This person cannot feel anything; there is a coldness or numbness that inhabits her or him, and no matter what they try to do, they can't fix it, reconnect, or feel in any way. They are incapable of tears or even of feeling anything if someone else cries. They feel nothing, even if they view some terrible human suffering or tragedy.

This is a remedy for sexual abuse, incest and rape survivors. It will help them reconnect with their sexuality in a positive manner and encourage the feelings to return once again. If a person leaves his or her body during intercourse, this remedy will help ground one and keep one in the body, aware of everything, rather than "checking out." (*Note:* For anyone who has been sexually abused, I often suggest the following natural essence formula: Phal. 3272/3280 Orchid, Yellow Columbine and Prickly Poppy).

Nickname. Emotional-Disconnect Essence.

Positive Qualities:

1. Helps the person get behind whatever the wound or root of the problem is and brings it to their attention to help resolve it.

2. For men who are abusers or for female survivors of abuse/rape/incest by a male. This is a male remedy, but women can use it too.

3. Right ovary pain will respond to this remedy. Activity experienced in the abdomen in general, including the intestinal tract. Hearing may become more acute. Mental clarity will improve. Headaches that start at the temples or back of skull may be helped.

4. Used for anyone who has encased oneself in a tube or behind a wall for protective purposes after suffering from a particular traumatic circumstance.

5. Brings up more masculine (right-sided) energy to help people stand their ground and stand on their own two feet.

6. Good for any kind of sexual abuse, particularly oral sexual abuse.

7. Disconnection from the world or losing consciousness or leaving your body due to a traumatic circumstance — disassociation.

8. It will bring up the issues that have wounded you and help you see and clearly identify them so that you can resolve them.

Note: If you have PTSD or know that you were traumatized on a serious level, it would be wise to use this remedy when you are in the care of a therapist or some individual who understands the healing process involved.

This remedy should not be used by a person who is mentally or emotionally unstable — unless they are under the care and direction of a qualified therapist — because it *will* bring up those issues to be dealt with.

Primary Chakra. All chakras are influenced by this remedy, particularly the heart chakra and root chakra. This remedy, because it is basically white — corresponding to the crown chakra, which deals with all colors — will go to the chakras that are involved with the trauma and clear them.

Symbol. Butterfly with wings spread to fly. Freeing up of one's self from a hardened cocoon that was placed around the self in order to protect it from further trauma or violence.

Doctrine of Signatures. White petals of orchid remind me of the wings of a butterfly. The inner lip of the orchid shows a person standing with arms open and legs wide, with yellow-colored thighs and bright red spots that look like menses blood. It also reminds me of a woman with her legs open and her genitals exposed.

Homeopathic Remedy Considerations. Homeopathic remedies can be used in conjunction with this essence. Anacardium, the "gangster" remedy for sociopathic, disassociative or disconnected-from-feelings type of people. Natrum Muriaticum, where there is a loss of all feelings, a disconnection from them, and putting up thick walls and hiding behind them in silence. Inability to cry. If emotions suddenly start flowing, one may think of Pulsatilla for help in controlling them. Or, if the shock and trauma appear, Aconitum Napellus should be considered to ameliorate these powerful feelings. Providing the person fits these symptoms and others that need to be taken by a homeopath first, these remedies can be used.

Dosage. Once a day until bottle is used up — usually 25 to 28 days. Stop taking if too many memories, feelings or emotions begin to overwhelm you. Begin taking again after you've worked through the items brought up by the remedy. Consult with your therapist before taking, and work with her/him closely while on this remedy.

Miltoniopsis Pansy Orchid.

Miltoniopsis has six white, paper thin, very delicate-looking petals. On three of the petals, there is less magenta coloring; it is in horizontal stripes on two of them, and vertical on a third one. There is a froglike creature on the column at the center of this orchid, a bright, vivid yellow with magenta/red vertical stripes on it. At the bottom of the "frog" the colors flare out in a semicircle around it on the lower petal and become red-orange, then the color moves back into radiating magenta stripes that look like a skirt. These stop and there is a white border, then the dark magenta color below it surrounded in white. There is no fragrance to this orchid. There are four flowers on the "spike" stem. There are four more buds on another spike that have yet to blossom.

Folklore. None — it is a human-made hybrid orchid, also called "Pansy Orchid."

Indications. The ability to nurture the self and deal with mothering and nurturing issues with one's mother or with women in general. This is for anyone who has had a bad relationship with his or her mother and wants to repair this wound with her. If our mother has wounded us, we struggle on several levels with this. First of all, if she is still alive, we must interact with her. Second, the female energy within ourselves (the left side of the body) has been wounded too. If we continue to avoid our mother in the outside, external world, we are simultaneously suppressing our feminine/female/mothering energy within ourselves. The net result: We aren't operating fully or completely as human beings — we're in denial, rage, humiliation or some other emotionally "stuck" position, so the energy can't be released, transformed or utilized in a more positive direction or way.

This orchid remedy allows us the conscious choice to begin to remember and bring up whatever mother issues we have and begin to heal them. Although you may never be able to fully resolve the mother issue with the human who bore you, you can change yourself and your attitudes toward her — which is where this remedy will create the healing. It does not necessarily mean you're going to "fix" your mother and make all things right with her. The real aim of this remedy is getting you to see her differently, in a more compassionate, understanding and forgiving light. And when you can do that, you are also being compassionate, understanding and forgiving of yourself and your inner female. Then, true

healing takes place.

This remedy is of special use for those who were adopted, put in an orphanage or put through a series of foster homes, never really able to be mother-nurtured in the positive sense. If you came out of a family where the mother was never there (the Super Mom of the 80s and 90s or a family where mother was physically there but never there for you emotionally to nurture you as you needed), then this is the remedy for you.

Nickname. Inner Mother Essence.

Positive Qualities:

1. Allows us to once again feel mother-nurtured within ourselves. This remedy heals the inner mother issue and, in so doing, gives us a warm, protective sense about ourselves and our female energy.

2. Releases the feminine energy so that we can be more creative, more in touch with our own unique abilities as artist, musician or writer.

3. May bring up repressed memories from this lifetime about you and mother. Or, warm memories of "family," in which you enjoyed yourself.

4. May bring up memories from past lifetimes in regard to your mother (as relates to the mother you have in this lifetime or someone in your life who was your mother in a past lifetime).

5. Will bring a sense of joy, playfulness and happiness. The ability to laugh and play like a child and to see laughter in our humanity without making fun of ourselves in a negative sense.

6. A wonderful sense of wanting to hug yourself because you like and love yourself.

7. The need to rock yourself — purchase of a rocking chair may be in order for some of you, to re-create the rocking of yourself in your mother's arms; at least the reminiscence of it, even if it never happened, you can now create for yourself and receive the warm nurturing that comes from the rocking motion.

8. Clearing of the mental faculties and more clarity about now in your life.

9. Any physical or emotional tension connected with your mother will dissolve and you will become much more relaxed and "laid back."

10. May address headaches that start at the temple or back of head. Numbness of lips or a burning sensation in the facial region. Ache in the right eye region. Relaxation of neck and shoulder region. Dryness of eyes.

Primary Chakra. The heart chakra is the primary focus of this remedy. Secondly, it moves to the head, and this includes the brow and crown chakra. As with any mother issue, the heart is certainly going to be involved.

Symbol. A mother in a rocking chair, holding an infant in her arms, smiling down at it and holding it close to her breast as she gently rocks back and forth.

Doctrine of Signatures. The froglike column reminds me of an infant, with its arms spread outward and upward, waiting to be lifted and held by its mother. There is a "happy face" to this orchid as one looks at it, as if it is smiling joyfully at you with this small infant/frog symbol at the center of her flower.

Homeopathic Remedy Considerations. Lac Humanum, mother's breast milk, is currently used for those who have lost their mother's connection either outwardly or inwardly. Lac Caninum, dog's milk, was used until recently for those — especially women and minorities — who felt like "second-class citizens" or who were treated with less respect than a white male.

Other Uses. One client taking this orchid essence has been having repeated past-life flashes in which she'll see the scene in color, hear the voices and be able to retain everything about the encounter. Sometimes she gets this in the dream state but it also occurs during her waking hours. She reports of never having this happen to her before. This *might* be a past-life memory essence, although more research needs to be done to verify its authenticity in this arena.

Red and Yellow Bromeliad

Red/yellow Bromeliads are from the Epiphytes family, a cousin to the orchids. They grow in South and Central America, absorbing water from the droplets dripping downward through the jungle canopy, funneling into the center of the plant. Bromeliads are often sold in nurseries and you can see their bright central flower, which really looks more like brightly painted leaves than a true "blossom."

The Red and Yellow Bromeliad is flame-shaped, with the inner two-thirds a bright, fire-engine red and the outer portion outlined in bright, golden yellow. It indeed looks like a living flame. Its Doctrine of Signatures shows that it *funnels* water and can be watered only through the central core of itself — a unique feature. A person who might need this essence is someone who needs to be "watered" in a very particular way. Of course, water is symbolic of emotions, and since the watering system of this plant is unique, it can apply to people who need a unique emotional watering of themselves as human beings.

Another unique and interesting feature of bromeliads in general is that they bloom only once. This means that the plant gathers and holds its energy, its survival for that one shot at producing its bloom so that its seeds will drop and propagate once again; but it's one time only. There's a gathering and storing of energy at every level of this plant. What people might need such an essence? Possibly, people who have come from very harsh, dysfunctional families, who have retreated deep within themselves in order to survive and, as a result, feel as if life may have taken away from them or cheated them in some way. There is a drawing-in with this essence and with these people, a cloistering or capturing of their "flame of life," possibly to hold it safe from outer attacks. This external source doesn't always have to be a family situation; it could be the threatened loss of a job or a move to another state or country, for example.

If you touch a bromeliad blossom, you find that it is tough and feels inflexible to the fingers. There is no fragrance to it, either. It is a very self-sufficient plant that relies on no one and nothing around it in order to survive — except for the precious drops of water drip-drip-dripping from the jungle canopy above, downward into its funnel-like form. Another interesting facet with this bromeliad is that the yellow outlining the flower turns with age to a bright green color. This suggests that the Root chakra, which is red, and the Solar Plexus chakra, which is yellow, can be transformed through the heart, green in color.

The way the plant is formed — all its leaves circular, lifted upward, and looking like a big funnel — says something of the psychology of the people who need this essence. They are people who may have gotten little watering or emotional sustenance and have learned, in order to survive, to greedily take everything they can from others or a situation, much like the plant takes errant drops of water dripping haphazardly off leaves above it. There can be a selfish, centering quality to these people who thirst for emotional sustenance or watering. As a result, this essence should be considered for people who take, take, take, who suck off your or other people's energy, for example. Psychic vampires (and there are many of them out there who do this unconsciously because they are so emotionally needy) can stop this by taking the correct bromeliad essence.

Nickname. Sociopathic Essence.

Indications. For irritable, aggressive, premeditating people, feelings of being unloved/unappreciated, fear, manipulation of others or situations, suspicion of others' intents toward them, loss of self-esteem/confidence, despondence, mood-swings, depression with anger attached to it, wanting to physically injure someone else, desire to kill or destroy another being — human, animal or insect.

There is much anger, usually barely controlled, or even uncontrolled, with this essence.

Positive Qualities:

1. Helps people realize their connection with all beings.

2. Helps them deal with and redirect any negative emotions, such as anger, irritability, physical assault, destructive behavior or any of the above conditions, into one of positive expression.

3. Turns off their ability to psychically suck off other people's energy fields.

4. Transforms their fear/anger/hatred into compassionate understanding of themselves in relation to the person or situation that it's directed against.

5. A very male energy essence. Good for aggressive males or females with "gangster" mentality.

6. Will help undo sociopathic behavior (homeopathy must be used in conjunction with this essence in this particular case).

7. Transforms destructive behavior in infant, child or adult into positive expressions.

8. The ability to transmute or transform destructive behavior into a reconnection with the heart chakra, which will allow a flow of feelings to begin once again and help to halt such negative behavior.

9. For anyone who abuses others in any form — physically, mentally, emotionally or spiritually. Especially useful in cases where the abuser was abused sexually but has now hardened and turned around to do it to other victims.

10. An essence for anyone incarcerated in a jail or prison.

11. Will help those who are decidedly premeditating in their behavior on a negative playing field. For people who deliberately, in passive/aggressive modes of behavior, snipe at others.

12. Of use in alcoholic families where the alcoholic or drug user is dominating and using his/her anger and physical size to threaten or in some way keep others "in line," out of fear of losing control of the situation.

Primary Chakra. Root chakra (red) and Solar Plexus chakra (yellow).

Secondary Chakra. Heart chakra (green), Brow chakra (purple) and Crown chakra (white).

Symbol. A bright, living flame that can either burn and destroy itself and others through destructive behavior, or that can light the way for the self and others.

Doctrine of Signatures. A living flame. Called the "cistern plant" because it funnels all water into one direct channel to be absorbed by its roots. For self-centered, narcissistic, selfishly oriented people who funnel all their energy into themselves and never invest anything in anyone outside themselves, for survival reasons (usually due to severe dysfunctional childhood).

Homeopathic Remedy Considerations. Anacardium is the "gangster" and sociopathic-behavior remedy, while Platina is a remedy for the dominating, self-centered, sometimes violent type. Nux Vomica is one of the major abuser remedies, for these fully capable of violence on any level. The Sulphur type is more than likely arrogant, self-centered and self-serving, while Sepia in its final stage of imbalance can become broodingly hostile, irritable and disconnected entirely from his/her emotional matrix.

Other considerations. The Red and Yellow Bromeliad is a very powerful essence to work with. The provers who took this essence could not finish out the seven-day trial on it because it made them so irritable, angry and wanting to become violent that it was causing havoc in their personal and professional lives! This is a powerful essence and deserves to be considered in cases of violence of any kind.

This is just a peek at the orchid family and its cousin the bromeliads. There is a wealth of information out there on these incredible flowers and how they can help us become better human beings — to help ourselves and then reflect that outward to others and the world around us.

Dosage is usually four drops four times daily, but this can change, based upon a person's individual need. For instance, in a crisis, the drops can be taken every five minutes until the crisis has passed.

NATURAL ESSENCE MATERIA MEDICA

Similar to Bach Flower Remedies, natural essences are grown at La Casa de Madre Tierra, The House of Mother Earth, the author's home near Sedona, Arizona.

Each essence has a particular personality, skill or talent, and these short definitions will help you decide if one or more are for you. The essences are of immense help during homeopathic treatment on a constitutional level, for children or for anyone going through some acute crisis. I routinely utilize my "friends" when treating a patient homeopathically — with excellent and often profound results.

Write down the ones that fit your mental or emotional state, or that will help you tackle a particular issue. To order, see Appendix C at the back of the book.

Note: For those who are alcohol-sensitive, and for infants and young children, we offer vegetable glycerine or vinegar as a preservative. Unless otherwise specified, all our natural essences are in a traditional brandy base.

Dosage: Using no more than six combined remedies at a time, you may use four drops of each essence under your tongue four times daily, or they may be "mixed" — four drops of each essence into an eight-ounce glass of water — and sipped. I recommend three glasses daily. Or, for an acute crisis: four drops under the tongue every five minutes until the symptoms ease.

Orchids, Bromeliads And Exotics

1. **Phalaenopsis 3272/3280 (Hakalau Wonder X Hawaiian Snowfall) Orchid:** Resolution of emotional disconnection issues. Healing sexual issues/incest/rape. For a person who feels dead, numb or loss of emotional feelings, a sense of disconnection. For Post-Traumatic Stress Disorder (PTSD).

2. **"Booncho" White Kasem (Dendrobium) Orchid:** Sexual trust. Enables sexual incest/rape survivors to trust their ability to love another even after this type of wounding.

3. **Bromeliad (red/yellow):** Sociopathic behavior. For angry, malicious, premeditating child/person who delights in striking at another person's vulnerability. Bossy, militaristic, egotistical or sociopathic behavior. Remedy for violent gang members.

4. **Bromeliad (red):** Spiritual connector. Allows a person to transcend their own day-to-day living and get in touch with the deeper, more spiritual parts of themselves.

5. **Gower Ramsey (Butterfly) Orchid:** Transformation. Used in cases where negative feelings thrive, transforming them to the opposite: joy, contentment and being glad to be alive.

6. **Miltoniopsis (Pansy) Orchid:** Inner Mother essence. Helps to bring up and resolve any unhealed issues between you and your mother.

7. **Cymbidium Pink Orchid:** Heart Speaks essence. Allows you to speak and communicate clearly what you are feeling — your heartfelt passions. Articulation.

8. **Cymbidium Green Orchid:** Woman's Transition essence. Whether you are pregnant, starting menopause or entering puberty, this remedy is about connecting with your sexuality as a woman-mother-child-old crone. Very powerful and warming.

9. **Cymbidium White Orchid:** Stop-craving-sweets-and-sugar essence. This remedy halts addictive cravings for anything sweet; be it pastries, chocolate, cookies or whatever.

10. **Cymbidium Yellow Orchid:** When-you've-had-a-bad-day essence. Uplifting even to the most depressed or despairing person, this essence brings an incredible smile to the face of anyone who takes it.

11. **Ti "Corn" Plant (Hawaiian):** Releasing old sexual dysfunction issues. This essence brings lost or forgotten memories of past hurts regarding our sexuality. Excellent remedy for rape/incest survivors.

Trees

1. **Almond blossom:** Inner Child essence. Happy, childlike and playful. To be connected with our positive child essence.

2. **Pear blossom:** Reproductive issues in women/miscarriage/abortion; loss of a baby; helps heal those issues.

3. **Peach blossom:** Positive mothering skills. Healing of the "mother wound" in both genders when dealing with a new baby in the family.

4. **Nectarine blossom:** Prejudice. Dealing with prejudices and releasing them.

5. **Willow:** The crutch essence. For those who cling to others — codependent behavior.

6. **Magnolia blossom:** Healing the feminine wound. For both genders. For women, allowing them to get in touch with their true femininity and expressing it on all levels and in all ways.

7. **Plum blossom:** (Testing stage.)

8. **Apricot blossom:** Codependence and putting the person in touch with those conditioned responses.

9. **Sour Cherry blossom:** Bitterness essence. Identifies the bitterness or bitter issues in our lives and helps resolve them.

10. **Bing Cherry blossom:** Negative emotions essence. Fears, anxieties, rage and hatred are released and resolved.

Bulb Plants

1. **Muscari (Grape Hyacinth):** (Testing stage.)

2. **Hyacinth (white):** (Testing stage.)

3. **Tulip (yellow/orange/white/black):** (Testing stage.)

4. **Amaryllis (pink/white):** Emotional release essence. Releasing old emotional issues. May be good for edema/urinary/kidney system.

5. **Anemone de Caen (red with black center):** Freedom-from-family-issues essence. Empowering selfhood via dealing with issues relating to our family dysfunction.

6. **Anemone Blanda:** (Testing stage.)

7. **Allium (purple):** (Testing stage.)

8. **Anthurium (red):** Male sexuality essence. Helps males integrate sexuality with heart/emotions and creates reconnection.

9. **Cyclamen (purple):** Self-esteem-building essence. Allows the person to get in touch with their self-esteem/confidence.

10. **Ranunculus (pink/black):** Injured-heart essence. Heals love-related issues/grief.

11. **Iris (yellow):** Releases old thought patterns (harbored negative emotions) that stunt our growth.

12. **Iris (burgundy/wine):** Creates connection between emotions and mental realm if disconnected via trauma.

13. **Oriental Lily (pink):** Sexual dysfunction essence. Helps release sexual/emotional dysfunction issues and return to a healthy sex life.

High Sierra/Tahoe Wildflowers

1. **Mountain Paintbrush:** Artistic codependence essence. For people who use/lean on others and won't use their own creativity or energy to accomplish things in life, using others as a crutch instead.

2. **California Fuchsia:** Dealing swiftly and positively with major life challenges.

3. **Alpine Smartweed:** Trapped-feelings essence. For those who hold on to emotional hurts or memories, unable to release them.

4. **Meadow Goldenrod:** Illumination essence. Good for heart-wound issues, healing them and replacing them with a constant state of joy about living life.

Sonoran Desert Wildflowers

1. **"Ladybug" Desert Paintbrush:** For those who cling to others and live their lives voyeuristically through another instead of living a full and creative life on their own.

2. **Penstemon (pink):** Passion-for-living essence. In need of courage, faith, strength and passion.

3. **Mariposa Lily (white):** Personal integrity essence. Awakening our higher self/values/morals.

4. **Crested Prickly Poppy:** Shadow (Carl Jung) issues essence. Our dark side is revealed and worked through positively. Shadow integration.

5. **Mexican Mormon Tea:** (Testing stage.)

6. **Bladderpod:** Negative-emotions-release essence. Releases angers, anxieties, fears; powerful urinary system cleanser. Genius-like inspirations and creativity.

7. **Desert Anemone:** (Testing stage.)

8. **Tesajo (Christmas Cholla):** (Testing stage.)

9. **Desert Hyacinth:** (Testing stage.)

10. **Prince's Rock Cress:** (Testing stage.)

11. **Barberry "Hollygrape":** Inflexible-opinions essence. For highly opinionated/prejudicial people.

High mental activity.

12. **Blackfoot Daisy:** (Testing stage.)

13. **Desert Globemallow:** Appraisal essence. The ability to see ourselves very clearly — as well as seeing others with unimpaired vision.

14. **Hedgehog Cactus (magenta):** Maternal instincts essence. Appreciating one's sensuality. For pregnant women who are disconnected from their condition and the baby they carry.

15. **Cholla (yellow):** Releases people from their mental state and forges a connection with their heart/feelings.

16. **Desert Chicory (white):** Hidden-strengths essence. Integrating our consciousness with our spiritual qualities. Tapping into our hidden strengths.

17. **Owls Clover:** The victim essence. For mental victim/co-dependent behavior and releasing it.

18. **Scorpionweed:** The abuser essence. For abusive male or female. Stops abusive behavior on any level — particularly violent physical attackers.

19. **Ocotillo:** Emotional expression essence. Inability to express your emotions, inability to understand your feelings. Inspires creativity based upon your emotional foundation.

20. **Spanish Bayonet Yucca:** Military mentality essence. For aggressive, irritable, belligerent, overbearing people who control other people's lives.

21. **Evening Primrose (yellow):** Mental cleanser essence. Mentally reconnects us with the aspects of living life through cleansing ourselves in some manner; getting rid of unwanted opinions or fixed ideas that can make us toxic.

22. **Evening Primrose (white):** Toxicity cleanser essence. A general cleanser of all chakras on all levels of ourselves; gets rid of toxicity.

23. **Evening Primrose (pink):** Toxic family cleanser essence. Cleansing ourselves regarding our family/relationships; deals with heart-related issues and cleans them up.

24. **Sea Pink:** Childlike joy essence. Reclaiming our inner-child integration and feeling childlike joy.

25. **Yarrow:** Boundaries essence. For those who have problems putting up boundaries and saying no. Good for codependent types — gives them strength and resolve to stand their ground.

26. **Prickly Pear:** Entrapped essence. For those who feel trapped. It will give you personal freedom.

27. **Snakeweed:** Confrontation-of-fears essence. In instances where fear rules you, and you can't act appropriately. This addresses any fear, especially confrontation with others.

28. **Erigonum Abertianum "Venus":** Heart-chakra-opening essence. For those who have suffered heart wounds, have closed down and refuse to open back up. Depression.

29. **Century Plant:** Breakthrough essence. Utilized for those who want to "break through" whatever is holding them back or retarding their forward motion or growth. Powerful.

30. **Saguaro Cactus:** The protector essence. Imbues people with a sense of taking care of themselves and expressing their skills and talents.

Traditional Garden Flowers

1. **Calendula (yellow/gold):** Gentle healer essence. The need for deep healing of mind/emotions that will occur in a gentle, soothing manner.

2. **Papaver Poppy (yellow/green/orange):** (Testing stage.)

3. **Foxglove (grandmother) (purple):** (Testing stage.)

4. **Megan, Rose (pink):** Stress-reducing essence. Soothes and calms agitated parasympathetic nervous system.

5. **Astarte, Rose (lavender):** Right-brain-stimulating essence. Gateway to right-brain activity, learning to trust one's own intuition.

6. **Delilah, Rose (orange/yellow):** Pregnant mother essence. Specifically for uterus/womb when carrying baby, maintains strength of placenta. Childbirth essence.

7. **Bellis Perennis (pink/yellow):** Shock/trauma essence. Protects person's emotional and mental state during a crisis/emergency that happens to self or another. Shock/trauma essence.

8. **Cottage Pinks (pink/red):** Energy-burst essence. For burst of energy on any level, particularly the physical one. For fatigue/tiredness.

9. **Mom's Rose (orange/yellow):** Loss-of-loved-one essence. Heals shock/trauma experienced through the heart/feelings (divorce, death of a loved one, etc.).

10. **Limestone Columbine (yellow/purple):** (Testing stage.)

11. **Crimson Columbine (red/yellow):** (Testing stage.)

12. **Colville's Columbine (yellow):** Heart-head connecting essence. Links highly emotional people to their mental/left-brain sphere so they can think clearly and logically through crisis or life events.

13. **Tree Peony (pink):** Powerful emotional essence. Deals with deep-rooted emotional issues and reveals and dissolves them.

14. **Lilac (purple):** Inflexibility, lack of higher vision or purpose.

15. **Jupiter's Beard:** (Testing stage.)

16. **Bleeding Heart:** Sexual dysfunction essence. Heals sexual issues; frigidity, impotence; helps orgasm return.

17. **Echo Blue:** Creative ideas essence. Creative ideas — good for writers and speakers, or anyone in a creative field.

18. **African Daisy:** Angry outbursts essence. For anger, irritability and stomach nausea/ulcers.

19. **Shasta Daisy:** Trusting-your-intuition essence. Enables you to trust what you know and then act upon it accordingly.

Gemstones

1. **Agate:** Protector essence. Protects person from psychic attack. Prevents loss of energy to another person.

2. **Amber:** Grounds person and stops spacy behavior. Stability.

3. **Amethyst:** Lifts person to a higher level of consciousness. Aids alcoholics. Do not use on hyperactive people.

4. **Apatite:** Calms the nervous system.

5. **Apophyllite:** Vision-quest essence. Promotes meditation and emphasizes person's spiritual qualities.

6. **Aquamarine:** Mother Nature's tranquilizer essence. Natural tranquilizer for any kind of stress. Insomnia.

7. **Aventurine (green):** Self-worth essence. Promotes value of self through ability to love oneself.

8. **Bloodstone:** Aids healing of any heart-related injury on any level. Powerful healer.

9. **Chrysoprase:** For those who are rigid in their mental outlook.

10. **Citrine:** Aids in concentration, improved memory; for senility or poor memory.

11. **Coral:** Improves circulation.

12. **Diamond:** Insights into ourselves.

13. **Emerald:** Powerful cleanser via the heart. Supports the immune system.

14. **Fire Opal:** High energy, vitality; addresses codependence.

15. **Flint:** Cuts through to root cause or main issue of problem.

16. **Fluorite:** Strengthens mental capacities; helps to focus.

17. **Garnet (red):** General vitality and energy boost. Hot flashes.

18. **Hematite:** Aids in stabilizing a person on any and all levels.

19. **Jade:** Digs out repressed/suppressed heart-related issues.

20. **Lapis Lazuli:** Allows person to communicate more clearly.

21. **Moldavite:** Heart injury and connecting with the repressed/suppressed root cause. UFO and alien consciousness.

22. **Moonstone:** Feminine-integration essence. Getting in touch with feelings/emotions/right brain.

23. **Obsidian:** Reflection essence. Reflects suppressed/repressed issues and mirrors them to the person on a conscious level.

24. **Opal:** Brings out emotions from individuals who are disconnected from them.

25. **Peridot:** Powerful immune-system supporter. Heart issues and cleansing of them.

26. **Pyrite:** Helps people to value themselves; self-esteem issues.

27. **Petrified Wood:** Helps disorganized, "spacy" individuals to ground.

28. **Red Jasper:** Bestows a sense of protection on the individual.

29. **Rhodochrosite:** Past traumas involving heart/head are brought forward to be healed.

30. **Rhodonite:** Supports self-esteem and confidence.

31. **Rose Quartz:** Helps release old, conditioned tapes that have occurred. Self-love issues.

32. **Ruby:** Powerful energizer on all levels; don't use on Cancer patients.

33. **Rutilated Quartz:** Soothes stressed nervous system and generally stressed-out individuals.

34. **Sapphire (blue):** Enables us to accurately see ourselves — faults as well as strengths. Perception of the self.

35. **Sequoia, petrified:** Zen Buddhist essence. The ability to accept whatever life is throwing at you without "drama queen" antics. It blends your feelings with your mental activity and creates harmony. Right-left brain connector bridge.

36. **Smoky Quartz:** Digs out unconscious issues that we've buried.

37. **Sodalite:** Improves intuitive knowing and a trust in that process.

38. **Tiger's Eye:** Brings a sense of value to the self.

39. **Topaz (gold):** Brings sunlight back into a person's life; a sense of hope. Depression.

40. **Tourmaline:**
    (a) **Black:** releases negativity, fears, anxieties.
    (b) **Pink:** connects primitive responses with heart.
    (c) **Green:** cleans out toxic conditions in the body on any level.
    (d) **Blue** (Indicolite): Speaking up for ourselves.

41. **Unakite:** healing past hurts/wounds of the heart/emotions.

Natural Essence Formulas

Over the years I've found that certain combinations of natural essences help people to direct their time, energy, emotion and spiritual growth. Frequently, these formulas have been used in conjunction with homeopathic constitutional treatment to speed up or alleviate some of the discomfort of the healing process.

PTSD Formula: This is used for anyone coming out of a battling-family situation, where the child has suffered mental, emotional or physical abuse. It is also used for adults suffering from anxiety or panic attacks that have resulted in some "wartime" crisis in their lives, be it growing up in an abusive family, living with an abusive spouse or surviving some kind of manmade or natural catastrophe. Phalaenopsis 3272/3280 Orchid, "Booncho" White Kasem Orchid, Red/Yellow Bromeliad, Colville's Columbine, Century Plant and Yarrow combination (pink/yellow/white).

Codependence No More: This is used to help break the victim's dependence mentality and to stop him leaning on others or continually giving power away to others in some form. This is for victims of spousal abuse, for anyone who can't say no and mean it, or for a person who has trouble setting up boundaries and maintaining them. For anyone who is a doormat to the world and who gives, gives, gives but doesn't know how to receive. Yarrow combination (pink/yellow/white), Century Plant, Owls Clover, Magnolia, Apricot and Cyclamen (purple).

Gangster Attitude: This combination helps teenagers in particular to stop and think about what they are doing or not doing. It gives a person conscience, consideration and sensitivity toward others instead of being selfish and self-centered. At its extreme, it can be used with sociopathic personality types who exhibit disconnection from their families, communities, or the world in general. Red/Yellow Bromeliad, Gower Ramsey Butterfly Orchid, Yellow Iris, Mountain Paintbrush, Century Plant and Colville's Columbine.

Sexual Dysfunction: This can occur for many reasons — some of them consciously known and others that are deeply buried in our subconscious. For those who experience any kind of sexual dysfunction, for whatever reason, and want to regain a normal sex life and feel comfortable with their sexuality again. Oriental Lily, Hedgehog Cactus, Pink Penstemon, Bleeding Heart and "Booncho" White Kasem Orchid. (If a woman, add Magnolia. If a man, add Red Antherium.

Therapy Formula: This is used for those who are undergoing any type of therapy and want to break old conditional patterns or dig up issues buried in the unconscious. Crested Prickly Poppy, Century Plant, Obsidian, Ti Corn Plant, Amaryllis (pink/white) and Bladderpod.

"Space Cadet" Formula: For those who are ungrounded. This is a condition that exists in many who astrally leave their physical bodies because life is too hard, too stressful or painful for them to endure. If there is forgetfulness, inability to finish any kind of project, or a loss of discipline, this formula will help "ground" the person and put him back in his body so he can be one hundred percent present.

Petrified Sequoia, Hematite and Snakeweed.

Grief Formula: This is for anyone who has experienced heartbreak of some kind. This may or may not include mild or acute depression. It can be the loss of a loved one, a favorite pet, moving and leaving friends or family behind, loss of a job, loss of status, divorce or any other crisis that brings on emotional grief. Bloodstone, Almond Blossom, Ranunculi (pink/black), Evening Primrose (pink), Century Plant, Mom's Rose and Bellis Perennis.

Depression Formula: Sea Pink, Century Plant, Prickly Pear, Gower Ramsey Butterfly Orchid and California Fuschia.

To order see Appendix B.

CHAPTER FIFTEEN
Cell Salts

Cell salts, inorganic minerals that inhabit the cells of the body and are instrumental in maintaining health, have been known in Europe since the early 1800's. In India they have been known since Vedic times. The man who modernized the use of cell-salt therapy was Dr. William H. Schuessler of Oldenburg, Germany, a homeopath looking for a simple, unified system of treatment.

Schuessler based his experiments with cell salts on the ideas of Professor Moleschott of Rome University, who stated that the structure and functions of the organs depended upon the presence of inorganic constiuents, what Schuessler later termed *cell salts* because the mineral salts are used in such minute quantities that they can be absorbed immediately.

Constituting only five per cent of the body, inorganic matter is nevertheless very important to the overall functioning of the body. Every cell in the body contains many of these mineral salts, which are necessary for all metabolism. Without them no organic material can be digested or eliminated. They also give strength and rigidity to the bones of the skeleton. They aid in the building of the soft tissue, such as muscles, cartilage and blood cells. And their solubility within the fluids of the body helps determine the acid-alkaline metabolism as well as other secretions, such as digestive juices and saliva.

Schuessler's contention, later embraced by other homeopaths, was that if a small portion of a person's cells were deficient in one of the inorganic salts, symptoms would occur. If enough cells did not get an adequate amount of a salt, a disease would eventually manifest. By thoroughly studying the symptoms produced, Schuessler was able to determine which cell salt to give as therapy. And he found that treating the problem with the cell salts relieved the symptoms and restored health.

CELL SALTS AND ASTROLOGY

Although there are hundreds of minerals in the body, Schuessler considered the 12 mineral salts essential to health. Astrologers have traditionally assigned each of these cell salts to one of the signs of the zodiac, as follows:

Aries—kali phosphoricum
Taurus—natrum sulphuricum
Gemini—kali muriaticum
Cancer—calcarea fluorica
Leo—magnesia phosphorica
Virgo—kali sulphuricum
Libra—natrum phosphoricum
Scorpio—calcarea sulphurica
Sagittarius—silicea
Capricorn—calcarea phosphorica

Aquarius—natrum muriaticum
Pisces—ferrum phosphoricum.

And based on these correlations, many astrologers have suggested that a person should take the cell salt ruled by his or her sun sign plus the cell salt ruled by the opposite sign. For example, a person born with the Sun in Aries should take both kali phosphoricum and natrum phosphoricum, ruled by Libra, Aries' opposite sign.

Another theory is that a person should take the cell salts ruled by the signs that natal Saturn and the natal South Node occupy. The reasoning behind this theory is that Saturn always indicates a shortage of something—in this case, a cell salt—and the South Node indicates any inherent weakness or "leak" in a natal chart.

But neither of these theories is foolproof. As Bob Mulligan, a medical astrologer who lives in Naples, Florida, has realized, no one system is going to be accurate 100 per cent of the time because cell salt needs vary with each individual. Many astrological factors, not just the placement of the Sun or one or two planets, will determine a person's needs.

Mulligan, who has traveled three times to India to study with homeopathic physicians there, uses an astrological procedure also followed by Inez Carey and Vanda Sawtel to ascertain a person's potential for deficiencies in cell salts by looking at the natal chart. First he examines the placements of the Sun and its opposite sign; second, the Moon and its opposite sign; third, Saturn and its opposite sign; fourth, the South Node and its opposite sign; and last, Mercury and its opposite sign.

He does not believe that the placement of Saturn alone provides enough information: although the placement of Saturn may indicate the root cause of an ailment, it does not indicate a deficiency. Instead, Mulligan believes that any combination of the planets mentioned may indicate what cell salts are needed. He has also found that house placement is sometimes more important than sign placement. And he has recognized that the skill of the medical astrologer counts a great deal toward determining what cell salts should be used.

Because of the unreliability of any one astrological system for administering cell salts, it is best for a medical astrologer to match a person's symptoms against the symptomology listed in *Dr. Schuessler's Biochemistry* by J. B. Chapman, M.D., and *then* look at the natal chart to determine the root of the ailment. A medical astrologer also needs to look carefully at the natal chart to find out what amount of a cell salt should be administered under a doctor's guidance. As I've indicated, each person's bodily needs are different. No one can really be considered "normal." Some individuals need more than the normal amount of a medicaton; others, less.

To determine a person's degree of sensitivity to cell salts, a medical astrologer should look carefully at Neptune, Pisces, Virgo and the Moon in a natal chart.

For instance, Neptune conjunct another planet, especially Mars, will suggest that a person needs a lower dosage than is considered normal—usually ½ of the adult dose for adults and ½ of the children's dose for children. Neptune within eight degrees of the Tenth House or First House cusp will also indicate a drug-sensitive individual. (Neptune in the First House and not conjunct the Ascendant may or may not indicate a drug-sensitive person: the degree of sensitivity will probably depend upon the number of aspects Neptune makes with other natal planets, with more than two hard aspects indicating an individual who needs lower dosages of drugs.) Furthermore, Neptune in the Sixth House in hard aspect with two or more other natal planets suggests that the person will have allergic reactions to drugs in general and therefore need only ½ the normal dosage of cell salts.

If the Moon, which rules over the fluid tides of the body, is a singleton or the handle of a bucketlike configuration in a chart, occupying the First or Tenth House cusp within eight degrees, the person will probably need only ½ dosage. If the Moon is conjunct Neptune, the individual will be especially sensitive to drugs. And, since Neptune rules Pisces and Virgo is Pisces' polar opposite, any person with natal planets in Pisces or Virgo will more than likely be sensitive to all drugs, including cell salts.

ADMINISTERING CELL SALTS

Any medical astrologer suggesting the use of cell salts must make careful and accurate diagnosis. Although cell salts are relatively nondangerous, an individual can still upset his or her bodily functions by taking them indiscriminately. Silicea especially, considered the most dangerous of the cell salts, should be used with caution and with the help of a professional in the health field familiar with tissue therapy, since it has an inherent cutting, slicing action. And cell salts should not be mixed and matched according to a person's whim. For best results one or perhaps two only should be used at one time: strict homeopaths prescribe only one remedy at a time.

Like any other medication, cell salts should be used sparingly and only when needed. Unlike vitamin and mineral supplements, they are not to be taken

forever. And unless a homeopathic physician prescribes them, they should not be taken continuously over a long period of time: to do so invites a metabolic imbalance that may become dangerous.

Doctors often use cell salts as adjuncts to medication already prescribed, and they sometimes suggest using them as preventive measures, much as we would take large doses of vitamin C to stave off a cold we feel coming on. The salts should be taken between meals without the aid of water or any other liquid. Made in a milk-lactose base and tasting very sweet, they disappear within seconds when placed beneath the tongue and allowed to melt. Children even treat them like candy. But people with allergies to milk or lactose should not take them.

The suggested dosages for the cell salts are found in the *Materia Medica*, the homeopathic physician's Bible. These doses were arrived at by thousands of doctors using them on patients over the years and discerning which potencies seemed to reap the best results. The standard potencies are 3X and 6X, or 3/10 and 6/10, the basic homeopathic strengths: when homeopaths refer to 3X, they mean that 3/10 of a cell is contained in the milk lactose that acts as a carrier and filler for the cell. For chronic and long-lasting ailments, however, 12X to 30X may be prescribed. And there are some homeopathic remedies that go up to 5,000X or more on occasion.

Since cell salts are becoming more and more popular, they can be purchased in most health food stores. They can usually be purchased more economically, however, from Standard Homeopathic Co., P.O. Box 61067, Los Angeles CA 90061—the oldest homeopathic pharmaceutical company in the United States.

THE 12 CELL SALTS

Calcarea Fluorica
Astrological Ruler: Cancer.

Synonyms: Calcium fluoride, calc. fluor. and fluoride of lime.

Characteristics: This tissue salt is found in large quantities on the surface of the bones, in the enamel of the teeth and in the fibers of the skin, muscles and blood vessels. It adds elasticity to these parts.

Deficiency Symptoms: Any part of the body that cracks or splits when ordinary folding or bending takes place points toward a deficiency of calcera fluorica. The symptoms include cracked lips, cold sores at the corners of the mouth, a fissured tongue that looks rutted and loss of enamel on the teeth. There may also be splitting of the skin near the anus, hemorrhoids, chapped hands and skin that feels hard or thickened.

Other symptoms indicating that calcarea fluorica is needed are hardening of the arteries or veins, especially in cases involving varicose veins, and enlargement of the knuckles or other joints. Some people may experience a continual coughing or tickling in the throat, causing irritation. Receding gums loosened teeth and small, yellow lumps beneath the skin may appear. And eye-related problems, such as blurred vision after straining the eyes, pain in the eyes and even cataracts, may occur.

Calcarea Phosphorica

Astrological Ruler: Capricorn.

Synonyms: Calcium phosphate, calc. phos. and phosphate of lime.

Characteristics: Commonly referred to as the "bone remedy", this salt is the most abundant of the 12 in the body. Fifty-seven per cent of all bones are made up of calcarea phosphorica. Without it no bones can form, or they will not form properly. It is concerned with the gastric juice secretions in the stomach and albumin, used in strengthening bones.

If a person experiences a broken bone or if teeth are not forming correctly or are decaying before their time, calcarea phosphorica has quick, restorative powers after the onset of an acute conditon. And it can aid in rapid recovery, since it helps to rebuild new blood corpuscles.

Deficiency Symptoms: Circulation to the extremities may be affected with lack of aclcarea phosphorica: cold feet, a sensation that the arms or legs are asleep and numbness or coldness of limbs may be evident, espcecially during weather changes. In addition, itching may occur and freckles or copper-colored spots may appear on the skin.

In addition, any type of bone trouble in any part of the body is suspect of being caused by a deficiency in this tissue salt. Bones around the ears may hurt. There may also be teething problems in infants or poor tooth formation or decay.

Simple anemia may be exacerbated by insufficient calcarea phosphorica as well. Caused by the onset of menstruation, simple anemia as well as other types of anemia has responded well to treatment with calcerea phosphorica. Lower backaches caused by the menstrual cycle have also responded favorably.

Problems with digestion may be caused by a deficiency of this cell salt, too. There may be great deal of flatulence and a swelling of the abdomen as well as craving for bacon, ham and salted or smoked meats. By improving gastric juice secretion so that food is properly broken down and assimilated, the cell salt alleviates a heaviness in the stomach, when food seems to lie there in a lump.

Infants who sweat heavily in the region of the head may also need calcarea phosphorica. Colicky pain may be present in the abdominal region, which will appear sunken and flattened. And children will tend to vomit easily.

Calcarea Sulphurica

Astrological Ruler: Scorpio.

Synonyms: Calcium sulphate, calc. sulph., sulphate of lime, gypsum and plaster of Paris.

Characteristics: This tissue salt is responsible for the destruction of worn-out red blood cells, the remnants of which, if not effectively dealt with will reach the mucous membranes and skin, creating a lag in healing time. Thus yellow, thick, lumpy mucous discharges from any part of the body will respond to calcera sulphurica, especially since the sulphates are derivatives of sulfur, the great cleanser in the human body.

Deficiency Symptoms: If the red blood cells are not destroyed and washed out of the body, they build up, creating pimples, including pimples under the hair, lumps, tumors, cysts and even lupus vulgaris, a chronic, progressive ulcération of the skin, indicating tuberculosis of the skin. Any clogging from these dead cells can cause numerous other symptoms, such as boils, abscesses and external or internal ulcers.

The orifices of the body can be greatly affected by a lack of calcarea sulphurica because it is through the orifices that the body sloughs off its dead cells. As a result there may be sinus discharge or heavy ear wax discharge: in fact, deafness may even be caused by the wax buildup. In addition, there may be inflammation of the eyes along with a thick, yellow discharge as the tear ducts are trying to get rid of the dead material. In extreme cases vision may be reduced and the cornea will turn a smoky color.

Other symptoms induced by a lack of calcarea sulphurica are excessive bleeding and poor healing time for a cut or scratch. The soles of the feet will burn and itch seemingly for no reason. And there will be chest congestion resembling pneumonia in its last stages: thick, lumpy, yellow mucus will be coughed up. Calcera sulphurica is very often used in the last stages of a cold, flu or chest congestion to clear out the mucus so that recovery can be made more rapidly.

Ferrum Phosphoricum

Astrological Ruler: Pisces.

Synonyms: Ferric phosphate, ferr. phos. and phosphate of iron.

Characteristics: Because ferrum phosphoricum is a metal salt it is concerned with the health of the red blood cells. Without enough of the cell salt weakened red corpuscles cannot fight off infection easily and sickness may ensue. For this reason many homeopaths use ferrum phosphoricum in attacking many ailments. And because of its general influence within the body ferrum phosphoricum is often used with other tissue salts. A potency of 3X of ferrum phosphoricum is said to increase the hemoglobin count.

Found primarily in the hemoglobin of the red blood cells but also in smaller quantities in every cell except nerve cells, ferrum phosphoricum may be pulverized and sprinkled over a bleeding wound to halt the flow or at least lessen it. In cases of cuts from razors two small tablets crushed up and applied externally will halt the bleeding quickly and painlessly. The powder can also be sniffed to stop a nosebleed.

Deficiency Symptoms: The major symptom of a lack of ferrum phosphoricum is anemia. A person may look extremely pale. Moreover, muscle fibers will lose their strength and make a person feel weak: fatigue and malaise may be attributed to oncoming anemia. And there may be sensitivity to cold drafts and cold weather, a side effect of anemia. Anyone experiencing such symptoms should see a doctor for a red blood cell count.

Other symptoms of a deficiency are a predisposition toward colds and chest congestion, extreme sensitivity to any noise, which may be jarring to the body, a feeling as though "sleep sand" were under the eyelids and blurred vision.

Kali Muriaticum

Astrological Ruler: Gemini.

Synonyms: Kali mur. and chloride of potassium.

Characteristics: This salt is found in the blood, muscles, nerves, brain cells and intercellular fluid. It unites with albumin to form fibrin. Found in every tissue of the body except for the bones, fibrin is a whitish filament protein instrumental in clotting of the blood and coagulation in general. Its filaments are interlaced and entangled with the red and white blood cells and platelets to form the clot. It is also partly responsible for helping cells maintain their proper shapes.

Deficiency Symptoms: A release of albumin indicates a lack of kali muriaticum. There will be a thick, white mucous discharge. The tongue may be white or grey-coated. And drainage from any orifice may occur.

Symptoms connected with a cold or chest congestion may also appear with a deficiency of this cell salt. The lymph glands may swell and be sore. There may be earaches and other middle ear problems: snapping sounds may take place within the ear. And there may be hoarseness or loss of voice.

Other symptoms indicating a shortage of kali muriaticum are constipation and indigestion from eating foods containing fat; heavy, dark clotting during a woman's menstruation; and rheumatic fever, including swelling around the joints.

Kali Phosphoricum

Astrological Ruler: Aries.

Synonyms: Kali phos. and phosphate of potassium.

Characteristics: Kali phosphoricum is found in the fluids and tissue of the body, with the highest concentration in the brain and nerves. Homeopaths consider it one of the greatest nerve remedies because it is especially effective on the sympathetic nervous system. Any muscular debility disease is also said to respond favorably to this tissue salt.

Uniting with albumin, this salt is very helpful in creating the tissue of the brain known as the grey matter.

Deficiency Symptoms: Mental fatigue and nervous exhaustion are the two major symptoms. People who are constantly tense and nervous, who work too hard without adequate rest and fray their fragile nervous systems, are probably deficient in the cell salt. Kali phosphoricum helps to rejuvenate and soothe so that an individual is able to continue.

Headaches, perhaps caused by too much studying, reading or work-related tension, are another common symptom. There may also be a humming or buzzing sound in the ears, and the breath may be offensive and fetid.

In women menstruation may be late and scanty. In both sexes the urine may be extremely yellow and diarrhea may be common.

Mental depression, malaise, prostration and bodily weakness are some of the other signals of a deficiency of kali phosphoricum. People who become easily frightened or hysterical will often respond favorably to this tissue salt. Since there tends to be a restabilization process that takes place with kali phosphoricum, it lifts people up from depression and brings people down from the heights of exaggerated emotional stress.

Kali Sulphuricum

Astrological Ruler: Virgo.

Synonyms: Kali sulph. and sulphate of potash.

Characteristics: Kali sulphuricum carries oxygen to the skin and coverings of the mucous and serous membranes. One of the cleansers, as all sulfur-bearing nutrients are, it is concerned with the oil secretions of the body, especially of the hair and skin. It also promotes the flow of perspiration that is responsible for keeping the skin "breathing." It may be thought of as the oil we put in our engines to keep the bodily parts functioning smoothly.

Deficiency Symptoms: The skin is one of the most important elimination channels for toxins besides the kidneys: if the pores are allowed to clog up with dead cells, toxins will be held within the body, eventually precipitating imbalance and illness. Such clogging may occur with a lack of kali sulphuricum. Skin conditions that might occur include scaling, burning and itching skin, a light, crusty dryness on the surface, wet eczema, psoriasis, nettle-rash eruptions and seborrhea.

A deficiency of kali sulphuricum can also cause chills and inflammatory pain because the cells are not getting sufficient oxygen. There may be respiratory infections, which tend to take on a rattling noise and are accompanied by a hoarseness. Nasal passages may clog and discharge a yellow, slimy mucus.

In addition, people with this deficiency tend to dislike warm or overheated rooms and will escape outside to get some fresh air. They may feel pain at the nape of the neck, in the back and in the limbs: the pain will tend to shift and wander, sometimes confusing both patient and doctor.

Magnesia Phosphorica

Astrological Ruler: Leo

Synonyms: Mag. phos. and phosphate of magnesium.

Characteristics: Known as the "antispasmodic remedy", magnesia phosphorica works in the white nerve fibers of the nerves and mucles. It also assists the bones, brain, spine, sperm, teeth and blood. The tissue salt uses albumin and water to form a liquid that feeds the white threads or fibers.

Deficiency Symptoms: Without enough magnesia phosphorica to form a liquid with albumin cramping of the muscles and inflammation of the nerves may take place. There may be spasms and shooting pains wherever the cramps exist. The cramps may occur in the calves, where the sciatica nerve becomes inflamed. Or there may be pain that starts in the lower back, goes through the buttocks and down the thighs into the calves. There may also be a weakness in the arms and hands, with the fingertips becoming numb. And the hands may shake involuntarily.

Gastic disorders are other signals of a deficiency of magnesia phosphorica. There may be a great deal of flatulent colic of the kind that will make a person bend over double with pain. There may also be belching, extreme gas and a bloated sensation.

Furthermore, angina pectoris may occur. There can be spasms in the heart as well as palpitations along the constricting pains across the chest.

And with insufficient magnesia phosphorica

women may experience menstrual problems, such as menses that come too early or a great deal of neuralgic pain in the ovaries.

Natrum Muriaticum

Astrological Ruler: Aquarius.

Synonyms: Nat. mur. and chloride of sodium.

Characteristics: Commonly known as ordinary table salt, natrum muriaticum regulates the degree of moisture within the cells. The cell salt is responsible for how much water enters or leaves the cells: if too much flows in, then the cells, gorged on the intercellular fluid, lose their shapes.

Natrum muriaticum also controls the amount of hydrochloric acid that enters the stomach during digestion. If too little hydrochloric acid is available, many problems can occur.

Deficiency Symptoms[1]: Various problems with the eyes may result from a lack of natrum muriaticum. The eyeballs may feel bruised when pressed. There may be a burning sensation in the eyes. And there may be pain when a person looks down.

In addition, a numbness or tingling sensation may take place in the tongue or the extremities. The heart and chest may feel constricted. The pulse may be intermittent when a person is lying down. Palms may be hot and perspiring. And hangnails may occur.

Natrum Phosphoricum

Astrological Ruler: Libra.

Synonyms: Nat. phos. and phosphate of sodium.

Characteristics: Natrum phosphoricum is found in the blood, muscles, nerves, brain cells and intercellular fluids. Its chemical action is to split up lactic acid into carbonic acid. It also promotes the absorption of water from the decomposed lactic acid. Another of its important jobs is to maintain the balance between alkalinity and acidity. And it promotes absorption of water.

Deficiency Symptoms: If the acid-alkaline metabolism is out of balance, a person may have acidosis. If he or she wears jewelry, the skin may turn green or black from the chemical interaction of the metal against the skin—a major signal that the acid level in the body is abnormally high. The gastric system may also be affected, with the possibility of heartburn, burping, a tight sensation throughout the

---

[1] No one should make the mistake of taking table salt for any of these symptoms of deficiency. The cell salt natrum muriaticum has been torn apart at high speeds (tritutrated) to such a degree that it is immediately absorbed; on the other hand, salt granules have not been broken down so that this swift assimilation takes place. And as I've indicated in Chapter Eight, most Americans consume too much sodium, especially in the form of table salt.

chest or ulcers in the stomach. Instead of an antacid tablet, natrum phosphoricum will eliminate such problems.

Several other symptoms may occur with a lack of this cell salt. The eyes may discharge a golden-yellow, creamy mucus. The same type of mucus may be found in the mouth, especially on the back of the tongue and the roof of the mouth. Itching may occur on the skin, particularly the ankles. Feet may be cold during the day and burning at night. And hives—another way for excess acid to be released through the skin pores—are fairly common.

Natrum Sulphuricum

Astrological Ruler: Taurus.

Synonyms: Nat. sulph., sulphate of sodium and Glauber's salt.

Characteristics: This inorganic mineral is found only intercellularly in the fluids. It controls the amount of bile that is secreted into the duodenum to break down food, aids and regulates the elimination of unwanted water in the body and gets rid of excess liquid from the blood and serum.

Because of natrum sulphuricum's affinity with water, people who suffer deficiencies of the cell salt should not live near water: the best climate is one that is sunny, warm and dry. These people will feel the most minute fluctuation in humidity, and they tend to feel worse when the humidity is high.

Deficiency Symptoms: With a lack of natrum sulphuricum there may be an accumulation of water in the connective tissue, a yellow, watery secretion on the skin and a coating at the base of the tongue. During the spring of each year there can be a return of skin problems.

Moreover, the mouth will have a bitter taste to it. The eyelids will contain granular sand, and there will be a burning at the corners of the eyes. Poor digestion will cause headaches, a bloated feeling and excessive bile. Liver problems may also arise.

Damp weather will bring on an array of uncomfortable symptoms, such as humid asthma, melancholy, tendencies toward mania, difficulty in breathing and a proclivity for catching influenza.

Silicea

Astrological Ruler: Sagittarius.

Synonyms: Silica and oxide of silicon.

Characteristics: Found in small amounts in the human body, silicea is abundant in the vegetable kingdom. It is involved with the bones, joints, glands, skin and mucous surfaces. Its action is deep and long-lasting, working upon the organic substances of the body. It gives strength to fingernails and bones, a glossy shine to hair and good vision to the eyes. Silicea also keeps the pores of the skin open and the enamel of the teeth strong to ward off tooth decay.

Known to homeopaths as the "surgeon's knife," this cell salt must be administered with care. Its sharp, lance-shaped needles cut. In cases involving pulmonary tuberculosis or any type of wasting or atrophic disease, silicea should not be given because the sharp lancets will cut into the newly healed scar tissue and release the tubercular infection into unaffected areas.

Silicea is usually given to people known to have imperfect assimilation of nutrients.

Deficiency Symptoms: With an insufficient amount of silicea there may be abcesses, boils or other festering skin conditions. The eyes may get sties, ulcers of the cornea or eventually even cataracts.

Other symptoms include hair that falls out or loses its sheen, roaring sounds in the ear, the sensation of hair being on the tongue, a prickling sensation in the tonsils, the swelling of parotid glands, sleepwalking, white spots on the nails, icy cold or sweaty feet, hands or underarms and cracks at the ends of the fingers.

APPENDIX A

Homeopathic Information: //

Hahnemann Pharmacy
Tel: 1-888-427-6422

1. Free catalog on products/price list
2. Homeopathic kits: Travelers Kit,
   Natural Cycles Kit, Injury Kit

Standard Homeopathic Co.
P.O. Box 61067
Los Angeles, CA 90061
Tel: (800) 624-9659

1. Calm's Forte
2. Other Homeopathic combinations and
   single remedies
3. Tincture of Hydrangea

National Center for Homeopathy
801 N. Fairfax St., Suite 306
Alexandria, VA 22314
Tel: (703) 548-7790
Fax: (703) 548-7792

1. Send for free brochures on Homeopathy
2. Call to find the Homeopathic doctor
   nearest to you
3. National and international directories of
   Homeopathic practitioners can be purchased for a nominal fee
4. Homeopathic home kits and books available for purchase
5. Two-week lay and professional courses
   offered every summer

Blue Turtle Flower & Gem Essences //

Blue Turtle Publishing
P.O. Box 2513
Cottonwood, AZ 86326
Tel/Fax: 1-520-634-9298
Email: docbones@sedona.net
Website: www.medicinegarden.com

1. Free Catalog
2. Yearly seminars
3. Essences for sale

Homeopathic Directory (to locate physician nearest you): ///

National Center for Homeopathy
801 N. Fairfax St., Suite 306
Alexandria, VA 22314
Tel: (703) 548-7790
Fax: (703) 548-7792

APPENDIX B

To order a free Natural Essence Catalog, contact Blue Turtle Publishing, P.O. Box 2513, Cottonwood, AZ
86326 or e-mail: docbones@sedona.net, or Fax (520) 634-9298. Visa/Mastercard accepted.

APPENDIX C

HOMEOPATHIC CORRESPONDENCE COURSE
The British Institute of Homeopathy is recognized worldwide as one of the best correspondence courses on learning basic through advanced Homeopathy. For more information and a brochure, contact:

Dr. Terry Jacobs, DI Hom,
Registrar
The British Institute of Homeopathy
520 Washington Blvd., Suite 423
Marina Del Rey, CA 90292
Tel: (310) 306-5408
Fax: (310) 827-5766

APPENDIX D

Med-Scan Technique software and medical transits software are available from:

Cosmic Patterns
6212 NW 43rd Street, Suite B
Gainesville, FL 32653
Tel: (352) 373-1504

NOTE: You must be either an M.D., D.O., D.C. or N.D. to purchase software (or an astrologer who will use this software for research purposes only). Please include copy of state medical liscense with order.

APPENDIX E

OTHER BOOKS BY EILEEN NAUMAN
1. *HELP! and Homeopathy,* 310 pages, $16.95, Blue Turtle Publishing, P.O. Box 2513, Cottonwood, AZ 86326. Homeopathic book. What to do in an emergency before 911 arrives. Fifty first aid remedies, a materia medica, and how to dose, how often and when not to depending upon the emergency. This book is for any parent or spouse and is valuable at-home or vacationing emergencies.
2. *Soul Recovery and Extraction* by Ai Gvhdi Waya (Eileen Nauman), 86 pages, $9.95, Blue Turtle Publishing, P.O. Box 2513, Cottonwood, AZ 86326. Shamanism and healing. This is about regaining the fragments of one's soul energy that have been trapped, lost or stolen either by another person or through traumatic incident that has occurred in one's life. Signs of soul loss. Directory of trained shamanic facilitators by Eileen Nauman in the back of the book.
3. *Beauty in Bloom: Homeopathy to Support Menopause.* To come out in 2000 and to be published by Blue Turtle Publishing. How to deal with the symptoms of menopause by utilizing the correct homeopathic remedy. Vitamins and minerals that are necessary during this time of change in a woman's life, as well as flower essences that can address the symptoms.
4. *21st Century Epidemics and Homeopathy.* To come out in 2000 and the be published by Blue Turtle Publishing. Homeopathy to address the coming epidemics such as Hanta Virus, Dengue Fever, Malaria, Ebola, Anthrax, Measles, and Mumps, among many others. Antibiotics are failing us. Only homeopathy stands between us and these super bugs. Remedies for each acute medical emergency.

Glossary of Medical Terms

17-Ketosteroid A test to determine endocrine problems related to the adrenal glands.

absorption Assimilation of nutrients, water or other liquids through some bodily surface, e.g., digested food being absorbed through the intestinal walls.

acid Any substance characterized by a sour taste and neutralizes basic substances, such as gallic acid, found in tea and vinegar.

acid-alkaline metabolism The balance of acids to alkalies within the body. The proper ratio approximates four parts alkali to one part acid.

acidosis A condition within the body wherein an accumulation of acids occurs, likely to appear when a person eats acidic foods with regularity. It may be caused by many ailments. Most often, it will create indigestion, heartburn, tenseness, nervousness and an inability to relax.

acute Pertaining to any condition that comes on suddenly; a rapid onset of an ailment which has a short course such as a flu, cold or fever.

adenoid Lymphatic tissue having the appearance of a gland. The area may become infected, halt or partially block passage or air or impair hearing, especially in your children.

adrenal glands Triangular-shaped glands located atop each kidney. Each consists of a tough outer layer of tissue known as the *cortex*; the inner part is called the *medulla*. These glands are responsible for a number of hormonal functions, including producing adrenalin and cortisone. They are also called the *suprarenal* glands.

alkali Any substance that will neutralize an acid, producing a salt or, when combined with fatty acids, producing a soap.

anemia A reduction in the number of red blood cells circulating in the circulatory system.

aneurysm A weakness in the wall of a vessel, producing a ballooning outward or distension. If the vessel ruptures, it can be fatal.

angina A disease characterized by a sense of suffocation or sudden attacks that may cause a person to choke or nearly suffocate.

antigens Any substance, such as bacteria, toxins or foreign blood cells, that trigger the body to produce antibodies to fight off invaders.

aorta The main trunk of the arterial system, approximately three centimeters in width. It is found in the center of the body and down both legs.

arrhythmia Irregularity of the heart action; loss of rhythm for any number of reasons.

arteriosclerosis The thickening, hardening or loss of elasticity of the walls of arteries.

atherosclerosis A form of arteriosclerosis, wherein lipid or plaque deposits accumulate and cause partial or complete blockage of blood in an area.

atrophy A wasting away or shriveling of some part of the body or cell. The term may be applied to many conditions, such as muscle atrophy, nerve atrophy or ovary atrophy, which takes place at menopause.

avidin A protein found in raw egg white, said to inhibit uptake of the vitamin biotin.

back The spinal column, composed of the cervical, thoracic, lumbar and sacroiliac regions.

bacteria Organisms that are unicellular. Bacteria are beneficial or harmful to the body, depending upon what they are.

barium enema A test to find ulcers or tumors in the large intestine.

biliary Pertaining to the ducts that convey bile from the liver.

bile A straw-colored fluid secreted by the liver, stored in the gallbladder and released into the duodenum during the digestion phase. Bile contains pigments, such as bilirubin, cholesterol and lecithin.

BMR. Basal metabolism rate, which indicates how well the body uses its metabolic energy.

brachycardia Slowed heart action. The heart beats much slower than it should.

Bright's disease A loose term used for either acute or chronic kidney ailments. The disease usually involves water retention.

brittle diabetes A disease characterized by unpredictable needs for insulin. Blood sugar may rise and fall sharply, endangering a patient's life.

BUN A blood, urea and nitrogen test for ailments pertaining to the kidney.

bursitis Inflammation of the bursa between the muscles and tendons of the shoulder and/or knee. May be referred to as "tennis elbow" or "housemaid's knee."

caffeine An alkaloid found in coffee and tea that stimulates the central nervous system and behaves as a diuretic. Too much caffeine will leach out valuable minerals and vitamins from the body.

calcify To form stones, usually found in the kidney, although they may be found in many other parts of the body. The term also means to deposit calcium salts, resulting in hardening and petrifying of organs.

calculi Calcium-bearing stones.

capillary The most minute of all blood vessels. Capillaries connect the smallest arteries with the smallest veins.

carbohydrates A chemical group consisting of sugars, glycogen, starches, dextrins, etc. carbohydrates are our basic sources of energy.

cardiac Pertaining to the heart and to the opening of the esophagus into the stomach.

caries Decay and disintegration of tooth or bone.

cardiovascular Pertaining to the heart and blood vessels.

carotene A yellow pigment found in both plant and animal tissue, especially carrots. It is a precursor to vitamin A.

cataract Opacity of the lens of the eye, blocking vision and eventually causing blindness if surgery is not performed.

catarrh An old physician's term for any inflammation occurring to the mucous membranes.

CBC Complete blood count, a test to help discern anemia.

cecum The portion that forms the first part of the large intestines.

cell The smallest unit of living matter found in all animals and plants.

central nervous system A bodily system comprised of the brain, spinal cord, their nerves and the end organs that control all voluntary functions of the body.

cerebral Pertaining to the largest part of the brain, known as the cerebrum.

chemotherapy Application of drugs to treat cancer.

cholecystography An x-ray test to examine the gallbladder.

cholesterol A sterol-related substance found in all animals, including humans. It is found in the bile, skin, blood and brain. High cholesterol deposits are directly related to heart and artery problems.

chronic Pertaining to diseases which are of long duration or showing very little change or sluggish progression and are of long continuance.

circulatory system A system within the cardiac system used to transport blood or lymph. It includes the heart, blood vessels, arteries, veins and sinuses.

cirrhosis A chronic ailment of the liver.

cleft palate A fissure (crack, split or division) located in the roof of the mouth.

coferment A coenzyme.

coenzyme A nonprotein substance produced by cells and essential in the formation of certain enzymes. As partners, coenzymes help vitamins and minerals join enzymes to aid in particular chemical functions.

colic A spasm ocurring in any hollow or tubal soft organ and accompanied with pain. It may occur in the bile ducts, intestines, abdomen associated with menstrual cycle, renal or in the uterine area.

colitis Inflammation in the colon (large intestine).

colon Another word for the large intestine.

cone A receptor cell of the retina that discerns color.

coronary Encircling, such as the blood vessels that supply blood to the heart. The term is usually applied to diseases having to do with atherosclerosis, in which partial or complete clogging of the artery to the heart causes a heart attack.

cortex The outer portion or layer of tissue on an organ, such as the cortex of the adrenal glands.

corticosterone A hormone released by the adrenal gland cortex. It helps to regulate the potassium-sodium metabolism and influences the carbohydrate metabolism.

cortisone A hormone secreted by the adrenal gland cortex. It aids in the metabolism of fats, carbohydrates, proteins, sodium and potassium.

creatinine The end product of creatine metabolism, found in higher levels in renal diseases.

cretinism Infantile hypothyroidism may arise from thyroid agenesis or inadequate maternal intake of iodine during gestation. It appears during the first years of life and results in stunting bodily growth and of mental development. untreated. The disease may strike newborn infants, leaving them mentally and physically impaired for the rest of their lives. The **crisis** The turning point of any condition or disease. It may be accompanied by a break in the fever, profuse sweating and deep, healing sleep.

Cushing's syndrome Excessive hormonal secretion from the adrenal gland cortex and overproduction of the glucocorticoids.

cyclical albuminuria Periodic amounts of albumin found in the urine, a sign of renal impairment.

cyst A closed sac or wall that contains fluid, semifluid or solid material.

cystitis It is a disease characterized by inflammation of the bladder and causes painful urination.

D and C D and C is a term for dilation of the cervix and curettage of the uterus, a procedure performed on women to halt excessive menstrual hemorrhaging conditions, to correct other uterine conditions or to abort a fetus.

deficiency A lack of some thing, such as a vitamin or mineral missing in proper amounts, so that the body is unable to maintain health.

degeneration Partial deterioration or complete impairment of some part of the body; gradual loss of the ability to maintain normal functions.

delirium tremens   Hallucinations seen and heard by alcoholics. The experience results in states of anxiety, excitement and incoherent behavior.

dermatitis   Inflammation of the skin. The outer layer of the skin becomes itchy and red.

detoxification   Removal of toxins or other bodily poisons through a natural diet, colonics, herbs, etc.

diabetes   A sugar disorder. Several types of diabetes may occur — brittle, insipidus, juvenile-onset and mellitus.

dilation   Expansion or opening of an organ, vessel or orifice.

diuretic   Drugs used to increase the secretion of urine from the body thereby forcing excess water from the body also. Diuretics drugs are particularly hard on the adrenal glands and kidneys.

diverticulitis   Inflammation of the intestines. Stool matter sits in pockets, causing festering conditions.

diverticulosis   Stagnation of fecal material in sacs located in colon, but without the symptoms or inflammation associated with diverticulitis.

dropsy   An antiquated term meaning edema or water retention.

duodenum   The first 11 inches of the small intestine, connected to the bottom of the stomach. The pyloric valve opens from the stomach and gradually empties the food into the duodenum, where pancreatic and gallbladder secretions pour into it. The food is then reduced to chyme. The duodenum is very important for proper emulsification of food so that nutrients may be absorbed as they pass through the intestinal tract.

dystrophy   An ailment caused by poor nutrition. It is most often known as muscular dystrophy, wherein the muscles atrophy or gradually waste away.

eczema   A disease of the skin, characterized by scales, scabs, pustules or crusty deposits. It may be caused by a variety of conditions, ranging from an allergic reaction to bacterial infection.

edema   Excessive water retention somewhere in the body, usually the hands or legs. Edema may be caused by a sodium-potassium imbalance. There may be swelling of the fingers or ankles.

electrolyte   A substance, such as an acid, base or salt, that acts as a conductor of electrical current within the body. It is commonly known as an "electrolyte balance" and is of concern to people who experience prolonged vomiting or diarrhea.

endocarditis   Inflammation in the lining of the membrane surrounding the heart muscle.

endocrine   Pertaining to a ductless gland that secretes hormones directly into the blood or lymph stream. The following are considered the principal endocrine glands: anterior/posterior pituitary, thyroid, parathyroid, adrenal, testes and ovaries. There is a debate about whether pineal and thymus are glands or not.

endocrinologist   One who studies the endocrine glands; a doctor specializing in how the ductless glands affect the body.

enuresis   Involuntary urination. Commonly known as "bed-wetting." Children seem to suffer from this problem sometimes because of emotional instability surrounding them. Enuresis may also be caused by organic malfunctions, such as urethral irritation.

enzyme   A complex protein that is able to induce chemical changes in other substances without change occurring within itself.

epilepsy   Attacks brought on by a disturbed brain function, often referred to as petite or grand mal seizures.

epiphyseal closure   The secondary bone formation in the skull area that takes place in children.

erysipelas   Localized swelling or inflammation of the skin followed by fever and chills. If erysipelas goes untreated, nephritis, abscesses or septicemia may occur.

erythrocyte   Commonly known as a red blood cell. It is a mature red cell.

estrogen   A female hormone responsible for such secondary sex characteristics as the beginning of menstruation.

eustachian tube   The auditory tube which extends from the middle ear to the pharynx.

fallopian tube   A tube that extends from the uterus and ends very near the ovary, from which the egg is expelled. The egg then travels down the Fallopian tube to lodge itself within the uterus. If fertilized, the egg is the beginning of a baby; if not, it is washed out during the menstrual cycle.

feces   Body waste excreted from the intestinal tract; also known as fecal matter or stool.

ferrous   Containing iron, used in compounds such as ferrous fumarate, gluconate or sulphate.

fibrillation   Movements of the heart, quivering or incomplete contractions; an irregular heart beat.

fibrin   A white, filamentlike protein responsible for coagulation after thrombin converts it to fibrinogen.

fibrosis   Formation of fiberlike material that may occur anywhere in the body.

fissure   A groove, slit or furrow. The word normally occurs in the phrase "fissured tongue," a condition that may occur with certain B vitamin deficiencies.

flatulence   Gas lodging in the stomach and intestinal region.

free radical   An atom or group of atoms having at least one unpaired electron and participating in various reactions. Free radicals are often believed responsible for wrinkles occurring with age.

fructose   A fruit sugar.

gallbladder   A pear-shaped organ beneath the liver that holds the bile made by the liver.

gallstone   A cholesterol bilirubin or protein stone that may form in the gallbladder or in the duct leading from that organ.

gastric   Pertaining to the stomach; used to refer to digestion.

gastroenteritis   Inflammation of the mucous membrane of the stomach and intestine.

gastrointestinal   Pertaining to the stomach and intestinal tract.

gene   The basic unit of heredity.

genitourinary   Pertaining to the genitals and urinary organs.

gigantism   Abnormal development of the human body. Gigantism may be caused by endocrine (pituitary) problems. The hands, feet and face may be distorted by overgrowth.

gland   An organ or structure that secretes. It may or may not be an endocrine gland.

glaucoma   A disease that increases pressure within the eyeball and results in atrophy of the optic nerve. Blindness is the result.

glomeruli   Pertaining to the kidneys. These are the capillary blood vessels found in clusters. They may become inflamed, causing renal difficulties.

glucagon   A substance secreted by the alpha cells of the pancreas. Glucagon breaks down glycogen and stimulates release of glucose from the liver, increasing the blood sugar.

glucose   A sugar. Glucose is an intermediate step in the carbohydrate metabolism. Once in the liver it is converted into glycogen.

glucose tolerance test   A three- to six-hour test to determine blood sugar levels of an individual. The curve frequently does not start to indicate a problem until the fourth, fifth or even sixth hour. The test is used to determine diabetes as well as hypoglycemia.

glycogen   The chemical form in which carbohydrates are stored in the body for conversion into sugar when needed.

goiter   Enlargement of the thyroid gland, usually caused by lack of sufficient iodine in the diet.

gout   Disease marked by acute arthritis and inflammation of the joints. Urate crystals settle in any part of the body, but usually the feet or other joints.

gravel   Crystals that are usually made up of calcium, oxalate or uric acid; another term for stones that may be found in the organs of the body.

heart   A hollow contracting organ consisting of muscle. The heart contains three layers: the outer layer is referred to as the epicardium; middle, myocardium; and inner, endocardium. The thin membrane sac that holds the heart is referred to as the pericardium.

heme   The iron containing nonprotein portion of hemoglobin.

hemoglobin   The iron-containing pigment of the red blood cells. Hemoglobin's function is to carry oxygen from the lungs to every part of the body.

hemorrhage   To bleed excessively, either internally or externally.

hemosiderosis   The loss of hemosiderin. This condition may occur in hemolytic or pernicious anemia or a chronic infection.

hepatitis   Inflammation of the liver through virus or toxicity.

herpes   Commonly know as "cold sores" or "fever blisters." A virus.

hiatus hernia   Protrusion of the stomach up through the mediastinal cavity and the diaphragm.

high blood pressure   An increase in the blood pressure, also known as hypertension.

hormone   A substance released by an organ, gland or part of the body and conveyed via the bloodstream to another area of the body and increasing activity via chemical action.

hydrochloric acid   Known as HCl. It is found in the gastric juices and aids in the digestive process.

hydrolysis   Any reaction in which water is involved.

hyper   Fast, overworking, excess, e.g., *hyperthyroid*.

hyperkalemia   Excessive amounts of potassium in the blood.

hyperparathyroidism   Excessive secretion of calcium that may result in kidney disease.

hyperpituitarism   Overactivity of the anterior pituitary gland that may result in growth-related problems.

hyperthyroidism   Excessive hormonal secretions by the thyroid gland that will increase the basal metabolic rate.

hypertrophy   Increase of an organ or structure not caused by the formation of tumors.

hyperventilation   Forced or quickened breathing that

results in loss of carbon dioxide. Hyperventilation usually occurs to people who are highly anxious.

hypervitaminosis Overdosage of a vitamin.

hypo Slow, sluggish, underworking, e.g., *hypothyroid*.

hypoadrenalism Known as adrenal insufficiency. The adrenal glands fail to put out enough hormones to do the work demanded within the body.

hypocalcemia Low levels of calcium in the blood.

hypoglycemia Low blood sugar. This disease is on the upswing in the United States. It is finally being diagnosed as an organic problem rather than strictly a mental/psychological problem.

hypokalemia Low levels of potassium in the body. Edema may occur as a consequence.

hypoparathyroidism Low level secretions from the parathyroid. Blood calcium levels may fall as a consequence.

hypopituitarism Diminished hormone secretion of the pituitary gland, especially the anterior portion.

hypothalamus A part of the brain related to the pituitary gland. The hypothalamus helps control metabolic activities.

hypothyroidism Decreased thyroid function that affects the basal metabolism. Removal or loss of functioning thyroid tissue can cause myxedema.

in vitro Pertaining to test experiments performed in glass test tubes rather than on living specimens.

in vivo Pertaining to tests and experiments performed on living bodies or organisms.

inorganic In chemistry anything occurring in nature that is independent from living things.

insomnia The inability to get to sleep; tossing and turning all night and feeling unrested in the morning.

insulin A hormone secreted by beta cells in the islands of Langerhans of the pancreas. Insulin is needed to maintain proper metabolism of the blood sugar levels.

intracellular Within the cell itself.

intravenous Within a vein or veins. The term refers to a method of feeding or infusion in which a needle is placed in a vein, the tubing is secured and then a fluid preparation is fed to the patient, thereby circumventing digestion completely.

intrinsic factor A substance found in the gastric system that helps B vitamins be absorbed more fully by the body.

iridology Study of the iris of the eye to determine disease.

irradiation Application of roentgen, radium or ultraviolet rays on a person or other material.

islands of Langerhans Clusters of cells within the pancreas that secrete insulin, also known as *islets of Langerhans.*

isoniazid An antibacterial compound used in treating tuberculosis.

IVP A test to discern renal problems.

jaundice A condition that turns the skin yellow. It may be due to obstruction of bile ducts, destruction of red blood cells or a disturbance of the liver cell function.

lactobacillus A bacterium that produces lactic acid and is responsible for the souring of milk. Lactobacillus acidophilus, known to yogurt lovers, produces lactic acid by fermenting sugar found in milk.

laparotomy Surgical section of the abdominal wall.

larynx Known as the voice box. The larynx contains the vocal cords.

lateral sclerosis A hardening of tissue, similar to multiple sclerosis but involving the spinal column.

lecithin A fatty substance found in the body and made in part from inositol and cholin.

leukemia A disease wherein white blood cells grow without restraint.

leukocyte A white blood cell.

leukopenia Abnormal decrease of white blood cells in the body.

lipid Pertaining to fat or fat-like substance.

lymph An alkaline fluid found in the lymphatic system.

lymphocyte A lymph or white blood cell without cytoplasmic granules. Lymphocytes represent between 20 to 50 per cent of all white blood cells.

macrocyte A larger-than-normal red blood cell.

malabsorption Inadequate absorption of nutrients through the intestinal tract.

malic acid An acid in apples. When made into vinegar and consumed, the acid turns alkaline upon entering the gastric juices. It is helpful in reestablishing the acid-alkaline balance of the body.

malnutrition Lack of correct foods to sustain bodily health or malabsorption that inhibits uptake of nutrients essential for health.

malocclusion Imperfect development of teeth. A malocclusion may be loss of teeth or abnormal growth of the jaw. The bite is affected.

malpractice Negligent or improper treatment of a patient by a person or persons in the medical profession.

massotherapy   The art and practice of therapeutic massage. Massotherapists attend two-year colleges and are licensed by the AMA of each state.

mastication   The ability to chew one's food; chewing.

megaloblastic   Pertaining to an abnormally large red blood cell found in pernicious anemia.

megavitamin   Massive doses of a single nutrient given for therapeutic reasons.

metabolism   The physical and chemical changes that take place in the body.

mineral   An inorganic substance occurring naturally in nature; not of animal or plant derivation.

mitochondria   Slender filaments that are sources of energy to a cell. They are also involved in protein synthesis and the lipid metabolism.

multiple sclerosis   A chronic disease of the central nervous system. Muscle control, coordination and speech may be affected.

myasthenia gravis   A disease producing extreme muscular weakness from lack of acetylcholine. Nerve impulses fail to produce contractions of the muscles.

myelin   A fatty substance surrounding the nerve fibers and helping to make up the myelin sheaths.

myelitis   Inflammation of the bone marrow or spinal cord.

myocardial   Pertaining to the middle layer of muscle of the heart.

myxedema   Hypothyroidism caused by removal or loss of functioning thyroid tissue. Characteristics of the disease are relatively hard edema of subcutaneous tissue, dryness and loss of hair, subnormal temperature, hoarseness, muscle weakness, and slow return of muscle after a tendon jerk to the neutral position. Also known as Gull's disease.

naturopathy   A method of healing that does not incorporate drug therapy. Instead, naturopathy employs techniques of natural healing that include the use of light, air, heat, water and massage.

nephritis   Inflammation of one or both kidneys, causing retention of urine and other toxins normally filtered from the blood.

nerve   A bundle or group of nerve fibers outside the central nervous system. Nerves are connected to the brain, spinal cord and other parts of the body.

neuritis   Inflammation of a nerve or nerves.

nutrient   Food that gives the body nourishment to sustain life.

organic   Pertaining to a substance derived from animals or plants.

osteoarthritis   A chronic ailment involving the joints. Destruction of cartilage, bone overgrowth and spur formation are common.

osteopathy   A branch of medicine employing attention to nutritional needs and bodily manipulation.

osteoporosis   A disease of the bones, which become porous, soften or widen.

ovary   One of two female glands responsible for production of the ovum (egg).

ovaritis   Inflammation of the ovary.

oxalic acid   Toxic acid that helps to coagulate blood. When eaten in excess, (e.g., too much chocolate, too many cranberries or too much chard), oxalic acid can inhibit the metabolism.

pancreas   A gland that produces internal as well as external secretions. Some of these secretions are hormonal and concern insulin and the carbohydrate processes.

pancreatitis   Inflammation of the pancreas.

parathyroid gland   Endocrine glands embedded or close to the thyroid gland. The parathyroids secretes parathormone, a hormone which controls the calcium-phosphorus metabolism.

Parkinson's disease   A chronic nervous disorder characterized by tremors and muscular weakness.

peptic ulcer   An ulcer in the lower part of the esophagus, stomach or duodenum.

pericarditis   Inflammation of the pericardium, the tissue sac containing the heart muscle.

peristalsis   A wavelike motion that occurs in the hollow tubing of the body and aids in digestion. The contraction-relaxation of the muscles within the tubing moves the digested food through the intestinal tract.

pernicious   Pertaining to harmful or destructive blood ailments, such as anemia. Pernicious anemia can be fatal if not treated.

peritonitis   Inflammation of the lining of the abdominal cavity.

phlebitis   Inflammation in the veins, usually of the legs or arms. Phlebitis can be dangerous or fatal if not treated.

phospholipid   A lipoid substance, such as lecithin, that has a base of phosphorus, fatty acids and nitrogen.

pineal   A pine cone-shaped body in the brain; loosely referred to as an endocrine gland.

pituitary gland   Master gland of the body located in the brain. The pituitary consists of an anterior and posterior portion.

polycythemia   Excessive red blood cells in the body.

polyp   A tumor or growth with a root or stem system. A polyp tends to bleed easily and can become malignant.

portal system   An opening in an organ, the intestines or circulation.

postpartum   After the birth of a child.

prostate   A gland surrounding the neck of the bladder in men. The prostate may become enlarged or inflamed in later life.

psoriasis   A skin condition characterized by pink or red scaling occurring externally in patches.

pulmonary   Relating to the lungs, to the pulmonary artery, or to the aperture leading from the right ventricle into the pulmonary artery.

pyruvic acid   An important acid that plays a role in the Krebs cycle and the metabolism of carbohydrates, fats and amino acids.

renal   Pertaining to the kidneys.

retina   The part of the eye which receives the image formed by the lens.

rheumatic fever   Sudden onset of a fever from a bacteria. Rheumatic fever may cause damage to the heart and kidneys if not arrested in time. It often causes heart murmurs.

rhinitis   Inflammation of the nasal mucous lining.

RNA   A nucleic acid that plays an important part in carrying information from the nucleus to cytoplasmic sites.

rods   Long, slender sensory bars within the retina that respond to very faint light.

scarlet fever   A contagious disease that erupts suddenly after an incubation period. Scarlet fever may damage the kidneys.

sciatica   The largest nerve in the body. The sciatica begins at the sacral region of the spine and extends down through the pelvis to the heels. It frequently gives problems in the area of the buttocks, hips or thighs.

sclerosis   Hardening of any organ or tissue.

serum calcium test   A test to determine the amount of calcium in the body.

serum creatinine test   A test to detect ailments in the kidneys.

sickle cell   An abnormally shaped red blood cell that looks like a crescent.

sigmoid colon   The lower part of the large intestines; the descending colon.

SGOT Test   A test to determine heart ailments.

SMA   A series of blood chemistry tests to determine how the bodily functions are performing.

sodium-potassium test   A test to indicate the balance between sodium and potassium.

spleen   A dark red, oval-shaped body responsible for formation of blood cells.

stasis   Stagnation.

stroke   A sudden, unexpected attack, such as a brain hemorrhage, that induces paralysis elsewhere in the body.

T-3, T-4, T-7 Test   A test to determine if the thyroid is hypo, hyper or normal.

testes   Reproductive glands located in the scrotum of men. They produce sperm.

thrombin   An enzyme that mixes with fibrinogen to make fibrin, a blood clot to cease loss of escaping blood.

thymus   An organ located above the heart that may or may not be an endocrine gland. The thymus manufactures thymocytes, which help keep immunity systems alert to invading bacteria or viruses.

thyroid   An endocrine gland located in the throat that is responsible for how iodine is used in the body.

thyroxine   One of the two hormones released by the thyroid gland.

total lipid test   A test to determine the amount of cholesterol in the body.

toxins   Any poisonous substance of a plant or animal origin.

trachea   A tube that allows the flow of air to reach the lungs.

upper GI   A test to discern ulcers, hiatal hernias and disturbances in the esophagus.

uremic toxemia   Uremic poisoning. The condition usually occurs to women in their third trimester of pregnancy. It can be very dangerous if not monitored.

ureters   Tubes extending from the kidneys down to the bladder so that waste can be excreted from the body in the form of urine.

urethra tube   A tube extending from the neck of the bladder to the outside of the body.

vaginitis   Inflammation of the vagina.

viscid   Adhering, jellylike or sticky.

vitiligo   White patches of skin surrounded by black or darker tissue. This condition occurs to black people who live in tropical regions. The cause is unknown.

Bibliography

Airola, Paavo. Are You Confused? Phoenix: Health Plus, 1971.

. . .How to Get Well. Phoenix: Health Plus, 1974.

. . .How to Keep Slim, Healthy and Young with Juice Fasting. Phoenix: Health Plus, 1971.

American Medical Association. Handbook of Nutrition. Toronto: Blakison, 1951.

. . .The Vitamins. New York: American Medical Association. 1939.

Angier, Bradford. Field Guide to Edible Wild Plants. Harrisburg, PA: Stackpole Books, 1974.

Arano, Luisa Cogliati. The Medieval Health Handbook Tacuinum Sanitatis. New York: George Braziller, 1976.

Association of Vitamin Chemists. Methods of Vitamin Assay. London: Interscience Publishers, 1966.

Attfield, John. Chemistry: General, Medical and Pharmaceutical. Boston: Henry C. Lea's Son, 1883.

Bach, Edward, M.D. & F. J. Wheeler, M.D. The Bach Flower Remedies. (three books in one - Heal Thyself, The Twelve Healers, The Bach Remedies Repertory) New Canaan, CT: Keats Publishing, Inc., 1979.

Ballentine, Rudolph. Diet and Nutrition. Honesdale, PA: Himalayan International Institute, 1978.

Barnes, Broda O. and Lawrence Galton. Hypothyroidism. New York: Thomas Y. Crowell, 1976.

Bender, Arnold E. Dictionary of Nutrition and Food Technology. Boston: Newnes-Butterworths, 1975.

Bendix, G. Press Point Therapy. Mahopac, NY: American Family Publishing, 1976.

Bennett, Thomas P. and Earl Frieden. Modern Topics in Biochemistry. New York: MacMillan, 1967.

Bentley, K.W., ed. The Chemistry of Natural Products. London: Interscience Publishers, 1965.

Best, Charles Herbert and Norman Taylor. Physiological Basis of Medical Practice. Baltimore: Waverly Press, 1937.

Birch, C.G. and L. F. Green. Molecular Structure and Function of Food Carbohydrates. New York: John Wiley, 1973.

Boericke, William. A Compendium of the Principles of Homeopathy. Mokelumn Hill, CA: Health Research, 1971.

. . .Materia Medica with Repertory. Philadelphia: Boericke & Runyon, 1927.

. . .Pocket Manual of Homeopathic Materia Medica. Philadelphia: Boericke & Runyan, 1928.

. . .and Willis Dewey. The Twelve Tissue Remedies of Schuessler. New Delhi: B. B. Join, 1971.

Borland, Douglas, M., MD. Homeopathy for Mother and Infant.

Bowen, Cuthbert. Materia Medica, Pharmacy and Therapeutics. Philadelphia: F. A. Davis, 1888.

Bragg, Paul C. Bragg's Apple Cider Vinegar System. Desert Hot Springs, CA: Health Science, 1967.

Butler, Glenworth Reeve. The Diagnostics of Internal Medicine. New York: D. Appleton, 1922.

Carey, G. W. and I. E. Perry. The Zodiac and the Salts of Salvation. New York: Samuel Wieser, 1973.

Cecil, Russel L. and Robert F. Loeb. Textbook of Medicine. Philadelphia: W. B. Saunders, 1956.

Chapman, J. E. and E. L. Perry. The Biochemic Handbook. St. Louis: D. Foemue, 1966.

. . .Dr. Schuessler's Biochemistry. London: New Era Laboratories, 1975.

Chapman, Estee. How to Use the 12 Tissue Salts. Wellingborough, Northamptomshire: Thorsons, n.d.

Chargoff, Erwin and J. N. Davidson. The Nucleic Acids. 2 vols. New York: Academic Press, 1955.

Christian, Henry A. Principles and Practice of Medicine. New York: D. Appleton-Century, 1944.

Christopher, John R. Dr. Christopher Talks on Rejuvenation through Elimination. Provo, UT: Christopher, 1976.

. . .Dr. Christopher's Three Day Cleansing Program and Mucousless Diet. Provo, UT: Christopher, 1969.

. . .The Incurables. Provo, UT: Christopher, 1977.

. . .School of Natural Healing. Provo, UT: Bi-World, 1977.

Comar, C. L. and Felix Bronner. Mineral Metabolism. New York: Academic Press, 1963.

Committee on Food Protection, National Research Council. Food Chemicals Codex II. Washington, D.C.: National Academy of Sciences, 1972.

Conn, Eric E. and P. K. Strumpt. Outlines of Biochemistry. New York: John Wiley, 1972.

Coulter, Catherine R.   Portraits of Homeopathic Medicine. North Atlantic Books: 1986.

Culbreth, David M. R.   Materia Medica and Pharmacology. Mokelumne Hill, CA: Health Research, 1977.

Culpepper, Nicholas. Culpepper's Herbal Remedies. Hollywood: Wilshire, 1973.

Cummings, Stephen and Dana Ullman. Everybody's Guide to Homeopathic Medicines, J. P. Tarcher, 1984 .

Cushman, Wesley, P., ed.   Positive Health. Columbus: Charles E. Merrill, 1965.

DaCosta, John Chalmers.   Modern Surgery. Philadelphia: W. B. Saunders, 1923.

Dana, Mrs. William Starr.   How to Know the Wild Flowers. New York: Cover Publications, 1963.

Dath, Heinrich.   Medical Astrology.   Mokelumne Hill, CA: Health Research, 1971.

Davidson, James Norman.   Davidson's The Biochemistry of the Nucleic Acids. London: Chapman & Hall, 1976.

Davidson, Victor S.   Science of Iridiagnosis. Westville, Natal, South Africa: Essence of Health, n.d.

Davidson, William M.   Medical Astrology and Health.   Monroe, NY: Astrological Bureau, 1973.

Davis, Adelle.   Let's Get Well.   New York: Harcourt, Brace & World, 1965.

Dennis, Frederic S.   System of Surgery.   2 vols. Philadelphia: Lea Brothers, 1895.

DeVore, Nicholas. Encyclopedia of Astrology. New York: Bonanza Books, 1967.

DiCyan, Erwin.   Vitamins in Your Life.   New York: Simon & Schuster, 1974.

Duffy, William.   Sugar Blues.   New York: Warner Books, 1975.

Ebertin, Reinhold.   Applied Cosmobiology. Tulpenweg, West Germany: Ebertin-Verlag, 1972.

. . .The Combination of Stellar Influences. Tulpenweg, West Germany: Ebertin-Verlag, 1972.

. . .Fixed   Stars   and   their   Interpretations. Aalen/Wuertt, West Germany: Ebertin-Verlag, 1971.

Ehret, Arnold. Prof. Arnold Ehret's Mucousless Diet Healing System. Beaumont, CA: Ehret Literature, 1977.

Ellis, John M. and James Presley.   Vitamin B6: The Doctor's Report.   New York: Harper & Row, 1973.

Ferner, H.,and J. Staubesand.   Atlas of Human Anatomy.   3 vols.   New York: Hafner Press, 1974.

Gabriel, Ingrid.   Herbs Identifier and Handbook. New York: Sterling, 1977.

Garten, M. O.   The Health Secrets of a Naturopathic Doctor.   West Nyach NY: Parker, 1976.

Gibson, D. M., M.D.   First Aid Homeopathy in Accidents   and   Injuries.   London: British Homeopathic Association, n.d.

Glands and Your Health.   Melbourne: Science of Life Books, n.d.

Goodwin, T. W.   The Biosynthesis of Vitamins and Related Compounds. London: Academic Press, 1963.

Gray, Henry.   Gray's Anatomy.   Philadelphia: Running Press, 1974.

Grieve, M.   A Modern Herbal.   2 vols.   New York: Dover Publications, 1971.

Hampel, Clifford A. and Gessner G. Hawley.   Glossary   of   Chemical   Terms.   New York: Van Nostran Reinhold, 1976.

Hansen, Oscar.   Materia Medica and Therapeutics of Rare Homeopathic Remedies.   Mokelumn Hill, CA: Health Research, 1899.

Hermann, Matthias.   Herbs and Medicinal Flowers. New York: Galahad Books, 1973.

Herscu, Paul, N.D.   The Homeopathic Treatment of Children.   Berkeley, CA: North Atlantic Books, 1991.

Hirst, Barton Cooke.   A Text Book of Obstetrics. Philadelphia: Saunders, 1903.

Horvilleur, Alain, M.D.   The Family Guide to Homeopathy.   Virginia: Health and Homeopathy Publishing, 1986.

Jacobson, Roger A.   The Language of Uranian Astrology.   Frandsville, WI: Uranian Publications, 1975.

Jansky, Robert Carl.   Astrology, Nutrition and Health.   Rockport, MA: Para Research, 1977.

Jennings, I. W.   Vitamins in Endocrine Metabolism. Springfield, IL: C. Thomas, 1970.

Jensen, William A.   The Plant Cell.   Belmont, CA: Wadsworth, 1965.

Jones, Eli G.   Definite Medication.   Boston: Therapeutic, 1974.

Jouanny, Jacques.   The Essential of Homeopathic Therapeutics.   Boiron Labs.

. . .The Essentials of Homeopathic Materia Medica. Boiron Labs.

Kadans, Joseph M. Modern Encyclopedia of Herbs. West Nyack, NY: Parker, 1970.

Karlson, P.   Introduction to Modern Biochemistry. New York: Academic Press, 1968.

Keeton, William T. Biological Science. New York: W. W. Norton, 1972.

Kent, James T., M.D. Lectures on Homeopathic Materia Medica. 1904. Reprint. New Delhi: Jain, 1974.

. . .Repertory of the Homeopathic Materia Medica.

1877. Reprint. New Delhi: Jain, 1982.

Kirschmann, John D. Nutrition Almanac. New York: McGraw-Hill, 1975.

Kittler, Glenn D. Laetrile: Nutritional Control for Cancer with Vitamin B17. Denver: Royal Publications, 1978.

Kloss, Jethro. Back to Eden. New York: Beneficial Books, 1971.

Krebs, Ernst T., Jr. Vitamin B15. Moscow: McNaughton Foundation, 1968.

Kroeger, Hanna. Instant Vitamin-Mineral Locator. n.p.: Hanna Kroeger, 1972.

Kutsky, Roman J. Handbook of Vitamins and Hormones. New York: Van Nostrand Reinhold, 1973.

Leonard, Jon N., J. L. Hofer and N. Pritikin. Live Longer Now. New York: Ace Books, 1974.

Malstrom, Stan and Marie Myer. Own Your Own Body. [United States}: Bell Press, 1977.

McElroy, William D. Cell Physiology and Biochemistry. New York: Prentice-Hall, 1964.

Meyer, Joseph E. The Herbalist. n.p.: Clarence Meyer, 1976.

Miller, Amy Bess. Shaker Herbs. New York: Clarkson N. Potter, 1976.

Miller, Marjorie A. and Lutie C. Leavell. Anatomy and Physiology. 6th ed. New York: MacMillan, 1972.

Mills, C. F. Trace Element Metabolism in Animals. London: E. & S. Livingstone, 1970.

Millspaugh, Charles F. American Medicinal Plants. New York: Cover Publications, 1974.

Morrison, Robert Thornton and Robert Neilson Boyd. Organic Chemistry. Boston: Allyn & Bacon, 1973.

Moullin, C. W. Mansell. Moullin's Treatise on Surgery. Philadelphia: P. Blakiston's Son, 1898.

Niggemann, Hans. The Principles of the Uranian System. New York: Niggemann, 1961.

Panos, Maeismund, M.D. and Jane Heimlich. Homeopathic Medicine at Home. Los Angeles: J. P. Tarcher, 1980.

Passwater, Richard A. Super Nutrition. New York: Dial Press, 1975.

Perry, Edward L. Luyties Homeopathic Practice. St. Louis, Formur, 1974.

Pike, R. L. and M. L. Brown. Nutrition: An Integrated Approach. 2nd ed. New York: John Wiley, 1975.

Powell, E. F. Biochemic Prescriber. N. Devon, Exeter: Health Science Press, 1972.

Rafelson, Max E. and Stephen B. Blinkley. Basic Biochemistry. New York: MacMillan, 1968.

Robson, Vivian E. The Fixed Stars and Constellations in Astrology. New York: Samuel Weiser, 1969.

Rodale, J. I., et al. The Complete Book of Minerals for Health. Emmaus, PA: Rodale Books, 1972.

. . .The Complete Book of Vitamins. Emmaus, PA: Rodale Press, 1977.

. . .Vitamins, Your Memory and Your Mental Attitude. Emmaus, PA: Rodale Press, 1977.

. . .Magnesium, the Nutrient that Could Change Your Life. New York: Jove Publications, 1968.

Rose, Jeanne. Herbs and Things. New York: Grosset & Dunlap, 1976.

Rudolph, Ludwig. Rules for Planetary Pictures. Franksville, WI: Poseidon Books, 1959.

Santiago, Grisolia, Rafael Baguenat and Frederico Mayor. The Urea Cycle. New York: John Wiley, 1976.

Santwani, M. T., M.D. Common Ailments of Children and Their Homeopathic Treatment. New Delhi: Jain, 1979.

Sawtel, Vanda. Astrology Biochemistry. Rustington, Sussex: Health Science Press, 1972.

Sebrell, W. H., Jr. and Robert S. Harris, eds. The Vitamins. 2 vols. New York: Academic Press, 1972.

Shook, Edward E. Elementary Treatise in Herbology. 2 vols. Beaumont, CA: Trinity Center Press & CSA Press, 1974.

Shute, Wilfrid E. Vitamin E for Ailing and Healthy Hearts. New York: Pyramid Books, 1972.

Smith, Trevor, M.D. A Woman's Guide to Homeopathic Medicine. Thorsons: 1982.

. . .Homeopathic Medicine. Thorsons: 1982

. . .The Homeopathic Treatment of Emotional Illness. Thorsons: 1982.

Snyder, Arthur W. Foods that Preserve the Alkaline Reserve. Los Angeles: Hansen's 1962.

. . .Nature's Way to Health. Los Angeles: Hansen's, 1969.

. . .Vitamins and Minerals. Los Angeles: Hansen's, 1969.

Sober, Herbert A. Handbook of Biochemistry. Cleveland National Institute of Health, 1968.

Steiner, Robert R. and Harold Edelhoch. Molecules and Life. Princeton: D. Van Nostrand, 1965.

Stewart, P. R. and D. S. Letham, eds. The Ribonucleic Acids. New York: Springer-Verlag, 1973.

Ternay, Andrew L., Jr. Contemporary Organic Chemistry. Philadelphia: W. B. Saunders, 1976.

Thomas, Clayton L., ed. Taber's Cyclopedic Medical Dictionary. Philadelphia: Davis, 1977.

Tilkian, Sarko M. and Ara G. Tilkian. Clinical Implications of Laboratory Tests. St. Louis: C. V.

Mosby, 1979.

Tobe, John H. Golden Treasury of Knowledge. [Canada]: Provoker Press, 1973.

. . .Proven Herbal Remedies. New York: Pyramid Books, 1973.

Venkstern, T. V. The Primary Structure of Transfer RNA. New York: Plenum Press, 1977.

Vogel, H. J., ed. Nucleic Acid-Protein Recognition. New York: Academic Press, 1977.

Wade, Carlson. Natural Hormones: The Secret of Youthful Health. West Nyack, NY: Parker, 1972.

Walker, Norman W. Colon Health. Phoenix: O'-Sullivan Woodside, 1979.

. . .Raw Vegetable Juices. Phoenix: Norwalk Press, 1936.

Wallach, Jacques. Interpretation of Diagnostic Tests. New York: Little, Brown, 1978.

Williams, Eakin, et al. The Biochemistry of B Vitamins. New York: Reinhold, 1950.

Yablonsky, Harvey A. Chemistry. New York: Thomas Y. Crowell, 1975.

Yemm, J. R. The Medical Herbalist. Hollywood: Wilshire, 1977.

Index

Drosera, 247
 See: Homeopathic remedy
Drowning
 See: Asphyxia
 Antimonium Tart., 240, 246
 Carbo. Veg., 242
Drug addiction
 See: Addiction
Drug toxicity
 Crab Apple, 230, 237
 Nux Vomica, 244, 248
Drugs
 ACTH, 170
 amethopterin, 176
 ammonium chloride, 184
 antibiotics, 172, 179
 anticonvulsant, 177
 antidotes, bad effects of — Nux Vomica,
  244, 248
 aspirin, 184, 207, 217, 219
 barbituates, 184
 chloramphenicol, 166
 chloromycetin, 196
 chloroquine, 207
 combating side effects, 185
 contraceptives, 171, 177
 cortisone, 160, 168, 170, 184, 217, 219
 DCA, 219
 dexamethasone, 196
 digitalis, 219
 digitoxin, 210
 diuretics, 163, 170, 211
 estradiol, 215
 estrogen, 168
 indomethacin, 184
 isoniazide, 168
 lithium, 219
 methotrexate (MTX), 176
 natural antibiotic, 225
 neomycin, 196
 penicillin, 164, 168, 196
 prednisone, 186, 196
 semicarbazide hormones, 168
 sensitivity, 22
 steroids, 160, 168, 196, 207
 stilbestrol, 184
 streptidine, 179
 streptomine, 179
 streptomycin, 168, 177, 179, 196
 sulfa types, 161, 172, 175, 177
 tetracycline, 211
 thiazide, 219
 thiouracil, 184
 thyroxine, 211, 217
Dumbcane, 300
Dysfunctional family
 Chicory, 230, 235

E

E, vitamin, 186, 266
 astrological ruler, 186
 deficiency symptoms, 188
 dosages, 187
 history & characteristics, 187
 recent clinical developments, 188
 sources, 186
 synonyms, 186
 synthetic forms, 186
 toxicity, 188
 unit of potency, 187
Ears
 ache — Belladonna, 241, 246

— Chamomilla, 242, 247
buzzing sounds — Kali Phos., 248
ear drum, 20
eustachian tubes, 19
humming or buzzing sound — Kali
 Phos., 248
infections — Belladonna, 241, 246
Meniere's syndrome, 170
noise sensitivity, 211
ringing — China Off., 242
tinnitis, 157
— Plumbum, 249
vomiting, 170
Echinacea, 247, 294
 See: Homeopathic remedies
Echo Blue Essence, 317
Eczema
 See: Skin disorders
El-nath, 15
El-scheratain, 15
Elderly
 See: Aging
 Lycopodium, 248
Electric shock injuries
 Nat. Mur., 248
Electric shock treatment
 Nat. Mur., 248
Elephant Ear, 300
Elm, 230, 236
Emerald Gemstone Essence, 317
Emotional
 cries easily — Pulsatilla, 245, 249
 overemotional — Pulsatilla, 245, 249
Emotions, negative
 See: Mental diseases/emotional problems
 aggressive — Holly, 230, 235
 anger — Anacardium, 246
 — Staphysagria, 249
 ashamed of body/self — Crab Apple,
  230, 237
 bitterness — Willow, 230, 236
 change, resists any kind of — Walnut,
  230, 235
 confidence, lack of — Larch, 230, 235
 confidence, loss of — Elm, 230, 236
 critical — Beech, 230, 237
 cruel — Vine, 230, 237
 despondent — Elm, 230, 236
 dictator — Vine, 230, 237
 disgust, with self — Crab Apple, 230,
  237
 dissatifaction — Wild Oat, 230, 233
 dominated by others — Cerato, 230, 232
 domineering — Vine, 230, 237
 dread — Kali Phos., 248
 envy — Holly, 230, 235
 fanatical — Vervain, 230, 237
 fault-finding — Beech, 230, 237
 greed — Holly, 230, 235
 greedy for authority — Vine, 230, 237
 hard — Vine, 230, 237
 hatred — Holly, 230, 235
 high-strung — Vervain, 230, 237
 hopelessness — Gorse, 230, 232
 impatient — Chestnut Bud, 230, 234
 — Impatiens, 230, 234
 jealous — Holly, 230, 235
 martyr — Rock Water, 230, 237
 Monday morning blahs — Hornbeam,
  230, 232
 overwhelmed by life in general
 — Olive, 230, 233

overwhelmed by responsibilities
 — Elm, 230, 236
possessive — Holly, 230, 235
resentment — Willow, 230, 236
resists any kind of change — Walnut,
 230, 235
rigid outlook — Rock Water, 230, 237
ruthless — Vine, 230, 237
saps others of energy — Heather, 230, 234
 — Honeysuckle, 230, 233
self-disgust — Crab Apple, 230, 237
self-pity — Willow, 230, 236
selfish — Holly, 230, 235
stalker remedy — Chicory, 230, 235
strict — Rock Water, 230, 237
struggle without hope — Oak, 230, 237
unfullfilled — Wild Oat, 230, 233
will, lack of — Wild Rose, 230, 236
Emphysema
 See: Lungs
 Antimonium Tart., 240, 246
Endocrine glands
 See individual glands
 adrenals, 261
 Libra, 23, 24
 Magnesium, 210
 ovaries, 263
 pancreas, 262
 parathyroid, 260
 pineal, 265
 pituitary, 258
 testes, 264
 thymus, 261
 thyroid, 259
Epilepsy, 17
 Aconite, 240, 246
 anticonvulsant drugs, 177
 Kali Brom., 248
 Tarentula, 250
Erigonum Abertianum "Venus" Essence,
 317
Estrogen, 21, 168, 169, 184, 187
 replacement — Folliculinum, 247
 — Oophorinum, 248
Eucalyptus (blue gum tree), 280
Eupatorium Perforatum, 243, 247
 See: Homeopathic remedies
Euphrasia, 247
 See: Homeopathic remedies
Evening Primrose Essence
 (pink), 316
 (white), 316
 (yellow), 316
Exhaustion
 physical — Nat. Carb., 248
 — Olive, 230, 233
 — Wild Rose, 230, 236
Extremities, numbness
 Rhododendron, 249
Eyes, 17, 20, 27, 28
 Bitot's spots, 157
 black dots before — Phosphorus, 245, 249
 blackened — Ledum, 244, 248
 bloodshot — Arnica, 165, 215
 blow to — Symphytum, 245, 250
 bruised feeling — Ruta Grav., 245, 249
 bulbar conjunctivitis, 165
 cataracts, 19, 24, 27
 conjunctivitis, 198
 cornea changes, 165
 discharge from tear ducts — Kali Brom.,
  248

Eyes (cont.)
    glasses changed often, 224
    glaucoma, 19, 24, 27, 156, 174
    grit beneath lids, 165
    floaters — Phosphorus, 245, 249
    half open in sleep, 211
    inflammation — Aconite, 240, 246
    injury — Hypericum, 244, 247
    inositol, 180
    light-sensitive — Nux Vomica, 244, 248
    myelo-optic neuropathy, 181
    nearsightedness, 160
    night blindness, 157
    pink eye, 198
    sleepy sand, 157
    splitting of outer skin, 165
    sties — Pulsatilla, 245, 249
    — Sulphur, 245, 250
    strain — Gelsemium, 243, 247
    — Pilocarpus Mic., 249
    swollen, 214
    trauma (surgery or otherwise) — Symphytum, 245, 250
    tumors, 28
    watering, 165
    white spots before — Pilocarpus Mic., 249
    xerosis, 157
    yellow cast, 211

F

F, vitamin, 193
    See: Fatty acids
    See: Oil
Fainting
    Aconite, 240, 246
    Nux Moschata, 248
Fatty acids, 193
    astrological ruler, 193
    deficiency symptoms, 194
    dosages, 193
    history & characteristics, 193
    recent clinical developments, 194
    sources, 193
    synonyms, 193
    synthetic forms, 193
    toxicity, 193
    unit of potency, 193
Fear (of)
    See: Mental diseases
    Aconite, 240, 246
    anxiety attack — Aconite, 240, 246
    — Rock Rose, 230, 231
    Aspen, 230, 232
    being alone — Arsenicum, 241, 246
    — Lycopodium, 248
    — Mimulus, 230, 231
    being robbed — Arsenicum, 241, 246
    death — Arsenicum, 241, 246
    dentist — Aconite, 240, 246
    dogs — Causticum, 247
    insomnia — Aconite, 240, 246
    panic attack — Aconite, 240, 246
    — Rock Rose, 230, 231
    paralyzed with — Gelsemium, 243, 247
    surgery — Aconite, 240, 246
    tests — Gelsemium, 243, 247
Feet, 28, 29
    bunions, 28
    burning sensation, 163, 181
    coldness, 28
    cramping toes, 197
    deformed, 28, 29

itching, 181
pain, 28, 181
sore — Silicea, 249
stinging, 208
swelling, 24, 206
weak arches, 29
Fennel, 289
Fenugreek, 294
Ferrum Met., 247
    See: Homeopathic remedies
Ferrum Phosphoricum, 247, 322-323
    See: Homeopathic remedies
Fever
    Belladonna, 241, 246
    Eupatorium Perf., 243, 247
    Gelsemium, 243, 247
    high — Millefolium, 248
    responds to nothing else — Ferrum Phos., 247
    Rhus Tox., 245, 249
    unknown origin — Ferrum Phos., 247
Fever blisters
    See: Cold sores
Fingernails
    breaking easily, 225, 226
    brittle, 194
    flattened, 208
    keeping healthy, 193, 205
    white spots, 228
Fire Opal Gemstone Essence, 317
Fissures
    Silicea, 249
Fixed stars, 14-16
Flint Gemstone Essence, 317
Flu
    aching muscles & bones — Eupatorium Perf., 243, 247
    relapse — Gelsemium, 243, 247
    Scutellaria Lat., 249
    sore skin — Eupatorium Perf., 243, 247
Fluorite Gemstone Essence, 317
Folic acid, 176
    astrological ruler, 176
    deficiency symptoms, 177
    dosages, 177
    history & characteristics, 176
    recent clinical developments, 177
    sources, 176
    synonyms, 176
    synthetic forms, 176
    toxicity, 177
    unit of potency, 176
Folliculinum, 247
    See: Homeopathic remedies
Fomalhaut, 16
Food allergy reactions
    Apis, 240
Foxglove, 300
Fractures
    Arnica, 241
    Hypericum, 244, 247
    Symphytum, 245, 250
Free radicals, 187, 221
    See: Selenium
    See: Vitamin E
Fringe Tree, 294

G

Gallbladder, 26, 27
    attack — Chelidonium, 247
    bile flow, 193
    Chelidonium, 247

lecithin, 26
obstruction of bile duct, 26, 156
promoting bile production, 172
spasms, 26
stones, 174, 194
Ganglia, nerve
    Calc., Fluor., 246
    Ruta Grav., 245, 249
    Silicea, 249
Gangrene
    Echinacea, 247
Garlic, 289-290
Garnet Gemstone Essence, 317
Gelsemium (yellow jasmine), 243, 247, 280
    See: Homeopathic remedies
Gemini, 19, 232, 234, 242, 243, 244, 245,
    246, 247, 248, 249
    Jupiter in, 19
    Mars in, 19
    Mercury in, 19
    Moon in, 19
    Neptune in, 20
    Pluto in, 20
    Saturn in, 19
    Sun in, 19
    Uranus in, 20
    Venus in, 19
Gentian, 230, 232, 234, 280
Glaucoma, 174
    See: Eyes
Goiter
    Calc. Fluor., 246
Golden Chain, 300
Goldenseal, 294-295
Gonorrhea
    Medorrhinum, 248
    Nat. Sulph., 248
    Petroselinum, 249
    Thuja Occ., 250
Gorse, 230, 232, 234, 266
Gout, 25, 26, 182
    Iodum, 247
    Kali Brom., 248
    Mag. Phos., 248
    Nat. Sulph., 248
    of knees, 26
    of toes — Rhododendron, 249
    Plumbum, 249
    Urtica Urens, 250
Gower Ramsey (Butterfly) Orchid Essence, 315
Graphites, 247
    See: Homeopathic remedies
Grief
    formula, natural essence, 319
    Ignatia, 244, 247
    Water Violet, 230, 234
Grindelia, 280
Guaiacum, 280
Guilt-ridden
    Pine, 230, 236
Gums
    bleeding — Hepar. Sulph., 243, 247
    — Phosphorus, 245, 249

H

Hades, 12
Haematoxylon, 280
Hair
    balding, 177
    brittle, 225, 226
    dandruff, 194

Sex (cont.)
 loss of interest, 208
 — Onosmodium, 248
 — Oophorinum, 248
 — Plumbum, 249
Sexual abuse
 Crab Apple, 230, 237
 Ignatia, 244, 247
 Staphysagria, 249
Sexual Dysfunction Formula, 318
Shasta Daisy Essence, 317
Shellfish, antidotes bad effects
 Urtica Urens, 250
Shock
 Aconite, 240, 246
 Arnica, 241
 Ignatia, 244, 247
 Star of Bethlehem, 230, 236
Silicea, 249, 325
 See: Homeopathic remedies
Sinus, 224
 See: Nose
 cavities, 20
 Chestnut Bud, 230, 234
 infections — Hepar Sulph., 243, 247
 — Kali Bichrom., 248
Sinusitis
 Hepar Sulph., 243, 247
 Kali Bichrom., 248
Skin disorders
 See: Herpes
 See: Ringworm
 See: Warts
 acne, 169, 194
 — Nat. Brom., 248
 ailments — Hepar Sulph., 243, 247
 black pores — Nitricum Acidum, 248
 burning — Sulphur, 245, 250
 cancer, 197
 canker sores, 166
 darkening of, 166
 dermatitis, 156, 167, 226
 — Crab Apple, 230, 237
 dry, 157, 173, 194, 198
 — Sulphur, 243, 247
 eczema, 176, 194, 219, 226
 — Nat. Mur., 248
 — Petroleum, 249
 — Sulphur, 245, 250
 — Tellurium, 250
 eruptions, 166
 — Urtica Urens, 250
 flaking, 164, 194
 fungus — Phosphorus, 245, 249
 gray cast, 173
 greasy — Nat. Mur., 248
 herpes zoster, 163
 itching, 26, 173
 — Sulphur, 243, 247
 liver spots, 157
 lupus erythematosus, 176
 pigmentation change, 166, 176
 psoriasis, 26, 226
 — Crab Apple, 230, 237
 — Kali Brom., 248
 — Petroleum, 249
 — Sulphur, 245, 250
 rapid healing of, 157, 264
 scaly, 173
 — Sulphur, 243, 247
 seborrhea, 169
 sharkskin appearance, 164

 splotches on, 166
 sunburn, 176, 198, 264, 268
 tumors, 191
 vitamin E, 188
 vitiligo, 176
 whiteheads, 164
 wrinkled, 157
Skullcap, 298
Sleeping pills, 161
 hypercalcemia, 160
 smoking, 94
 vitamin C, 184
 vitamin D, 160
Slippery Elm, 281, 298-299
Smallpox
 Millefolium, 248
Smoky Quartz Gemstone Essence, 318
Snakebite
 Lachesis, 248
Snakeweed Essence, 316
Sneezing
 Sabadilla, 249
Sodalite Gemstone Essence, 318
Sodium, 222
 astrological ruler, 222
 deficiency symptoms, 223
 dosages, 223
 history & characteristics, 222
 recent clinical developments, 224
 sources, 222
 synthetic forms, 222
 toxicity, 223
 unit of potency, 222
Sodium-potassium exchange, 17, 20, 164,
  218, 219, 222
 See: Adrenal glands
 apple cider vinegar, 112
 edema, 21, 168, 169, 172, 187
 high blood pressure, 165
 lowering sodium levels, 165
 puffiness, 197, 206
Solid extracts, 281
Sore throat
 painless — Belladonna, 241, 246
Sour Cherry Blossom Essence, 315
South Aselli, 15
Southern Scales, The, 15
"Space Cadet" Formula, 319
Spanish Bayonet Yucca Essence, 316
Speech
 aphasia, 17
 impediments, 17
 slow — Baryta Carb., 246
Spinal injuries
 Physostigma, 249
Spinal meningitis
 Nat., Sulph., 248
 Physostigma, 249
Spleen, 22, 23
 enlargement — Ceanothus, 247
 high white count, 23
Spongia Tosta, 245
 See: Homeopathic remedies
Sprains — Ruta Grav., 245, 249
 See: Muscle injuries
Spurge Laurel, 301
Squaw Vine, 299
Squills, 281
Stalker remedy
 See: Love, possessive/obsessive
 Chicory, 230, 235
Stammering

Stramonium, 250
Staphysagria, 249
 See: Homeopathic remedies
Star of Bethlehem, 229, 230, 236
Sterility, 214
 Platina, 249
Stings
 any insect — Apis Mellifica, 240
 honey bee — Apis Mellifica, 240
 wasp — Apis Mellifica, 240
Stomach, 20, 21
 See: Digestive disorders
Stramonium, 250
 See: Homeopathic remedies
Strawberry leaves, 299
Stress
 vitamin C, 186
Strokes
 Aconite, 240, 246
 Arnica, 241
 Belladonna, 241, 246
 strengthening walls, 175
 vitamin E, 188
Sudden Infant Death Syndrome (SIDS),
  173, 212
 See: Infants
Suffocation
 See: Asphyxia
 Antimonium Tart., 246
Sugar, 98, 100
 craving — Argentum Nit., 246
 — Carbo. Veg., 242, 247
 damage from, 198
 dextromaltose, 100
 eating too much — Nat. Phos., 248
 molasses, 100, 113
 Sepia, 249
 sucrose, 100
 turbo, 100
Suicide
 Cherry Plum, 230, 231
 Mimulus, 230, 231
 Rock Rose, 230, 231
Sulfa drugs, 161
 See: Drugs
Sulfur, 225
 astrological ruler, 225
 deficiency symptoms, 226
 dosages, 225
 history & characteristics, 225
 recent clinical developments, 226
 sources, 225
 synthetic forms, 225
 toxicity, 225
 unit of potency, 225
Sulphur, 245, 263, 264, 265, 267, 268
 See: Homeopathic remedies
Summer heat, worse
 Nat. Carb., 248
Sun, 4, 234, 246, 247
 See specific astrological signs
 Sun-Ascendant, 41
 Sun-Jupiter, 38, 272
 Sun-Mars, 37, 272
 Sun-Mercury, 36
 Sun-Moon, 36
 Sun-Neptune, 40, 272
 Sun-Pluto, 40, 272
 Sun-Saturn, 39, 272
 Sun-Uranus, 39, 272
 Sun-Venus, 37
Sunburn, 176, 263, 268